AN INTRODUCTION TO THE OPERATIONS WITH SERIES

AN INTRODUCTION TO THE OPERATIONS WITH SERIES

BY

I. J. SCHWATT, PH.D.

PROFESSOR OF MATHEMATICS, UNIVERSITY OF PENNSYLVANIA

SECOND EDITION

CHELSEA PUBLISHING COMPANY
NEW YORK

SECOND EDITION

THE PRESENT, SECOND, EDITION IS A REPRINT, WITH CORRECTIONS, OF THE FIRST EDITION OF 1924

LIBRARY OF CONGRESS CATALOG CARD NUMBER 61-17957

REPRINTED BY ARRANGEMENT WITH THE UNIVERSITY OF PENNSYLVANIA PRESS

PRINTED IN THE UNITED STATES OF AMERICA

TO

JOSIAH H. PENNIMAN, PH.D., LL.D., L.H.D.

PROVOST OF THE UNIVERSITY OF PENNSYLVANIA
AS A SIGN OF GRATITUDE AND APPRECIATION
THIS BOOK IS AFFECTIONATELY DEDICATED
BY THE AUTHOR

PREFACE

The matter contained in this book had its inception in the author's effort to obtain the value for the sum of the series of powers of natural numbers, in an explicit form and without the use of the Bernoulli numbers. This problem led to the study of the higher derivatives of functions of functions, which in turn required certain principles in operations with series, which had to be established. By means of these and other principles, methods for the expansion of certain functions and the summation of various types of series were devised and other topics developed.

Since as a rule only the simpler tests are needed to determine the validity of the expansions in the various parts of the book, the criteria for convergence which are so fully covered in other texts have been omitted. Although much of the work is believed to be new and, it is hoped, will prove of interest to mathematicians, the material has been so presented that it ought to be possible for anyone who has a good knowledge of the Calculus to read it comprehendingly.

The author was fortunate in being able to avail himself of the criticisms and suggestions of his friend and colleague, Dr. H. H. Mitchell, Professor of Mathematics at the University of Pennsylvania. The author wishes to express his gratitude to Mr. William A. Redding, a member of the Board of Trustees of the University of Pennsylvania and President of the University Press, who by securing the funds has made the publication of the book possible. His cordial thanks are due also to Mr. E. W. Mumford, Secretary of the University of Pennsylvania, for the solicitude and untiring efforts with which he has attended to the many questions that arose in connection with the negotiations for the printing of the book, and during its passage through the Press.

I. J. SCHWATT.

University of Pennsylvania,
Philadelphia, Pa., U.S.A.,
April, 1924.

TABLE OF CONTENTS

CHAPTER I.

HIGHER DERIVATIVES OF FUNCTIONS OF FUNCTIONS AND THEIR EXPANSIONS.

1. SEVERAL methods for obtaining the higher derivative of a function of a function have been given,* but they are not altogether convenient for purposes of application. Some of the leading treatises on Calculus† give the general derivatives of only the simplest functions, and in most cases the derivatives are obtained by special devices or by induction. Also in the expansion of functions the first few derivatives are as a rule found by actual differentiation, and in this way only the first few terms of the expansion are derived.

In the following we shall obtain the higher derivatives of certain classes of functions of functions and their expansions.

2. Given $$y=(a_0+a_1x+a_2x^2)^p=u^p, \tag{1}$$

where p is any real number.

To find $\frac{d^ny}{dx^n}$.

Letting $$a_1+2a_2x=u_1, \tag{2}$$

then by actual differentiation we have

$$\frac{dy}{dx}=pu^{p-1}u_1,$$

$$\frac{d^2y}{dx^2}=2(p_2)u^{p-2}u_1^2+2(p_1)u^{p-1}a_2,$$

$$\frac{d^3y}{dx^3}=6(p_3)u^{p-3}u_1^3+12(p_2)u^{p-2}u_1a_2,$$

$$\frac{d^4y}{dx^4}=24(p_4)u^{p-4}u_1^4+72(p_3)u^{p-3}u_1^2a_2+24(p_2)u^{p-2}a_2^2. \tag{3}$$

* Faa de Bruno, *Quarterly Journal of Mathematics*, vol. i. p. 359.—Goursat—Hedrick, *A Course in Mathematical Analysis*, vol. i. p. 34.—Arbogast, *Du Calcul des Dérivatives*, p. 15.—Williamson, *Differential Calculus*, p. 88.—Schlömilch, *Zeitschrift für Mathematik und Physik*, vol. iii. p. 65.—Saalschütz, *Vorlesungen über die Bernoullischen Zahlen*, 1893, p. 67.—Fujisawa, *Journal of the College of Science, Imperial University of Tokyo*, vol. vi. p. 174.—Meyer, *Grunerts Archiv der Mathematik und Physik*, vol. ix. p. 96.—Worpitzky, *Lehrbuch der Differential und Integralrechnung*, vol. i. p. 140.—Todhunter, *Differential Calculus*, p. 148.—Bertrand, *Traité de Calcul Différential et de Calcul Intégral*, vol. i. p. 140.—Edwards, *The Differential Calculus*, pp. 57 and 449.—Czuber, *Vorlesungen über Differential und Integralrechnung*.—Price, *A Treatise on Infinitesimal Calculus*, vol. i.—Dini, *Lezioni di Analisi Infinitesimale*, part i. p. 361.—Stolz, *Grundzüge der Differential und Integralrechnung*, p. 121.—Genocchi-Peano, *Calcolo Differenziale*, p. 52.

† Edwards, Williamson, Bertrand, Todhunter, Czuber, Serret, Schlömilch, Harnack, Kiepert and others.

This may be written symbolically thus:

$$\frac{d^4y}{dx^4}=4!\sum_{k=0}^{2}\binom{p}{4-k}\binom{4-k}{k}u^{p-4+k}u_1^{4-2k}a_2^{k}. \tag{4}$$

Again

$$\frac{d^5y}{dx^5}=5!\left[\binom{p}{5}u^{p-5}u_1^{5}+\binom{p}{4}4u^{p-4}u_1^{3}a_2+\binom{p}{3}3u^{p-3}u_1a_2^{2}\right]$$

$$=5!\sum_{k=0}^{2}\binom{p}{5-k}\binom{5-k}{k}u^{p-5+k}u_1^{5-2k}a_2^{k}. \tag{5}$$

We now assume

$$\frac{d^ny}{dx^n}=n!\sum_{k=0}^{\left[\frac{n}{2}\right]}\binom{p}{n-k}\binom{n-k}{k}u^{p-n+k}u_1^{n-2k}a_2^{k}, \tag{6}$$

where $\left[\frac{n}{2}\right]$ denotes the integral part of $\frac{n}{2}$.

We shall show that the form (6) holds also for $\frac{d^{n+1}y}{dx^{n+1}}$.

Now one of the terms of the derivative of the kth term of (6) is of the same power in u and u_1 as one of the terms of the derivative of the $(k+1)^{\text{st}}$ term of (6). The sum of these two terms of equal powers in u and u_1 gives the $(k+1)^{\text{st}}$ term of the derivative of (6). This term is

$$n!\,u^{p-(n+1)+k}u_1^{n+1-2k}\left[\binom{p}{n-k}\binom{n-k}{k}(p-n+k)\right.$$

$$\left.+2\binom{p}{n-k+1}\binom{n-k+1}{k-1}(n-2k+2)\right]a_2^{k}$$

$$=n!\,u^{p-(n+1)+k}u_1^{n+1-2k}(n+1)\binom{p}{n+1-k}\binom{n+1-k}{k}a_2^{k}. \tag{7}$$

We then obtain

$$\frac{d^{n+1}y}{dx^{n+1}}=(n+1)!\sum_{k=0}^{\left[\frac{n+1}{2}\right]}\binom{p}{n+1-k}\binom{n+1-k}{k}u^{p-(n+1)+k}u_1^{n+1-2k}a_2^{k}. \tag{8}$$

But since (8) is of the same form as (6), we conclude that (6) is universally true.

3. To find the expansion of (1) in powers of x.

By Maclaurin's theorem we have

$$y=\sum_{n=0}^{\infty}\left.\frac{d^ny}{dx^n}\right]_{x=0}\frac{x^n}{n!}, \tag{9}$$

and by means of (6) we obtain

$$y=\sum_{n=0}^{\infty}x^n\sum_{k=0}^{\left[\frac{n}{2}\right]}\binom{p}{n-k}\binom{n-k}{k}a_0^{p-n+k}a_1^{n-2k}a_2^{k}. \tag{10}$$

If p is a positive integer, the upper limit of n is $2p$. For, from $\binom{p}{n-k}$, $n-k$ cannot be greater than p. And since $\left[\frac{n}{2}\right]$ is the greatest value which k may assume, $n-k=n-\left[\frac{n}{2}\right]=\left[\frac{n+1}{2}\right]$ cannot be greater than p, or n cannot be greater than $2p$.

4. If
$$y=(a_0+a_1x+a_2x^2+a_3x^3)^p=u^p, \tag{11}$$
we find
$$\frac{d^ny}{dx^n}=n!\sum_{k=0}^{\left[\frac{2}{3}n\right]}\frac{1}{2^k}\binom{p}{n-k}\sum_{\beta=0}^{\left[\frac{k}{2}\right]}\left(\frac{2}{3}\right)^{\beta}\binom{n-k}{k-\beta}\binom{k-\beta}{\beta}u^{p-n+k}u_1^{n-2k+\beta}u_2^{k-2\beta}u_3^{\beta}, \tag{12}$$
where
$$u_1=a_1+2a_2x+3a_3x^2,$$
$$u_2=2a_2+6a_3x,$$
$$u_3=6a_3,$$

and by Maclaurin's theorem we obtain
$$y=\sum_{n=0}^{\infty}x^n\sum_{k=0}^{\left[\frac{2}{3}n\right]}\binom{p}{n-k}\sum_{\beta=0}^{\left[\frac{k}{2}\right]}\binom{n-k}{k-\beta}\binom{k-\beta}{\beta}a_0^{p-n+k}a_1^{n-2k+\beta}a_2^{k-2\beta}a_3^{\beta}. \tag{13}$$

Similarly, if
$$y=(a_0+a_1x+a_2x^2+a_3x^3+a_4x^4)^p=u^p, \tag{14}$$
$$\frac{d^ny}{dx^n}=n!\sum_{k=0}^{\left[\frac{3}{4}n\right]}\frac{1}{2^k}\binom{p}{n-k}\sum_{\beta=0}^{\left[\frac{2}{3}k\right]}\left(\frac{2}{3}\right)^{\beta}\binom{n-k}{k-\beta}\sum_{\gamma=0}^{\left[\frac{\beta}{2}\right]}\left(\frac{3}{4}\right)^{\gamma}\binom{k-\beta}{\beta-\gamma}\binom{\beta-\gamma}{\gamma}$$
$$u^{p-n+k}u_1^{n-2k+\beta}u_2^{k-2\beta+\gamma}u_3^{\beta-2\gamma}u_4^{\gamma}, \tag{15}$$
where
$$u_1=\frac{du}{dx},\quad u_2=\frac{d^2u}{dx^2},\quad u_3=\frac{d^3u}{dx^3},\quad u_4=\frac{d^4u}{dx^4}.$$

The expansion of y is then readily obtained.

In general, if
$$y=\left(\sum_{m=0}^{r}a_mx^m\right)^p=u^p,\text{ where } p \text{ is any real number,} \tag{16}$$
then
$$\frac{d^ny}{dx^n}=n!\sum_{k_1=0}^{\left[\frac{r-1}{r}n\right]}\frac{1}{2^{k_1}}\binom{p}{n-k_1}\sum_{k_2=0}^{\left[\frac{r-2}{r-1}k_1\right]}\left(\frac{2}{3}\right)^{k_2}\binom{n-k_1}{k_1-k_2}\sum_{k_3=0}^{\left[\frac{r-3}{r-2}k_2\right]}\left(\frac{3}{4}\right)^{k_3}\binom{k_1-k_2}{k_2-k_3}\cdots$$
$$\sum_{k_{r-1}=0}^{\left[\frac{k_{r-2}}{2}\right]}\left(\frac{r-1}{r}\right)^{k_{r-1}}\binom{k_{r-3}-k_{r-2}}{k_{r-2}-k_{r-1}}\binom{k_{r-2}-k_{r-1}}{k_{r-1}}u^{p-n+k_1}u_1^{n-2k_1+k_2}\cdots$$
$$u_{r-2}^{k_{r-3}-2k_{r-2}+k_{r-1}}u_{r-1}^{k_{r-2}-2k_{r-1}}u_r^{k_{r-1}}, \tag{17}$$
where $u_t=\dfrac{d^t}{dx^t}u,\ u_0=u.$ (18)

By means of (17) we obtain the Multinomial Theorem in the form
$$y=\sum_{n=0}^{\infty}x^n\sum_{k_1=0}^{\left[\frac{r-1}{r}n\right]}\binom{p}{n-k_1}\sum_{k_2=0}^{\left[\frac{r-2}{r-1}k_1\right]}\binom{n-k_1}{k_1-k_2}\cdots\sum_{k_{r-1}=0}^{\left[\frac{k_{r-2}}{2}\right]}\binom{k_{r-3}-k_{r-2}}{k_{r-2}-k_{r-1}}\binom{k_{r-2}-k_{r-1}}{k_{r-1}},$$
$$a_0^{p-n+k_1}a_1^{n-2k_1+k_2}a_2^{k_1-2k_2+k_3}\cdots a_{r-2}^{k_{r-3}-2k_{r-2}+k_{r-1}}a_{r-1}^{k_{r-2}-2k_{r-1}}a_r^{k_{r-1}}.* \tag{19}$$

* The Multinomial Theorem as ordinarily given (see for instance Chrystal, *Text Book of Algebra*, part ii. pp. 15 and 16) restricts the exponent p to positive integers. The above method also establishes a definite way in which the succession of the operations is to be performed.

If in (10) we let $p=-1$, and $a_0=a_1=a_2=1$, we have

$$\frac{1}{1+x+x^2}=\sum_{n=0}^{\infty}(-1)^n x^n \sum_{k=0}^{\left[\frac{n}{2}\right]}(-1)^k\binom{n-k}{k}.$$

On the other hand,

$$\frac{1}{1+x+x^2}=\frac{1-x}{1-x^3}=\sum_{\alpha=0}^{1}(-1)^{\alpha}\sum_{m=0}^{\infty}x^{3m+\alpha}.$$

Comparing coefficients of equal powers of x, we obtain

$$\text{for } n=3m, \quad \sum_{k=0}^{\left[\frac{3m}{2}\right]}(-1)^k\binom{3m-k}{k}=(-1)^m;$$

$$\text{for } n=3m+1, \quad \sum_{k=0}^{\left[\frac{3m+1}{2}\right]}(-1)^k\binom{3m+1-k}{k}=(-1)^m$$

$$\text{for } n=3m+2, \quad \sum_{k=0}^{\left[\frac{3m+2}{2}\right]}(-1)^k\binom{3m+2-k}{k}=0;$$

or

$$\sum_{k=0}^{\left[\frac{n}{2}\right]}(-1)^k\binom{n-k}{k}=\frac{1}{2}\left[(-1)^{\left[\frac{n}{3}\right]}+(-1)^{\left[\frac{n+1}{3}\right]}\right],$$

$$n=3m+\gamma, \quad \gamma=0,\ 1,\ 2.$$

Derive from (13)

$$\sum_{k=0}^{\left[\frac{2n}{3}\right]}(-1)^k\sum_{\alpha=0}^{\left[\frac{k}{2}\right]}\binom{n-k}{k-\alpha}\binom{k-\alpha}{\alpha}=\frac{1}{2}\left[1+(-1)^{\left[\frac{n}{2}\right]}\right],$$

$$n=4m+\gamma, \quad \gamma=0,\ 1,\ 2,\ 3;$$

and by means of (15)

$$\sum_{k=0}^{\left[\frac{3n}{4}\right]}(-1)^k\sum_{\alpha=0}^{\left[\frac{2k}{3}\right]}\binom{n-k}{k-\alpha}S_{\beta}=\frac{1}{2}\left[(-1)^{\left[\frac{n}{5}\right]}+(-1)^{\left[\frac{n+3}{5}\right]}\right],$$

$$n=5m+\gamma, \quad \gamma=0,\ 1,\ 2,\ 3,\ 4,$$

and

$$S_{\beta}=\sum_{\beta=0}^{\left[\frac{\alpha}{2}\right]}\binom{k-\alpha}{\alpha-\beta}\binom{\alpha-\beta}{\beta}.$$

5. The above expansions can also be obtained by the repeated application of the Binomial Theorem, and without the use of Calculus.

To illustrate the method we shall find the expansion of (11).

Now (11) may be written thus:

$$y=\sum_{n=0}^{\infty}\binom{p}{n}a_0^{\,p-n}x^n v^n, \tag{20}$$

where

$$v=a_1+a_2x+a_3x^2. \tag{21}$$

We then have

$$v^n = \sum_{\beta=0}^{n} \binom{n}{\beta} a_1^{n-\beta} x^\beta (a_2 + a_3 x)^\beta$$

$$= \sum_{\beta=0}^{n} \binom{n}{\beta} a_1^{n-\beta} x^\beta \sum_{k=0}^{\beta} \binom{\beta}{k} a_2^{\beta-k} a_3^k x^k$$

$$= \sum_{\beta=0}^{n} \binom{n}{\beta} a_1^{n-\beta} \sum_{k=0}^{\beta} \binom{\beta}{k} a_2^{\beta-k} a_3^k x^{\beta+k}. \quad (22)$$

Letting

$$\beta + k = k', \quad (23)$$

and dropping the accent, then

$$v^n = \sum_{\beta=0}^{n} \binom{n}{\beta} a_1^{n-\beta} \sum_{k=\beta}^{2\beta} \binom{\beta}{k-\beta} a_2^{2\beta-k} a_3^{k-\beta} x^k.* \quad (24)$$

Now

$$\sum_{\beta=0}^{n} \sum_{k=\beta}^{2\beta} A_{\beta,k} = \sum_{k=0}^{2n} \sum_{\beta=\left[\frac{k+1}{2}\right]}^{k} A_{\beta,k},\dagger \quad (25)$$

and by means of (25), (24) changes to

$$v^n = \sum_{k=0}^{2n} x^k \sum_{\beta=\left[\frac{k+1}{2}\right]}^{k} \binom{n}{\beta} \binom{\beta}{k-\beta} a_1^{n-\beta} a_2^{2\beta-k} a_3^{k-\beta}. \quad (26)$$

Letting $k - \beta = \beta'$,

$$v^n = \sum_{k=0}^{2n} x^k \sum_{\beta=0}^{\left[\frac{k}{2}\right]} \binom{n}{k-\beta} \binom{k-\beta}{\beta} a_1^{n-k+\beta} a_2^{k-2\beta} a_3^\beta. \quad (27)$$

Applying (26) to (20) gives

$$y = \sum_{n=0}^{\infty} \binom{p}{n} a_0^{p-n} \sum_{k=0}^{2n} x^{n+k} \sum_{\beta=0}^{\left[\frac{k}{2}\right]} \binom{n}{k-\beta} \binom{k-\beta}{\beta} a_1^{n-k+\beta} a_2^{k-2\beta} a_3^\beta. \quad (28)$$

Letting $n + k = k'$,

$$y = \sum_{n=0}^{\infty} \binom{p}{n} a_0^{p-n} \sum_{k=n}^{3n} x^k \sum_{\beta=0}^{\left[\frac{k-n}{2}\right]} \binom{n}{k-n-\beta} \binom{k-n-\beta}{\beta} a_1^{2n-k+\beta} a_2^{k-n-2\beta} a_3^\beta. \quad (29)$$

Now, by means of the principle

$$\sum_{n=0}^{\infty} \sum_{k=n}^{3n} A_{n,k} = \sum_{k=0}^{\infty} \sum_{n=\left[\frac{k+2}{3}\right]}^{k} A_{n,k},\ddagger \quad (30)$$

* In (23) the variable is k. Now if $k=0$, then $k'=\beta$, and if $k=\beta$, $k'=2\beta$. Therefore as k passes from 0 to β, k' goes from β to 2β. Now, from (23), $k=k'-\beta$. Substituting this value for k in the expression under the second summation sign in (24) we have

$$\sum_{k'=\beta}^{2\beta} \binom{\beta}{k'-\beta} a_2^{2\beta-k'} a_3^{k'-\beta} x^{k'}.$$

† Expanding the first member, we have

$$S = \sum_{k=0}^{0} A_{0,k} + \sum_{k=1}^{2} A_{1,k} + \sum_{k=2}^{4} A_{2,k} + \ldots + \sum_{k=n}^{2n} A_{n,k}.$$

Writing the terms with equal indices of k in columns and adding these columns gives the desired result.

‡ The proof is similar to the one for (25).

with due regard to the convergency of the series involved, (29) becomes

$$y=\sum_{k=0}^{\infty} x^k \sum_{n=\left[\frac{k+2}{3}\right]}^{k} \binom{p}{n} a_0^{p-n} \sum_{\beta=0}^{\left[\frac{k-n}{2}\right]} \binom{n}{k-n-\beta}\binom{k-n-\beta}{\beta} a_1^{2n-k+\beta} a_2^{k-n-2\beta} a_3^{\beta}. \quad (31)$$

Letting $k-n=n'$,

$$y=\sum_{k=0}^{\infty} x^k \sum_{n=0}^{\left[\frac{2}{3}k\right]} \binom{p}{k-n} \sum_{\beta=0}^{\left[\frac{n}{2}\right]} \binom{k-n}{n-\beta}\binom{n-\beta}{\beta} a_0^{p-k+n} a_1^{k-2n+\beta} a_2^{n-2\beta} a_3^{\beta}, \quad (32)$$

which is the same as (13), n and k being interchanged.

6. We shall illustrate the above by a few examples.

(i) Given
$$y=\sin^{-1}x, \quad (33)$$
to find $\frac{d^n y}{dx^n}$ and the expansion of y in powers of x.

Now
$$\frac{d^n y}{dx^n}=\frac{d^{n-1}}{dx^{n-1}}\frac{1}{\sqrt{1-x^2}}, \quad (34)$$
and by (6),

$$\frac{d^{n-1}}{dx^{n-1}}(1-x^2)^{-\frac{1}{2}}=(n-1)!\sum_{k=0}^{\left[\frac{n-1}{2}\right]}(-1)^k\binom{-\frac{1}{2}}{n-1-k}\binom{n-1-k}{k}(1-x^2)^{-n+\frac{1}{2}+k}(-2x)^{n-1-2k}. \quad (35)$$

But
$$\binom{-\frac{1}{2}}{n-1-k}=\frac{(-1)^{n-k-1}}{2^{2n-2k-2}}\binom{2n-2k-2}{n-k-1}, \quad (36)$$

and since
$$\binom{2n-2k-2}{n-k-1}\binom{n-k-1}{k}=\binom{2n-2k-2}{n-1}\binom{n-1}{k},$$
therefore

$$\frac{d^n y}{dx^n}=\frac{(n-1)!}{2^{n-1}}\frac{x^{n-1}}{(1-x^2)^n(1-x^2)^{-\frac{1}{2}}}\sum_{k=0}^{\left[\frac{n-1}{2}\right]}\binom{2n-2k-2}{n-1}\binom{n-1}{k}\frac{(1-x^2)^k}{x^{2k}}. \quad (37)$$

To find the expansion of y we let in (35), $x=0$; then $\left.\frac{d^n y}{dx^n}\right]_{x=0}=0$, except when $n=2k+1$.

Hence n must be odd, and as the exponent of x is then $2n-2k$, k can have the value n only.

Writing in (35) $2n+1$ for n, and then n for k, we have

$$\left.\frac{d^{2n+1}y}{dx^{2n+1}}\right]_{x=0}=(-1)^n(2n)!\binom{-\frac{1}{2}}{n}; \quad (38)$$

therefore
$$\sin^{-1}x=\sum_{n=0}^{\infty}\left.\frac{d^{2n+1}y}{dx^{2n+1}}\right]_{x=0}\frac{x^{2n+1}}{(2n+1)!}$$
$$=\sum_{n=0}^{\infty}(-1)^n\binom{-\frac{1}{2}}{n}\frac{x^{2n+1}}{2n+1!}; \quad (39)$$

and since $$\binom{-\frac{1}{2}}{n}=\frac{(-1)^n}{2^{2n}}\binom{2n}{n},$$

$$\sin^{-1}x=\sum_{n=0}^{\infty}\frac{1}{2^{2n}}\binom{2n}{n}\frac{x^{2n+1}}{2n+1},^{*}\quad -1<x<1. \tag{40}$$

(ii) Show that $$\tan^{-1}x=\sum_{n=0}^{\infty}(-1)^n\frac{x^{2n+1}}{2n+1},\quad -1\leqq x\leqq 1. \tag{41}$$

(iii) To find the coefficient of x^{2p} in the expansion of $y=(\tan^{-1}x)^2$.

Now, by Leibnitz's theorem,

$$\left.\frac{d^ny}{dx^n}\right]_{x=0}=\sum_{k=0}^{n}\binom{n}{k}\frac{d^{n-k}}{dx^{n-k}}\tan^{-1}x\left.\frac{d^k}{dx^k}\tan^{-1}x\right]_{x=0}, \tag{42}$$

and since, for $x=0$, the terms in the second member of (42) corresponding to $k=0$ and $k=n$ vanish, we have

$$\left.\frac{d^ny}{dx^n}\right]_{x=0}=\sum_{k=1}^{n-1}\binom{n}{k}\frac{d^{n-k-1}}{dx^{n-k-1}}\frac{1}{1+x^2}\left.\frac{d^{k-1}}{dx^{k-1}}\frac{1}{1+x^2}\right]_{x=0}. \tag{43}$$

Now, by (6),

$$\frac{d^{n-k-1}}{dx^{n-k-1}}\frac{1}{1+x^2}=(-1)^{n-k-1}(n-k-1)!\sum_{\alpha=0}^{\left[\frac{n-k-1}{2}\right]}(-1)^{\alpha}\binom{n-k-1-\alpha}{\alpha}(1+x^2)^{-n+k+\alpha}(2x)^{n-k-1-2\alpha} \tag{44}$$

with a similar form for $\frac{d^{k-1}}{dx^{k-1}}\frac{1}{1+x^2}$.

We then obtain

$$\left.\frac{d^ny}{dx^n}\right]_{x=0}=(-1)^n\sum_{k=1}^{n-1}\binom{n}{k}(n-k-1)!\,(k-1)!\sum_{\alpha=0}^{\left[\frac{n-k-1}{2}\right]}(-1)^{\alpha}\binom{n-k-1-\alpha}{\alpha}\sum_{\beta=0}^{\left[\frac{k-1}{2}\right]}(-1)^{\beta}\binom{k-1-\beta}{\beta}(2x)^{n-k-1-2\alpha+k-1-2\beta}\Big]_{x=0} \tag{45}$$

$$=0,\text{ except when } n-k-1-2\alpha+k-1-2\beta=0. \tag{46}$$

We shall now show that under the condition (46),

$$n-k-1-2\alpha=0\quad\text{and}\quad k-1-2\beta=0. \tag{47}$$

For, let $n-k-1-2\alpha>0$, then, from (46), $k-1-2\beta<0$. (48)

But from $\binom{k-1-\beta}{\beta}$, follows $k-1-2\beta\geqq 0$; therefore the assumption (48) is not tenable. Similarly $n-k-1-2\alpha$ cannot be less than zero, which proves the correctness of (47).

* In the *Differential Calculus* by Williamson, p. 68—Todhunter, p. 92—Edwards, p. 85, and other authors, the first few terms of the expansion are found by the method of Undetermined Coefficients.

The result (40) can also be obtained by expanding $\frac{1}{\sqrt{1-x^2}}$ by the Binomial Theorem and then integrating term by term.

It then follows that

$$\alpha=\frac{n-k-1}{2} \quad \text{and} \quad \beta=\frac{k-1}{2}$$

are the only values α and β can have, and (45) reduces to

$$\left.\frac{d^ny}{dx^n}\right]_{x=0}=(-1)^n(-1)^{\frac{n-2}{2}}n!\sum_{k=1}^{n-1}\frac{1}{(n-k)k}. \tag{49}$$

Now, since $n-k=2\alpha+1$ and $k=2\beta+1$, it follows that k must be odd and consequently n must be even.

Therefore

$$\left.\frac{d^{2n}y}{dx^{2n}}\right]_{x=0}=(-1)^{n-1}(2n)!\sum_{k=1}^{n}\frac{1}{2n-2k+1}\,\frac{1}{2k-1}, \tag{50}$$

and

$$(\tan^{-1}x)^2=\sum_{n=1}^{\infty}(-1)^{n-1}x^{2n}\sum_{k=1}^{n}\frac{1}{2n-2k+1}\,\frac{1}{2k-1}. \tag{51}$$

But

$$\frac{1}{2n-2k+1}\,\frac{1}{2k-1}=\frac{1}{2n}\left(\frac{1}{2n-2k+1}+\frac{1}{2k-1}\right).$$

Letting $n-k=k'$, then

$$\sum_{k=1}^{n}\frac{1}{2n-2k+1}\,\frac{1}{2k-1}=\frac{1}{n}\sum_{k=1}^{n}\frac{1}{2k-1}; \tag{52}$$

therefore

$$(\tan^{-1}x)^2=\sum_{n=1}^{\infty}(-1)^{n-1}\frac{x^{2n}}{n}\sum_{k=1}^{n}\frac{1}{2k-1}, \tag{53}$$

and the coefficient of x^{2p} in the expansion is

$$(-1)^{p-1}\frac{1}{p}\sum_{k=1}^{p}\frac{1}{2k-1}. \tag{54}$$

This result can also be obtained as follows:

$$(\tan^{-1}x)^2=\sum_{k=1}^{\infty}(-1)^{k-1}\frac{x^{2k-1}}{2k-1}\sum_{n=1}^{\infty}(-1)^{n-1}\frac{x^{2n-1}}{2n-1} \quad \text{by (41)} \tag{55}$$

$$=\sum_{k=1}^{\infty}\frac{1}{2k-1}\sum_{n=1}^{\infty}\frac{(-1)^{n+k}}{2n-1}x^{2(n+k)-2}.$$

Letting $n+k=n'$, then

$$(\tan^{-1}x)^2=\sum_{k=1}^{\infty}\frac{1}{2k-1}\sum_{n=k+1}^{\infty}(-1)^n\frac{x^{2n-2}}{2n-2k-1}. \tag{56}$$

Applying the principle

$$\sum_{k=a}^{\infty}\sum_{n=k+a}^{\infty}A_{k,n}=\sum_{n=2a}^{\infty}\sum_{k=a}^{n-a}A_{k,n}\text{*} \tag{57}$$

* Expanding the first member, we have

$$S=\sum_{\beta=0}^{\infty}A_{a,\,2a+\beta}+\sum_{\beta=0}^{\infty}A_{a+1,\,2a+1+\beta}+\sum_{\beta=0}^{\infty}A_{a+2,\,2a+2+\beta}+\cdots.$$

Adding S in columns gives

$$S=\sum_{\beta=0}^{0}A_{a+\beta,\,2a}+\sum_{\beta=0}^{1}A_{a+\beta,\,2a+1}+\sum_{\beta=0}^{2}A_{a+\beta,\,2a+2}+\cdots=\sum_{k=2a}^{\infty}\sum_{n=a}^{k-a}A_{n,k}.$$

to (56), we have

$$(\tan^{-1}x)^2 = \sum_{n=2}^{\infty}(-1)^n x^{2n-2}\sum_{k=1}^{n-1}\frac{1}{2n-2k-1}\,\frac{1}{2k-1}$$

$$= \sum_{n=1}^{\infty}(-1)^{n-1}x^{2n}\sum_{k=1}^{n}\frac{1}{2n-2k+1}\,\frac{1}{2k-1}, \tag{58}$$

which is the same as (51).

(iv) Given $$y=(1+x^2)^p\sin^{-1}x, \tag{59}$$

where p is any real number. To find the expansion of y.

Now, by Leibnitz's theorem,

$$\frac{d^ny}{dx^n}=\sum_{k=0}^{n}\binom{n}{k}\frac{d^{n-k}}{dx^{n-k}}(1+x^2)^p\,\frac{d^k}{dx^k}\sin^{-1}x. \tag{60}$$

Then, by means of (6) and (35), we obtain

$$\frac{d^ny}{dx^n}=n!\sum_{k=1}^{n}\frac{(-1)^{k-1}}{k}\sum_{\alpha=0}^{\left[\frac{n-k}{2}\right]}\binom{p}{n-k-\alpha}\binom{n-k-\alpha}{\alpha}(1+x^2)^{p-n+k+\alpha}$$

$$\sum_{\beta=0}^{\left[\frac{k-1}{2}\right]}(-1)^\beta\binom{-\frac{1}{2}}{k-1-\beta}\binom{k-1-\beta}{\beta}(1-x^2)^{\beta-k+\frac{1}{2}}(2x)^{n-1-2\alpha-2\beta}. \tag{61}$$

Now $\left.\dfrac{d^ny}{dx^n}\right]_{x=0}=0$, except when $n-1=2\alpha+2\beta$,

or $$n-k+k-1=2\alpha+2\beta. \tag{62}$$

But from $\binom{n-k-\alpha}{\alpha}$, $\qquad n-k\geqq 2\alpha$,

and from $\binom{k-1-\beta}{\beta}$, $\qquad k-1\geqq 2\beta$.

If we assume $n-k>2\alpha$, then by (62) $k-1<2\beta$,

and if we assume $k-1>2\beta$, then $\qquad n-k<2\alpha$.

Therefore only $$n-k=2\alpha \quad\text{and}\quad k-1=2\beta \tag{63}$$

are admissible, and n and k must both be odd.

Writing $2n+1$ for n and $2k+1$ for k in (63), we have

$$n-k=\alpha \quad\text{and}\quad \beta=k.$$

We then obtain

$$\left.\frac{d^{2n+1}y}{dx^{2n+1}}\right]_{x=0}=(2n+1)!\sum_{k=0}^{2n+1}\frac{(-1)^k}{2k+1}\binom{p}{n-k}\binom{-\frac{1}{2}}{k}. \tag{64}$$

But from $\binom{p}{n-k}$, $n-k\geqq 0$, and k cannot be greater than n.

Therefore $$y=\sum_{n=0}^{\infty}x^{2n+1}\sum_{k=0}^{n}\frac{1}{2^{2k}}\binom{p}{n-k}\binom{2k}{k}\frac{1}{2k+1}. \tag{65}$$

This result can be obtained more directly thus:
Applying the expansions

$$(1+x^2)^p=\sum_{k=0}^{\infty}\binom{p}{k}x^{2k} \quad \text{and} \quad \sin^{-1}x=\sum_{n=0}^{\infty}(-1)^n\binom{-\frac{1}{2}}{n}\frac{x^{2n+1}}{2n+1}$$

to (59), we have

$$y=\sum_{k=0}^{\infty}\binom{p}{k}\sum_{n=0}^{\infty}(-1)^n\binom{-\frac{1}{2}}{n}\frac{x^{2(k+n)+1}}{2n+1}. \tag{66}$$

Letting $n+k=n'$, then

$$y=\sum_{k=0}^{\infty}(-1)^k\binom{p}{k}\sum_{n=k}^{\infty}(-1)^n\binom{-\frac{1}{2}}{n-k}\frac{x^{2n+1}}{2n-2k+1}. \tag{67}$$

Now

$$\sum_{k=0}^{\infty}\sum_{n=k}^{\infty}A_{k,n}=\sum_{n=0}^{\infty}\sum_{k=0}^{n}A_{k,n},^* \tag{68}$$

with due regard to the convergency of the expansions.

Applying the principle in (68) to (67), we obtain

$$y=\sum_{n=0}^{\infty}(-1)^n x^{2n+1}\sum_{k=0}^{n}(-1)^k\binom{p}{k}\binom{-\frac{1}{2}}{n-k}\frac{1}{2n-2k+1}. \tag{69}$$

Letting $n-k=k'$, then

$$y=\sum_{n=0}^{\infty}x^{2n+1}\sum_{k=0}^{n}(-1)^k\binom{p}{n-k}\binom{-\frac{1}{2}}{k}\frac{1}{2k+1},$$

which is the same as (65).

(v) Show by both methods given in (iv) that

$$(1+x^2)^p\tan^{-1}x=\sum_{n=0}^{\infty}x^{2n+1}\sum_{k=0}^{n}(-1)^k\binom{p}{n-k}\frac{1}{2k+1} \tag{70}$$

and

$$(1+x^m)^p\log(1+x)=\sum_{n=1}^{\infty}(-1)^{n-1}x^n\sum_{k=0}^{\left[\frac{n-1}{m}\right]}\frac{(-1)^{mk}}{n-mk}\binom{p}{k}. \tag{71}$$

(vi) To expand $y=\log(7x^2-5x+3)$ in powers of x. (72)
We have

$$\frac{dy}{dx}=(14x-5)u, \text{ where } u=(7x^2-5x+3)^{-1} \quad \text{and} \quad \frac{d^ny}{dx^n}=\frac{d^{n-1}}{dx^{n-1}}[(14x-5)u].$$

Then, by Leibnitz's theorem,

$$\frac{d^ny}{dx^n}=\sum_{k=0}^{n-1}\binom{n-1}{k}\frac{d^{n-1-k}}{dx^{n-1-k}}(14x-5)\frac{d^k}{dx^k}u$$

$$=(14x-5)\frac{d^{n-1}}{dx^{n-1}}u+14(n-1)\frac{d^{n-2}}{dx^{n-2}}u. \tag{73}$$

* Expanding the first member gives

$$S=\sum_{n=0}^{\infty}A_{0,n}+\sum_{n=1}^{\infty}A_{1,n}+\sum_{n=2}^{\infty}A_{3,n}+\dots.$$

Writing the terms with equal indices of n in columns and adding these columns, we obtain

$$S=\sum_{k=0}^{0}A_{k,0}+\sum_{k=0}^{1}A_{k,1}+\sum_{k=0}^{2}A_{k,2}+\dots=\sum_{n=0}^{\infty}\sum_{k=0}^{n}A_{k,n}.$$

Now, by (6),

$$\left.\frac{d^{n-1}u}{dx^{n-1}}\right]_{x=0}=\frac{1}{5}\left(\frac{5}{3}\right)^n(n-1)!\sum_{k=0}^{\left[\frac{n-1}{2}\right]}(-1)^k\binom{n-1-k}{k}\left(\frac{21}{25}\right)^k \tag{74}$$

and

$$\left.\frac{d^{n-2}u}{dx^{n-2}}\right]_{x=0}=\frac{3}{25}\left(\frac{5}{3}\right)^n(n-2)!\sum_{k=0}^{\left[\frac{n-2}{2}\right]}(-1)^k\binom{n-2-k}{k}\left(\frac{21}{25}\right)^k. \tag{75}$$

Then, by means of (74) and (75), we obtain from (73)

$$\left.\frac{d^ny}{dx^n}\right]_{x=0}=-\left(\frac{5}{3}\right)^n(n-1)!\left[\sum_{k=0}^{\left[\frac{n-1}{2}\right]}(-1)^k\binom{n-1-k}{k}\left(\frac{21}{25}\right)^k\right.$$
$$\left.-2\sum_{k=0}^{\left[\frac{n-2}{2}\right]}(-1)^k\binom{n-2-k}{k}\left(\frac{21}{25}\right)^{k+1}\right]. \tag{76}$$

Hence
$$y=\log 3-\sum_{n=1}^{\infty}\frac{1}{n}\left(\frac{5}{3}\right)^nS_nx^n, \tag{77}$$

where S_n is the expression within the brackets of (76).

This expression may be reduced as follows.

We may write

$$\frac{1}{n}S_n=\frac{1}{n}+\frac{1}{n}\left[\sum_{k=1}^{\left[\frac{n-1}{2}\right]}(-1)^k\binom{n-1-k}{k}\left(\frac{21}{25}\right)^k+2\sum_{k=1}^{\left[\frac{n}{2}\right]}(-1)^k\binom{n-1-k}{k-1}\left(\frac{21}{25}\right)^k\right]. \tag{78}$$

Now, since the upper limit of the first summation is $\left[\frac{n}{2}\right]$, if n is odd, and the term corresponding to $k=\left[\frac{n}{2}\right]$ is zero, if n is even, therefore

$$\frac{1}{n}S_n=\frac{1}{n}+\frac{1}{n}\sum_{k=1}^{\left[\frac{n}{2}\right]}(-1)^k\left(\frac{21}{25}\right)^k\left[\binom{n-1-k}{k}+2\binom{n-1-k}{k-1}\right]. \tag{79}$$

But
$$\binom{n-1-k}{k}+2\binom{n-1-k}{k-1}=\frac{n}{n-k}\binom{n-k}{k}; \tag{80}$$

hence
$$\frac{1}{n}S_n=\frac{1}{n}+\sum_{k=1}^{\left[\frac{n}{2}\right]}\frac{(-1)^k}{n-k}\binom{n-k}{k}\left(\frac{21}{25}\right)^k$$
$$=\sum_{k=0}^{\left[\frac{n}{2}\right]}\frac{(-1)^k}{n-k}\binom{n-k}{k}\left(\frac{21}{25}\right)^k, \tag{81}$$

and
$$y=\log 3-\sum_{n=1}^{\infty}\left(\frac{5}{3}\right)^nx^n\sum_{k=0}^{\left[\frac{n}{2}\right]}\frac{(-1)^k}{n-k}\binom{n-k}{k}\left(\frac{21}{25}\right)^k. \tag{82}$$

In general, if $y=\log(a_0+a_1x+a_2x^2)$, then

$$y=\log a_0-\sum_{n=1}^{\infty}(-1)^n\left(\frac{a_1}{a_0}\right)^nx^n\sum_{k=0}^{\left[\frac{n}{2}\right]}\frac{(-1)^k}{n-k}\binom{n-k}{k}\left(\frac{a_0a_2}{a_1^2}\right)^k,$$

from which
$$\log(1-x+x^2)=-\sum_{n=1}^{\infty}x^n\sum_{k=0}^{\left[\frac{n}{2}\right]}\frac{(-1)^k}{n-k}\binom{n-k}{k}.$$

This result can also be obtained without the use of Calculus as follows. We may write

$$y=\log a_0+\log\left(1+\frac{a_1}{a_0}x+\frac{a_2}{a_0}x^2\right).$$

Then

$$y=\log a_0-\sum_{k=1}^{\infty}\frac{(-1)^k}{k}\left(\frac{a_1}{a_0}x+\frac{a_2}{a_0}x^2\right)^k$$

$$=\log a_0-\sum_{k=1}^{\infty}\frac{(-1)^k}{k}\sum_{a=0}^{k}\binom{k}{a}\left(\frac{a_1}{a_0}\right)^{k-a}\left(\frac{a_2}{a_0}\right)^{a}x^{k+a}.$$

Letting $k+a=n$, then

$$y=\log a_0-\sum_{k=1}^{\infty}\frac{(-1)^k}{k}\sum_{n=k}^{2k}\binom{k}{n-k}\left(\frac{a_1}{a_0}\right)^{2k-n}\left(\frac{a_2}{a_0}\right)^{n-k}x^n.$$

But

$$\sum_{k=1}^{\infty}\sum_{n=k}^{2k}A_{k,n}=\sum_{n=1}^{\infty}\sum_{k=0}^{\left[\frac{n}{2}\right]}A_{n-k,n};$$

therefore

$$y=\log a_0-\sum_{n=1}^{\infty}(-1)^n x^n\sum_{k=0}^{\left[\frac{n}{2}\right]}\frac{(-1)^k}{n-k}\binom{n-k}{k}\left(\frac{a_1}{a_0}\right)^{n-2k}\left(\frac{a_2}{a_0}\right)^k$$

$$=\log a_0-\sum_{n=1}^{\infty}(-1)^n\left(\frac{a_1}{a_0}\right)^n x^n\sum_{k=0}^{\left[\frac{n}{2}\right]}\frac{(-1)^k}{n-k}\binom{n-k}{k}\left(\frac{a_0a_2}{a_1^2}\right)^k.$$

Now $\log(1-x+x^2)=\log\frac{1+x^3}{1+x}=\sum_{n=1}^{\infty}(-1)^{n-1}\frac{x^{3n}}{n}-\sum_{n=1}^{\infty}(-1)^{n-1}\frac{x^n}{n}$,

then

$$\sum_{n=1}^{\infty}(-1)^{n-1}\frac{x^n}{n}=\sum_{n=1}^{\infty}(-1)^{n-1}\frac{x^{3n}}{3n}-\sum_{n=1}^{\infty}(-1)^{n-1}\frac{x^{3n-1}}{3n-1}+\sum_{n=1}^{\infty}(-1)^{n-1}\frac{x^{3n-2}}{3n-2};$$

therefore

$$\log(1-x+x^2)=-\sum_{n=1}^{\infty}(-1)^n\left[\frac{2x^{3n}}{3n}+\frac{x^{3n-1}}{3n-1}-\frac{x^{3n-2}}{3n-2}\right],$$

and we obtain

$$\sum_{k=0}^{\left[\frac{3m}{2}\right]}\frac{(-1)^k}{3m-k}\binom{3m-k}{k}=(-1)^m\frac{2}{3m},$$

$$\sum_{k=0}^{\left[\frac{3m-1}{2}\right]}\frac{(-1)^k}{3m-1-k}\binom{3m-1-k}{k}=(-1)^m\frac{1}{3m-1},$$

$$\sum_{k=0}^{\left[\frac{3m-2}{2}\right]}\frac{(-1)^k}{3m-2-k}\binom{3m-2-k}{k}=(-1)^{m-1}\frac{1}{3m-2}.$$

7. We shall next derive a formula for the higher derivative of a function of a function which is applicable to a wider class of functions.

If $y=\phi(u)$ and $u=f(x)$, then

$$\frac{d^ny}{dx^n}=\sum_{k=1}^{n}\frac{(-1)^k}{k!}\sum_{a=1}^{k}(-1)^a\binom{k}{a}u^{k-a}\frac{d^n}{dx^n}u^a\frac{d^ky}{du^k}. \tag{83}$$

To prove this formula we proceed as follows.

By actual differentiation we find

$$\frac{dy}{dx}=\frac{dy}{du}\frac{du}{dx}=\phi'(u)\frac{du}{dx},$$

$$\frac{d^2y}{dx^2}=\phi'(u)\frac{d^2u}{dx^2}+\phi''(u)\left(\frac{du}{dx}\right)^2,$$

$$\frac{d^3y}{dx^3}=\phi'(u)\frac{d^3u}{dx^3}+3\phi''(u)\frac{d^2u}{dx^2}\frac{du}{dx}+\phi''(u)\left(\frac{du}{dx}\right)^3,$$

....

$$\frac{d^ny}{dx^n}=\frac{A_1}{1!}\phi'(u)+\frac{A_2}{2!}\phi''(u)+\frac{A_3}{3!}\phi'''(u)+\ldots+\frac{A_n}{n!}\phi^{(n)}(n)$$

$$=\sum_{k=1}^{n}\frac{A_k}{k!}\phi^{(k)}(u), \tag{84}$$

where the A's depend on u and not on y. For a definite u the values of the A's are therefore the same whatever $y=\phi(u)$ might be.

Letting $$y=\phi(u)=u,$$

then $$\frac{d^nu}{dx^n}=A_1. \tag{85}$$

Assuming $$y=\phi(u)=u^2,$$

we have $$\frac{d^nu^2}{dx^n}=\binom{2}{1}A_1u+\binom{2}{2}A_2. \tag{86}$$

If we let $$y=u^3,$$

then $$\frac{d^nu^3}{dx^n}=\binom{3}{1}A_1u^2+\binom{3}{2}A_2u+\binom{3}{3}A_3; \tag{87}$$

and if we assume $y=u^p$, we obtain

$$\frac{d^nu^p}{dx^n}=\binom{p}{1}A_1u^{p-1}+\binom{p}{2}A_2u^{p-2}+\ldots+\binom{p}{1}A_{p-1}u+A_p. \tag{88}$$

Solving the set of equations (85)–(88) for A_k, we have

$$A_k=\begin{vmatrix} 1 & 0 & 0 & \ldots\ 0 & D^nu \\ 2u & 1 & 0 & \ldots\ 0 & D^nu^2 \\ 3u^2 & \binom{3}{2}u & 1 & \ldots\ 0 & D^nu^3 \\ \ldots & \ldots & \ldots & \ldots & \ldots \\ (k-1)u^{k-2} & \binom{k-1}{2}u^{k-3} & \binom{k-1}{3}u^{k-4} & \ldots\ 1 & D^nu^{k-1} \\ ku^{k-1} & \binom{k}{2}u^{k-2} & \binom{k}{3}u^{k-3} & \ldots\ ku & D^nu^k \end{vmatrix}. \tag{89}$$

8. The following method will render the value of A_k in the form of a single summation.

By means of (85) we obtain from (86)

$$A_2=\frac{d^nu^2}{dx^n}-\binom{2}{1}u\frac{d^nu}{dx^n}. \tag{90}$$

Applying (85) and (90) to (87) gives

$$A_3=\frac{d^n u^3}{dx^n}-\binom{3}{1}u\frac{d^n u^2}{dx^n}+\binom{3}{2}u^2\frac{d^n u}{dx^n},$$

or written symbolically,

$$A_3=\sum_{k=0}^{2}(-1)^k\binom{3}{k}u^k\frac{d^n}{dx^n}u^{3-k}.$$

Letting $3-k=k'$, then

$$A_3=(-1)^3\sum_{k=1}^{3}(-1)^k\binom{3}{k}u^{3-k}\frac{d^n}{dx^n}u^k. \tag{91}$$

In a similar way we find

$$A_4=(-1)^4\sum_{k=1}^{4}(-1)^k\binom{4}{k}u^{4-k}\frac{d^n}{dx^n}u^k. \tag{92}$$

We now assume

$$A_k=(-1)^k\sum_{\alpha=1}^{k}(-1)^\alpha\binom{k}{\alpha}u^{k-\alpha}\frac{d^n}{dx^n}u^\alpha, \tag{93}$$

and will show that this form holds also for A_{k+1}.

Letting $y=u^{k+1}$, then

$$\frac{d^n}{dx^n}u^{k+1}=\binom{k+1}{1}A_1u^k+\binom{k+1}{2}A_2u^{k-1}+\dots+\binom{k+1}{1}A_ku+A_{k+1}, \tag{94}$$

from which

$$A_{k+1}=\frac{d^n u^{k+1}}{dx^n}-\sum_{\alpha=1}^{k}\binom{k+1}{\alpha}A_\alpha u^{k+1-\alpha}, \tag{95}$$

and by means of (93) we have

$$A_{k+1}=\frac{d^n u^{k+1}}{dx^n}-\sum_{\alpha=1}^{k}(-1)^\alpha\binom{k+1}{\alpha}u^{k+1-\alpha}\sum_{\beta=1}^{\alpha}(-1)^\beta\binom{\alpha}{\beta}u^{\alpha-\beta}\frac{d^n}{dx^n}u^\beta. \tag{96}$$

Denoting the double summation in (96) by S, and since

$$\sum_{\alpha=1}^{k}\sum_{\beta=1}^{\alpha}A_{\alpha,\beta}=\sum_{\beta=1}^{k}\sum_{\alpha=\beta}^{k}A_{\alpha,\beta},^* \tag{97}$$

therefore

$$S=\sum_{\beta=1}^{k}(-1)^\beta u^{k+1-\beta}\frac{d^n}{dx^n}u^\beta\sum_{\alpha=\beta}^{k}(-1)^\alpha\binom{k+1}{\alpha}\binom{\alpha}{\beta}. \tag{98}$$

But

$$\binom{k+1}{\alpha}\binom{\alpha}{\beta}=\binom{k+1}{\beta}\binom{k+1-\beta}{\alpha-\beta},$$

hence

$$S=\sum_{\beta=1}^{k}(-1)^\beta\binom{k+1}{\beta}u^{k+1-\beta}\frac{d^n}{dx^n}u^\beta\sum_{\alpha=\beta}^{k}(-1)^\alpha\binom{k+1-\beta}{\alpha-\beta}. \tag{99}$$

Now, letting $\alpha-\beta=\alpha'$ in

$$S_1=\sum_{\alpha=\beta}^{k}(-1)^\alpha\binom{k+1-\beta}{\alpha-\beta}, \tag{100}$$

* The proof is similar to the one for (68).

then
$$S_1=(-1)^\beta\sum_{\alpha=0}^{k-\beta}(-1)^\alpha\binom{k+1-\beta}{\alpha}$$
$$=(-1)^\beta\sum_{\alpha=0}^{k+1-\beta}(-1)^\alpha\binom{k+1-\beta}{\alpha}-(-1)^{k+1}=(-1)^k. \tag{101}$$

Applying (101) to (99) gives
$$S=(-1)^k\sum_{\beta=1}^{k}(-1)^\beta\binom{k+1}{\beta}u^{k+1-\beta}\frac{d^n}{dx^n}u^\beta. \tag{102}$$

Then, by means of (102), we obtain from (96)
$$A_{k+1}=\frac{d^nu^{k+1}}{dx^n}+(-1)^k\sum_{\beta=1}^{k}(-1)^\beta\binom{k+1}{\beta}u^{k+1-\beta}\frac{d^n}{dx^n}u^\beta$$
$$=(-1)^{k+1}\sum_{\beta=1}^{k+1}(-1)^\beta\binom{k+1}{\beta}u^{k+1-\beta}\frac{d^n}{dx^n}u^\beta, \tag{103}$$
which is the same as (93), except that $k+1$ appears in place of k.

Substituting (93) in (84) gives (83).

9. For the purpose of illustrating some of the methods of the operation with series, we shall show the validity of (83) in the following manner.

We have
$$\frac{dy}{dx}=\frac{dy}{du}\frac{du}{dx};$$
$$\frac{d^2y}{dx^2}=\frac{d^2u}{dx^2}\frac{dy}{du}+\left(\frac{du}{dx}\right)^2\frac{d^2y}{du^2}. \tag{104}$$

Now
$$\frac{d^2u^2}{dx^2}=2\left(\frac{du}{dx}\right)^2+2u\frac{d^2u}{dx^2},$$

from which
$$\left(\frac{du}{dx}\right)^2=\frac{1}{2!}\left[\binom{2}{0}\frac{d^2u^2}{dx^2}-\binom{2}{1}u\frac{d^2u}{dx^2}\right]. \tag{105}$$

Applying (105) to (104), we obtain
$$\frac{d^2y}{dx^2}=\frac{d^2u}{dx^2}\frac{dy}{du}+\frac{1}{2!}\left[\binom{2}{0}\frac{d^2u^2}{dx^2}-\binom{2}{1}u\frac{d^2u}{dx^2}\right]\frac{d^2y}{du^2}$$
$$=\sum_{k=1}^{2}\frac{(-1)^k}{k!}\sum_{\alpha=1}^{k}(-1)^\alpha\binom{k}{\alpha}u^{k-\alpha}\frac{d^2u^\alpha}{dx^2}\frac{d^ky}{du^k}. \tag{106}$$

Thus (83) holds for $n=1$ and $n=2$, and we shall show that it holds true in general.

Differentiating (83) with respect to x, we have
$$\frac{d^{n+1}y}{dx^{n+1}}=\sum_{k=1}^{n}\frac{(-1)^k}{k!}\sum_{\alpha=1}^{k}(-1)^\alpha\binom{k}{\alpha}u^{k-\alpha}\frac{d^nu^\alpha}{dx^n}\frac{du}{dx}\frac{d^{k+1}y}{du^{k+1}}$$
$$+\sum_{k=2}^{n}\frac{(-1)^k}{k!}\sum_{\alpha=1}^{k-1}(-1)^\alpha\binom{k}{\alpha}(k-\alpha)u^{k-\alpha-1}\frac{d^nu^\alpha}{dx^n}\frac{du}{dx}\frac{d^ky}{du^k}$$
$$+\sum_{k=1}^{n}\frac{(-1)^k}{k!}\sum_{\alpha=1}^{k}(-1)^\alpha\binom{k}{\alpha}u^{k-\alpha}\frac{d^{n+1}u^\alpha}{dx^{n+1}}\frac{d^ky}{du^k}. \tag{107}$$

We shall designate the double summations in (107) in order by S_1, S_2 and S_3.

Then, since
$$\frac{1}{k!}\binom{k}{\alpha}(k-\alpha)=\frac{1}{(k-1)!}\binom{k-1}{\alpha},$$
we may write
$$S_2=-\sum_{k=2}^{n}\frac{(-1)^{k-1}}{(k-1)!}\sum_{\alpha=1}^{k-1}(-1)^{\alpha}\binom{k-1}{\alpha}u^{k-1-\alpha}\frac{d^n u^{\alpha}}{dx^n}\frac{du}{dx}\frac{d^k y}{du^k}. \tag{108}$$

Letting $k-1=k'$, then
$$S_2=-\sum_{k=1}^{n-1}\frac{(-1)^k}{k!}\sum_{\alpha=1}^{k}(-1)^{\alpha}\binom{k}{\alpha}u^{k-\alpha}\frac{d^n u^{\alpha}}{dx^n}\frac{du}{dx}\frac{d^{k+1}y}{dx^{k+1}}. \tag{109}$$

Now (109) with sign changed is equal to S_1 minus the term in S_1 corresponding to $k=n$; therefore
$$S_1+S_2=\frac{(-1)^n}{n!}\left(\sum_{\alpha=1}^{n}(-1)^{\alpha}\binom{n}{\alpha}u^{n-\alpha}\frac{d^n u^{\alpha}}{dx^n}\frac{du}{dx}\right)\frac{d^{n+1}y}{dx^{n+1}}. \tag{110}$$

Then, by means of
$$\frac{1}{n!}\binom{n}{\alpha}=\frac{1}{(n+1)!}\binom{n+1}{\alpha}(n+1-\alpha)$$
and
$$(n+1-\alpha)u^{n-\alpha}\frac{du}{dx}\frac{d^n u^{\alpha}}{dx^n}=\frac{d}{dx}\left(u^{n+1-\alpha}\frac{d^n u^{\alpha}}{dx^n}\right)-u^{n+1-\alpha}\frac{d^{n+1}u^{\alpha}}{dx^{n+1}},$$
(110) becomes
$$S_1+S_2=\frac{(-1)^{n+1}}{(n+1)!}\sum_{\alpha=1}^{n+1}(-1)^{\alpha}\binom{n+1}{\alpha}u^{n+1-\alpha}\frac{d^{n+1}u^{\alpha}}{dx^{n+1}}\frac{d^{n+1}y}{du^{n+1}}$$
$$+\frac{(-1)^n}{(n+1)!}\sum_{\alpha=1}^{n+1}(-1)^{\alpha}\binom{n+1}{\alpha}\frac{d}{dx}\left(u^{n+1-\alpha}\frac{d^n u^{\alpha}}{dx^n}\right)\frac{d^{n+1}y}{du^{n+1}}. \tag{111}$$

Let
$$(-1)^{n+1}\sum_{\alpha=1}^{n+1}(-1)^{\alpha}\binom{n+1}{\alpha}\frac{d}{dx}\left(u^{n+1-\alpha}\frac{d^n u^{\alpha}}{dx^n}\right)$$
$$=(-1)^{n+1}\frac{d}{dx}\sum_{\alpha=0}^{n+1}(-1)^{\alpha}\binom{n+1}{\alpha}u^{n+1-\alpha}\frac{d^n u^{\alpha}}{dx^n}=P. \tag{112}$$

Now
$$(-1)^{n+1-\alpha}\binom{n+1}{\alpha}u^{n+1-\alpha}=((r^{n+1-\alpha}))(1-ur)^{n+1},^{*}\quad\frac{dr}{dx}=0, \tag{113}$$
and
$$\frac{d^n u^{\alpha}}{dx^n}=((r^{\alpha}))\frac{d^n}{dx^n}\frac{1}{1-ur}; \tag{114}$$
then by means of (113) and (114), (112) becomes
$$P=\frac{d}{dx}((r^{n+1}))(1-ur)^{n+1}\frac{d^n}{dx^n}\frac{1}{1-ur}. \tag{115}$$

But
$$\frac{d^n}{dx^n}\frac{1}{1-ur}=\frac{\sum_{k=0}^{n}A_k r^k}{(1-ur)^{n+1}},$$
where A_k is a function of x only.

* Where $((r^{n+1-\alpha}))(1-ur)^{n+1}$ denotes the coefficient of $r^{n+1-\alpha}$ in the expansion of $(1-ur)^{n+1}$.

Therefore $$P=\frac{d}{dx}((r^{n+1}))\sum_{k=0}^{n}A_k r^k=0, \tag{116}$$

and $$S_1+S_2=\frac{(-1)^{n+1}}{(n+1)!}\sum_{\alpha=1}^{n+1}(-1)^\alpha\binom{n+1}{\alpha}u^{n+1-\alpha}\frac{d^{n+1}u^\alpha}{dx^{n+1}}\frac{d^{n+1}y}{du^{n+1}}. \tag{117}$$

But the second member in (117) may be obtained by letting $k=n+1$ in S_3; hence

$$\frac{d^{n+1}y}{dx^{n+1}}=\sum_{k=1}^{n+1}\frac{(-1)^k}{k!}\sum_{\alpha=1}^{k}(-1)^\alpha\binom{k}{\alpha}u^{k-\alpha}\frac{d^{n+1}u^\alpha}{dx^{n+1}}\frac{d^k y}{du^k}. \tag{118}$$

This result being of the same form as (83), it holds true for all values of n.

10. In the following a few applications of (83) are given.

(i) By means of (83) to find (10), which is the expansion of (1).

Letting in (1) $$a_1x+a_2x^2=u,$$

then $$y=(a_0+u)^p, \tag{119}$$

and by (83),

$$\frac{d^ny}{dx^n}=\sum_{k=0}^{n}\frac{(-1)^k}{k!}\sum_{\beta=0}^{k}(-1)^\beta\binom{k}{\beta}(a_1x+a_2x^2)^{k-\beta}\frac{d^n}{dx^n}(a_1x+a_2x^2)^\beta\frac{d^ky}{du^k} \tag{120}$$

Now $$\frac{d^nu^\beta}{dx^n}=\frac{d^n}{dx^n}\sum_{\gamma=0}^{\beta}\binom{\beta}{\gamma}a_1{}^{\beta-\gamma}a_2{}^\gamma x^{\beta+\gamma}$$

$$=n!\sum_{\gamma=0}^{\beta}\binom{\beta}{\gamma}\binom{\beta+\gamma}{n}a_1{}^{\beta-\gamma}a_2{}^\gamma x^{\beta+\gamma-n}, \tag{121}$$

and $$\frac{d^ky}{du^k}=k!\binom{p}{k}(a_0+u)^{p-k}. \tag{122}$$

Applying (121) and (122) to (120), we have

$$\frac{d^ny}{dx^n}=n!\,y\sum_{k=0}^{n}(-1)^k\binom{p}{k}\frac{1}{y^{k/p}}\sum_{\beta=0}^{k}(-1)^\beta\binom{k}{\beta}(a_1+a_2x)^{k-\beta}$$
$$\sum_{\gamma=0}^{\beta}\binom{\beta}{\gamma}\binom{\beta+\gamma}{n}a_1{}^{\beta-\gamma}a_2{}^\gamma x^{k-n+\gamma}, \tag{123}$$

and $$\left.\frac{d^ny}{dx^n}\right]_{x=0}=0,\text{ except when } k-n+\gamma=0,\text{ or } \gamma=n-k, \tag{124}$$

in which case

$$\left.\frac{d^ny}{dx^n}\right]_{x=0}=n!\sum_{k=0}^{n}(-1)^k\binom{p}{k}\sum_{\beta=0}^{k}(-1)^\beta\binom{k}{\beta}\binom{\beta}{n-k}\binom{\beta+n-k}{n}a_0{}^{p-k}$$
$$a_1{}^{2k-n}a_2{}^{n-k}. \tag{125}$$

Now from $\binom{k}{\beta}$, $k\geqq\beta$, and from $\binom{\beta+n-k}{n}$, $\beta\geqq k$; hence $\beta=k$. It then follows from $\binom{\beta}{n-k}=\binom{k}{n-k}$, that $k\geqq\left[\frac{n+1}{2}\right]$.

Therefore $$\left.\frac{d^ny}{dx^n}\right]_{x=0}=n!\sum_{k=\left[\frac{n+1}{2}\right]}^{n}\binom{p}{k}\binom{k}{n-k}a_0{}^{p-k}a_1{}^{2k-n}a_2{}^{n-k}. \tag{126}$$

Letting $$n-k=k',$$

then $$y=\sum_{n=0}^{\infty} x^n \sum_{k=0}^{\left[\frac{n}{2}\right]} \binom{p}{n-k}\binom{n-k}{k} a_0^{p-n+k} a_1^{n-2k} a_2^{k}, \tag{127}$$

which is the same as (10).

(ii) Given $$y=(1+x^m)^p, \tag{128}$$

where m and p are any real numbers.

To find $\frac{d^n y}{dx^n}$.

Letting in (83) $u=x^m$, we have

$$\frac{d^n y}{dx^n}=\frac{n!\,y}{x^n}\sum_{k=0}^{n}(-1)^k\binom{p}{k}\frac{x^{mk}}{y^{k/p}}\sum_{\alpha=0}^{k}(-1)^{\alpha}\binom{k}{\alpha}\binom{m\alpha}{n}. \tag{129}$$

If p is negative, we may write

$$\binom{-p}{k}=(-1)^k\binom{p+k-1}{k}. \tag{130}$$

If m is a positive integer, then from $\binom{m\alpha}{n}$ it follows $\alpha \geqq \frac{n}{m}$, and that $\left[\frac{m+n-1}{m}\right]$ is the smallest value α may assume. Then

$$\frac{d^n y}{dx^n}=\frac{n!\,y}{x^n}\sum_{k=\left[\frac{m+n-1}{m}\right]}^{n}(-1)^k\binom{p}{k}\frac{x^{mk}}{y^{k/p}}\sum_{\alpha=\left[\frac{m+n-1}{m}\right]}^{k}(-1)^{\alpha}\binom{k}{\alpha}\binom{m\alpha}{n}. \tag{131}$$

(iii) Given $$y=x^q(1+x^m)^p, \tag{132}$$

where q, m and p are any real numbers.

To find $\frac{d^n y}{dx^n}$.

By Leibnitz's theorem,

$$\frac{d^n y}{dx^n}=\sum_{k=0}^{n}\binom{n}{k}\frac{d^{n-k}}{dx^{n-k}}x^q\,\frac{d^k}{dx^k}(1+x^m)^p. \tag{133}$$

Applying (129) and

$$\frac{d^{n-k}}{dx^{n-k}}x^q=\binom{q}{n-k}(n-k)!\,x^{q-n+k}$$

to (133), we obtain

$$\frac{d^n y}{dx^n}=\frac{n!\,y}{x^n}\sum_{k=0}^{n}\binom{q}{n-k}\sum_{\alpha=0}^{k}(-1)^{\alpha}\binom{p}{\alpha}\frac{x^{m\alpha}}{(1+x^m)^{\alpha}}\sum_{\beta=0}^{\alpha}(-1)^{\beta}\binom{\alpha}{\beta}\binom{m\beta}{k}. \tag{134}$$

Now $$S_1=\sum_{\beta=0}^{\alpha}(-1)^{\beta}\binom{\alpha}{\beta}\binom{m\beta}{k}=0, \text{ if } k<\alpha, \tag{135}$$

as this principle depends on

$$S_2=\sum_{\beta=1}^{\alpha}(-1)^{\beta}\binom{\alpha}{\beta}\beta^{\gamma}=0, \text{ if } \gamma<\alpha. \tag{136}$$

We shall prove (136) first.

From $$(e^x-1)^\alpha=(-1)^\alpha(1-e^x)^\alpha=(-1)^\alpha\sum_{\beta=0}^{\alpha}(-1)^\beta\binom{\alpha}{\beta}e^{\beta x}$$

$$=(-1)^\alpha\sum_{\gamma=0}^{\infty}\frac{x^\gamma}{\gamma!}\sum_{\beta=1}^{\alpha}(-1)^\beta\binom{\alpha}{\beta}\beta^\gamma, \tag{137}$$

we conclude that $$S_2=(-1)^\alpha\gamma! \text{ times } ((x^\gamma))(e^x-1)^\alpha. \tag{138}$$

Now $$(e^x-1)^\alpha=x^\alpha\left(1+\frac{x}{2!}+\frac{x^2}{3!}+\dots\right)^\alpha, \tag{139}$$

and since in (139) x^α is the lowest power of x,
therefore $$S_2=0, \text{ if } \gamma<\alpha. \tag{140}$$

We are now prepared to prove (135).

Since $\binom{m\beta}{k}$ is a polynomial in β of degree k, we may write

$$\binom{m\beta}{k}=\frac{1}{k!}\sum_{\gamma=0}^{k}A_\gamma\beta^\gamma, \tag{141}$$

where A_γ is independent of β.

Therefore $$S_1=\frac{1}{k!}\sum_{\beta=0}^{\alpha}(-1)^\beta\binom{\alpha}{\beta}\sum_{\gamma=0}^{k}A_\gamma\beta^\gamma$$

$$=\frac{1}{k!}\sum_{\gamma=0}^{k}A_\gamma\sum_{\beta=1}^{\alpha}(-1)^\beta\binom{\alpha}{\beta}\beta^\gamma. \tag{142}$$

Now, if $k<\alpha$, and since $\gamma\leqq k$, hence $\gamma<\alpha$.
But $S_2=0$, if $\gamma<\alpha$; therefore from (142) also $S_1=0$.
Then (134) becomes

$$\frac{d^ny}{dx^n}=\frac{n!y}{x^n}\sum_{k=0}^{n}\binom{q}{n-k}\sum_{\alpha=0}^{\infty}(-1)^\alpha\binom{p}{\alpha}\frac{x^{m\alpha}}{(1+x^m)^\alpha}\sum_{\beta=0}^{\alpha}(-1)^\beta\binom{\alpha}{\beta}\binom{m\beta}{k} \tag{143}$$

$$=\frac{n!y}{x^n}\sum_{\alpha=0}^{\infty}(-1)^\alpha\binom{p}{\alpha}\frac{x^{m\alpha}}{(1+x^m)^\alpha}\sum_{\beta=0}^{\alpha}(-1)^\beta\binom{\alpha}{\beta}\sum_{k=0}^{n}\binom{q}{n-k}\binom{m\beta}{k}. \tag{144}$$

Now $$\sum_{k=0}^{n}\binom{q}{n-k}\binom{m\beta}{k}=\sum_{k=0}^{n}((x^{n-k}))(1+x)^q((x^k))(1+x)^{m\beta}$$

$$=((x^n))(1+x)^{q+m\beta}$$

$$=\binom{q+m\beta}{n}. \tag{145}$$

Applying (145) to (144), we have

$$\frac{d^ny}{dx^n}=\frac{n!y}{x^n}\sum_{\alpha=0}^{\infty}(-1)^\alpha\binom{p}{\alpha}\frac{x^{m\alpha}}{(1+x^m)^\alpha}\sum_{\beta=0}^{\alpha}(-1)^\beta\binom{\alpha}{\beta}\binom{q+m\beta}{n}. \tag{146}$$

And since $$\sum_{\beta=0}^{\alpha}(-1)^\beta\binom{\alpha}{\beta}\binom{q+m\beta}{n}=0, \text{ if } \alpha>n,^* \tag{147}$$

therefore α cannot be greater than n, and we obtain

$$\frac{d^ny}{dx^n}=\frac{n!y}{x^n}\sum_{\alpha=0}^{n}(-1)^\alpha\binom{p}{\alpha}\frac{x^{m\alpha}}{(1+x^m)^\alpha}\sum_{\beta=0}^{\alpha}(-1)^\beta\binom{\alpha}{\beta}\binom{q+m\beta}{n}. \tag{148}$$

* The proof is the same as for (135).

(iv) We shall find the expansion of (72) also by means of (83). Letting $7x^2-5x=u$, then by (83),

$$\frac{d^ny}{dx^n}=\sum_{k=1}^{n}\frac{(-1)^k}{k!}\sum_{\alpha=1}^{k}(-1)^{\alpha}\binom{k}{\alpha}(7x^2-5x)^{k-\alpha}\frac{d^n}{dx^n}(7x^2-5x)^{\alpha}\frac{d^k}{du^k}\log(3+u). \quad (149)$$

But $$\frac{d^n}{dx^n}(7x^2-5x)^{\alpha}=(-1)^{\alpha}n!\sum_{\beta=0}^{\alpha}(-1)^{\beta}\binom{\alpha}{\beta}5^{\alpha-\beta}7^{\beta}\binom{\alpha+\beta}{n}x^{\alpha+\beta-n}, \quad (150)$$

and $$\frac{d^k}{du^k}\log(3+u)=\frac{d^{k-1}}{du^{k-1}}\frac{1}{3+u}=(-1)^{k-1}\frac{(k-1)!}{(3+u)^k}. \quad (151)$$

Applying (150) and (151) to (149) gives

$$\frac{d^ny}{dx^n}=n!\sum_{k=1}^{n}\frac{1}{k}\sum_{\alpha=1}^{k}\binom{k}{\alpha}(7x-5)^{k-\alpha}\sum_{\beta=1}^{\alpha}(-1)^{\beta-1}\binom{\alpha}{\beta}\binom{\alpha+\beta}{n}5^{\alpha-\beta}7^{\beta}\frac{x^{k+\beta-n}}{(3+u)^k}. \quad (152)$$

Then $\left.\frac{d^ny}{dx^n}\right]_{x=0}=0$, unless $\beta=n-k$, in which case

$$\left.\frac{d^ny}{dx^n}\right]_{x=0}=(-1)^{n-1}n!\sum_{k=1}^{n}\frac{1}{k}\sum_{\alpha=1}^{k}(-1)^{\alpha}\binom{k}{\alpha}\binom{n+\alpha-k}{n}\binom{\alpha}{n-k}\left(\frac{7}{5}\right)^n\left(\frac{25}{21}\right)^k. \quad (153)$$

Now from $\binom{n+\alpha-k}{n}$, $\alpha\geqq k$, and from $\binom{k}{\alpha}$, $k\geqq\alpha$; hence $\alpha=k$, and (153) becomes

$$\left.\frac{d^ny}{dx^n}\right]_{x=0}=(-1)^{n-1}n!\left(\frac{7}{5}\right)^n\sum_{k=1}^{n}\frac{(-1)^k}{k}\binom{k}{n-k}\left(\frac{25}{21}\right)^k. \quad (154)$$

We then have

$$y=\log 3+\sum_{n=1}^{\infty}(-1)^{n-1}\left(\frac{7}{5}\right)^n x^n\sum_{k=1}^{n}\frac{(-1)^k}{k}\binom{k}{n-k}\left(\frac{25}{21}\right)^k. \quad (155)$$

But since $k\geqq n-k$, $\left[\frac{n+1}{2}\right]$ is the smallest value of k, therefore

$$y=\log 3+\sum_{n=1}^{\infty}(-1)^{n-1}\left(\frac{7}{5}\right)^n x^n\sum_{k=\left[\frac{n+1}{2}\right]}^{n}\frac{(-1)^k}{k}\binom{k}{n-k}\left(\frac{25}{21}\right)^k; \quad (156)$$

and letting $n-k=k'$, we obtain

$$y=\log 3-\sum_{n=1}^{\infty}\left(\frac{5}{3}\right)^n x^n\sum_{k=0}^{\left[\frac{n}{2}\right]}\frac{(-1)^k}{n-k}\binom{n-k}{k}\left(\frac{21}{25}\right)^k,$$

which is the same as (82).

(v) Given $$y=(1-x^3+x^7)^p, \quad (157)$$

where p is any real number.

To find the expansion of y.

Let $x^3-x^7=u$; then

$$\frac{d^nu^{\alpha}}{dx^n}=\frac{d^n}{dx^n}\sum_{\beta=0}^{\alpha}(-1)^{\beta}\binom{\alpha}{\beta}x^{3\alpha+4\beta}=n!\sum_{\beta=0}^{\alpha}(-1)^{\beta}\binom{\alpha}{\beta}\binom{3\alpha+4\beta}{n}x^{3\alpha+4\beta-n}, \quad (158)$$

and $$\frac{d^k}{du^k}(1-u)^p=(-1)^k k!\binom{p}{k}(1-u)^{p-k}. \quad (159)$$

Applying (158) and (159) to (83), we have

$$\frac{d^ny}{dx^n}=n!\sum_{k=1}^{n}(-1)^k\binom{p}{k}(1-u)^{p-k}\sum_{a=1}^{k}(-1)^a\binom{k}{a}(1-x^4)^{k-a}\sum_{\beta=1}^{a}(-1)^\beta \binom{a}{\beta}\binom{3a+4\beta}{n}x^{3k+4\beta-n}. \quad (160)$$

Then $$\left.\frac{d^ny}{dx^n}\right]_{x=0}=0, \text{ unless } 3k+4\beta=n; \quad (161)$$

and since $3a+4\beta \geqq n$, it follows that $3a-3k\geqq 0$, and $a\geqq k$. But from $\binom{k}{a}$, $a\leqq k$; hence $a=k$, and

$$\left.\frac{d^ny}{dx^n}\right]_{x=0}=n!\sum_{k=1}^{n}\binom{p}{k}\sum_{\beta=0}^{k}(-1)^\beta\binom{k}{\beta}\binom{3k+4\beta}{n}\left.x^{3k+4\beta-n}\right]_{x=0}. \quad (162)$$

The solutions of $3k+4\beta=n$ are,

$$\left.\begin{aligned}k&=k_0, \quad k_0-4, \ \dots, \ k_0-4(m-1),\\ \beta&=\beta_0, \quad \beta_0+3, \ \dots, \ \beta_0+3(m-1),\end{aligned}\right\} \quad (163)$$

where $$k_0=4\left[\frac{n}{3}\right]-n \quad \text{and} \quad \beta_0=n-3\left[\frac{n}{3}\right].$$

Now $\beta\leqq k$, hence $\beta_0+3(m-1)\leqq k_0-4(m-1)$, or

$$m\leqq 1+\left[\frac{n}{3}\right]-\frac{2n}{7}.$$

Therefore

$$\left.\frac{d^ny}{dx^n}\right]_{x=0}=(-1)^n n!\sum_{m=1}^{\left[1+\left[\frac{n}{3}\right]-\frac{2n}{7}\right]}(-1)^{\left[\frac{n}{3}\right]-m-1}\binom{p}{4\left[\frac{n}{3}\right]-n-4(m-1)}\binom{4\left[\frac{n}{3}\right]-n-4(m-1)}{n-3\left[\frac{n}{3}\right]+3(m-1)} \quad (164)$$

and $$(1-x^3+x^7)^p=\sum_{n=0}^{\infty}(-1)^n x^n\sum_{m=1}^{\left[1+\left[\frac{n}{3}\right]-\frac{2n}{7}\right]}(-1)^{\left[\frac{n}{3}\right]-m-1}\binom{p}{4\left[\frac{n}{3}\right]-n-4(m-1)}\binom{4\left[\frac{n}{3}\right]-n-4(m-1)}{n-3\left[\frac{n}{3}\right]+3(m-1)}. \quad (165)$$

Expanding (157) by the Binomial Theorem, we have

$$y=\sum_{k=0}^{\infty}\sum_{\beta=0}^{k}(-1)^{k+\beta}\binom{p}{k}\binom{k}{\beta}x^{3k+4\beta},$$

and continuing as above we obtain (165).

Show that

$$(1+x^7)^{p_1}(1-x^3)^{p_2}$$

$$=\sum_{n=0}^{\infty}(-1)^{\left[\frac{2n}{7}\right]}x^n\sum_{k=0}^{\left[\frac{n}{3}\right]-\left[\frac{2n}{7}\right]}(-1)^k\binom{p_1}{n-3\left[\frac{2n}{7}\right]-3k}\binom{p_2}{-2n+7\left[\frac{2n}{7}\right]+7k}.^* \quad (166)$$

* For additional expansions see Appendix.

(vi) Given $y=e^{cx^p}$, p any real number.

To find $\frac{d^ny}{dx^n}$.

Letting in (83) $u=cx^p$, then

$$\frac{d^ny}{dx^n}=\frac{n!\,y}{x^n}\sum_{k=1}^{n}\frac{(-1)^k}{k!}c^kx^{pk}\sum_{\alpha=1}^{k}(-1)^\alpha\binom{k}{\alpha}\binom{p\alpha}{n}, \tag{167}$$

and if p is a positive integer,

$$\frac{d^ny}{dx^n}=\frac{n!\,y}{x^n}\sum_{k=\left[\frac{n+p-1}{p}\right]}^{n}\frac{(-1)^k}{k!}c^kx^{pk}\sum_{\alpha=\left[\frac{n+p-1}{p}\right]}^{k}(-1)^\alpha\binom{k}{\alpha}\binom{p\alpha}{n}. \tag{168}$$

11. We shall next obtain a formula by which the higher derivatives of

$$\left(\frac{x^2}{x^3-1}\right)^p,\quad \frac{x^p}{\sin^p x},\quad \frac{x^p}{(e^x-1)^p}$$

and similar expressions can be more readily found than by (83).

If u is a function of x, we shall show that

$$\frac{d^n}{dx^n}u^{-p}=p\binom{n+p}{p}\sum_{k=1}^{n}\frac{(-1)^k}{p+k}\binom{n}{k}u^{-p-k}\frac{d^n}{dx^n}u^k. \tag{169}$$

Letting $y=u^p$, then

$$\frac{d^n}{dx^n}u^p=\sum_{k=1}^{n}(-1)^k\binom{p}{k}\sum_{\alpha=1}^{k}(-1)^\alpha\binom{k}{\alpha}u^{p-\alpha}\frac{d^n}{dx^n}u^\alpha,\text{ by (83)},$$

$$=\sum_{\alpha=1}^{n}(-1)^\alpha u^{p-\alpha}\frac{d^n}{dx^n}u^\alpha\sum_{k=\alpha}^{n}(-1)^k\binom{k}{\alpha}\binom{p}{k},\text{ by (97)}; \tag{170}$$

and since
$$\binom{k}{\alpha}\binom{p}{k}=\binom{p}{\alpha}\binom{p-\alpha}{k-\alpha}, \tag{171}$$

$$\frac{d^n}{dx^n}u^p=\sum_{\alpha=1}^{n}(-1)^\alpha\binom{p}{\alpha}u^{p-\alpha}\frac{d^n}{dx^n}u^\alpha\sum_{k=\alpha}^{n}(-1)^k\binom{p-\alpha}{k-\alpha}. \tag{172}$$

Letting $k-\alpha=k'$, then

$$S=\sum_{k=\alpha}^{n}(-1)^k\binom{p-\alpha}{k-\alpha}=(-1)^\alpha\sum_{k=0}^{n-\alpha}(-1)^k\binom{p-\alpha}{k}; \tag{173}$$

and letting $n-\alpha-k=k'$,

$$S=(-1)^n\sum_{k=0}^{n-\alpha}(-1)^k\binom{p-\alpha}{n-\alpha-k}$$

$$=(-1)^n\sum_{k=0}^{n-\alpha}((x^k))(1+x)^{-1}((x^{n-\alpha-k}))(1+x)^{p-\alpha}$$

$$=(-1)^n((x^{n-\alpha}))(1+x)^{p-\alpha-1}$$

$$=(-1)^n\binom{p-\alpha-1}{n-\alpha}. \tag{174}$$

Then (170) becomes, changing α into k,

$$\frac{d^n}{dx^n}u^p=(-1)^n\sum_{k=1}^{n}(-1)^k\binom{p}{k}\binom{p-k-1}{n-k}u^{p-k}\frac{d^n}{dx^n}x^k. \tag{175}$$

If p is negative, then

$$\binom{-p}{k}=(-1)^k\binom{p+k-1}{k}, \tag{176}$$

$$\binom{-p-k-1}{n-k}=(-1)^{n-k}\binom{n+p}{n-k}, \tag{177}$$

and

$$\binom{p+k-1}{k}\binom{n+p}{n-k}=p\binom{n+p}{p}\binom{n}{k}\frac{1}{p+k}. \tag{178}$$

Applying (176)–(178) to (175) gives (169).

(i) Given

$$y=\left(\frac{x^2}{x^3-1}\right)^p. \tag{179}$$

To find $\dfrac{d^ny}{dx^n}$.

Letting $\dfrac{1}{y^{1/p}}=u$, then by (169),

$$\frac{d^n}{dx^n}u^{-p}=n!\,p\binom{n+p}{n}\sum_{k=1}^{n}\frac{(-1)^k}{p+k}\binom{n}{k}\left(\frac{x^3-1}{x^2}\right)^{-p-k}\frac{d^n}{dx^n}\left(x-\frac{1}{x^2}\right)^k \tag{180}$$

$$=n!\,p\binom{n+p}{n}\sum_{k=1}^{n}\frac{(-1)^k}{p+k}\binom{n}{k}\frac{1}{(x^3-1)^{p+k}}\sum_{\alpha=1}^{k}(-1)^\alpha\binom{k}{\alpha}\binom{k-3\alpha}{n}x^{3k-3\alpha+2p-n}. \tag{181}$$

Now if $x=0$, $3k-3\alpha=n-2p$, and $n\geqq 2p$, then

$$\left.\frac{d^n}{dx^n}u^{-p}\right]_{x=0}=(-1)^n(-1)^{\frac{n+p}{3}}n!\,p\binom{n+p}{n}\sum_{k=1}^{n}\frac{(-1)^k}{p+k}\binom{n}{k}\binom{2p+2k-1}{n}\binom{k}{\frac{n+p}{3}-p}, \tag{182}$$

and

$$\left(\frac{x^2}{x^3-1}\right)^p=p\sum_{n=2p}^{\infty}(-1)^n(-1)^{\frac{n+p}{3}}x^n\binom{n+p}{n}\sum_{k=1}^{n}\frac{(-1)^k}{p+k}\binom{n}{k}\binom{2p+2k-1}{n}\binom{k}{\frac{n+p}{3}-p}, \tag{183}$$

only those values of n being admissible for which $n+p$ is a multiple of 3.

(ii) Glaisher* obtains the coefficients of the expansion of

$$\frac{x}{\log(1+x)}$$

in the form of determinants. The method used cannot, however, be conveniently applied to the expansion of the more general form

$$y=\frac{x^p}{\log^p(1+x)}. \tag{184}$$

* *The Messenger of Mathematics*, vol. vi. p. 50.

Now, letting
$$u=\frac{\log(1+x)}{x},\tag{185}$$
then, since
$$u^{-p-k}\Big]_{x\doteq 0}=1,$$
we have by (169),
$$\frac{d^n}{dx^n}\left[\frac{\log(1+x)}{x}\right]^{-p}_{x\doteq 0}=p\binom{n+p}{n}\sum_{k=1}^{n}\frac{(-1)^k}{p+k}\binom{n}{k}\frac{d^n}{dx^n}u^k\Big]_{x\doteq 0}.\tag{186}$$

To find $\frac{d^n}{dx^n}u^k\Big]_{x\doteq 0}$, we write
$$x^k u^k=\log^k(1+x),\ \text{by (185)};$$
then by Leibnitz's theorem,
$$\sum_{a=0}^{n+k}\binom{n+k}{a}\frac{d^{n+k-a}}{dx^{n+k-a}}x^k\frac{d^a}{dx^a}u^k\Big]_{x\doteq 0}=\frac{d^{n+k}}{dx^{n+k}}\log^k(1+x)\Big]_{x\doteq 0}.\tag{187}$$

Now as the first member of (187) vanishes except when $a=n$, therefore
$$\binom{n+k}{n}k!\frac{d^n}{dx^n}u^k\Big]_{x\doteq 0}=\frac{d^{n+k}}{dx^{n+k}}\log^k(1+x)\Big]_{x\doteq 0}$$
and
$$\frac{d^n}{dx^n}u^k\Big]_{x\doteq 0}=\frac{n!}{(n+k)!}\frac{d^{n+k}}{dx^{n+k}}\log^k(1+x)\Big]_{x\doteq 0}.\tag{188}$$

But
$$\frac{d^m}{dx^m}\log^k(1+x)\Big]_{x\doteq 0}=\frac{d^m}{dx^m}\log^k x\Big]_{x\doteq 1},\tag{189}$$
and by successive differentiation we find
$$\frac{d^m}{dx^m}\log^k x=\frac{(-1)^{m-1}}{x^m}\sum_{a=1}^{m}(-1)^{a-1}Q_{m-1,m-a}\binom{k}{a}a!(\log x)^{k-a};\tag{190}$$
hence
$$\frac{d^{n+k}}{dx^{n+k}}\log^k(1+x)\Big]_{x\doteq 0}=\frac{d^{n+k}}{dx^{n+k}}\log^k x\Big]_{x\doteq 1}$$
$$=(-1)^n k!\,Q_{n+k-1,n}.\tag{191}$$

Applying (191) to (188), we have
$$\frac{d^n}{dx^n}u^k\Big]_{x\doteq 0}=(-1)^n\frac{n!\,k!}{(n+k)!}Q_{n+k-1,n}.\tag{192}$$

Then by means of (192) we obtain from (186),
$$\frac{d^n}{dx^n}u^{-p}\Big]_{x\doteq 0}=(-1)^n n!\,p\binom{n+p}{n}\sum_{k=1}^{n}\frac{(-1)^k}{p+k}\binom{n}{k}\frac{k!}{(n+k)!}Q_{n+k-1,n}\tag{193}$$
and
$$\frac{x^p}{\log^p(1+x)}=\frac{1}{(p-1)!}\sum_{n=1}^{\infty}(-1)^n(n+p)!\,x^n\sum_{k=1}^{n}\frac{(-1)^k}{(n+k)!\,(n-k)!}Q_{n+k-1,n}.\tag{194}$$

We shall now show that $Q_{n,k}$ is the sum of the products of the numbers 1, 2, 3, ..., n taken k at a time.

Letting $m-a=a'$ in (190), we have
$$\frac{d^m}{dx^m}\log^k x=\frac{1}{x^m}\sum_{a=0}^{m-1}(-1)^a Q_{m-1,a}\frac{d^{m-a}}{d(\log x)^{m-a}}\log^k x.\tag{195}$$

If we let D represent the operation of differentiation with respect to $\log x$, then

$$\frac{d}{dx}\log^k x = \frac{1}{x} D \log^k x, \tag{196}$$

$$\frac{d^2}{dx^2}\log^k x = \frac{1}{x^2} D^2 \log^k x - \frac{1}{x^2} D \log^k x$$

$$= \frac{1}{x^2} D(D-1)\log^k x. \tag{197}$$

If we now assume that

$$\frac{d^m}{dx^m}\log^k x = \frac{1}{x^m} D(D-1)\dots(D-m+1)\log^k x, \tag{198}$$

we find by differentiation that

$$\frac{d^{m+1}}{dx^{m+1}}\log^k x = \frac{1}{x^{m+1}} D(D-1)\dots(D-m)\log^k x, \tag{199}$$

thus completing the induction.

An expression for $Q_{n,k}$ will be given in a subsequent chapter.

12. The higher derivatives of functions may also be found from their expansions, if they can be readily obtained without the use of Calculus. The processes, however, by which the results are arrived at are in most cases very laborious. The methods will be illustrated by the following examples.

(i) Given $y=(1+x^m)^p$, m and p being real numbers.

To find $\frac{d^n y}{dx^n}$ from the expansion

$$y = \sum_{k=0}^{\infty} \binom{p}{k} x^{mk}. \tag{200}$$

From (200)

$$\frac{d^n y}{dx^n} = n! \sum_{k=0}^{\infty} \binom{p}{k}\binom{mk}{n} x^{mk-n}. \tag{201}$$

Introducing in the second member of (201) the function

$$y(1+x^m)^{-p} = y\sum_{\alpha=0}^{\infty}\binom{-p}{\alpha} x^{m\alpha} = 1,$$

we obtain

$$\frac{d^n y}{dx^n} = \frac{n!\,y}{x^n}\sum_{\alpha=0}^{\infty}\binom{-p}{\alpha}\sum_{k=0}^{\infty}\binom{p}{k}\binom{mk}{n} x^{m(k+\alpha)}. \tag{202}$$

Letting $k+\alpha=\alpha'$ gives

$$\frac{d^n y}{dx^n} = \frac{n!\,y}{x^n}\sum_{\alpha=0}^{\infty}\binom{-p}{\alpha}\sum_{k=\alpha}^{\infty}\binom{p}{k}\binom{mk}{n} x^{mk+\alpha}. \tag{203}$$

Then by means of (68) and letting $k-\alpha=\alpha'$, (203) becomes

$$\frac{d^n y}{dx^n} = \frac{n!\,y}{x^n}\sum_{k=0}^{\infty} x^{mk}\sum_{\alpha=0}^{k}\binom{-p}{k-\alpha}\binom{p}{\alpha}\binom{m\alpha}{n}. \tag{204}$$

Now $$\binom{-p}{k-\alpha}=\sum_{\beta=0}^{k-\alpha}(-1)^{\beta}\binom{p-\alpha}{\beta}\binom{-\alpha-\beta}{k-\alpha-\beta}.^{*} \tag{205}$$

Letting $\alpha+\beta=\beta'$, then

$$\binom{-p}{k-\alpha}=(-1)^{\alpha}\sum_{\beta=\alpha}^{k}(-1)^{\beta}\binom{-\beta}{k-\beta}\binom{p-\alpha}{\beta-\alpha}. \tag{206}$$

But $$\binom{p}{\alpha}\binom{p-\alpha}{\beta-\alpha}=\binom{p}{\beta}\binom{\beta}{\alpha}; \tag{207}$$

hence $$\binom{-p}{k-\alpha}=(-1)^{\alpha}\frac{1}{\binom{p}{\alpha}}\sum_{\beta=\alpha}^{k}(-1)^{\beta}\binom{-\beta}{k-\beta}\binom{p}{\beta}\binom{\beta}{\alpha} \tag{208}$$

and $$\frac{d^ny}{dx^n}=\frac{n!\,y}{x^n}\sum_{k=0}^{\infty}x^{mk}\sum_{\alpha=0}^{k}(-1)^{\alpha}\binom{m\alpha}{n}\sum_{\beta=\alpha}^{k}(-1)^{\beta}\binom{p}{\beta}\binom{-\beta}{k-\beta}\binom{\beta}{\alpha}$$

$$=\frac{n!\,y}{x^n}\sum_{k=0}^{\infty}x^{mk}\sum_{\beta=0}^{k}(-1)^{\beta}\binom{p}{\beta}\binom{-\beta}{k-\beta}\sum_{\alpha=0}^{\beta}(-1)^{\alpha}\binom{\beta}{\alpha}\binom{m\alpha}{n}, \text{ by (68)},$$

$$=\frac{n!\,y}{x^n}\sum_{\beta=0}^{\infty}(-1)^{\beta}\binom{p}{\beta}\sum_{\alpha=0}^{\beta}(-1)^{\alpha}\binom{\beta}{\alpha}\binom{m\alpha}{n}\sum_{k=\beta}^{\infty}\binom{-\beta}{k-\beta}x^{mk}, \text{ by (97)}. \tag{209}$$

But $$\sum_{k=\beta}^{\infty}\binom{-\beta}{k-\beta}x^{mk}=\sum_{k=0}^{\infty}\binom{-\beta}{k}x^{m(k+\beta)}=\frac{x^{m\beta}}{(1+x^m)^{\beta}};$$

therefore $$\frac{d^ny}{dx^n}=\frac{n!\,y}{x^n}\sum_{\beta=0}^{\infty}(-1)^{\beta}\binom{p}{\beta}\frac{x^{m\beta}}{(1+x^m)^{\beta}}\sum_{\alpha=0}^{\beta}(-1)^{\alpha}\binom{\beta}{\alpha}\binom{m\alpha}{n}. \tag{210}$$

Now, if $\beta>n$, $$\sum_{\alpha=0}^{\beta}(-1)^{\alpha}\binom{\beta}{\alpha}\binom{m\alpha}{n}=0, \text{ by (135)};$$

we then obtain

$$\frac{d^ny}{dx^n}=\frac{n!\,y}{x^n}\sum_{k=0}^{n}(-1)^{k}\binom{p}{k}\frac{x^{mk}}{(1+x^m)^{k}}\sum_{\alpha=0}^{k}(-1)^{\alpha}\binom{k}{\alpha}\binom{m\alpha}{n},$$

which is the same as (129).

* Any Binomial Coefficient can be expressed as the sum of the products of two or more Binomial Coefficients.

$$\binom{a}{b}=\sum_{k=0}^{b}\binom{a-x}{k}\binom{x}{b-k}, \text{ where } x>b-k \text{ and } <a-k;$$

$$\binom{-a}{b}=(-1)^{b}\binom{b+a-1}{b}=(-1)^{b}\sum_{k=0}^{b}\binom{a}{k}\binom{b-1}{b-k}.$$

We then have

$$\binom{-p}{k-a}=(-1)^{k-a}\binom{k-a+p-1}{\beta+k-a-\beta}=(-1)^{k-a}\sum_{\beta=0}^{k-a}((x^{\beta}))(1+x)^{p-a}((x^{k-a-\beta}))(1+x)^{k-1}$$

$$=(-1)^{k-a}\sum_{\beta=0}^{k-a}\binom{p-a}{\beta}\binom{k-1}{k-a-\beta},$$

and by means of $\binom{k-1}{k-a-\beta}=(-1)^{k-a-\beta}\binom{-a-\beta}{k-a-\beta}$, we obtain (205).

(ii) Given $y=e^{cx^p}$, p any real number. (211)

To find $\frac{d^ny}{dx^n}$ from the expansion

$$y=\sum_{k=0}^{\infty}\frac{c^kx^{pk}}{k!}. \tag{212}$$

Then
$$\frac{d^ny}{dx^n}=\frac{n!}{x^n}\sum_{k=0}^{\infty}\frac{c^k}{k!}\binom{pk}{n}x^{pk}. \tag{213}$$

Introducing in (213) the function

$$ye^{-cx^p}=y\sum_{a=0}^{\infty}(-1)^a\frac{c^a}{a!}x^{pa}=1,$$

we have
$$\frac{d^ny}{dx^n}=\frac{n!\,y}{x^n}\sum_{a=0}^{\infty}\frac{(-1)^a}{a!}\sum_{k=0}^{\infty}\frac{c^{a+k}}{k!}\binom{pk}{n}x^{p(a+k)}. \tag{214}$$

Letting $a+k=a'$, and applying (68) to the result, we obtain

$$\frac{d^ny}{dx^n}=\frac{n!\,y}{x^n}\sum_{k=0}^{\infty}\frac{c^k}{k!}x^{pk}\sum_{a=0}^{k}(-1)^a\binom{k}{a}\binom{p\,\overline{k-a}}{n}. \tag{215}$$

Letting $k-a=a'$, then

$$\frac{d^ny}{dx^n}=\frac{n!\,y}{x^n}\sum_{k=0}^{\infty}\frac{(-1)^k}{k!}c^kx^{pk}\sum_{a=0}^{k}(-1)^a\binom{k}{a}\binom{pa}{n}; \tag{216}$$

and since, if $k>n$, $\sum_{a=0}^{k}(-1)^a\binom{k}{a}\binom{pa}{n}=0$, by (135),

therefore
$$\frac{d^ny}{dx^n}=\frac{n!\,y}{x^n}\sum_{k=1}^{n}\frac{(-1)^k}{k!}c^kx^{pk}\sum_{a=1}^{k}(-1)^a\binom{k}{a}\binom{pa}{n},$$

which is the same as (167).

CHAPTER II.

HIGHER DERIVATIVES OF TRIGONOMETRIC FUNCTIONS AND THEIR EXPANSIONS.

1. We shall first find the expansions of $\sin x$ and $\cos x$.

(i) If $y = \sin x$, then
$$\frac{d^n y}{dx^n} = \sin\left(x + \frac{n\pi}{2}\right) \tag{1}$$
and
$$y = \sum_{n=0}^{\infty} \frac{d^n y}{dx^n}\Big]_{x=0} \frac{x^n}{n!}. \tag{2}$$
Now
$$\frac{d^n y}{dx^n}\Big]_{x=0} = \sin\frac{n\pi}{2}$$
$$= 0, \text{ if } n \text{ is even,}$$
$$= (-1)^{\left[\frac{n}{2}\right]}, \text{ if } n \text{ is odd.} \tag{3}$$
Writing $2n+1$ for n in (2), and since
$$\frac{d^{2n+1} y}{dx^{2n+1}}\Big]_{x=0} = (-1)^n, \text{ by (3),}$$
therefore
$$y = \sum_{n=0}^{\infty} (-1)^n \frac{x^{2n+1}}{(2n+1)!}. \tag{4}$$

(ii) If $y = \cos x$, then
$$\frac{d^n y}{dx^n} = \cos\left(x + \frac{n\pi}{2}\right), \tag{5}$$
and
$$\frac{d^n y}{dx^n}\Big]_{x=0} = \cos\frac{n\pi}{2}$$
$$= (-1)^{\left[\frac{n}{2}\right]}, \text{ if } n \text{ is even,}$$
$$= 0, \text{ if } n \text{ is odd.}$$
We then obtain
$$y = \sum_{n=0}^{\infty} (-1)^n \frac{x^{2n}}{(2n)!}. \tag{6}$$

2. (i) Given
$$y = \tan x. \tag{7}$$
To find $\frac{d^n y}{dx^n}$ and the expansion of y.

Now
$$y = \frac{2i}{e^{2ix}+1} - i,$$
and
$$\frac{d^n y}{dx^n} = 2i \frac{d^n}{dx^n} \frac{1}{u+1}, \text{ where } u = e^{2ix}. \tag{8}$$

Then, by Ch. I. (83),

$$\frac{d^n y}{dx^n}=(2i)^{n+1}\sum_{k=1}^{n}\sum_{\alpha=1}^{k}(-1)^\alpha\binom{k}{\alpha}\alpha^n\frac{u^k}{(u+1)^{k+1}}. \tag{9}$$

But

$$\frac{u^k}{(u+1)^{k+1}}=\frac{(\cos x+i\sin x)^{k-1}}{2^{k+1}\cos^{k-1}x\cos^2 x}$$

$$=\frac{1}{2^{k+1}}\sec^{k+1}x\,(\cos\overline{k-1}\,x+i\sin\overline{k-1}\,x)\,; \tag{10}$$

and since $\frac{d^n y}{dx^n}$ is real, then, by means of (10), we obtain from (9)

$$\frac{d^{2n}}{dx^{2n}}\tan x=(-1)^{n+1}2^{2n}\sum_{k=1}^{2n}\frac{1}{2^k}\sec^{k+1}x\sin(k-1)x\sum_{\alpha=1}^{k}(-1)^\alpha\binom{k}{\alpha}\alpha^{2n} \tag{11}$$

and

$$\frac{d^{2n+1}}{dx^{2n+1}}\tan x=(-1)^{n+1}2^{2n+1}\sum_{k=1}^{2n+1}\frac{1}{2^k}\sec^{k+1}x\cos(k-1)x\sum_{\alpha=1}^{k}(-1)^\alpha\binom{k}{\alpha}\alpha^{2n+1}. \tag{12}$$

Combining (11) and (12) gives

$$\frac{d^n}{dx^n}\tan x=(-1)^{\left[\frac{n+2}{2}\right]}2^n\sum_{k=1}^{n}\frac{1}{2^k}\sec^{k+1}x\sin\left(\frac{\pi}{2}\beta+\overline{k-1}\,x\right)\sum_{\alpha=1}^{k}(-1)^\alpha\binom{k}{\alpha}\alpha^n, \tag{13}$$

where $\beta=\frac{1-(-1)^n}{2}$.

Now

$$\tan x=\sum_{n=1}^{\infty}\frac{d^n}{dx^n}\tan x\Big]_{x=0}\frac{x^n}{n!}, \tag{14}$$

and since

$$\frac{d^{2n}}{dx^{2n}}\tan x\Big]_{x=0}=0,\ \text{by (12)}, \tag{15}$$

and

$$\frac{d^{2n+1}}{dx^{2n+1}}\tan x\Big]_{x=0}=(-1)^{n-1}2^{2n+1}\sum_{k=1}^{2n+1}\frac{1}{2^k}\sum_{\alpha=1}^{k}(-1)^\alpha\binom{k}{\alpha}\alpha^{2n+1},\ \text{by (13)}\,; \tag{16}$$

therefore

$$\tan x=\sum_{n=0}^{\infty}(-1)^{n-1}\frac{x^{2n+1}}{(2n+1)!}2^{2n+1}\sum_{k=1}^{2n+1}\frac{1}{2^k}\sum_{\alpha=1}^{k}(-1)^\alpha\binom{k}{\alpha}\alpha^{2n+1}. \tag{17}$$

This result can also be obtained in the following way :

Writing

$$\frac{u^k}{(u+1)^{k+1}}=\frac{1}{2^{k+1}}\sec^2 x(1+i\tan x)^{k-1} \tag{18}$$

in place of (10), then (9) becomes

$$\frac{d^n y}{dx^n}=(2i)^{n+1}\sec^2 x\sum_{k=1}^{n}\frac{1}{2^{k+1}}(1+i\tan x)^{k-1}\sum_{\alpha=1}^{k}(-1)^\alpha\binom{k}{\alpha}\alpha^n. \tag{19}$$

Separating the expansion of $(1+i\tan x)^{k-1}$ into its real and imaginary parts, we have

$$(1+i\tan x)^{k-1}=N_{2\beta}+iN_{2\beta+1},$$

where

$$N_{2\beta}=\sum_{\beta=0}^{\left[\frac{k-1}{2}\right]}(-1)^\beta\binom{k-1}{2\beta}\tan^{2\beta}x, \tag{20}$$

and
$$N_{2\beta+1}=\sum_{\beta=0}^{\left[\frac{k-2}{2}\right]}(-1)^{\beta}\binom{k-1}{2\beta+1}\tan^{2\beta+1}x. \tag{21}$$

Therefore, when n is even,

$$\frac{d^{2n}}{dx^{2n}}\tan x=(-1)^{n-1}2^{2n}\sec^2 x\sum_{k=1}^{2n}\frac{1}{2^k}\sum_{a=1}^{k}(-1)^a\binom{k}{a}a^{2n}N_{2\beta+1}, \tag{22}$$

and when n is odd,

$$\frac{d^{2n+1}}{dx^{2n+1}}\tan x=(-1)^{n-1}2^{2n+1}\sec^2 x\sum_{k=1}^{2n+1}\frac{1}{2^k}\sum_{a=1}^{k}(-1)^a\binom{k}{a}a^{2n+1}N_{2\beta}. \tag{23}$$

Combining (22) and (23), we have

$$\frac{d^n}{dx^n}\tan x=(-1)^{\left[\frac{n+2}{2}\right]}2^n\sec^2 x\sum_{k=1}^{n}\frac{1}{2^k}\sum_{a=1}^{k}(-1)^a\binom{k}{a}a^nN_{2\beta+\gamma}, \tag{24}$$

where $\gamma=\dfrac{1+(-1)^n}{2}$.

To find the expansion of $\tan x$, we let $x=0$ in (24), and then obtain (16), and finally (17).

We arrive at (16) more directly by letting $x=0$ in (9).

(ii) The expansion of $y=\tan x$ can also be obtained without the use of Calculus.

We have
$$y=\frac{\sin x}{(1-\sin^2 x)^{\frac{1}{2}}}=\sum_{k=0}^{\infty}(-1)^k\binom{-\frac{1}{2}}{k}\sin^{2k+1}x. \tag{25}$$

To find the expansion of $\sin^{2k+1}x$ we proceed as follows:

$$\sin^{2k+1}x=\frac{(-1)^{k-1}i}{2^{2k+1}}(e^{ix}-e^{-ix})^{2k+1} \tag{26}$$

$$=\frac{(-1)^{k-1}i}{2^{2k+1}}\sum_{a=0}^{2k+1}(-1)^a\binom{2k+1}{a}e^{(2k+1-2a)ix}$$

$$=\frac{(-1)^{k-1}}{2^{2k+1}}\sum_{n=0}^{\infty}i^{n+1}\frac{x^n}{n!}\sum_{a=0}^{2k+1}(-1)^a\binom{2k+1}{a}(2k+1-2a)^n. \tag{27}$$

We shall first reduce

$$S=\sum_{a=0}^{2k+1}(-1)^a\binom{2k+1}{a}(2k+1-2a)^n. \tag{28}$$

Now

$$S=\sum_{a=0}^{k}(-1)^a\binom{2k+1}{a}(2k+1-2a)^n+\sum_{a=k+1}^{2k+1}(-1)^a\binom{2k+1}{a}(2k+1-2a)^n. \tag{29}$$

Designating in (29) the first summation by S_1 and the second summation by S_2, and letting in S_2, $2k+1-a=a'$, then

$$S_2=-\sum_{a=0}^{k}(-1)^a\binom{2k+1}{a}(2a-2k-1)^n$$

$$=(-1)^{n-1}\sum_{a=0}^{k}(-1)^a\binom{2k+1}{a}(2k+1-2a)^n=(-1)^{n-1}S_1. \tag{30}$$

Applying (30) to (29) gives

$$S=[1+(-1)^{n-1}]S_1 \tag{31}$$

$$=0, \text{ when } n \text{ is even.} \tag{32}$$

But if n is odd and $\gtreqless k$, we obtain from (31)

$$S=2\sum_{a=0}^{k}(-1)^a\binom{2k+1}{a}(2k+1-2a)^{2n+1}. \tag{33}$$

Letting $k-a=a'$,

$$S=2(-1)^k\sum_{a=0}^{k}(-1)^a\binom{2k+1}{k-a}(2a+1)^{2n+1}. \tag{34}$$

Then, by means of (34) and remembering that $n\gtreqless k$, (27) becomes

$$\sin^{2k+1}x=\frac{1}{2^{2k}}\sum_{n=k}^{\infty}(-1)^n\frac{x^{2n+1}}{(2n+1)!}\sum_{a=0}^{k}(-1)^a\binom{2k+1}{k-a}(2a+1)^{2n+1}. \tag{35}$$

Applying (35) to (25) gives

$$\tan x=\sum_{k=0}^{\infty}\frac{(-1)^k}{2^{2k}}\binom{-\frac{1}{2}}{k}\sum_{n=k}^{\infty}(-1)^n\frac{x^{2n+1}}{(2n+1)!}\sum_{a=0}^{k}(-1)^a\binom{2k+1}{k-a}(2a+1)^{2n+1}, \tag{36}$$

from which, by means of $\binom{-\frac{1}{2}}{k}=\frac{(-1)^k}{2^{2k}}\binom{2k}{k}$ and the principle, Ch. I. (68), we obtain

$$\tan x=\sum_{n=0}^{\infty}(-1)^n\frac{x^{2n+1}}{(2n+1)!}\sum_{k=0}^{n}\frac{1}{2^{4k}}\binom{2k}{k}\sum_{a=0}^{k}(-1)^a\binom{2k+1}{k-a}(2a+1)^{2n+1}. \tag{37}$$

3. (i) Given $y=\sec x$.* (38)

To find $\frac{d^ny}{dx^n}$ and the expansion of y.

Letting in Ch. I. (83) $u=\cos x$, we have

$$\frac{d^ny}{dx^n}=\sum_{k=1}^{n}\sum_{a=1}^{k}(-1)^a\binom{k}{a}u^{-a-1}\frac{d^n}{dx^n}u^a \tag{39}$$

$$=\sum_{a=1}^{n}(-1)^a\sec^{a+1}x\frac{d^n}{dx^n}\cos^a x\sum_{k=a}^{n}\binom{k}{a}, \text{ by Ch. I. (97).} \tag{40}$$

But

$$\sum_{k=a}^{n}\binom{k}{a}=((x^a))\sum_{k=a}^{n}(1+x)^k$$

$$=((x^{a+1}))[(1+x)^{n+1}-(1+x)^a]$$

$$=\binom{n+1}{a+1}, \tag{41}$$

* Stern, *Journal für Mathematik*, vol. 79, pp. 67–98, finds by actual differentiation the higher derivatives of $F(x)=\operatorname{sech} x$ in terms of $A=\frac{2}{e^x+e^{-x}}$, $Z=\left(\frac{e^x-e^{-x}}{e^x+e^{-x}}\right)^2$ and $B=\frac{2Z}{e^x-e^{-x}}$, up to

$$F^{(7)}(x)=B(1385-7266Z+10920Z^2-5040Z^3),$$

$$F^{(8)}(x)=A(1385-24568Z+83664Z^2-100800Z^3+40320Z^4),$$

but does not give a general form of the higher derivative.

Shovelton, *Quarterly Journal of Mathematics*, vol. 46, pp. 220–247.

and (40) becomes

$$\frac{d^n y}{dx^n} = \sum_{k=1}^{n} (-1)^k \binom{n+1}{k+1} \sec^{k+1} x \frac{d^n}{dx^n} \cos^k x. \tag{42}$$

Now

$$\frac{d^n}{dx^n} \cos^k x = \frac{1}{2^k} \frac{d^n}{dx^n} (e^{ix} + e^{-ix})^k$$

$$= \frac{1}{2^k} \frac{d^n}{dx^n} \sum_{\alpha=0}^{k} \binom{k}{\alpha} e^{(k-2\alpha)ix}$$

$$= \frac{i^n}{2^k} \sum_{\alpha=0}^{k} \binom{k}{\alpha} (k-2\alpha)^n e^{(k-2\alpha)ix}, \tag{43}$$

and we obtain

$$\frac{d^n y}{dx^n} = i^n \sum_{k=1}^{n} \frac{(-1)^k}{2^k} \binom{n+1}{k+1} \sec^{k+1} x \sum_{\alpha=0}^{k} \binom{k}{\alpha} (k-2\alpha)^n [\cos(k-2\alpha)x + i \sin(k-2\alpha)x]. \tag{44}$$

Then when n is even,

$$\frac{d^{2n}}{dx^{2n}} \sec x = (-1)^n \sum_{k=1}^{2n} \frac{(-1)^k}{2^k} \binom{2n+1}{k+1} \sec^{k+1} x \sum_{\alpha=0}^{k} \binom{k}{\alpha} (k-2\alpha)^{2n} \cos(k-2\alpha)x, \tag{45}$$

and when n is odd,

$$\frac{d^{2n+1}}{dx^{2n+1}} \sec x = (-1)^{n-1} \sum_{k=1}^{2n+1} \frac{(-1)^k}{2^k} \binom{2n+2}{k+1} \sec^{k+1} x \sum_{\alpha=0}^{k} \binom{k}{\alpha} (k-2\alpha)^{2n+1} \sin(k-2\alpha)x. \tag{46}$$

Combining (45) and (46) gives

$$\frac{d^n}{dx^n} \sec x = (-1)^{\left[\frac{n+1}{2}\right]} \sum_{k=1}^{n} \frac{(-1)^k}{2^k} \binom{n+1}{k+1} \sec^{k+1} x \sum_{\alpha=0}^{k} \binom{k}{\alpha} (k-2\alpha)^n \cos\left(\frac{\pi}{2}\beta - k + 2\alpha\right)x, \tag{47}$$

where $\beta = \dfrac{1-(-1)^n}{2}$.

To express (45)–(47) in terms of powers of $\sec x$ and $\tan x$.

From

$$\cos rx + i \sin rx = (\cos x + i \sin x)^r,$$

we have

$$\cos rx = \sum_{\beta=0}^{\left[\frac{r}{2}\right]} (-1)^\beta \binom{r}{2\beta} \cos^{r-2\beta} x \sin^{2\beta} x \tag{48}$$

and

$$\sin rx = \sum_{\beta=0}^{\left[\frac{r-1}{2}\right]} (-1)^\beta \binom{r}{2\beta+1} \cos^{r-2\beta-1} x \sin^{2\beta+1} x. \tag{49}$$

Then, by means of (48) and (49), we obtain from (45)

$$\frac{d^{2n}}{dx^{2n}} \sec x = (-1)^n \sum_{k=1}^{2n} \frac{(-1)^k}{2^k} \binom{2n+1}{k+1} \sum_{\alpha=0}^{k} \binom{k}{\alpha} (k-2\alpha)^{2n} \sec^{2\alpha+1} x \sum_{\beta=0}^{\left[\frac{k}{2}\right]-\alpha} (-1)^\beta \binom{k-2\alpha}{2\beta} \tan^{2\beta} x, \tag{50}$$

and from (46),

$$\frac{d^{2n+1}}{dx^{2n+1}}\sec x=(-1)^{n-1}\sum_{k=1}^{2n+1}\frac{(-1)^k}{2^k}\binom{2n+2}{k+1}\sum_{a=0}^{k}\binom{k}{a}(k-2a)^{2n+1}\sec^{2a+1}x$$

$$\sum_{\beta=0}^{\left[\frac{k-1}{2}\right]-a}(-1)^{\beta}\binom{k-2a}{2\beta+1}\tan^{2\beta+1}x. \quad (51)$$

Combining (50) and (51) gives

$$\frac{d^n}{dx^n}\sec x=(-1)^{\left[\frac{n+1}{2}\right]}\sum_{k=1}^{n}\frac{(-1)^k}{2^k}\binom{n+1}{k+1}\sum_{a=0}^{k}\binom{k}{a}(k-2a)^n\sec^{2a+1}x$$

$$\sum_{\beta=0}^{\left[\frac{k-\gamma}{2}\right]-a}(-1)^{\beta}\binom{k-2a}{2\beta+\gamma}\tan^{2\beta+\gamma}x, \quad (52)$$

where $\gamma=\dfrac{1-(-1)^n}{2}$.

Letting $x=0$, then

$$\left.\frac{d^{2n}}{dx^{2n}}\sec x\right]_{x=0}=(-1)^n\sum_{k=1}^{2n}\frac{(-1)^k}{2^k}\binom{2n+1}{k+1}\sum_{a=0}^{k}\binom{k}{a}(k-2a)^{2n}, \quad (53)$$

since $\tan^{2\beta}x]_{x=0}=1$, for $\beta=0$ only.

And $$\left.\frac{d^{2n+1}}{dx^{2n+1}}\sec x\right]_{x=0}=0.$$

To reduce (53), we shall show that

$$S=\sum_{a=0}^{k}\binom{k}{a}(k-2a)^{2n}=2\sum_{a=0}^{\left[\frac{k-1}{2}\right]}\binom{k}{a}(k-2a)^{2n}. \quad (54)$$

For, if k is even,

$$S=\sum_{a=0}^{\frac{k}{2}-1}\binom{k}{a}(k-2a)^{2n}+\sum_{a=\frac{k}{2}+1}^{k}\binom{k}{a}(k-2a)^{2n}.$$

Letting in the second summation $k-a=a'$, then

$$S=2\sum_{a=0}^{\frac{k-2}{2}}\binom{k}{a}(k-2a)^{2n}.$$

If k is odd, the upper limit of S is $\dfrac{k-1}{2}$.

Then, by means of (53) and (54), we find

$$\sec x=\sum_{n=0}^{\infty}(-1)^n\frac{x^{2n}}{(2n)!}\sum_{k=1}^{2n}\frac{(-1)^k}{2^{k-1}}\binom{2n+1}{k+1}\sum_{a=0}^{\left[\frac{k-1}{2}\right]}\binom{k}{a}(k-2a)^{2n}. \quad (55)$$

This result can also be obtained by letting $x=0$ in (44).

(ii) Another form of the nth derivative and the expansion of $\sec x$ is arrived at in the following manner.

From $y = \sec x$, we have
$$\frac{d^n y}{dx^n} = 2\frac{d^n}{dx^n}\frac{e^{ix}}{e^{2ix}+1}, \tag{56}$$
and by Leibnitz's theorem,
$$\frac{d^n y}{dx^n} = 2\sum_{k=0}^{n}\binom{n}{k}\frac{d^{n-k}}{dx^{n-k}}e^{ix}\frac{d^k}{dx^k}\frac{1}{e^{2ix}+1}. \tag{57}$$

Now
$$\frac{d^{n-k}}{dx^{n-k}}e^{ix} = i^{n-k}e^{ix}, \tag{58}$$

and
$$\frac{d^k}{dx^k}\frac{1}{e^{2ix}+1} = \frac{(2i)^k}{e^{2ix}+1}\sum_{\alpha=0}^{k}\frac{e^{2i\alpha x}}{(e^{2ix}+1)^\alpha}\sum_{\beta=0}^{\alpha}(-1)^\beta\binom{\alpha}{\beta}\beta^k. \tag{59}$$

Then, by means of (58) and (59), (57) becomes
$$\frac{d^n y}{dx^n} = i^n \sec x\sum_{k=0}^{n}\binom{n}{k}2^k\sum_{\alpha=1}^{k}\frac{e^{2i\alpha x}}{(e^{2ix}+1)^\alpha}\sum_{\beta=0}^{\alpha}(-1)^\beta\binom{\alpha}{\beta}\beta^k. \tag{60}$$

Now
$$\frac{e^{2i\alpha x}}{(e^{2ix}+1)^\alpha} = \frac{1}{2^\alpha}(1+i\tan x)^\alpha$$
$$= \frac{1}{2^\alpha}(N_{2\gamma}+iN_{2\gamma+1}), \tag{61}$$

where $N_{2\gamma}$ and $N_{2\gamma+1}$ are of the same form as (20) and (21) respectively, except that α is written in place of $k-1$.

Applying (61) to (60), we have
$$\frac{d^n y}{dx^n} = i^n\sec x\sum_{\alpha=0}^{n}\frac{1}{2^\alpha}(N_{2\gamma}+iN_{2\gamma+1})\sum_{\beta=0}^{\alpha}(-1)^\beta\binom{\alpha}{\beta}\sum_{k=\alpha}^{n}\binom{n}{k}(2\beta)^k, \text{ by Ch. I. (97).} \tag{62}$$

And since $\sum_{\beta=0}^{\alpha}(-1)^\beta\binom{\alpha}{\beta}\beta^k = 0$, if $k<\alpha$, by Ch. I. (136),

therefore
$$\frac{d^n y}{dx^n} = i^n\sec x\sum_{\alpha=0}^{n}\frac{1}{2^\alpha}(N_{2\gamma}+iN_{2\gamma+1})\sum_{\beta=0}^{\alpha}(-1)^\beta\binom{\alpha}{\beta}\sum_{k=0}^{n}\binom{n}{k}(2\beta)^k. \tag{63}$$

Now
$$\sum_{k=0}^{n}\binom{n}{k}(2\beta)^k = (1+2\beta)^n,$$
and (63) becomes
$$\frac{d^n y}{dx^n} = i^n\sec x\sum_{\alpha=0}^{n}\frac{1}{2^\alpha}(N_{2\gamma}+iN_{2\gamma+1})\sum_{\beta=0}^{\alpha}(-1)^\beta\binom{\alpha}{\beta}(1+2\beta)^n. \tag{64}$$

Then, from (61) and (64), we obtain
$$\frac{d^{2n}}{dx^{2n}}\sec x = (-1)^n\sec x\sum_{\alpha=0}^{2n}\frac{1}{2^\alpha}\sum_{\gamma=0}^{\left[\frac{\alpha}{2}\right]}(-1)^\gamma\binom{\alpha}{2\gamma}\tan^{2\gamma}x\sum_{\beta=0}^{\alpha}(-1)^\beta\binom{\alpha}{\beta}(1+2\beta)^{2n}, \tag{65}$$
and
$$\frac{d^{2n+1}}{dx^{2n+1}}\sec x = (-1)^{n-1}\sec x\sum_{\alpha=0}^{2n+1}\frac{1}{2^\alpha}\sum_{\gamma=0}^{\left[\frac{\alpha-1}{2}\right]}(-1)^\gamma\binom{\alpha}{2\gamma+1}\tan^{2\gamma+1}x\sum_{\beta=0}^{\alpha}(-1)^\beta\binom{\alpha}{\beta}(1+2\beta)^{2n+1}. \tag{66}$$

Combining (65) and (66), we have ,

$$\frac{d^n}{dx^n}\sec x=(-1)^{\left[\frac{n+1}{2}\right]}\sec x\sum_{\alpha=0}^{n}\frac{1}{2^\alpha}\sum_{\gamma=0}^{\left[\frac{\alpha-\delta}{2}\right]}(-1)^\gamma\binom{\alpha}{2\gamma+\delta}\tan^{2\gamma+\delta}x\sum_{\beta=0}^{\alpha}(-1)^\beta \binom{\alpha}{\beta}(1+2\beta)^n, \quad (67)$$

where $\delta=\frac{1-(-1)^n}{2}$.

Then, from (65),

$$\left.\frac{d^{2n}}{dx^{2n}}\sec x\right]_{x=0}=(-1)^n\sum_{\alpha=0}^{2n}\frac{1}{2^\alpha}\sum_{\beta=0}^{\alpha}(-1)^\beta\binom{\alpha}{\beta}(1+2\beta)^{2n}, \quad (68)$$

and from (66),

$$\left.\frac{d^{2n+1}}{dx^{2n+1}}\sec x\right]_{x=0}=0.$$

Therefore

$$\sec x=\sum_{n=0}^{\infty}(-1)^n\frac{x^{2n}}{(2n)!}\sum_{\alpha=0}^{2n}\frac{1}{2^\alpha}\sum_{\beta=0}^{\alpha}(-1)^\beta\binom{\alpha}{\beta}(1+2\beta)^{2n}. \quad (69)$$

(iii) Still another form for the derivative and the expansion of $\sec x$ is found as follows.

We have

$$\left.\frac{d^n}{dx^n}\sec x\right]_{x=0}=i^n\left.\frac{d^n}{dx^n}\frac{2}{e^x+e^{-x}}\right]_{x=0}. \quad (70)$$

Letting

$$e^x=u \quad\text{and}\quad \frac{2}{e^x+e^{-x}}=y, \quad (71)$$

then

$$\frac{d^ny}{dx^n}=\sum_{k=0}^{n}\frac{(-1)^k}{k!}\sum_{\alpha=0}^{k}(-1)^\alpha\binom{k}{\alpha}u^{k-\alpha}\frac{d^n}{dx^n}u^\alpha\frac{d^k}{du^k}\left(\frac{1}{u+i}+\frac{1}{u-i}\right) \quad (72)$$

$$=\sum_{k=0}^{n}\frac{(u+i)^{k+1}+(u-i)^{k+1}}{(u^2+1)^{k+1}}u^k\sum_{\alpha=0}^{k}(-1)^\alpha\binom{k}{\alpha}\alpha^n. \quad (73)$$

And letting

$$u=\cot\theta,$$

whence

$$u+i=\frac{e^\theta}{\sin\theta} \quad\text{and}\quad u-i=\frac{e^{-\theta}}{\sin\theta}. \quad (74)$$

Then, by means of (74), (72) changes to

$$\frac{d^ny}{dx^n}=\sum_{k=0}^{n}\frac{2\cos(k+1)\theta}{\operatorname{cosec}^{k+1}\theta}e^{kx}\sum_{\alpha=0}^{k}(-1)^\alpha\binom{k}{\alpha}\alpha^n$$

$$=2\sum_{k=0}^{n}\frac{\cos[(k+1)\cot^{-1}e^x]}{(e^{2x}+1)^{\frac{k+1}{2}}}e^{kx}\sum_{\alpha=0}^{k}(-1)^\alpha\binom{k}{\alpha}\alpha^n. \quad (75)$$

Therefore

$$\left.\frac{d^n}{dx^n}\sec x\right]_{x=0}=i^n\sqrt{2}\sum_{k=0}^{n}\frac{1}{2^{k/2}}\cos(k+1)\frac{\pi}{4}\sum_{\alpha=0}^{k}(-1)^\alpha\binom{k}{\alpha}\alpha^n, \quad (76)$$

and as n must be even,

$$\sec x=1+\sqrt{2}\sum_{n=1}^{\infty}(-1)^n\frac{x^{2n}}{(2n)!}\sum_{k=1}^{2n}\frac{1}{2^{k/2}}\cos(k+1)\frac{\pi}{4}\sum_{\alpha=1}^{k}(-1)^\alpha\binom{k}{\alpha}\alpha^{2n}. \quad (77)$$

The expansion (77) can also be obtained by the following method:

We have $$\sec x=\frac{2e^{ix}}{e^{2ix}+1}=i\left(\frac{1}{1+ie^{ix}}-\frac{1}{1-ie^{ix}}\right)=iy\,; \tag{78}$$

then $$\frac{d^n}{dx^n}\sec x=i\frac{d^ny}{dx^n}.$$

Letting, in Ch. I. (83), $u=ie^{ix}$, we have

$$\frac{d^ny}{dx^n}=\sum_{k=1}^{n}(-1)^k\sum_{a=1}^{k}(-1)^a\binom{k}{a}a^n i^{n+k}e^{kix}\left[\frac{(-1)^k}{(1+ie^{ix})^{k+1}}-\frac{1}{(1-ie^{ix})^{k+1}}\right]. \tag{79}$$

But $$1+ie^{ix}=2\cos\left(\frac{\pi}{4}+\frac{x}{2}\right)e^{\left(\frac{\pi}{4}+\frac{x}{2}\right)i} \tag{80}$$

and $$1-ie^{ix}=-2\sin\left(\frac{\pi}{4}+\frac{x}{2}\right)e^{\left(\frac{\pi}{4}+\frac{x}{2}\right)i}. \tag{81}$$

Applying (80) and (81) to (79), and proceeding as before, (77) is obtained.

(iv) The expansion of $\sec x$ can also be found without the use of calculus.

Now $$\sec x=\frac{1}{(1-\sin^2x)^{1/2}}=\sum_{k=0}^{\infty}(-1)^k\binom{-\frac{1}{2}}{k}\sin^{2k}x. \tag{82}$$

Following the method which has led to (27), we find

$$\sin^{2k}x=\frac{(-1)^k}{2^{2k}}\sum_{n=0}^{\infty}i^n2^n\frac{x^n}{n!}\sum_{a=0}^{2k}(-1)^a\binom{2k}{a}(k-a)^n, \tag{83}$$

and as n must be even,

$$\sin^{2k}x=\frac{(-1)^k}{2^{2k}}\sum_{n=0}^{\infty}(-1)^n2^{2n}\frac{x^{2n}}{(2n)!}\sum_{a=0}^{2k}(-1)^a\binom{2k}{a}(k-a)^{2n}. \tag{84}$$

Now $\sum_{a=0}^{2k}(-1)^a\binom{2k}{a}(k-a)^{2n}=0$, if $n<k$, by Ch. I. (135),

$$=2(-1)^k\sum_{a=1}^{k}(-1)^a\binom{2k}{k-a}a^{2n},\ \text{if } n\geqq k;$$

therefore $$\sin^{2k}x=\frac{1}{2^{2k-1}}\sum_{n=k}^{\infty}(-1)^n2^{2n}\frac{x^{2n}}{(2n)!}\sum_{a=1}^{k}(-1)^a\binom{2k}{k-a}a^{2n}. \tag{85}$$

Applying (85) to (82), we obtain, by means of Ch. I. (68),

$$\sec x=2\sum_{n=1}^{\infty}(-1)^n2^{2n}\frac{x^{2n}}{(2n)!}\sum_{k=1}^{n}\frac{1}{2^{4k}}\binom{2k}{k}\sum_{a=1}^{k}(-1)^a\binom{2k}{k-a}a^{2n}. \tag{86}$$

4. (i) Given $$y=\cot x. \tag{87}$$

To find $\frac{d^ny}{dx^n}$.

Now $$y=i+\frac{2i}{e^{2ix}-1}; \tag{88}$$

then $$\frac{d^ny}{dx^n}=2i\frac{d^n}{dx^n}\frac{1}{e^{2ix}-1}=2i\frac{d^n}{dx^n}y_1 \tag{89}$$

But, by Ch. I. (83),

$$\frac{d^n y_1}{dx^n} = (2i)^n \sum_{k=1}^{n} \sum_{\alpha=1}^{k} (-1)^\alpha \binom{k}{\alpha} \alpha^n \frac{u^k}{(u-1)^{k+1}}, \quad u = e^{2ix}. \tag{90}$$

Now
$$\frac{u^k}{(u-1)^{k+1}} = \frac{(\cos x + i \sin x)^{k-1}}{2^{k+1} i^{k+1} \sin^2 x \sin^{k-1} x}$$

$$= -\frac{1}{2^{k+1}} \operatorname{cosec}^2 x (1 - i \cot x)^{k-1} \tag{91}$$

and
$$(1 - i \cot x)^{k-1} = M_{2\beta} - i M_{2\beta+1}, \tag{92}$$

where
$$M_{2\beta} = \sum_{\beta=0}^{\left[\frac{k-1}{2}\right]} (-1)^\beta \binom{k-1}{2\beta} \cot^{2\beta} x, \tag{93}$$

and
$$M_{2\beta+1} = \sum_{\beta=0}^{\left[\frac{k-2}{2}\right]} (-1)^\beta \binom{k-1}{2\beta+1} \cot^{2\beta+1} x. \tag{94}$$

Applying (92) to (90), we have from (89),

$$\frac{d^{2n}}{dx^{2n}} \cot x = (-1)^{n-1} 2^{2n} \operatorname{cosec}^2 x \sum_{k=1}^{2n} \frac{1}{2^k} \sum_{\alpha=1}^{k} (-1)^\alpha \binom{k}{\alpha} \alpha^{2n} M_{2\beta+1} \tag{95}$$

and
$$\frac{d^{2n+1}}{dx^{2n+1}} \cot x = (-1)^n 2^{2n+1} \operatorname{cosec}^2 x \sum_{k=1}^{2n+1} \frac{1}{2^k} \sum_{\alpha=1}^{k} (-1)^\alpha \binom{k}{\alpha} \alpha^{2n+1} M_{2\beta}. \tag{96}$$

Combining (95) and (96) gives

$$\frac{d^n}{dx^n} \cot x = (-1)^{\left[\frac{n-1}{2}\right]} 2^n \operatorname{cosec}^2 x \sum_{k=1}^{n} \frac{1}{2^k} \sum_{\alpha=1}^{k} (-1)^\alpha \binom{k}{\alpha} \alpha^n \sum_{\beta=0}^{\left[\frac{k-2+\gamma}{2}\right]} (-1)^\beta \binom{k-1}{2\beta+1-\gamma} \cot^{2\beta+1-\gamma}, \tag{97}$$

where
$$\gamma = \frac{1-(-1)^n}{2}.$$

(ii) We shall next find the expansion of

$$y = x \cot x. \tag{98}$$

We have
$$y = ix + \frac{2ix}{e^{2ix} - 1} \tag{99}$$

and
$$\left.\frac{d^n y}{dx^n}\right]_{x \doteq 0} = (2i)^n \left.\frac{d^n}{dx^n} \frac{x}{e^x - 1}\right]_{x \doteq 0}. \tag{100}$$

Now
$$\frac{2x}{e^{2x} - 1} = \frac{x}{e^x - 1} - \frac{x}{e^x + 1}. \tag{101}$$

Letting $2x = z$, then

$$\frac{d^n}{dx^n} \frac{2x}{e^{2x} - 1} = 2^n \frac{d^n}{dz^n} \frac{z}{e^z - 1} = 2^n \frac{d^n}{dx^n} \frac{x}{e^x - 1}, \tag{102}$$

and, by means of (102), we obtain from (101)

$$\left.\frac{d^n}{dx^n} \frac{x}{e^x - 1}\right]_{x \doteq 0} = -\frac{1}{2^n - 1} \left.\frac{d^n}{dx^n} \frac{x}{e^x + 1}\right]_{x \doteq 0}. \tag{103}$$

But
$$\frac{d^n}{dx^n}\frac{x}{e^x+1}=\sum_{k=0}^{n}\binom{n}{k}\frac{d^{n-k}}{dx^{n-k}}x\frac{d^k}{dx^k}\frac{1}{e^x+1}$$
$$=x\frac{d^n}{dx^n}\frac{1}{e^x+1}+n\frac{d^{n-1}}{dx^{n-1}}\frac{1}{e^x+1}; \tag{104}$$
hence
$$\left.\frac{d^ny}{dx^n}\right]_{x\doteq 0}=-\frac{(2i)^n n}{2^n-1}\left.\frac{d^{n-1}}{dx^{n-1}}\frac{1}{e^x+1}\right]_{x\doteq 0}. \tag{105}$$

Applying
$$\left.\frac{d^{n-1}}{dx^{n-1}}\frac{1}{e^x+1}\right]_{x\doteq 0}=\sum_{k=1}^{n-1}\frac{1}{2^{k+1}}\sum_{\alpha=1}^{k}(-1)^\alpha\binom{k}{\alpha}\alpha^{n-1}, \text{ by Ch. I. (83)}, \tag{106}$$
(105) becomes
$$\left.\frac{d^ny}{dx^n}\right]_{x\doteq 0}=-\frac{(2i)^n n}{2^n-1}\sum_{k=1}^{n-1}\frac{1}{2^{k+1}}\sum_{\alpha=1}^{k}(-1)^\alpha\binom{k}{\alpha}\alpha^{n-1}. \tag{107}$$

Therefore n must be even, and we obtain
$$x\cot x=1-\sum_{n=1}^{\infty}(-1)^n\frac{n2^{2n}}{2^{2n}-1}\frac{x^{2n}}{(2n)!}\sum_{k=1}^{2n-1}\frac{1}{2^k}\sum_{\alpha=1}^{k}(-1)^\alpha\binom{k}{\alpha}\alpha^{2n-1}. \tag{108}$$

5. (i) Given
$$y=\operatorname{cosec} x. \tag{109}$$

To find $\frac{d^ny}{dx^n}$ in terms of powers of $\operatorname{cosec} x$ and $\cot x$.

Let $u=\sin x$; then, by Ch. I. (83),
$$\frac{d^ny}{dx^n}=\sum_{k=1}^{n}(-1)^k\binom{n+1}{k+1}\operatorname{cosec}^{k+1}x\frac{d^n}{dx^n}\sin^k x. \tag{110}$$

Now
$$\sin^k x=(-1)^k\frac{i^k}{2^k}\sum_{\alpha=0}^{k}(-1)^\alpha\binom{k}{\alpha}e^{(k-2\alpha)ix} \tag{111}$$
and
$$\frac{d^n}{dx^n}\sin^k x=(-1)^k\frac{i^{n+k}}{2^k}\sum_{\alpha=0}^{k}(-1)^\alpha\binom{k}{\alpha}(k-2\alpha)^n e^{(k-2\alpha)ix}; \tag{112}$$
therefore
$$\frac{d^ny}{dx^n}=i^n\sum_{k=1}^{n}\frac{i^k}{2^k}\binom{n+1}{k+1}\operatorname{cosec}^{k+1}x\sum_{\alpha=0}^{k}(-1)^\alpha\binom{k}{\alpha}(k-2\alpha)^n(\cos x+i\sin x)^{k-2\alpha}. \tag{113}$$

But
$$(\cos x+i\sin x)^{k-2\alpha}=(-1)^\alpha i^k(\sin x-i\cos x)^{k-2\alpha}, \tag{114}$$
and separating $(\sin x-i\cos x)^{k-2\alpha}$ into its real and imaginary parts, (113) becomes
$$\frac{d^ny}{dx^n}=i^n\sum_{k=1}^{n}\frac{(-1)^k}{2^k}\binom{n+1}{k+1}\sum_{\alpha=0}^{k}\binom{k}{\alpha}(k-2\alpha)^n\operatorname{cosec}^{2\alpha+1}x(M_{2\beta}-iM_{2\beta+1}), \tag{115}$$
where
$$M_{2\beta}=\sum_{\beta=0}^{\left[\frac{k}{2}\right]-\alpha}(-1)^\beta\binom{k-2\alpha}{2\beta}\cot^{2\beta}x \tag{116}$$
and
$$M_{2\beta+1}=\sum_{\beta=0}^{\left[\frac{k-1}{2}\right]-\alpha}(-1)^\beta\binom{k-2\alpha}{2\beta+1}\cot^{2\beta+1}x. \tag{117}$$

Therefore

$$\frac{d^{2n}}{dx^{2n}}\operatorname{cosec} x = (-1)^n \sum_{k=1}^{2n} \frac{(-1)^k}{2^k}\binom{2n+1}{k+1}\sum_{\alpha=0}^{k}\binom{k}{\alpha}(k-2\alpha)^{2n}\operatorname{cosec}^{2\alpha+1}x\, M_{2\beta}, \qquad (118)$$

and

$$\frac{d^{2n+1}}{dx^{2n+1}}\operatorname{cosec} x = (-1)^n \sum_{k=1}^{2n+1} \frac{(-1)^k}{2^k}\binom{2n+2}{k+1}$$

$$\sum_{\alpha=0}^{k}\binom{k}{\alpha}(k-2\alpha)^{2n+1}\operatorname{cosec}^{2\alpha+1}x\, M_{2\beta+1}. \qquad (119)$$

Combining (118) and (119), we obtain

$$\frac{d^n}{dx^n}\operatorname{cosec} x = (-1)^{\left[\frac{n}{2}\right]} \sum_{k=1}^{n} \frac{(-1)^k}{2^k}\binom{n+1}{k+1}\sum_{\alpha=0}^{k}\binom{k}{\alpha}(k-2\alpha)^{n}\operatorname{cosec}^{2\alpha+1}x$$

$$\sum_{\beta=0}^{\left[\frac{k-\gamma}{2}\right]-\alpha}(-1)^\beta\binom{k-2\alpha}{2\beta+\gamma}\cot^{2\beta+\gamma}x, \qquad (120)$$

where

$$\gamma = \frac{1-(-1)^n}{2}.$$

(ii) Another form for the higher derivative of $y=\operatorname{cosec} x$ is found as follows:

Now

$$\frac{d^n y}{dx^n} = 2i\frac{d^n}{dx^n}y_1, \qquad (121)$$

where

$$y_1 = \frac{e^{ix}}{e^{2ix}-1}.$$

Then

$$\frac{d^n}{dx^n}y_1 = \sum_{k=0}^{n}\binom{n}{k}\frac{d^{n-k}}{dx^{n-k}}e^{ix}\frac{d^k}{dx^k}\frac{1}{e^{2ix}-1}, \qquad (122)$$

and, by Ch. I. (83),

$$\frac{d^k}{dx^k}\frac{1}{e^{2ix}-1} = 2^k i^k \sum_{\alpha=0}^{k}\frac{e^{2i\alpha x}}{(e^{2ix}-1)^{\alpha+1}}\sum_{\beta=0}^{\alpha}(-1)^\beta\binom{\alpha}{\beta}\beta^k. \qquad (123)$$

Hence

$$\frac{d^n}{dx^n}y_1 = i^n\frac{e^{ix}}{e^{2ix}-1}\sum_{k=0}^{n}\binom{n}{k}2^k\sum_{\alpha=0}^{k}\frac{e^{2i\alpha x}}{(e^{2ix}-1)^\alpha}\sum_{\beta=0}^{\alpha}(-1)^\beta\binom{\alpha}{\beta}\beta^k. \qquad (124)$$

Now, applying to (124) the method by which (64) was obtained from (62) and (63), we have from (121),

$$\frac{d^n y}{dx^n} = i^n\operatorname{cosec} x\sum_{\alpha=0}^{n}\frac{e^{2i\alpha x}}{(e^{2ix}-1)^\alpha}\sum_{\beta=0}^{\alpha}(-1)^\beta\binom{\alpha}{\beta}(1+2\beta)^n. \qquad (125)$$

But

$$\frac{e^{2i\alpha x}}{(e^{2ix}-1)^\alpha} = \frac{1}{2^\alpha}(1-i\cot x)^\alpha \qquad (126)$$

and

$$(1-i\cot x)^\alpha = M_{2\gamma} - iM_{2\gamma+1}, \qquad (127)$$

where $M_{2\gamma}$ and $M_{2\gamma+1}$ are the expressions in (93) and (94) respectively, except that α takes the place of $k-1$.

Hence

$$\frac{d^{2n}}{dx^{2n}}\operatorname{cosec} x = (-1)^n \operatorname{cosec} x \sum_{\alpha=0}^{2n} \frac{1}{2^\alpha} \sum_{\beta=0}^{\alpha} (-1)^\beta \binom{\alpha}{\beta} (1+2\beta)^{2n} M_{2\gamma} \tag{128}$$

and

$$\frac{d^{2n+1}}{dx^{2n+1}}\operatorname{cosec} x = (-1)^n \operatorname{cosec} x \sum_{\alpha=0}^{2n+1} \frac{1}{2^\alpha} \sum_{\beta=0}^{\alpha} (-1)^\beta \binom{\alpha}{\beta} (1+2\beta)^{2n+1} M_{2\gamma+1}. \tag{129}$$

Combining (128) and (129), we obtain

$$\frac{d^n}{dx^n}\operatorname{cosec} x = (-1)^{\left[\frac{n}{2}\right]} \operatorname{cosec} x \sum_{\alpha=0}^{n} \frac{1}{2^\alpha} \sum_{\beta=0}^{\alpha} (-1)^\beta \binom{\alpha}{\beta} (1+2\beta)^n \sum_{\gamma=0}^{\left[\frac{\alpha-\delta}{2}\right]} (-1)^\gamma \binom{\alpha}{2\gamma+\delta} \cot^{2\gamma+\delta} x, \tag{130}$$

where $$\delta = \frac{1-(-1)^n}{2}.$$

(iii) We shall next find the expansion of

$$y = x \operatorname{cosec} x. \tag{131}$$

Now $$y = \frac{2ixe^{ix}}{e^{2ix}-1} = \frac{ix}{e^{ix}+1} + \frac{ix}{e^{ix}-1}, \tag{132}$$

then

$$\left.\frac{d^n y}{dx^n}\right]_{x=0} = i^n \left[\frac{d^n}{dx^n}\frac{x}{e^x+1} - \frac{1}{2^n-1}\frac{d^n}{dx^n}\frac{x}{e^x+1}\right], \text{ by (103)},$$

$$= 2i^n \frac{2^{n-1}-1}{2^n-1} \left.\frac{d^n}{dx^n}\frac{x}{e^x+1}\right]_{x=0}$$

$$= 2ni^n \frac{2^{n-1}-1}{2^n-1} \left.\frac{d^{n-1}}{dx^{n-1}}\frac{1}{e^x+1}\right]_{x=0}; \tag{133}$$

and since n must be even, then, by means of (106), we have

$$\left.\frac{d^{2n}}{dx^{2n}} x \operatorname{cosec} x\right]_{x=0} = (-1)^n \frac{n(2^{2n-1}-1)}{2^{2n}-1} \sum_{k=1}^{2n-1} \frac{1}{2^{k-1}} \sum_{\alpha=1}^{k} (-1)^\alpha \binom{k}{\alpha} \alpha^{2n-1}, \tag{134}$$

and finally obtain

$$x \operatorname{cosec} x = 1 + \sum_{n=1}^{\infty} (-1)^n \frac{nx^{2n}}{(2n)!} \frac{2^{2n-1}-1}{2^{2n}-1} \sum_{k=1}^{2n-1} \frac{1}{2^{k-1}} \sum_{\alpha=1}^{k} (-1)^\alpha \binom{k}{\alpha} \alpha^{2n-1}. \tag{135}$$

(iv) Another method for expanding $y = x \operatorname{cosec} x$ is the following: Let $x = \sin^{-1}\theta$, then

$$y = \frac{\sin^{-1}\theta}{\theta} = \sum_{k=0}^{\infty} (-1)^k \binom{-\frac{1}{2}}{k} \frac{\theta^{2k}}{2k+1}, \text{ by Ch. I. (39)},$$

$$= 1 + \sum_{k=1}^{\infty} (-1)^k \binom{-\frac{1}{2}}{k} \frac{\sin^{2k} x}{2k+1}, \tag{136}$$

and by means of (85)

$$y=1+\sum_{k=1}^{\infty}\frac{1}{2^{4k-1}}\binom{2k}{k}\frac{1}{2k+1}\sum_{n=k}^{\infty}(-1)^n\frac{x^{2n}}{(2n)!}2^{2n}\sum_{a=1}^{k}(-1)^a\binom{2k}{k-a}a^{2n}. \quad (137)$$

Applying Ch. I. (67) to (137), we obtain

$$x\operatorname{cosec}x=1+\sum_{n=1}^{\infty}(-1)^n\frac{x^{2n}}{(2n)!}2^{2n}\sum_{k=1}^{n}\frac{1}{2^{4k-1}}\binom{2k}{k}\frac{1}{2k+1}\sum_{a=1}^{k}(-1)^a\binom{2k}{k-a}a^{2n}. \quad (138)$$

CHAPTER III.

SERIES OF BINOMIAL COEFFICIENTS.

In the preceding chapters we have had occasion to reduce Binomial Coefficients and to find the value of a series of them. We shall give here a few examples which will illustrate additional methods of the operations with Binomial Coefficients.

1. (i) To find the value of

$$S=\sum_{k=0}^{n}\binom{2n}{k}. \tag{1}$$

Let

$$S_1=\sum_{k=1}^{n}\binom{2n}{n+k}=\sum_{k=1}^{n}\binom{2n}{n-k}; \tag{2}$$

then

$$S+S_1=\sum_{k=0}^{2n}\binom{2n}{k}=(1+1)^{2n}=2^{2n}. \tag{3}$$

Letting $n-k=k'$ in (2), we have

$$S_1=\sum_{k=0}^{n-1}\binom{2n}{k}=\sum_{k=0}^{n}\binom{2n}{k}-\binom{2n}{n}$$

$$=S-\binom{2n}{n},$$

or

$$S-S_1=\binom{2n}{n}. \tag{4}$$

From (3) and (4), we then obtain

$$S=\frac{1}{2}\left[2^{2n}+\binom{2n}{n}\right]=2^{2n-1}+\binom{2n-1}{n-1} \tag{5}$$

and

$$S_1=\frac{1}{2}\left[2^{2n}-\binom{2n}{n}\right]=2^{2n-1}-\binom{2n-1}{n-1}. \tag{6}$$

(ii) To find the value of

$$S=\sum_{k=0}^{n}(-1)^k\binom{2n}{k}. \tag{7}$$

Let

$$S_1=(-1)^n\sum_{k=1}^{n}(-1)^k\binom{2n}{n+k}; \tag{8}$$

then
$$S+S_1=\sum_{k=0}^{2n}(-1)^k\binom{2n}{k}=(1-1)^n=0 \tag{9}$$

and
$$S-S_1=(-1)^n\binom{2n}{n}. \tag{10}$$

Therefore
$$S=\frac{(-1)^n}{2}\binom{2n}{n}=(-1)^n\binom{2n-1}{n-1} \tag{11}$$

and
$$S_1=\frac{(-1)^{n-1}}{2}\binom{2n}{n}=(-1)^{n-1}\binom{2n-1}{n-1}. \tag{12}$$

The results (11) and (12) might also be obtained as follows:

Letting in (7), $n-k=k'$, then

$$S=(-1)^n\sum_{k=0}^{n}(-1)^k\binom{2n}{n-k} \tag{13}$$

$$=(-1)^n\sum_{k=0}^{n}((x^k))(1+x)^{-1}((x^{n-k}))(1+x)^{2n}$$

$$=(-1)^n((x^n))(1+x)^{2n-1}$$

$$=(-1)^n\binom{2n-1}{n}=(-1)^n\binom{2n-1}{n-1}$$

$$=(-1)^n\binom{2n-1}{n-1}\frac{2n}{2n}=\frac{(-1)^n}{2}\binom{2n}{n},$$

which is the same as (11). In a similar way (12) is obtained.

(iii) To show that
$$\sum_{k=0}^{\left[\frac{n}{2}\right]}\binom{n}{2k}=\sum_{k=0}^{\left[\frac{n-1}{2}\right]}\binom{n}{2k+1}=2^{n-1}. \tag{14}$$

Designating the first and the second summations in (14) by S_1 and S_2 respectively, we have
$$S_1+S_2=\sum_{k=0}^{n}\binom{n}{k}=2^n. \tag{15}$$

Now, since
$$\binom{n}{2k}=\binom{n-1}{2k}+\binom{n-1}{2k-1}, \tag{16}$$

therefore
$$S_1=1+\sum_{k=1}^{\left[\frac{n}{2}\right]}\binom{n-1}{2k}+\sum_{k=1}^{\left[\frac{n}{2}\right]}\binom{n-1}{2k-1}$$

$$=\sum_{k=0}^{\left[\frac{n-1}{2}\right]}\binom{n-1}{2k}+\sum_{k=0}^{\left[\frac{n-1}{2}\right]}\binom{n-1}{2k+1} \tag{17}$$

and
$$S_2=\sum_{k=0}^{\left[\frac{n-1}{2}\right]}\binom{n-1}{2k+1}+\sum_{k=0}^{\left[\frac{n-1}{2}\right]}\binom{n-1}{2k}. \tag{18}$$

Then (15), (17) and (18) give (14).

(iv) Show that
$$\sum_{k=0}^{n}\binom{2n}{2k}=\sum_{k=0}^{n}\binom{2n}{2k+1}=2^{2n-1} \tag{19}$$

and
$$\sum_{k=0}^{n}\binom{2n+1}{2k}=\sum_{k=0}^{n}\binom{2n+1}{2k+1}=2^{2n}. \tag{20}$$

(v) To find the value of
$$S=\sum_{k=1}^{\left[\frac{n}{2}\right]}(-1)^k\binom{n}{2k}. \tag{21}$$

Let
$$S_1=\sum_{k=0}^{\left[\frac{n-1}{2}\right]}(-1)^k\binom{n}{2k+1}. \tag{22}$$

Now
$$S=\sum_{k=0}^{\left[\frac{n}{2}\right]}\binom{n}{2k}i^{2k} \tag{23}$$

and
$$S_1=\sum_{k=0}^{\left[\frac{n-1}{2}\right]}\binom{n}{2k+1}i^{2k}; \tag{24}$$

then
$$S+iS_1=\sum_{k=0}^{n}\binom{n}{k}i^k=(1+i)^n \tag{25}$$

and
$$S-iS_1=\sum_{k=0}^{n}(-1)^k\binom{n}{k}i^k=(1-i)^n. \tag{26}$$

But
$$(1+i)^n=(\sqrt{2})^n\left(\frac{1}{\sqrt{2}}+i\frac{1}{\sqrt{2}}\right)^n=(\sqrt{2})^n\left(\cos\frac{\pi}{4}+i\sin\frac{\pi}{4}\right)^n$$
$$=(\sqrt{2})^n e^{\frac{n\pi i}{4}}. \tag{27}$$

Similarly
$$(1-i)^n=(\sqrt{2})^n\left(\cos\frac{\pi}{4}-i\sin\frac{\pi}{4}\right)^n=(\sqrt{2})^n e^{-\frac{n\pi i}{4}}. \tag{28}$$

Then, by means of (27) and (28), we obtain from (25) and (26),
$$S=(\sqrt{2})^n\cos\frac{n\pi}{4} \tag{29}$$

and
$$S_1=(\sqrt{2})^n\sin\frac{n\pi}{4}. \tag{30}$$

Now
$$\cos\frac{n\pi}{4}=\frac{(-1)^{\left[\frac{n}{4}\right]}}{2}\left[1+(-1)^{\frac{n}{2}}\right],\quad \text{when } n \text{ is even,} \tag{31}$$
$$=(-1)^{\left[\frac{n+1}{4}\right]}\frac{1}{\sqrt{2}},\quad \text{when } n \text{ is odd;} \tag{32}$$

therefore $$\cos\frac{n\pi}{4}=\frac{1}{4}\left[(-1)^{\left[\frac{n+1}{4}\right]}\sqrt{2}\{1-(-1)^n\}+(-1)^{\left[\frac{n}{4}\right]}\left\{1+(-1)^{\frac{n}{2}}\right\}\{1+(-1)^n\}\right], \quad (33)$$

whether n be even or odd.

Similarly $$\sin\frac{n\pi}{4}=\frac{(-1)^{\left[\frac{n}{4}\right]}}{2}\left[1-(-1)^{\frac{n}{2}}\right], \text{ when } n \text{ is even,}$$

$$=(-1)^{\left[\frac{n-1}{4}\right]}\frac{1}{\sqrt{2}}, \qquad \text{when } n \text{ is odd;} \quad (34)$$

hence $$\sin\frac{n\pi}{4}=\frac{1}{4}\left[(-1)^{\left[\frac{n}{4}\right]}\left\{1-(-1)^{\frac{n}{2}}\right\}\{1+(-1)^n\}+(-1)^{\left[\frac{n-1}{4}\right]}\sqrt{2}\{1-(-1)^n\}\right], \quad (35)$$

whether n be even or odd.

Applying (33) to (29) and (35) to (30) gives the values of S and S_1.

We shall express $\cos\frac{n\pi}{4}$ and $\sin\frac{n\pi}{4}$ also as summations.

Now taking the sum of (27) and (28), we have

$$\cos\frac{n\pi}{4}=\frac{1}{2(\sqrt{2})^n}[(1+i)^n+(1-i)^n], \quad (36)$$

and their difference gives

$$\sin\frac{n\pi}{4}=\frac{1}{2i(\sqrt{2})^n}[(1+i)^n-(1-i)^n]. \quad (37)$$

But $$(1+i)^n=\sum_{k=0}^{\left[\frac{n}{2}\right]}(-1)^k\binom{n}{2k}+i\sum_{k=0}^{\left[\frac{n-1}{2}\right]}(-1)^k\binom{n}{2k+1} \quad (38)$$

and $$(1-i)^n=\sum_{k=0}^{\left[\frac{n}{2}\right]}(-1)^k\binom{n}{2k}-i\sum_{k=0}^{\left[\frac{n-1}{2}\right]}(-1)^k\binom{n}{2k+1}; \quad (39)$$

then by means of (38) and (39), we obtain from (36) and (37)

$$\cos\frac{n\pi}{4}=\frac{1}{(\sqrt{2})^n}\sum_{k=0}^{\left[\frac{n}{2}\right]}(-1)^k\binom{n}{2k} \quad (40)$$

and $$\sin\frac{n\pi}{4}=\frac{1}{(\sqrt{2})^n}\sum_{k=0}^{\left[\frac{n-1}{2}\right]}(-1)^k\binom{n}{2k+1}. \quad (41)$$

Applying (40) to (29) and (41) to (30) gives (21) and (22).

In a similar way we obtain by means of

$$\cos\frac{n\pi}{3}+i\sin\frac{n\pi}{3}=\frac{1}{2^n}(1+i\sqrt{3})^n$$

$$=\frac{1}{2^n}\left[\sum_{k=0}^{\left[\frac{n}{2}\right]}(-1)^k\binom{n}{2k}3^k+i\sqrt{3}\sum_{k=0}^{\left[\frac{n-1}{2}\right]}(-1)^k\binom{n}{2k+1}3^k\right], \quad (42)$$

and from the expression for $\cos\frac{n\pi}{3} - i\sin\frac{n\pi}{3}$, which is of the same form as (42), except that i is negative,

$$\cos\frac{n\pi}{3} = \frac{1}{2^n}\sum_{k=0}^{\left[\frac{n}{2}\right]}(-1)^k\binom{n}{2k}3^k \tag{43}$$

and

$$\sin\frac{n\pi}{3} = \frac{\sqrt{3}}{2^n}\sum_{k=0}^{\left[\frac{n-1}{2}\right]}(-1)^k\binom{n}{2k+1}3^k. \tag{44}$$

We also find

$$\cos\frac{n\pi}{5} = \frac{1}{2^{2n}}(1+\sqrt{5})^n\sum_{k=0}^{\left[\frac{n}{2}\right]}(-1)^k\binom{n}{2k}(5-2\sqrt{5})^k \tag{45}$$

and

$$\sin\frac{n\pi}{5} = \frac{1}{2^{2n}}(1+\sqrt{5})^n(5-2\sqrt{5})^{\frac{1}{2}}\sum_{k=0}^{\left[\frac{n-1}{2}\right]}(-1)^k\binom{n}{2k+1}(5-2\sqrt{5})^k. \tag{46}$$

(vi) Show by the method used in (v) that

$$\sum_{k=0}^{n}(-1)^k\binom{2n+1}{2k} = (-1)^{\left[\frac{n+1}{2}\right]}2^n, \tag{47}$$

$$\sum_{k=0}^{n}(-1)^k\binom{2n+1}{2k+1} = (-1)^{\left[\frac{n}{2}\right]}2^n, \tag{48}$$

$$\sum_{k=0}^{n}(-1)^k\binom{2n}{2k} = (-1)^{\left[\frac{n}{2}\right]}[1+(-1)^n]2^{n-1}, \tag{49}$$

$$\sum_{k=0}^{n-1}(-1)^k\binom{2n}{2k+1} = (-1)^{\left[\frac{n}{2}\right]}[1-(-1)^n]2^{n-1}. \tag{50}$$

(vii) The result (49) can also be obtained as follows:

Applying (16) to (49), we have

$$\sum_{k=0}^{n}(-1)^k\binom{2n}{2k} = (-1)^n + \sum_{k=0}^{n-1}(-1)^k\binom{2n-1}{2k} + \sum_{k=0}^{n-1}(-1)^k\binom{2n-1}{2k-1}$$

$$= (-1)^n + \sum_{k=0}^{n-1}(-1)^k\binom{2n-1}{2k} + \sum_{k=0}^{n-1}(-1)^k\binom{2n-1}{2n-2k}. \tag{51}$$

Letting in the second summation on the right $n-k=k'$, then

$$\sum_{k=0}^{n-1}(-1)^k\binom{2n-1}{2n-2k} = (-1)^n\sum_{k=1}^{n}(-1)^k\binom{2n-1}{2k} \tag{52}$$

$$= -(-1)^n + (-1)^n\sum_{k=0}^{n-1}(-1)^k\binom{2n-1}{2k}. \tag{53}$$

Applying (53) to (51) gives

$$\sum_{k=0}^{n}(-1)^k\binom{2n}{2k} = [1+(-1)^n]\sum_{k=0}^{n-1}(-1)^k\binom{2n-1}{2k}, \tag{54}$$

which by means of (47) gives (49).

2. (i) To find the value of

$$S = \sum_{k=0}^{n} \binom{p-k}{n-k}. \tag{55}$$

Now
$$S = \sum_{k=0}^{n} \binom{p-k}{p-n}$$

$$= ((x^{p-n})) \sum_{k=0}^{n} (1+x)^{p-k}$$

$$= ((x^{p-n+1}))[(1+x)^{p+1} - (1+x)^{p-n}]$$

$$= \binom{p+1}{p-n+1} = \binom{p+1}{n}. \tag{56}$$

(ii) To find the value of

$$S = \sum_{k=1}^{n} (-1)^{k-1} \binom{p}{n+1-k}. \tag{57}$$

We have
$$S = \sum_{k=1}^{n+1} (-1)^{k-1} \binom{p}{n+1-k} - (-1)^n \tag{58}$$

$$= \sum_{k=1}^{n+1} ((x^{k-1}))(1+x)^{-1}((x^{n+1-k}))(1+x)^{p} - (-1)^n$$

$$= ((x^n))(1+x)^{p-1} - (-1)^n$$

$$= \binom{p-1}{n} - (-1)^n. \tag{59}$$

(iii) To sum the series

$$S = \sum_{k=n}^{p-m} \binom{k}{n}\binom{p-k}{m}. \tag{60}$$

Now
$$\binom{k}{n} = \binom{k}{k-n} = (-1)^{k-n}\binom{-n-1}{k-n} \tag{61}$$

and
$$\binom{p-k}{m} = \binom{p-k}{p-k-m} = (-1)^{p-k-m}\binom{-m-1}{p-k-m}. \tag{62}$$

Applying (61) and (62) to (60), we have

$$S = (-1)^{p-n-m} \sum_{k=n}^{p-m} \binom{-n-1}{k-n}\binom{-m-1}{p-k-m} \tag{63}$$

$$= (-1)^{p-n-m} \sum_{k=n}^{p-m} ((x^{k-n}))(1+x)^{-n-1}((x^{p-k-m}))(1+x)^{-m-1} \tag{64}$$

$$= (-1)^{p-n-m}((x^{p-n-m}))(1+x)^{-n-m-2}$$

$$= (-1)^{p-n-m}\binom{-n-m-2}{p-n-m} = \binom{p+1}{p-n-m}. \tag{65}$$

(iv) To find the value of

$$S=\sum_{n=0}^{p}(-1)^n\binom{p}{n}\binom{m+n}{n}. \tag{66}$$

Since $\binom{m+n}{n}=\binom{m+n}{m}$ is a polynomial in n of degree m,

$$S=0,\text{ if } m<p,\text{ by Ch. I. (135).} \tag{67}$$

The result (67) and the value of S when $m=p$ and when m is greater than p can be obtained in the following way :

$$S=\sum_{n=0}^{p}(-1)^n\binom{p}{p-n}\binom{m+n}{n} \tag{68}$$

$$=\sum_{n=0}^{p}\binom{p}{p-n}\binom{-m-1}{n} \tag{69}$$

$$=\sum_{n=0}^{p}((x^{p-n}))(1+x)^p((x^n))(1+x)^{-m-1} \tag{70}$$

$$=((x^p))(1+x)^{p-m-1}=\binom{p-m-1}{p}=0,\text{ when } m<p, \tag{71}$$

$$=(-1)^p\binom{m}{p},\qquad\text{when } m>p, \tag{72}$$

$$=(-1)^p,\qquad\text{when } m=p. \tag{73}$$

3. (i) To express

$$S=\sum_{k=0}^{n}\binom{2k+1}{m} \tag{74}$$

as a polynomial in n.

Since, in (74), $2k+1\geqq m$,

$$S=\sum_{k=\left[\frac{m}{2}\right]}^{n}\binom{2k+1}{m}. \tag{75}$$

When m is even,

$$S=((x^m))\sum_{k=\frac{m}{2}}^{n}(1+x)^{2k+1} \tag{76}$$

$$=\tfrac{1}{2}((x^{m+1}))\frac{(1+x)^{2n+3}-(1+x)^{m+1}}{1+\frac{x}{2}}. \tag{77}$$

Denoting

$$\frac{(1+x)^{2n+3}}{1+\frac{x}{2}}\text{ by } S_1 \tag{78}$$

and

$$\frac{(1+x)^{m+1}}{1+\frac{x}{2}}\text{ by } S_2, \tag{79}$$

then

$$S_1=\sum_{\alpha=0}^{\infty}(-1)^\alpha\frac{x^\alpha}{2^\alpha}\sum_{\beta=0}^{2n+3}\binom{2n+3}{\beta}x^\beta. \tag{80}$$

Letting $\alpha+\beta=\alpha'$,

$$S_1=\sum_{\beta=0}^{2n+3}(-1)^\beta\binom{2n+3}{\beta}\sum_{\alpha=\beta}^{\infty}(-1)^\alpha x^\alpha\frac{1}{2^{\alpha-\beta}} \tag{81}$$

and

$$((x^{m+1}))S_1=(-1)^{m+1}\sum_{\beta=0}^{m+1}(-1)^\beta\binom{2n+3}{\beta}\frac{1}{2^{m+1-\beta}}. \tag{82}$$

Next

$$S_2=\sum_{\alpha=0}^{\infty}(-1)^\alpha\frac{x^\alpha}{2^\alpha}\sum_{\beta=0}^{m+1}\binom{m+1}{\beta}x^\beta$$

$$=\sum_{\beta=0}^{m+1}(-1)^\beta\binom{m+1}{\beta}\sum_{\alpha=\beta}^{\infty}(-1)^\alpha x^\alpha\frac{1}{2^{\alpha-\beta}}. \tag{83}$$

Letting $m+1-\beta=\beta'$, then

$$((x^{m+1}))S_2=(-1)^{m+1}\sum_{\beta=0}^{m+1}(-1)^{m+1-\beta}\binom{m+1}{\beta}\frac{1}{2^\beta}$$

$$=\frac{1}{2^{m+1}}. \tag{84}$$

Applying (82) and (84) to (77), we obtain

$$S=\frac{(-1)^{m-1}}{2^{m+2}}\left[\sum_{\beta=0}^{m+1}(-1)^\beta\binom{2n+3}{\beta}2^\beta+1\right]. \tag{85}$$

When m is odd, the result is the same as (85).

Therefore

$$\sum_{k=\left[\frac{m}{2}\right]}^{n}\binom{2k+1}{m}=\frac{(-1)^{m-1}}{2^{m+2}}\left[\sum_{\beta=0}^{m+1}(-1)^\beta\binom{2n+3}{\beta}2^\beta+1\right]. \tag{86}$$

While the second member in (86) is also a summation it is expressed as a polynomial in n, a form often required in mathematical work.

(ii) To express

$$S=\sum_{k=\left[\frac{m}{2}\right]}^{n}(-1)^k\binom{2k+1}{m} \tag{87}$$

as a polynomial in n.

When m is even,

$$\sum_{k=\frac{m}{2}}^{n}(-1)^k\binom{2k+1}{m}=((x^m))\sum_{k=\frac{m}{2}}^{n}(-1)^k(1+x)^{2k+1} \tag{88}$$

$$=((x^m))\frac{(-1)^{\frac{m}{2}}(1+x)^{m+1}+(-1)^n(1+x)^{2n+3}}{2+2x+x^2}. \tag{89}$$

We shall first find the expansion in powers of x of

$$S_1=\frac{(-1)^n(1+x)^{2n+3}}{2+2x+x^2}. \tag{90}$$

Now $(2+2x+x^2)^{-1}=\sum_{k=0}^{\infty}(-1)^k x^k \sum_{\alpha=0}^{\left[\frac{k}{2}\right]}(-1)^\alpha\binom{k-\alpha}{\alpha}\frac{1}{2^{\alpha+1}}$, by Ch. I. (10); (91)

therefore

$$S_1=(-1)^n\sum_{k=0}^{\infty}(-1)^k x^k \sum_{\alpha=0}^{\left[\frac{k}{2}\right]}(-1)^\alpha\binom{k-\alpha}{\alpha}\frac{1}{2^{\alpha+1}}\sum_{\beta=0}^{2n+3}\binom{2n+3}{\beta}x^\beta. \tag{92}$$

Letting $k+\beta=k'$, then

$$S_1=(-1)^n\sum_{\beta=0}^{2n+3}(-1)^\beta\binom{2n+3}{\beta}\sum_{k=\beta}^{\infty}(-1)^k x^k\sum_{\alpha=0}^{\left[\frac{k-\beta}{2}\right]}(-1)^\alpha\binom{k-\beta-\alpha}{\alpha}\frac{1}{2^{\alpha+1}}. \tag{93}$$

Hence

$$((x^m))S_1=(-1)^{n-m}\sum_{\alpha=0}^{m}(-1)^\alpha\binom{2n+3}{\alpha}\sum_{\beta=0}^{\left[\frac{m-\alpha}{2}\right]}(-1)^\beta\binom{m-\alpha-\beta}{\beta}\frac{1}{2^{\beta+1}}. \tag{94}$$

In a similar way we obtain

$$((x^m))\frac{(-1)^{\frac{m}{2}}(1+x)^{m+1}}{2+2x+x^2}=(-1)^{\frac{3m}{2}}\sum_{\alpha=0}^{m}(-1)^\alpha\binom{m+1}{\alpha}\sum_{\beta=0}^{\left[\frac{m-\alpha}{2}\right]}(-1)^\beta \binom{m-\alpha-\beta}{\beta}\frac{1}{2^{\beta+1}}. \tag{95}$$

Therefore

$$\sum_{k=\frac{m}{2}}^{n}(-1)^k\binom{2k+1}{m}=(-1)^m\sum_{\alpha=0}^{m}(-1)^\alpha\left[(-1)^{\frac{m}{2}}\binom{m+1}{\alpha}+(-1)^n\binom{2n+3}{\alpha}\right]\sum_{\beta=0}^{\left[\frac{m-\alpha}{2}\right]}(-1)^\beta\binom{m-\alpha-\beta}{\beta}\frac{1}{2^{\beta+1}}. \tag{96}$$

When m is odd, then by means of (94) and

$$((x^m))\frac{(-1)^{\frac{m-1}{2}}(1+x)^m}{2+2x+x^2}=(-1)^{\frac{3m-1}{2}}\sum_{\alpha=0}^{m}(-1)^\alpha\binom{m}{\alpha}\sum_{\beta=0}^{\left[\frac{m-\alpha}{2}\right]}(-1)^\beta\binom{m-\alpha-\beta}{\beta}\frac{1}{2^{\beta+1}}, \tag{97}$$

we obtain

$$\sum_{k=\frac{m-1}{2}}^{n}(-1)^k\binom{2k+1}{m}=(-1)^m\sum_{\alpha=0}^{m}(-1)^\alpha\left[(-1)^{\frac{m-1}{2}}\binom{m}{\alpha}+(-1)^n\binom{2n+3}{\alpha}\right]\sum_{\beta=0}^{\left[\frac{m-\alpha}{2}\right]}(-1)^\beta\binom{m-\alpha-\beta}{\beta}\frac{1}{2^{\beta+1}}. \tag{98}$$

Therefore whether m be even or odd,

$$\sum_{k=\left[\frac{m}{2}\right]}^{n}(-1)^k\binom{2k+1}{m}=(-1)^m\sum_{a=0}^{m}(-1)^a\left[(-1)^{\frac{m-\gamma}{2}}\binom{m+1-\gamma}{a}+(-1)^n\binom{2n+3}{a}\right]$$
$$\sum_{\beta=0}^{\left[\frac{m-a}{2}\right]}(-1)^\beta\binom{m-a-\beta}{\beta}\frac{1}{2^{\beta+1}}, \quad (99)$$

where $$\gamma=\frac{1-(-1)^m}{2}.$$

(iii) To express $$S=\sum_{k=0}^{n}(-1)^k\binom{m+k}{m} \quad (100)$$
as a polynomial in n.

Now $$S=\sum_{k=0}^{n}\binom{m+k}{k}-2\sum_{k=0}^{\left[\frac{n-1}{2}\right]}\binom{m+2k+1}{m}. \quad (101)$$

Letting $$S_1=\sum_{k=0}^{n}\binom{m+k}{k} \quad (102)$$

and $$S_2=\sum_{k=0}^{n}\binom{m+2k+1}{m}, \quad (103)$$

then $$S_1=((x^m))[(1+x)^m\sum_{k=0}^{n}(1+x)^k] \quad (104)$$
$$=\binom{n+m+1}{m+1}=\binom{n+m+1}{n}. \quad (105)$$

Next $$S_2=((x^m))[(1+x)^{m+1}\sum_{k=0}^{n}(1+x)^{2k}] \quad (106)$$
$$=\tfrac{1}{2}((x^{m+1}))S_3-\tfrac{1}{2}((x^{m+1}))S_4, \quad (107)$$

where $$S_3=\frac{(1+x)^{2n+m+3}}{1+\frac{x}{2}} \quad (108)$$

and $$S_4=\frac{(1+x)^{m+1}}{1+\frac{x}{2}}. \quad (109)$$

Then, by the method used in (ii), we obtain

$$\tfrac{1}{2}((x^{m+1}))S_3=\frac{(-1)^{m-1}}{2^{m+2}}\sum_{a=0}^{m+1}(-1)^a\binom{2n+m+3}{a}2^a \quad (110)$$

and $$\tfrac{1}{2}((x^{m+1}))S_4=\frac{(-1)^{m-1}}{2^{m+2}}\sum_{a=0}^{m+1}(-1)^a\binom{m+1}{a}2^a,$$
$$=\frac{(-1)^{m-1}}{2^{m+2}}(1-2)^{m+1}=\frac{1}{2^{m+2}}. \quad (111)$$

Applying (110) and (111) to (107), we have

$$S_2 = \frac{(-1)^{m-1}}{2^{m+2}} \left[\sum_{\alpha=0}^{m+1} (-1)^\alpha \binom{2n+m+3}{\alpha} 2^\alpha + (-1)^m \right]. \tag{112}$$

Then, by means of (105) and (112), we obtain from (101)

$$S = \binom{n+m+1}{n} + \frac{(-1)^m}{2^{m+1}} \left[\sum_{\alpha=0}^{m+1} (-1)^\alpha \binom{2\left[\frac{n-1}{2}\right]+m+3}{\alpha} 2^\alpha + (-1)^m \right] \tag{113}$$

$$= \frac{(-1)^m}{2^{m+1}} \left[(-1)^n \sum_{\alpha=0}^{m} (-1)^\alpha \binom{n+m+1}{\alpha} 2^\alpha + (-1)^m \right]. \tag{114}$$

This result can also be derived as follows:

From (100), $\qquad S = ((x^m)) \left[(1+x)^m \sum_{k=0}^{n} (-1)^k (1+x)^k \right] \tag{115}$

$$= \tfrac{1}{2}((x^m)) S_5 + \tfrac{1}{2}((x^m)) S_6, \tag{116}$$

where $\qquad S_5 = \dfrac{(1+x)^m}{1+\frac{x}{2}} \quad$ and $\quad S_6 = (-1)^n \dfrac{(1+x)^{n+m+1}}{1+\frac{x}{2}}. \tag{117}$

We then find $\quad ((x^m)) S_5 = \dfrac{1}{2^m} \tag{118}$

and $\qquad ((x^m)) S_6 = \dfrac{(-1)^{n+m}}{2^m} \sum_{\alpha=0}^{m} (-1)^\alpha \binom{n+m+1}{\alpha} 2^\alpha. \tag{119}$

Therefore $\quad S = \dfrac{(-1)^m}{2^{m+1}} \left[(-1)^n \sum_{\alpha=0}^{n} (-1)^\alpha \binom{n+m+1}{\alpha} 2^\alpha + (-1)^m \right], \tag{120}$

which is the same as (114).

    4. To express $\qquad S = \sum_{k=1}^{n} \binom{3k-2}{m} \tag{121}$

as a sum of polynomials in powers of n.

Now $\qquad S = ((x^m)) \sum_{k=1}^{n} (1+x)^{3k-2}$

$$= ((x^{m+1})) S_1 - ((x^{m+1})) S_2, \tag{122}$$

where $\qquad S_1 = \dfrac{(1+x)^{3n+1}}{3+3x+x^2} \tag{123}$

and $\qquad S_2 = \dfrac{1+x}{3+3x+x^2}. \tag{124}$

We find

$$\frac{1}{3+3x+x^2} = \frac{1}{3} \sum_{k=0}^{\infty} (-1)^k x^k \sum_{\alpha=0}^{\left[\frac{k}{2}\right]} (-1)^\alpha \binom{k-\alpha}{\alpha} \left(\frac{1}{3}\right)^\alpha, \text{ by Ch. I. (10).} \tag{125}$$

Then

$$S_1=\frac{1}{3}\sum_{k=0}^{\infty}(-1)^k x^k \sum_{\beta=0}^{k}(-1)^\beta\binom{3n+1}{\beta}\sum_{\alpha=0}^{\left[\frac{k-\beta}{2}\right]}(-1)^\alpha\binom{k-\beta-\alpha}{\alpha}\left(\frac{1}{3}\right)^\alpha \tag{126}$$

and

$$((x^{m+1}))S_1=\frac{(-1)^{m-1}}{3}\sum_{\alpha=0}^{m+1}(-1)^\alpha\binom{3n+1}{\alpha}\sum_{\beta=0}^{\left[\frac{m+1-\alpha}{2}\right]}(-1)^\beta\binom{m+1-\alpha-\beta}{\beta}\frac{1}{3^\beta}. \tag{127}$$

Similarly

$$S_2=\frac{1}{3}\sum_{k=0}^{\infty}(-1)^k x^k\sum_{\alpha=0}^{\left[\frac{k}{2}\right]}(-1)^\alpha\binom{k-\alpha}{\alpha}\frac{1}{3^\alpha}$$

$$+\frac{1}{3}\sum_{k=0}^{\infty}(-1)^k x^{k+1}\sum_{\alpha=0}^{\left[\frac{k}{2}\right]}(-1)^\alpha\binom{k-\alpha}{\alpha}\frac{1}{3^\alpha} \tag{128}$$

and

$$((x^{m+1}))S_2=\frac{(-1)^{m-1}}{3}\sum_{\alpha=0}^{\left[\frac{m+1}{2}\right]}(-1)^\alpha\binom{m+1-\alpha}{\alpha}\frac{1}{3^\alpha}$$

$$+\frac{(-1)^m}{3}\sum_{\alpha=0}^{\left[\frac{m}{2}\right]}(-1)^\alpha\binom{m-\alpha}{\alpha}\frac{1}{3^\alpha}. \tag{129}$$

Applying (127) and (129) to (122), we obtain

$$S=\frac{(-1)^{m-1}}{3}\left[\sum_{\alpha=0}^{m+1}(-1)^\alpha\binom{3n+1}{\alpha}\sum_{\beta=0}^{\left[\frac{m+1-\alpha}{2}\right]}(-1)^\beta\binom{m+1-\alpha-\beta}{\beta}\frac{1}{3^\beta}\right.$$

$$\left.-\sum_{\beta=0}^{\left[\frac{m+1}{2}\right]}(-1)^\beta\binom{m+1-\beta}{\beta}\frac{1}{3^\beta}+\sum_{\beta=0}^{\left[\frac{m}{2}\right]}(-1)^\beta\binom{m-\beta}{\beta}\frac{1}{3^\beta}\right]$$

$$=\frac{(-1)^{m-1}}{3}\left[\sum_{\alpha=1}^{m+1}(-1)^\alpha\binom{3n+1}{\alpha}\sum_{\beta=0}^{\left[\frac{m+1-\alpha}{2}\right]}(-1)^\beta\binom{m+1-\alpha-\beta}{\beta}\frac{1}{3^\beta}\right.$$

$$\left.+\sum_{\beta=0}^{\left[\frac{m}{2}\right]}(-1)^\beta\binom{m-\beta}{\beta}\frac{1}{3^\beta}\right]. \tag{130}$$

The results (82), (84), (94), (95), etc., could also have been derived by Maclaurin's theorem.

5. We shall find here the sum of a few series.

The methods applied in obtaining the results will be used in subsequent chapters.

(i) To find the value of

$$S=\sum_{k=1}^{n}(-1)^{k-1}\binom{n}{k}\sum_{m=1}^{k}\frac{1}{m}. \tag{131}$$

Now, by Ch. I. (97),

$$S=\sum_{m=1}^{n}\frac{1}{m}\sum_{k=m}^{n}(-1)^{k-1}\binom{n}{k}$$

$$=\sum_{m=1}^{n}\frac{1}{m}\left[-\sum_{k=0}^{n}(-1)^{k}\binom{n}{k}+\sum_{k=0}^{m-1}(-1)^{k}\binom{n}{k}\right]; \tag{132}$$

and since

$$\sum_{k=0}^{n}(-1)^{k}\binom{n}{k}=(1-1)^{n}=0,$$

therefore

$$S=\sum_{m=1}^{n}\frac{1}{m}\sum_{k=0}^{m-1}(-1)^{k}\binom{n}{k}. \tag{133}$$

To find the value of

$$S_1=\sum_{k=0}^{m-1}(-1)^{k}\binom{n}{k}, \tag{134}$$

we let

$$m-1-k=k';$$

then

$$S_1=(-1)^{m-1}\sum_{k=0}^{m-1}(-1)^{k}\binom{n}{m-1-k}$$

$$=(-1)^{m-1}\sum_{k=0}^{m-1}((x^{k}))(1+x)^{-1}((x^{m-1-k}))(1+x)^{n}$$

$$=(-1)^{m-1}\binom{n-1}{m-1}. \tag{135}$$

Applying (135) to (133), we obtain

$$S=\sum_{m=1}^{n}\frac{(-1)^{m-1}}{m}\binom{n-1}{m-1}=-\frac{1}{n}\sum_{m=1}^{n}(-1)^{m}\binom{n}{m}$$

$$=-\frac{1}{n}\left[\sum_{m=0}^{n}(-1)^{m}\binom{n}{m}-1\right]=\frac{1}{n}. \tag{136}$$

This result can also be obtained as follows:

Let

$$S_r=\sum_{k=1}^{n}(-1)^{k-1}\binom{n}{k}\sum_{m=1}^{k}\frac{r^{m}}{m}; \tag{137}$$

then

$$S=S_r]_{r=1}.$$

Now

$$\frac{dS_r}{dr}=\sum_{k=1}^{n}(-1)^{k-1}\binom{n}{k}\sum_{m=1}^{k}r^{m-1} \tag{138}$$

$$=\sum_{k=1}^{n}(-1)^{k-1}\binom{n}{k}\frac{1-r^{k}}{1-r} \tag{139}$$

$$=-\frac{1}{1-r}\left[\sum_{k=0}^{n}(-1)^{k}\binom{n}{k}-\sum_{k=0}^{n}(-1)^{k}\binom{n}{k}r^{k}\right] \tag{140}$$

$$=(1-r)^{n-1}. \tag{141}$$

Therefore $$S_r = -\frac{1}{n}(1-r)^n + C. \tag{142}$$

But when $r=0$, $$S_r = 0 \quad\text{and}\quad C = \frac{1}{n};$$

hence $$S_r = -\frac{1}{n}(1-r)^n + \frac{1}{n} \tag{143}$$

and $$S = \frac{1}{n}. \tag{144}$$

Show that $$\sum_{k=1}^{n}(-1)^{k-1}\binom{n}{k}\sum_{m=1}^{k}(-1)^m\frac{1}{m} = \frac{1-2^n}{n}. \tag{145}$$

(ii) To find the value of

$$S = \sum_{n=1}^{\infty}\frac{(-1)^{n-1}}{n}\sum_{k=1}^{n}\frac{1}{2k-1}. \tag{146}$$

Let $$S_r = \sum_{n=1}^{\infty}(-1)^{n-1}\frac{r^n}{n}\sum_{k=1}^{n}\frac{1}{2k-1}, \quad -1<r\leqq 1; \tag{147}$$

then $$S = S_r\big]_{r=1}.$$

Now, by Ch. I. (97), (147) becomes

$$S_r = \sum_{k=1}^{\infty}\frac{1}{2k-1}\sum_{n=k}^{\infty}(-1)^{n-1}\frac{r^n}{n}. \tag{148}$$

Letting $n-k=n'$,

$$S_r = \sum_{k=1}^{\infty}\frac{1}{2k-1}\sum_{n=0}^{\infty}(-1)^{n+k-1}\frac{r^{n+k}}{n+k} \tag{149}$$

and $$\frac{dS_r}{dr} = \sum_{k=1}^{\infty}\frac{1}{2k-1}\sum_{n=0}^{\infty}(-1)^{n+k-1}r^{n+k-1} \tag{150}$$

$$= \frac{1}{1+r}\sum_{k=1}^{\infty}(-1)^{k-1}\frac{r^{k-1}}{2k-1}$$

$$= \frac{1}{(1+r)r^{\frac{1}{2}}}\sum_{k=1}^{\infty}(-1)^{k-1}\frac{(r^{\frac{1}{2}})^{2k-1}}{2k-1}$$

$$= \frac{1}{(1+r)r^{\frac{1}{2}}}\tan^{-1}r^{\frac{1}{2}}, \text{ by Ch. I. (41).} \tag{151}$$

Therefore $$S_r = \int_0^r \frac{1}{(1+r)r^{\frac{1}{2}}}\tan^{-1}r^{\frac{1}{2}}\,dr$$

$$= (\tan^{-1}r^{\frac{1}{2}})^2 \tag{152}$$

and $$S = \frac{\pi^2}{16}. \tag{153}$$

(iii) To find the value of

$$S=\sum_{k=n}^{\infty}\binom{p+k-1}{k}\binom{k}{n}\frac{1}{2^k}. \tag{154}$$

Now
$$\binom{p+k-1}{k}=(-1)^k\binom{-p}{k};$$

hence
$$S=\sum_{k=n}^{\infty}(-1)^k\binom{-p}{k}\binom{k}{n}\frac{1}{2^k}; \tag{155}$$

and since
$$\binom{-p}{k}\binom{k}{n}=\binom{-p}{n}\binom{-p-n}{k-n},$$

$$S=\binom{-p}{n}\sum_{k=n}^{\infty}(-1)^k\binom{-p-n}{k-n}\frac{1}{2^k}. \tag{156}$$

Letting $k-n=k'$, then

$$S=\frac{(-1)^n}{2^n}\binom{-p}{n}\sum_{k=0}^{\infty}(-1)^k\binom{-p-n}{k}\frac{1}{2^k} \tag{157}$$

$$=\frac{(-1)^n}{2^n}\binom{-p}{n}(1-\tfrac{1}{2})^{-p-n}$$

$$=(-1)^n 2^p\binom{-p}{n}=2^p\binom{p+n-1}{n}. \tag{158}$$

(iv) To find the sum

$$S=\sum_{n=1}^{\infty}\sum_{k=1}^{n}\frac{1}{k}\binom{p-k}{n-k}r^n. \tag{159}$$

Now
$$S=\sum_{k=1}^{\infty}\frac{r^k}{k}\sum_{n=k}^{\infty}\binom{p-k}{n-k}r^{n-k},\ \text{by Ch. I. (97)}, \tag{160}$$

$$=\sum_{k=1}^{\infty}\frac{r^k}{k}(1+r)^{p-k}$$

$$=(1+r)^p\sum_{k=1}^{\infty}\frac{1}{k}\left(\frac{r}{1+r}\right)^k$$

$$=-(1+r)^p\log\left(1-\frac{r}{1+r}\right)=(1+r)^p\log(1+r). \tag{161}$$

(v) To find the value of

$$S=\sum_{n=1}^{\infty}\sum_{k=1}^{n}\frac{(-1)^{k-1}}{k}\binom{p}{n-k}r^n. \tag{162}$$

Now
$$S=\sum_{k=1}^{\infty}(-1)^{k-1}\frac{r^k}{k}\sum_{n=k}^{\infty}\binom{p}{n-k}r^{n-k} \tag{163}$$

$$=\sum_{k=1}^{\infty}(-1)^{k-1}\frac{r^k}{k}(1+r)^p=(1+r)^p\log(1+r). \tag{164}$$

This shows that (159) and (162) have the same values.

(vi) To find the sum of

$$S=\sum_{k=0}^{\infty}(-1)^k\binom{p+k}{n}r^k. \tag{165}$$

Letting $p+k=k'$, then

$$S=\frac{(-1)^p}{r^p}\sum_{k=p}^{\infty}(-1)^k\binom{k}{n}r^k \tag{166}$$

(a) If p is less than n,

$$S=\frac{(-1)^p}{r^p}\sum_{k=n}^{\infty}(-1)^k\binom{k}{k-n}r^k; \tag{167}$$

and letting $k-n=k'$,
$$S=(-1)^{n-p}r^{n-p}\sum_{k=0}^{\infty}\binom{-n-1}{k}r^k$$
$$=\frac{(-1)^{n-p}r^{n-p}}{(1+r)^{n+1}}. \tag{168}$$

(b) If p is greater than n,

$$S=\frac{(-1)^p}{r^p}\sum_{k=n}^{\infty}(-1)^k\binom{k}{n}r^k-\frac{(-1)^p}{r^p}\sum_{k=n}^{p-1}(-1)^k\binom{n}{k}r^k \tag{169}$$

$$=\frac{(-1)^{p-n}}{r^{p-n}(1+r)^{n+1}}+\frac{(-1)^{p-1}}{r^p}\sum_{k=n}^{p-1}(-1)^k\binom{k}{n}r^k. \tag{170}$$

Now, if $p<n$, the summation in (170) is zero; therefore (168) holds true whether p be greater or less than n.

Also
$$\sum_{k=0}^{\infty}\binom{p+k}{n}r^k=\frac{r^{n-p}}{(1-r)^{n+1}}-\frac{1}{r^p}\sum_{k=n}^{p-1}\binom{k}{n}r^k. \tag{171}$$

CHAPTER IV.

HIGHER DERIVATIVES OF POWERS OF TRIGONOMETRIC FUNCTIONS, AND THEIR EXPANSIONS.

1. GIVEN
$$y = \sin^p x, \tag{1}$$
to find $\dfrac{d^n y}{dx^n}$ in powers of $\sin x$ and $\cos x$, and the expansion of y in powers of x.

Now
$$y = \frac{(-1)^p i^p}{2^p} \frac{(e^{2ix}-1)^p}{e^{pix}} \tag{2}$$
and
$$\frac{d^n y}{dx^n} = \frac{(-1)^p i^p}{2^p} \frac{d^n}{dx^n} \frac{(e^{2ix}-1)^p}{e^{pix}}. \tag{3}$$

Then, by Leibnitz's theorem,
$$\frac{d^n y}{dx^n} = \frac{(-1)^p i^p}{2^p} \sum_{k=0}^{n} \binom{n}{k} \frac{d^{n-k}}{dx^{n-k}} e^{-pix} \frac{d^k}{dx^k} (e^{2ix}-1)^p ; \tag{4}$$
and since
$$\frac{d^{n-k}}{dx^{n-k}} e^{-pix} = (-1)^{n-k} p^{n-k} i^{n-k} e^{-pix}$$
and
$$\frac{d^k}{dx^k} (e^{2ix}-1)^p = (-1)^p 2^k i^k \sum_{a=0}^{p} (-1)^a \binom{p}{a} a^k e^{2iax},$$
therefore, from (4),
$$\frac{d^n y}{dx^n} = \frac{(-1)^n}{2^p} p^n i^{n+p} \sum_{k=0}^{n} (-1)^k \binom{n}{k} \left(\frac{2a}{p}\right)^k \sum_{a=0}^{p} (-1)^a \binom{p}{a} e^{-(p-2a)ix}. \tag{5}$$

But
$$\sum_{k=0}^{n} (-1)^k \binom{n}{k} \left(\frac{2a}{p}\right)^k = \frac{(p-2a)^n}{p^n};$$
hence
$$\frac{d^n}{dx^n} \sin^p x = \frac{(-1)^n}{2^p} i^{n+p} \sum_{a=0}^{p} (-1)^a \binom{p}{a} (p-2a)^n (\cos x - i \sin x)^{p-2a}. \tag{6}$$

This result can be obtained, without the use of Leibnitz's theorem, by taking the nth derivative of
$$\sin^p x = \frac{(-1)^p i^p}{2^p} \sum_{k=0}^{p} (-1)^k \binom{p}{k} e^{(p-2k)ix}$$
$$= \frac{i^p}{2^p} \sum_{k=0}^{p} (-1)^k \binom{p}{k} e^{-(p-2k)ix}.$$

Now, from (6), we have

$$\frac{d^{2n}}{dx^{2n}}\sin^{2p}x=\frac{(-1)^{n+p}}{2^{2p}}\sum_{k=0}^{2p}(-1)^k\binom{2p}{k}(2p-2k)^{2n}\cos(2p-2k)x. \tag{7}$$

Denoting by P_k the expression under the summation sign in (7), then

$$\sum_{k=0}^{2p}P_k=\sum_{k=0}^{p}P_k+\sum_{k=p+1}^{2p}P_k. \tag{8}$$

Letting in the second summation on the right $2p-k=k'$, we find

$$\sum_{k=0}^{2p}P_k=2\sum_{k=0}^{p}P_k. \tag{9}$$

Therefore
$$\frac{d^{2n}}{dx^{2n}}\sin^{2p}x=\frac{(-1)^{n+p}}{2^{2p-1}}\sum_{k=0}^{p}(-1)^k\binom{2p}{k}(2p-2k)^{2n}\cos(2p-2k)x. \tag{10}$$

In a similar way we obtain from (6),

$$\frac{d^{2n}}{dx^{2n}}\sin^{2p+1}x=\frac{(-1)^{n+p}}{2^{2p+1-1}}\sum_{k=0}^{p}(-1)^k\binom{2p+1}{k}(2p+1-2k)^{2n}\sin(2p+1-2k)x, \tag{11}$$

$$\frac{d^{2n+1}}{dx^{2n+1}}\sin^{2p}x=\frac{(-1)^{n+p+1}}{2^{2p-1}}\sum_{k=0}^{p}(-1)^k\binom{2p}{k}(2p-2k)^{2n+1}\sin(2p-2k)x, \tag{12}$$

$$\frac{d^{2n+1}}{dx^{2n+1}}\sin^{2p+1}x=\frac{(-1)^{n+p}}{2^{2p+1-1}}\sum_{k=0}^{p}(-1)^k\binom{2p+1}{k}(2p+1-2k)^{2n+1}\cos(2p+1-2k)x. \tag{13}$$

Letting, as in Ch. II. (48) and (49),

$$\cos(p-2k)x=\sum_{\alpha=0}^{\left[\frac{p}{2}\right]-k}(-1)^\alpha\binom{p-2k}{2\alpha}\cos^{p-2k-2\alpha}x\sin^{2\alpha}x=M_{2\alpha} \tag{14}$$

and
$$\sin(p-2k)x=\sum_{\alpha=0}^{\left[\frac{p-1}{2}\right]-k}(-1)^\alpha\binom{p-2k}{2\alpha+1}\cos^{p-2k-2\alpha-1}x\sin^{2\alpha+1}x=M_{2\alpha+1}, \tag{15}$$

and combining (10)–(13), gives

$$\frac{d^n}{dx^n}\sin^p x=\frac{(-1)^{\left[\frac{n+p+\Delta_1}{2}\right]}}{2^{p-1}}\sum_{k=0}^{\left[\frac{p}{2}\right]}(-1)^k\binom{p}{k}(p-2k)^n M_{2\alpha+\Delta_2}, \tag{16}$$

where
$$\Delta_1=(-1)^p\frac{1-(-1)^n}{2} \quad\text{and}\quad \Delta_2=\frac{1-(-1)^{n+p}}{2}.$$

If $p=1$, then from (16)

$$\frac{d^n}{dx^n}\sin x=(-1)^{\left[\frac{n+1}{2}\right]}M_{2\alpha+1}=(-1)^{\left[\frac{n+1}{2}\right]}\sin x,\quad\text{when } n \text{ is even,}$$

$$=(-1)^{\left[\frac{n}{n}\right]}M_{2\alpha}=(-1)^{\left[\frac{n}{2}\right]}\cos x,\qquad\text{when } n \text{ is odd.}$$

2. We shall now find the expansion of $\sin^p x$.

From (16) follows $$\frac{d^n}{dx^n}\sin^p x\Big]_{x\doteq 0}=0, \text{ if } \Delta_1=1, \tag{17}$$

that is when n is even and p is odd, or when n is odd and p is even.

But when n and p are both either even or odd, then $\Delta_2=0$, and since $a=0$ is the only value which may be assigned to a, $M_{2a}]_{x\doteq 0}=1$.

We then have

$$\frac{d^n}{dx^n}\sin^p x\Big]_{x\doteq 0}=\frac{(-1)^{\left[\frac{n+p+\Delta_1}{2}\right]}}{2^{p-1}}\sum_{k=0}^{\left[\frac{p}{2}\right]}(-1)^k\binom{p}{k}(p-2k)^n. \tag{18}$$

But, by Ch. I. (136), the second member of (18) vanishes for values of $n<\left[\begin{matrix}p\\ n<p\end{matrix}\right]$; therefore

$$\sin^p x=\frac{1}{2^{p-1}}\sum_{n=\left[\begin{smallmatrix}p\\ n=p\end{smallmatrix}\right]}^{\infty}(-1)^{\left[\frac{n+p+\Delta_1}{2}\right]}\frac{x^n}{n!}\sum_{k=0}^{\left[\frac{p}{2}\right]}(-1)^k\binom{p}{k}(p-2k)^n. \tag{19}$$

Now, if n and p are both even, then $\Delta_1=0$, and

$$\sin^p x=\frac{(-1)^{\frac{p}{2}}}{2^{p-1}}\sum_{n=\frac{p}{2}}^{\infty}(-1)^n\frac{x^{2n}}{(2n)!}\sum_{k=0}^{\left[\frac{p}{2}\right]}(-1)^k\binom{p}{k}(p-2k)^{2n}. \tag{20}$$

Letting in (20), $n-\frac{p}{2}=n'$, then

$$\sin^p x=\frac{(-1)^{\frac{p}{2}}}{2^{p-1}}\sum_{n=0}^{\infty}(-1)^{n+\frac{p}{2}}\frac{x^{2n+p}}{(2n+p)!}\sum_{k=0}^{\left[\frac{p}{2}\right]}(-1)^k\binom{p}{k}(p-2k)^{2n+p}; \tag{21}$$

and if n and p are both odd, then

$$\sin^p x=\frac{(-1)^{\frac{p-1}{2}}}{2^{p-1}}\sum_{n=\frac{p-1}{2}}^{\infty}(-1)^n\frac{x^{2n+1}}{(2n+1)!}\sum_{k=0}^{\left[\frac{p}{2}\right]}(-1)^k\binom{p}{k}(p-2k)^{2n+1}. \tag{22}$$

Letting now in (22) $n-\frac{p-1}{2}=n'$,

$$\sin^p x=\frac{(-1)^{\frac{p-1}{2}}}{2^{p-1}}\sum_{n=0}^{\infty}(-1)^{n+\frac{p-1}{2}}\frac{x^{2n+1+p}}{(2n+1+p)!}\sum_{k=0}^{\left[\frac{p}{2}\right]}(-1)^k\binom{p}{k}(p-2k)^{2n+1+p}. \tag{23}$$

Combining (21) and (23), we obtain

$$\sin^p x=\frac{1}{2^{p-1}}\sum_{n=0}^{\infty}(-1)^n\frac{x^{2n+p}}{(2n+p)!}\sum_{k=0}^{\left[\frac{p}{2}\right]}(-1)^k\binom{p}{k}(p-2k)^{2n+p}. \tag{24}$$

The expansion of $\sin^p x$ can be obtained more directly by letting $x=0$ in (6).

3. The expansion of $\sin^p x$ in powers of x can be found without the use of Maclaurin's theorem.

We have
$$\sin^p x = \frac{(e^{ix} - e^{-ix})^p}{2^p i^p}$$
$$= \frac{(-1)^p i^p}{2^p} \sum_{k=0}^{p} (-1)^k \binom{p}{k} e^{(p-2k)ix}, \tag{25}$$

and if p is even,
$$\sin^p x = \frac{(-1)^{\frac{p}{2}}}{2^p} \sum_{k=0}^{p} (-1)^k \binom{p}{k} \cos (p-2k)x. \tag{26}$$

Denoting by P_k the expression under the summation sign in (26), then
$$\sum_{k=0}^{p} P_k = \sum_{k=0}^{\frac{p}{2}-1} P_k + (-1)^{\frac{p}{2}} \binom{p}{\frac{p}{2}} + \sum_{k=\frac{p}{2}+1}^{p} P_k. \tag{27}$$

Letting $\frac{p}{2} - k = k'$ in the first summation of the second member of (27) and $k - \frac{p}{2} = k'$ in the second summation, we obtain
$$\sum_{k=0}^{p} P_k = 2 \sum_{k=1}^{\frac{p}{2}} (-1)^{k+\frac{p}{2}} \binom{p}{\frac{p}{2} - k} \cos 2kx + \binom{p}{\frac{p}{2}}. \tag{28}$$

Applying (28) to (26) gives
$$\sin^p x = \frac{1}{2^{p-1}} \sum_{k=1}^{\frac{p}{2}} (-1)^k \binom{p}{\frac{p}{2} - k} \cos 2kx + \frac{1}{2^p} \binom{p}{\frac{p}{2}}. \tag{29}$$

But
$$\cos 2kx = \sum_{n=0}^{\infty} (-1)^n \frac{(2kx)^{2n}}{(2n)!}; \tag{30}$$

therefore
$$\sin^p x = \frac{1}{2^{p-1}} \sum_{n=0}^{\infty} (-1)^n \frac{x^{2n}}{(2n)!} \sum_{k=1}^{\frac{p}{2}} (-1)^k \binom{p}{\frac{p}{2} - k} (2k)^{2n} + \frac{1}{2^p} \binom{p}{\frac{p}{2}}. \tag{31}$$

We shall now show that the term corresponding to $n = 0$ in (31) is equal to $-\frac{1}{2^p}\binom{p}{\frac{p}{2}}$, that is
$$\sum_{k=1}^{\frac{p}{2}} (-1)^k \binom{p}{\frac{p}{2} - k} = -\frac{1}{2} \binom{p}{\frac{p}{2}} \tag{32}$$

or
$$S = \sum_{k=0}^{\frac{p}{2}} (-1)^k \binom{p}{\frac{p}{2} - k} = \frac{1}{2} \binom{p}{\frac{p}{2}}. \tag{33}$$

Now
$$S = \sum_{k=0}^{\frac{p}{2}} [((x^k))(1+x)^{-1} \times ((x^{\frac{p}{2}-k}))(1+x)^p]$$
$$= ((x^{\frac{p}{2}}))(1+x)^{p-1} = \binom{p-1}{\frac{p}{2}} = \frac{1}{2} \binom{p}{\frac{p}{2}}. \tag{34}$$

Applying (32) to (31), we obtain

$$\sin^p x = \frac{1}{2^{p-1}} \sum_{n=1}^{\infty} (-1)^n \frac{x^{2n}}{(2n)!} \sum_{k=0}^{\frac{p}{2}} (-1)^k \binom{p}{\frac{p}{2}-k} (2k)^{2n}. \tag{35}$$

Letting $\frac{p}{2} - k = k'$, we have

$$\sin^p x = \frac{1}{2^{p-1}} \sum_{n=1}^{\infty} (-1)^{n+\frac{p}{2}} \frac{x^{2n}}{(2n)!} \sum_{k=0}^{\frac{p}{2}} (-1)^k \binom{p}{k} (p-2k)^{2n}. \tag{36}$$

But
$$\sum_{k=0}^{\frac{p}{2}} (-1)^k \binom{p}{k} (p-2k)^{2n} = \frac{1}{2} \sum_{k=0}^{p} (-1)^k \binom{p}{k} (p-2k)^{2n}$$
$$= 0, \text{ if } n < \frac{p}{2};$$

therefore
$$\sin^p x = \frac{1}{2^{p-1}} \sum_{n=\frac{p}{2}}^{\infty} (-1)^{n+\frac{p}{2}} \frac{x^{2n}}{(2n)!} \sum_{k=0}^{\frac{p}{2}} (-1)^k \binom{p}{k} (p-2k)^{2n}; \tag{37}$$

and letting $n - \frac{p}{2} = n'$, we obtain (24).

If p is odd, then from (25) we have

$$\sin^p x = \frac{(-1)^{\frac{p-1}{2}}}{2^p} \sum_{k=0}^{p} (-1)^k \binom{p}{k} \sin (p-2k) x. \tag{38}$$

Denoting by P_k the expression under the summation sign in (38), then

$$\sum_{k=0}^{p} P_k = \sum_{k=0}^{\frac{p-1}{2}} P_k + \sum_{k=\frac{p+1}{2}}^{p} P_k. \tag{39}$$

Letting $\frac{p-1}{2} - k = k'$ in the first summation of the second member of (39) and $k - \frac{p+1}{2} = k'$ in the second summation, then

$$\sum_{k=0}^{p} P_k = 2 \sum_{k=0}^{\frac{p-1}{2}} (-1)^{k+\frac{p-1}{2}} \binom{p}{\frac{p-1}{2}-k} \sin (2k+1) x. \tag{40}$$

Applying (40) to (38), we have

$$\sin^p x = \frac{1}{2^{p-1}} \sum_{k=0}^{\frac{p-1}{2}} (-1)^k \binom{p}{\frac{p-1}{2}-k} \sin (2k+1) x. \tag{41}$$

Substituting $\sin (2k+1)x = \sum_{n=0}^{\infty} (-1)^n (2k+1)^{2n+1} \frac{x^{2n+1}}{(2n+1)!}$

in (40), and then letting $\frac{p-1}{2} - k = k'$, we obtain from (41)

$$\sin^p x = \frac{1}{2^{p-1}} \sum_{n=0}^{\infty} (-1)^{n+\frac{p-1}{2}} \frac{x^{2n+1}}{(2n+1)!} \sum_{k=0}^{\frac{p-1}{2}} (-1)^k \binom{p}{k} (p-2k)^{2n+1} \tag{42}$$

But $\sum_{k=0}^{\frac{p-1}{2}}(-1)^k\binom{p}{k}(p-2k)^{2n+1}=\frac{1}{2}\sum_{k=0}^{p}(-1)^k\binom{p}{k}(p-2k)^{2n+1}=0,$

if $n<\frac{p-1}{2}$;

therefore

$$\sin^p x=\frac{1}{2^{p-1}}\sum_{n=\frac{p-1}{2}}^{\infty}(-1)^{n+\frac{p-1}{2}}\frac{x^{2n+1}}{(2n+1)!}\sum_{k=0}^{\frac{p-1}{2}}(-1)^k\binom{p}{k}(p-2k)^{2n+1}; \tag{43}$$

and letting in (43) $n-\frac{p-1}{2}=n'$, gives again (24).

4. To find $\frac{d^n}{dx^n}\cos^p x$ in powers of $\sin x$ and $\cos x$ and the expansion of $\cos^p x$ in powers of x.

Now
$$\cos^p x=\frac{1}{2^p}\sum_{k=0}^{p}\binom{p}{k}e^{(p-2k)ix}, \tag{44}$$

then
$$\frac{d^n}{dx^n}\cos^p x=\frac{i^n}{2^p}\sum_{k=0}^{p}\binom{p}{k}(p-2k)^n[\cos(p-2k)x+i\sin(p-2k)x] \tag{45}$$

and
$$\frac{d^{2n}}{dx^{2n}}\cos^p x=\frac{(-1)^n}{2^p}\sum_{k=0}^{p}\binom{p}{k}(p-2k)^{2n}\cos(p-2k)x. \tag{46}$$

Denoting by P_k the expression under the summation sign in (46), then if p be even and $n>0$,

$$\sum_{k=0}^{p}P_k=\sum_{k=0}^{\frac{p}{2}-1}P_k+\sum_{k=\frac{p}{2}+1}^{p}P_k. \tag{47}$$

Letting in the second summation on the right of (47) $p-k=k'$, gives

$$\sum_{k=0}^{p}P_k=2\sum_{k=0}^{\frac{p}{2}-1}P_k. \tag{48}$$

If p is odd,
$$\sum_{k=0}^{p}P_k=2\sum_{k=0}^{\frac{p-1}{2}}P_k. \tag{49}$$

Therefore
$$\sum_{k=0}^{p}P_k=2\sum_{k=0}^{\left[\frac{p-1}{2}\right]}P_k, \tag{50}$$

whether p be even or odd.

By means of (50), (46) becomes

$$\frac{d^{2n}}{dx^{2n}}\cos^p x=\frac{(-1)^n}{2^{p-1}}\sum_{k=0}^{\left[\frac{p-1}{2}\right]}\binom{p}{k}(p-2k)^{2n}\sum_{a=0}^{\left[\frac{p}{2}\right]-k}(-1)^a\binom{p-2k}{2a}$$

$$\cos^{p-2k-2a}x\sin^{2a}x. \tag{51}$$

In a similar way we obtain from (45)

$$\frac{d^{2n+1}}{dx^{2n+1}}\cos^p x = \frac{(-1)^{n-1}}{2^{p-1}} \sum_{k=0}^{\left[\frac{p-1}{2}\right]} \binom{p}{k} (p-2k)^{2n+1} \sum_{\alpha=0}^{\left[\frac{p-1}{2}\right]-k} (-1)^\alpha \binom{p-2k}{2\alpha+1} \cos^{p-2k-2\alpha-1}x \sin^{2\alpha+1}x. \quad (52)$$

Combining (51) and (52) gives

$$\frac{d^n}{dx^n}\cos^p x = \frac{(-1)^{\left[\frac{n+1}{2}\right]}}{2^{p-1}} \sum_{k=0}^{\left[\frac{p-1}{2}\right]} \binom{p}{k} (p-2k)^n \sum_{\alpha=0}^{\left[\frac{p-\Delta}{2}\right]-k} (-1)^\alpha \binom{p-2k}{2\alpha+\Delta} \cos^{p-2k-2\alpha-\Delta}x \sin^{2\alpha+\Delta}x, \quad (53)$$

where
$$\Delta = \frac{1-(-1)^n}{2}.$$

Letting $x=0$ in (53), then

$$\left.\frac{d^n}{dx^n}\cos^p x\right]_{x=0} = 0, \text{ unless } \Delta = 0,$$

in which case n is even, and since $\alpha=0$ is the only value which can be assigned to α, $M_{2\alpha}]_{x=0}=1$.

Now when $x=0$ and p is even, then for $n=0$, (47) changes to

$$\sum_{k=0}^{p} \binom{p}{k} = 2\sum_{k=0}^{\frac{p}{2}-1} \binom{p}{k} + \binom{p}{\frac{p}{2}} \quad (54)$$

$$= 2\sum_{k=0}^{\frac{p}{2}} \binom{p}{k} - \binom{p}{\frac{p}{2}}. \quad (55)$$

We then obtain

$$\cos^p x = \frac{1}{2^{p-1}} \sum_{n=0}^{\infty} (-1)^n \frac{x^{2n}}{(2n)!} \sum_{k=0}^{\left[\frac{p}{2}\right]} \binom{p}{k} (p-2k)^{2n} - \frac{1+(-1)^p}{2^{p+1}} \binom{p}{\frac{p}{2}}. \quad (56)$$

Denoting by C_0 the coefficient of x^0 in the expansion (56), then

$$C_0 = \frac{1}{2^{p-1}} \sum_{k=0}^{\left[\frac{p}{2}\right]} \binom{p}{k} - \frac{1+(-1)^p}{2^{p+1}} \binom{p}{\frac{p}{2}}, \quad (57)$$

and we shall show that $C_0=1$.

Now, if p is even, then from (55) we have

$$\sum_{k=0}^{\frac{p}{2}} \binom{p}{k} = \frac{1}{2}\sum_{k=0}^{p} \binom{p}{k} + \frac{1}{2}\binom{p}{\frac{p}{2}}$$

$$= \frac{1}{2}2^p + \frac{1}{2}\binom{p}{\frac{p}{2}}. \quad (58)$$

Applying (58) to (57) gives

$$C_0 = 1 + \frac{1}{2^p}\binom{p}{\frac{p}{2}} - \frac{1}{2^p}\binom{p}{\frac{p}{2}} = 1.$$

If p is odd, then from (56)

$$C_0 = \frac{1}{2^{p-1}} \sum_{k=0}^{\frac{p-1}{2}} \binom{p}{k} = \frac{1}{2^p} \sum_{k=0}^{p} \binom{p}{k} \text{ by (49).} \tag{59}$$

Therefore $C_0 = 1$, which is the first term of the expansion of $\cos^p x$, whether p be even or odd.

5. (i) Given $y = \tan^p x$. To express $\frac{d^n y}{dx^n}$ in powers of $\tan x$ and $\sec x$ and to find the expansion of y in powers of x.

Now $$\tan x = -i\left(1 - \frac{2}{e^{2ix}+1}\right)$$

and $$\frac{d^n}{dx^n} \tan^p x = (-1)^p i^p \sum_{k=0}^{p} (-1)^k \binom{p}{k} 2^k \frac{d^n}{dx^n} \frac{1}{(e^{2ix}+1)^k}. \tag{60}$$

But $$\frac{d^n}{dx^n} \frac{1}{(e^{2ix}+1)^k} = (2i)^n \sum_{\alpha=1}^{n} \binom{k+\alpha-1}{\alpha} \sum_{\beta=1}^{\alpha} (-1)^\beta \binom{\alpha}{\beta} \beta^n \frac{e^{2i\alpha x}}{(e^{2ix}+1)^{k+\alpha}} \tag{61}$$

and $$\frac{e^{2i\alpha x}}{(e^{2ix}+1)^{k+\alpha}} = \frac{\sec^{k+\alpha} x}{2^{k+\alpha}} (\cos x - i \sin x)^{k-\alpha}$$

$$= \frac{\sec^{2\alpha} x}{2^{k+\alpha}} (N_{2\gamma} - i N_{2\gamma+1}), \tag{62}$$

where $$N_{2\gamma} = \sum_{\gamma=0}^{\left[\frac{k-\alpha}{2}\right]} (-1)^\gamma \binom{k-\alpha}{2\gamma} \tan^{2\gamma} x \tag{63}$$

and $$N_{2\gamma+1} = \sum_{\gamma=0}^{\left[\frac{k-\alpha-1}{2}\right]} (-1)^\gamma \binom{k-\alpha}{2\gamma+1} \tan^{2\gamma+1} x. \tag{64}$$

Applying (61) and (62) to (60), we obtain

$$\frac{d^n}{dx^n} \tan^p x = (-1)^p i^{n+p} 2^n \sum_{k=1}^{p} (-1)^k \binom{p}{k} \sum_{\alpha=1}^{n} \binom{k+\alpha-1}{\alpha} \frac{\sec^{2\alpha} x}{2^\alpha}$$
$$\sum_{\beta=1}^{\alpha} (-1)^\beta \binom{\alpha}{\beta} \beta^n (N_{2\gamma} - i N_{2\gamma+1}). \tag{65}$$

From (65) we have

$$\frac{d^{2n}}{dx^{2n}} \tan^{2p} x = (-1)^{n+p} 2^{2n} \sum_{k=1}^{2p} (-1)^k \binom{2p}{k} \sum_{\alpha=1}^{2n} \binom{k+\alpha-1}{\alpha} \frac{\sec^{2\alpha} x}{2^\alpha} \sum_{\beta=1}^{\alpha} (-1)^\beta$$
$$\binom{\alpha}{\beta} \beta^{2n} N_{2\gamma}, \tag{66}$$

$$\frac{d^{2n}}{dx^{2n}} \tan^{2p+1} x = (-1)^{n+p+1} 2^{2n} \sum_{k=1}^{2p+1} (-1)^k \binom{2p+1}{k} \sum_{\alpha=1}^{2n} \binom{k+\alpha-1}{\alpha} \frac{\sec^{2\alpha} x}{2^\alpha} \sum_{\beta=1}^{\alpha} (-1)^\beta$$
$$\binom{\alpha}{\beta} \beta^{2n} N_{2\gamma+1}, \tag{67}$$

$$\frac{d^{2n+1}}{dx^{2n+1}}\tan^{2p}x=(-1)^{n+p}2^{2n+1}\sum_{k=1}^{2p}(-1)^k\binom{2p}{k}\sum_{a=1}^{2n+1}\binom{k+a-1}{a}\frac{\sec^{2a}x}{2^a}$$

$$\sum_{\beta=1}^{a}(-1)^\beta\binom{a}{\beta}\beta^{2n+1}N_{2\gamma+1}, \quad (68)$$

$$\frac{d^{2n+1}}{dx^{2n+1}}\tan^{2p+1}x=(-1)^{n+p}2^{2n+1}\sum_{k=1}^{2p+1}(-1)^k\binom{2p+1}{k}\sum_{a=1}^{2n+1}\binom{k+a-1}{a}\frac{\sec^{2a}x}{2^a}$$

$$\sum_{\beta=1}^{a}(-1)^\beta\binom{a}{\beta}\beta^{2n+1}N_{2\gamma}. \quad (69)$$

Combining (66)–(69) gives

$$\frac{d^n}{dx^n}\tan^p x=(-1)^{\left[\frac{n+p+\Delta_1}{2}\right]}2^n\sum_{k=1}^{p}(-1)^k\binom{p}{k}\sum_{a=1}^{n}\binom{k+a-1}{a}\frac{\sec^{2a}x}{2^a}$$

$$\sum_{\beta=1}^{a}(-1)^k\binom{a}{\beta}\beta^n N_{2\gamma+\Delta_2}, \quad (70)$$

where $\Delta_1=(-1)^n\dfrac{1-(-1)^p}{2}$ and $\Delta_2=\dfrac{1-(-1)^{n+p}}{2}$.

To find the expansion of $\tan^p x$ we have from (70) $\left.\dfrac{d^n}{dx^n}\tan^p x\right]_{x=0}=0$, unless $\Delta_2=0$, that is unless $n+p$ is even. Hence n and p must both be even or both be odd, and since $a=0$ is the only value which may be assigned to a, $N_{2\gamma}]_{x=0}=1$.

Therefore

$$\tan^p x=\sum_{n=0}^{\infty}(-1)^{\left[\frac{n+p+\Delta_1}{2}\right]}2^n\frac{x^n}{n!}\sum_{k=1}^{p}(-1)^k\binom{p}{k}\sum_{a=1}^{n}\binom{k+a-1}{a}\frac{1}{2^a}$$

$$\sum_{\beta=1}^{a}(-1)^\beta\binom{a}{\beta}\beta^n, \quad (71)$$

with the conditions following from above that n is even, if p is even and n is odd, if p is odd.

To reduce (71) we let

$$S=\sum_{k=1}^{p}(-1)^k\binom{p}{k}\binom{k+a-1}{a}. \quad (72)$$

Now $$\binom{k+a-1}{a}=\binom{k+a-1}{k-1}=(-1)^{k-1}\binom{-a-1}{k-1},$$

hence
$$S=-\sum_{k=1}^{p}\binom{p}{p-k}\binom{-a-1}{k-1}$$

$$=-\sum_{k=1}^{p}((x^{p-k}))(1+x)^p((x^{k-1}))(1+x)^{-a-1}$$

$$=-\binom{p-a-1}{p-1}=(-1)^p\binom{a-1}{p-1}. \quad (73)$$

Then, by means of (73), (72) becomes

$$\tan^p x = (-1)^p \sum_{n=0}^{\infty} (-1)^{\left[\frac{n+p+\Delta_1}{2}\right]} 2^n \frac{x^n}{n!} \sum_{\alpha=1}^{n} \binom{\alpha-1}{p-1} \frac{1}{2^\alpha} \sum_{\beta=1}^{\alpha} (-1)^\beta \binom{\alpha}{\beta} \beta^n. \quad (74)$$

Letting $n-p=n'$, then

$$\tan^p x = (-1)^p \sum_{n=0}^{\infty} (-1)^{\left[\frac{2n+p+\Delta_1}{2}\right]} 2^{n+p} \frac{x^{n+p}}{(n+p)!} \sum_{\alpha=p}^{n+p} \binom{\alpha-1}{p-1} \frac{1}{2^\alpha} \sum_{\beta=1}^{\alpha} (-1)^\beta \binom{\alpha}{\beta} \beta^{n+p}; \quad (75)$$

and since the powers of the expansion are even when p is even and odd when p is odd, therefore n must be even, and

$$\tan^p x = (-1)^p \sum_{n=0}^{\infty} (-1)^n 2^{2n+p} \frac{x^{2n+p}}{(2n+p)!} \sum_{\alpha=p}^{2n+p} \binom{\alpha-1}{p-1} \frac{1}{2^\alpha} \sum_{\beta=1}^{\alpha} (-1)^\beta \binom{\alpha}{\beta} \beta^{2n+p}. \quad (76)$$

This result could have been obtained from (65).
Letting $p=1$ in (76) gives the form Ch. II. (17).

(ii) The expansion of $\tan^p x$ may be also obtained in the following way:

We have
$$\tan^p x = \frac{\sin^p x}{(1-\sin^2 x)^{\frac{p}{2}}} = \sum_{k=0}^{\infty} (-1)^k \binom{-\frac{p}{2}}{k} \sin^{p+2k} x. \quad (77)$$

Now, by (24),

$$\sin^{p+2k} x = \frac{1}{2^{p+2k-1}} \sum_{n=0}^{\infty} (-1)^n \frac{x^{2n+p+2k}}{(2n+p+2k)!} \sum_{\alpha=0}^{\left[\frac{p}{2}\right]+k} (-1)^\alpha \binom{p+2k}{\alpha} (p+2k-2\alpha)^{2n+p+2k}. \quad (78)$$

Letting $n+k=n'$, then

$$\sin^{p+2k} x = \frac{1}{2^{p+2k-1}} \sum_{n=k}^{\infty} (-1)^{n-k} \frac{x^{2n+p}}{(2n+p)!} \sum_{\alpha=0}^{\left[\frac{p}{2}\right]+k} (-1)^\alpha \binom{p+2k}{\alpha} (p-2k-2\alpha)^{2n+p}. \quad (79)$$

Applying (79) to (77), then, by means of Ch. I. (68), we obtain

$$\tan^p x = \frac{1}{2^{p-1}} \sum_{n=0}^{\infty} (-1)^n \frac{x^{2n+p}}{(2n+p)!} \sum_{k=0}^{n} \frac{1}{2^{2k}} \binom{-\frac{p}{2}}{k} \sum_{\alpha=0}^{\left[\frac{p}{2}\right]+k} (-1)^\alpha \binom{p+2k}{\alpha} (p+2k-2\alpha)^{2n+p}. \quad (80)$$

Letting, if p is even, $\frac{p}{2}+k-\alpha=\alpha'$, we have

$$\tan^p x = \frac{(-1)^{\frac{p}{2}}}{2^{p-1}} \sum_{n=0}^{\infty} (-1)^n \frac{x^{2n+p}}{(2n+p)!} \sum_{k=0}^{n} \frac{(-1)^k}{2^{2k}} \binom{-\frac{p}{2}}{k} \sum_{\alpha=0}^{\frac{p}{2}+k} (-1)^\alpha \binom{p+2k}{\frac{p}{2}+k-\alpha} (2\alpha)^{2n+p}. \quad (81)$$

Similarly, if p is odd,

$$\tan^p x = \frac{(-1)^{\frac{p-1}{2}}}{2^{p-1}} \sum_{n=0}^{\infty} (-1)^n \frac{x^{2n+p}}{(2n+p)!} \sum_{k=0}^{n} \frac{(-1)^k}{2^{2k}} \binom{-\frac{p}{2}}{k} \sum_{\alpha=0}^{\frac{p-1}{2}+k} (-1)^\alpha \binom{p+2k}{\frac{p-1}{2}+k-\alpha} (2\alpha+1)^{2n+p}. \quad (82)$$

Therefore, whether p be even or odd,

$$\tan^p x = \frac{(-1)^{\left[\frac{p}{2}\right]}}{2^{p-1}} \sum_{n=0}^{\infty} (-1)^n \frac{x^{2n+p}}{(2n+p)!} \sum_{k=0}^{n} \frac{(-1)^k}{2^{2k}} \binom{-\frac{p}{2}}{k} \sum_{\alpha=0}^{\left[\frac{p}{2}\right]+k} (-1)^\alpha \binom{p+2k}{\left[\frac{p}{2}\right]+k-\alpha} (2\alpha+\Delta)^{2n+p}, \quad (83)$$

where

$$\Delta = \frac{1-(-1)^p}{2}.$$

6. (i) To find $\frac{d^n}{dx^n}\sec^p x$ in powers of $\sec x$ and $\tan x$ and the expansion of $\sec^p x$.*

Now

$$\sec^p x = \frac{2^p e^{pix}}{(e^{2ix}+1)^p}; \quad (84)$$

then, by Leibnitz's theorem,

$$\frac{d^n}{dx^n}\sec^p x = 2^p \sum_{k=0}^{n} \binom{n}{k} \frac{d^{n-k}}{dx^{n-k}} e^{pix} \frac{d^k}{dx^k} \frac{1}{(e^{2ix}+1)^p}. \quad (85)$$

But

$$\frac{d^k}{dx^k}\frac{1}{(e^{2ix}+1)^p} = \frac{(2i)^k}{(e^{2ix}+1)^p} \sum_{\alpha=0}^{p} \binom{p+\alpha-1}{\alpha} \frac{e^{2i\alpha x}}{(e^{2ix}+1)^\alpha} \sum_{\beta=0}^{\alpha} (-1)^\beta \binom{\alpha}{\beta} \beta^k \quad (86)$$

and

$$\frac{e^{2i\alpha x}}{(e^{2ix}+1)^\alpha} = \frac{1}{2^\alpha}(1+i\tan x)^\alpha = \frac{1}{2^\alpha}(N_{2\gamma}+iN_{2\gamma+1}), \quad (87)$$

where

$$N_{2\gamma} = \sum_{\gamma=0}^{\left[\frac{\alpha}{2}\right]} (-1)^\gamma \binom{\alpha}{2\gamma} \tan^{2\gamma} x \quad (88)$$

and

$$N_{2\gamma+1} = \sum_{\gamma=0}^{\left[\frac{\alpha-1}{2}\right]} (-1)^\gamma \binom{\alpha}{2\gamma+1} \tan^{2\gamma+1} x. \quad (89)$$

* Ely, *American Journal of Mathematics*, vol. v. p. 339, obtains by induction for odd powers of p,

$$\sec^p x = \frac{1}{(p-1)!} \sum_{n=0}^{\infty} \frac{x^{2n}}{(2n)!} \sum_{k=0}^{p'} S_{p'-k} E_{2n+2k}, \quad p = 2p'+1,$$

where S_n is the combination n at a time of $1^2, 3^2, 5^2, \dots, (p-2)^2$. No expression for S_n is given. The values of the E's (Euler's numbers) are obtained (*ibid.* p. 338) by multiplying

$$\sec x = 1 + E_2 \frac{x^2}{2!} + E_4 \frac{x^4}{4!} + \dots$$

by the expansion of $\cos x$, and equating coefficients of like powers of x.

Shovelton, *Quarterly Journal of Mathematics*, vol. 46, pp. 220–247, derives by means of the theory of *Finite Differences*,

$$\sec^r x = \sum_{n=0}^{\infty} (-1)^n 2^{4n} r x^{2n} \sum_{k=0}^{2n} (-1)^k \frac{1}{2^{2k}} \binom{2k+r-1}{k} \frac{1}{r+k} \Delta^k (\tfrac{1}{4}r)^{2n},$$

where

$$\Delta^k (\tfrac{1}{4}r)^{2n} = \sum_{\alpha=0}^{k} (-1)^\alpha \binom{k}{\alpha} (\tfrac{1}{4}r + k - \alpha)^{2n}.$$

Applying (86) and (87) to (85), we obtain, when n is even,

$$\frac{d^{2n}}{dx^{2n}}\sec^p x = (-1)^n p^{2n} \sec^p x \sum_{k=0}^{2n} \binom{2n}{k} \left(\frac{2}{p}\right)^k \sum_{\alpha=0}^{k} \frac{1}{2^\alpha} \binom{p+\alpha-1}{\alpha}$$

$$\sum_{\beta=0}^{\alpha} (-1)^\beta \binom{\alpha}{\beta} \beta^{2n} N_{2\gamma} \quad (90)$$

$$= (-1)^n p^{2n} \sec^p x \sum_{\alpha=0}^{2n} \frac{1}{2^\alpha} \binom{p+\alpha-1}{\alpha} \sum_{\beta=0}^{\alpha} (-1)^\beta \binom{\alpha}{\beta}$$

$$\sum_{k=\alpha}^{2n} \binom{2n}{k} \left(\frac{2\beta}{p}\right)^k N_{2\gamma}, \text{ by Ch. I. (97).} \quad (91)$$

Now, if $k<\alpha$, $\quad \sum_{\beta=0}^{\alpha} (-1)^\beta \binom{\alpha}{\beta} \beta^k = 0$, by Ch. I. (136);

and since

$$\sum_{k=0}^{2n} \binom{2n}{k} \left(\frac{2\beta}{p}\right)^k = \frac{1}{p^{2n}} (p+2\beta)^{2n},$$

therefore

$$\frac{d^{2n}}{dx^{2n}}\sec^p x = (-1)^n \sec^p x \sum_{\alpha=0}^{2n} \frac{1}{2^\alpha} \binom{p+\alpha-1}{\alpha} \sum_{\beta=0}^{\alpha} (-1)^\beta \binom{\alpha}{\beta} (p+2\beta)^{2n} N_{2\gamma}. \quad (92)$$

Similarly,

$$\frac{d^{2n+1}}{dx^{2n+1}}\sec^p x = (-1)^{n-1} \sec^p x \sum_{\alpha=1}^{2n+1} \frac{1}{2^\alpha} \binom{p+\alpha-1}{\alpha} \sum_{\beta=0}^{\alpha} (-1)^\beta \binom{\alpha}{\beta}$$

$$(p+2\beta)^{2n+1} N_{2\gamma+1}. \quad (93)$$

Combining (92) and (93), we obtain

$$\frac{d^n}{dx^n}\sec^p x = (-1)^{\left[\frac{n+1}{2}\right]} \sec^p x \sum_{\alpha=1}^{n} \frac{1}{2^\alpha} \binom{p+\alpha-1}{\alpha} \sum_{\beta=0}^{\alpha} (-1)^\beta \binom{\alpha}{\beta}$$

$$(p+2\beta)^n N_{2\gamma+\Delta}, \quad (94)$$

where

$$\Delta = \frac{1-(-1)^n}{2}.$$

If $p=1$, then (94) changes to Ch. II. (67).

Letting $x=0$ in (94), then

$$\left.\frac{d^n}{dx^n}\sec^p x\right]_{x=0} = 0, \text{ except when } \Delta = 0, \text{ that is, when } n \text{ is even.}$$

Then $\alpha=0$ is the only value which α may assume, and $N_{2\gamma}]_{x=0}=1$. Therefore

$$\left.\frac{d^{2n}}{dx^{2n}}\sec^p x\right]_{x=0} = (-1)^n \sum_{k=0}^{2n} \frac{1}{2^k} \binom{p+k-1}{k} \sum_{\alpha=0}^{k} (-1)^\alpha \binom{k}{\alpha} (p+2\alpha)^{2n} \quad (95)$$

and

$$\sec^p x = \sum_{n=0}^{\infty} (-1)^n \frac{x^{2n}}{(2n)!} \sum_{k=0}^{2n} \frac{1}{2^k} \binom{p+k-1}{k} \sum_{\alpha=0}^{k} (-1)^\alpha \binom{k}{\alpha} (p+2\alpha)^{2n}. \quad (96)$$

Letting in (96) $p=1$, the result is the same as Ch. II. (69).

(ii) The expansion of $\sec^p x$ can also be obtained as follows:

We have
$$\sec^p x = \frac{1}{(1-\sin^2 x)^{\frac{p}{2}}} = \sum_{n=0}^{\infty} (-1)^n \binom{-\frac{p}{2}}{n} \sin^{2n} x. \tag{97}$$

Writing $2p$ for p in (20) and then n for p gives

$$\sin^{2n} x = \frac{(-1)^n}{2^{2n-1}} \sum_{k=n}^{\infty} (-1)^k \frac{x^{2k}}{(2k)!} \sum_{\alpha=0}^{n} (-1)^\alpha \binom{2n}{\alpha} (2n-2\alpha)^{2k}. \tag{98}$$

Letting now $n-\alpha = \alpha'$, then

$$\sin^{2n} x = \frac{1}{2^{2n-1}} \sum_{k=n}^{\infty} (-1)^k 2^{2k} \frac{x^{2k}}{(2k)!} \sum_{\alpha=1}^{n} (-1)^\alpha \binom{2n}{n-\alpha} \alpha^{2k}; \tag{99}$$

and by means of (99), (97) becomes

$$\sec^p x = \sum_{n=0}^{\infty} (-1)^n \binom{-\frac{p}{2}}{n} \frac{1}{2^{2n-1}} \sum_{k=n}^{\infty} (-1)^k 2^{2k} \frac{x^{2k}}{(2k)!} \sum_{\alpha=1}^{n} (-1)^\alpha \binom{2n}{n-\alpha} \alpha^{2k}. \tag{100}$$

Applying to (100) the principle of Ch. I. (97) and interchanging k and n, we obtain

$$\sec^p x = 1 + 2 \sum_{n=1}^{\infty} (-1)^n 2^{2n} \frac{x^{2n}}{(2n)!} \sum_{k=1}^{n} (-1)^k \binom{-\frac{p}{2}}{k} \frac{1}{2^{2k}} \sum_{\alpha=1}^{k} (-1)^\alpha \binom{2k}{k-\alpha} \alpha^{2n}. \tag{101}$$

(iii) Another method for finding $\frac{d^n}{dx^n} \sec^p x$ and the expansion of $\sec^p x$ may be derived thus:

Letting $u = \cos x$ in Ch. I. (169), we have

$$\frac{d^n}{dx^n} \sec^p x = p \binom{n+p}{p} \sum_{k=1}^{n} \frac{(-1)^k}{p+k} \binom{n}{k} \cos^{-p-k} x \frac{d^n}{dx^n} \cos^k x; \tag{102}$$

then, by means of (53), we obtain

$$\frac{d^n}{dx^n} \sec^p x = (-1)^{\left[\frac{n+1}{2}\right]} p \binom{n+p}{n} \sec^p x \sum_{k=1}^{n} \frac{(-1)^k}{p+k} \frac{1}{2^{k-1}} \binom{n}{k} \sum_{\alpha=0}^{\left[\frac{k-1}{2}\right]} \binom{k}{\alpha} (k-2\alpha)^n$$
$$\sum_{\beta=0}^{\left[\frac{k-\Delta}{2}\right]-\alpha} (-1)^\beta \binom{k-2\alpha}{2\beta+\Delta} \sec^{2\alpha+2\beta+\Delta} x \sin^{2\beta+\Delta} x, \tag{103}$$

where
$$\Delta = \frac{1-(-1)^n}{2}.$$

Now $\left.\frac{d^n}{dx^n} \sec^p x\right]_{x=0} = 0$, unless $\Delta = 0$, or n is even, in which case $\beta = 0$;

therefore

$$\sec^p x = 1 + p \sum_{n=1}^{\infty} (-1)^n \binom{2n+p}{p} \frac{x^{2n}}{(2n)!} \sum_{k=1}^{2n} \frac{(-1)^k}{p+k} \frac{1}{2^{k-1}} \binom{2n}{k}$$
$$\sum_{\alpha=0}^{\left[\frac{k-1}{2}\right]} \binom{k}{\alpha} (k-2\alpha)^{2n}. \tag{104}$$

If $p=1$,

$$\sec x = 1+\sum_{n=1}^{\infty}(-1)^n \frac{x^{2n}}{(2n)!}\sum_{k=1}^{2n}\frac{(-1)^k}{2^{k-1}}\binom{2n+1}{k+1}\sum_{\alpha=0}^{\left[\frac{k-1}{2}\right]}\binom{k}{\alpha}(k-2\alpha)^{2n}, \tag{105}$$

which is the same as Ch. II. (55).

7. (i) To find $\dfrac{d^n}{dx^n}\cot^p x$ in powers of $\operatorname{cosec} x$ and $\cot x$.

Now

$$\cot^p x = i^p \sum_{k=0}^{p}\binom{p}{k}\frac{2^k}{(e^{2ix}-1)^k}, \tag{106}$$

from which

$$\frac{d^n}{dx^n}\cot^p x = 2^n i^{n+p}\sum_{k=1}^{p}\binom{p}{k}2^k\sum_{\alpha=1}^{n}\binom{k+\alpha-1}{\alpha}\frac{e^{2i\alpha x}}{(e^{2ix}-1)^{k+\alpha}}\sum_{\beta=1}^{\alpha}(-1)^\beta\binom{\alpha}{\beta}\beta^n. \tag{107}$$

But

$$\frac{e^{2i\alpha x}}{(e^{2ix}-1)^{k+\alpha}} = \frac{(-1)^k}{2^{k+\alpha}}\operatorname{cosec}^{2k}x\,(1-i\cot x)^{\alpha-k}$$

$$= \frac{(-1)^k}{2^{k+\alpha}}\operatorname{cosec}^{2k}x\,(N_{2\gamma}-iN_{2\gamma+1}), \tag{108}$$

where

$$N_{2\gamma} = \sum_{\gamma=0}^{\left[\frac{\alpha-k}{2}\right]}(-1)^\gamma\binom{\alpha-k}{2\gamma}\cot^{2\gamma}x \tag{109}$$

and

$$N_{2\gamma+1} = \sum_{\gamma=0}^{\left[\frac{\alpha-k-1}{2}\right]}(-1)^\gamma\binom{\alpha-k}{2\gamma+1}\cot^{2\gamma+1}x; \tag{110}$$

therefore

$$\frac{d^n}{dx^n}\cot^p x = 2^n i^{n+p}\sum_{k=1}^{p}(-1)^k\binom{p}{k}\operatorname{cosec}^{2k}x\sum_{\alpha=1}^{n}\binom{k+\alpha-1}{\alpha}\frac{1}{2^\alpha}$$
$$\sum_{\beta=0}^{\alpha}(-1)^\beta\binom{\alpha}{\beta}\beta^n(N_{2\gamma}-iN_{2\gamma+1}). \tag{111}$$

From (111) we obtain

$$\frac{d^{2n}}{dx^{2n}}\cot^{2p}x = (-1)^{n+p}2^{2n}\sum_{k=1}^{2p}(-1)^k\binom{2p}{k}\operatorname{cosec}^{2k}x\sum_{\alpha=1}^{2n}\binom{k+\alpha-1}{\alpha}\frac{1}{2^\alpha}$$
$$\sum_{\beta=1}^{\alpha}(-1)^\beta\binom{\alpha}{\beta}\beta^{2n}N_{2\gamma}, \tag{112}$$

$$\frac{d^{2n}}{dx^{2n}}\cot^{2p+1}x = (-1)^{n+p}2^{2n}\sum_{k=1}^{2p+1}(-1)^k\binom{2p+1}{k}\operatorname{cosec}^{2k}x\sum_{\alpha=1}^{2n}\binom{k+\alpha-1}{\alpha}\frac{1}{2^\alpha}$$
$$\sum_{\beta=1}^{\alpha}(-1)^\beta\binom{\alpha}{\beta}\beta^{2n}N_{2\gamma+1}, \tag{113}$$

$$\frac{d^{2n+1}}{dx^{2n+1}}\cot^{2p}x = (-1)^{n+p}2^{2n+1}\sum_{k=1}^{2p}(-1)^k\binom{2p}{k}\operatorname{cosec}^{2k}x\sum_{a=1}^{2n+1}\binom{k+a-1}{a}\frac{1}{2^a}$$
$$\sum_{\beta=1}^{a}(-1)^\beta\binom{a}{\beta}\beta^{2n+1}N_{2\gamma+1}, \quad (114)$$

$$\frac{d^{2n+1}}{dx^{2n+1}}\cot^{2p+1}x = (-1)^{n+p+1}2^{2n+1}\sum_{k=1}^{2p+1}(-1)^k\binom{2p+1}{k}\operatorname{cosec}^{2k}x$$
$$\sum_{a=1}^{2n+1}\binom{k+a-1}{a}\frac{1}{2^a}\sum_{\beta=1}^{a}(-1)^\beta\binom{a}{\beta}\beta^{2n+1}N_{2\gamma}. \quad (115)$$

Combining (112)-(115), we obtain

$$\frac{d^n}{dx^n}\cot^p x = (-1)^{\left[\frac{n+p-\Delta_1}{2}\right]}2^n\sum_{k=1}^{p}(-1)^k\binom{p}{k}\operatorname{cosec}^{2k}x\sum_{a=1}^{n}\binom{k+a-1}{a}\frac{1}{2^a}$$
$$\sum_{\beta=1}^{a}(-1)^\beta\binom{a}{\beta}\beta^n N_{2\gamma+\Delta_2}, \quad (116)$$

where $\Delta_1 = (-1)^p\dfrac{1-(-1)^n}{2}, \qquad \Delta_2 = \dfrac{1-(-1)^{n+p}}{2}.$

If $p=1$, then if n is even, (116) changes to Ch. II. (95), and if n is odd, to Ch. II. (96).

(ii) Letting $u=\tan x$ in Ch. I. (169), then in a way similar to 3 (iii) another form for $\cot^p x$ can be obtained.

(iii) To find the expansion of $\cot^p x$ in powers of x, we shall first find the expansion of $x^p\cot^p x$ in powers of x.

Letting $u = \dfrac{\tan x}{x}$, then, by Ch. I. (169), we have

$$\frac{d^n}{dx^n}(x^p\cot^p x)\Big]_{x=0} = \frac{d^n}{dx^n}\left(\frac{\tan x}{x}\right)^{-p}\Big]_{x=0}$$
$$= p\binom{n+p}{p}\sum_{k=1}^{n}\frac{(-1)^k}{p+k}\binom{n}{k}\frac{d^n}{dx^n}\left(\frac{\tan x}{x}\right)^k\Big]_{x=0}. \quad (117)$$

To find $\dfrac{d^n}{dx^n}\left(\dfrac{\tan x}{x}\right)^k$, we proceed as follows:

Taking the $(n+k)$th derivative of

$$x^k u^k = \tan^k x, \quad (118)$$

we have
$$\sum_{a=0}^{n+k}\binom{n+k}{a}\frac{d^{n+k-a}}{dx^{n+k-a}}x^k\frac{d^a}{dx^a}u^k\Big]_{x=0} = \frac{d^{n+k}}{dx^{n+k}}\tan^k x\Big]_{x=0}. \quad (119)$$

Now for $x=0$, the terms of the first member of (119) vanish, except for $a=n$, in which case

$$\binom{n+k}{n}\frac{d^k}{dx^k}x^k\frac{d^n}{dx^n}u^k\Big]_{x=0} = \frac{d^{n+k}}{dx^{n+k}}\tan^k x\Big]_{x=0} \quad (120)$$

or
$$\frac{d^n}{dx^n}u^k\Big]_{x=0} = \frac{n!}{(n+k)!}\frac{d^{n+k}}{dx^{n+k}}\tan^k x\Big]_{x=0}. \quad (121)$$

Then, by means of (121) and (70), we obtain from (117)

$$\frac{d^{2n}}{dx^{2n}}(x\cot x)^p\bigg]_{x=0}=(-1)^n\frac{(2n+p)!}{(p-1)!}\sum_{k=0}^{2n}\frac{1}{p+k}\binom{2n}{k}\frac{2^{2n+k}}{(2n+k)!}$$

$$\sum_{\alpha=k}^{2n+k}\binom{\alpha-1}{k-1}\frac{1}{2^\alpha}\sum_{\beta=1}^{\alpha}(-1)^\beta\binom{\alpha}{\beta}\beta^{2n+k}, \quad (122)$$

which is the coefficient of $\frac{x^{2n}}{(2n)!}$ in the expansion of $(x\cot x)^p$.

8. (i) Following the method in 6 (i), we obtain

$$\frac{d^{2n}}{dx^{2n}}\operatorname{cosec}^p x=(-1)^n\operatorname{cosec}^p x\sum_{\alpha=0}^{2n}\frac{1}{2^\alpha}\binom{p+\alpha-1}{\alpha}\sum_{\beta=0}^{\alpha}(-1)^\beta\binom{\alpha}{\beta}$$

$$(p+2\beta)^{2n}N_{2\gamma} \quad (123)$$

and

$$\frac{d^{2n+1}}{dx^{2n+1}}\operatorname{cosec}^p x=(-1)^n\operatorname{cosec}^p x\sum_{\alpha=0}^{2n+1}\frac{1}{2^\alpha}\binom{p+\alpha-1}{\alpha}\sum_{\beta=0}^{\alpha}(-1)^\beta\binom{\alpha}{\beta}$$

$$(p+2\beta)^{2n+1}N_{2\gamma+1}, \quad (124)$$

where

$$N_{2\gamma}=\sum_{\gamma=0}^{\left[\frac{\alpha}{2}\right]}(-1)^\gamma\binom{\alpha}{2\gamma}\cot^{2\gamma}x$$

and

$$N_{2\gamma+1}=\sum_{\gamma=0}^{\left[\frac{\alpha-1}{2}\right]}(-1)^\gamma\binom{\alpha}{2\gamma+1}\cot^{2\gamma+1}x.$$

Combining (123) and (124) gives

$$\frac{d^n}{dx^n}\operatorname{cosec}^p x=(-1)^{\left[\frac{n}{2}\right]}\operatorname{cosec}^p x\sum_{\alpha=0}^{n}\frac{1}{2^\alpha}\binom{p+\alpha-1}{\alpha}\sum_{\beta=0}^{\alpha}(-1)^\beta\binom{\alpha}{\beta}$$

$$(p+2\beta)^n N_{2\gamma+\Delta}, \quad (125)$$

where

$$\Delta=\frac{1-(-1)^n}{2}.$$

If $p=1$, (125) changes to Ch. II. (130).

(ii) By the method given in 6 (iii), we derive for $\frac{d^n}{dx^n}\operatorname{cosec}^p x$ an expression similar to (103).

9. To find the expansion of $x^p\operatorname{cosec}^p x$ in powers of x.

Letting in Ch. I. (169) $u=\frac{\sin x}{x}$, we obtain

$$\frac{d^n}{dx^n}(x\operatorname{cosec} x)^p\bigg]_{x=0}=\frac{d^n}{dx^n}\left(\frac{\sin x}{x}\right)^{-p}$$

$$=p\binom{n+p}{p}\sum_{k=1}^{n}\frac{(-1)^k}{p+k}\binom{n}{k}\frac{d^n}{dx^n}\left(\frac{\sin x}{x}\right)^k\bigg]_{x=0}. \quad (126)$$

Now

$$\frac{d^{n+k}}{dx^{n+k}}(x^k u^k)\bigg]_{x=0}=\frac{d^{n+k}}{dx^{n+k}}\sin^k x\bigg]_{x=0},$$

from which

$$\frac{d^n}{dx^n}u^k\bigg]_{x=0}=\frac{n!}{(n+k)!}\frac{d^{n+k}}{dx^{n+k}}\sin^k x\bigg]_{x=0}. \quad (127)$$

But
$$\frac{d^{n+k}}{dx^{n+k}}\sin^k x\Big]_{x=0} = \frac{i^n}{2^k}\sum_{\alpha=0}^{k}(-1)^\alpha\binom{k}{\alpha}(k-2\alpha)^{n+k}. \tag{128}$$

Therefore n must be even, and

$$\frac{d^{2n+k}}{dx^{2n+k}}\sin^k x\Big]_{x=0} = \frac{(-1)^n}{2^k}\sum_{\alpha=0}^{k}(-1)^\alpha\binom{k}{\alpha}(k-2\alpha)^{2n+k}$$
$$= \frac{(-1)^n}{2^{k-1}}\sum_{\alpha=0}^{\left[\frac{k-1}{2}\right]}(-1)^\alpha\binom{k}{\alpha}(k-2\alpha)^{2n+k}. \tag{129}$$

We then obtain

$$\frac{d^{2n}}{dx^{2n}}(x\operatorname{cosec} x)^p\Big]_{x=0} = (-1)^n p\binom{2n+p}{p}\sum_{k=1}^{2n}\frac{(-1)^k}{p+k}\frac{1}{2^{k-1}}\binom{2n}{k}$$
$$\sum_{\alpha=0}^{\left[\frac{k-1}{2}\right]}(-1)^\alpha\binom{k}{\alpha}(k-2\alpha)^{2n+k}, \tag{130}$$

which is the coefficient of $\frac{x^{2n}}{(2n)!}$ in the expansion of $x^p \operatorname{cosec}^p x$.

10. (i) To find the expansion of

$$y = \sin^p x\cos^q x, \tag{131}$$

in powers of x.

Now
$$\sin^p x = \frac{1}{2^p}\sum_{k=0}^{\infty}(-1)^k\frac{x^{2k+p}}{(2k+p)!}\sum_{\alpha=0}^{p}(-1)^\alpha\binom{p}{\alpha}(p-2\alpha)^{2k+p} \tag{132}$$

and
$$\cos^q x = \frac{1}{2^q}\sum_{n=0}^{\infty}(-1)^n\frac{x^{2n}}{(2n)!}\sum_{\beta=0}^{q}\binom{q}{\beta}(q-2\beta)^{2n}. \tag{133}$$

Letting in the product of (132) and (133) $n+k=n'$, we obtain

$$y = \frac{1}{2^{p+q}}\sum_{k=0}^{\infty}\frac{1}{(2k+p)!}\sum_{\alpha=0}^{p}(-1)^\alpha\binom{p}{\alpha}(p-2\alpha)^{2k+p}\sum_{n=k}^{\infty}(-1)^n\frac{x^{2n+p}}{(2n-2k)!}$$
$$\sum_{\beta=0}^{q}\binom{q}{\beta}(q-2\beta)^{2n-2k}; \tag{134}$$

and since
$$\frac{1}{(2k+p)!(2n-2k)!} = \frac{1}{(2n+p)!}\binom{2n+p}{2k+p},$$

therefore

$$y = \frac{1}{2^{p+q}}\sum_{n=0}^{\infty}(-1)^n\frac{x^{2n+p}}{(2n+p)!}\sum_{k=0}^{n}\binom{2n+p}{2k+p}\sum_{\alpha=0}^{p}(-1)^\alpha\binom{p}{\alpha}(p-2\alpha)^{2k+p}$$
$$\sum_{\beta=0}^{q}\binom{q}{\beta}(q-2\beta)^{2n-2k}. \tag{135}$$

To show that

$$S = \sum_{k=0}^{n}\binom{2n+p}{2k+p}\sum_{\alpha=0}^{p}(-1)^\alpha\binom{p}{\alpha}(p-2\alpha)^{2k+p}\sum_{\beta=0}^{q}\binom{q}{\beta}(q-2\beta)^{2n-2k} \tag{136}$$

reduces to $$\sum_{\alpha=0}^{q}\binom{q}{\alpha}\sum_{\beta=0}^{p}(-1)^{\beta}\binom{p}{\beta}(p+q-2\alpha-2\beta)^{2n+p}, \tag{137}$$

we distinguish between the cases when in (136) p is even and p is odd.

(*a*) Let $p=2m$, then

$$S=\sum_{k=0}^{n}\binom{2n+2m}{2k+2m}\sum_{\alpha=0}^{q}\binom{q}{\alpha}(q-2\alpha)^{2n-2k}\sum_{\beta=0}^{2m}(-1)^{\beta}\binom{2m}{\beta}(2m-2\beta)^{2k+2m}. \tag{138}$$

Letting $k+m=k'$,

$$S=\sum_{k=m}^{n+m}\binom{2n+2m}{2k}\sum_{\alpha=0}^{q}\binom{q}{\alpha}(q-2\alpha)^{2(n+m)-2k}\sum_{\beta=0}^{2m}(-1)^{\beta}\binom{2m}{\beta}(2m-2\beta)^{2k}; \tag{139}$$

and since $$\sum_{\beta=0}^{2m}(-1)^{\beta}\binom{2m}{\beta}(2m-2\beta)^{2k}=0, \text{ if } k<m,$$

therefore

$$S=\sum_{k=0}^{n+m}\binom{2n+2m}{2k}\sum_{\alpha=0}^{q}\binom{q}{\alpha}(q-2\alpha)^{2(n+m)-2k}\sum_{\beta=0}^{2m}(-1)^{\beta}\binom{2m}{\beta}(2m-2\beta)^{2k}. \tag{140}$$

Now $$S_1=\sum_{\beta=0}^{2m}(-1)^{\beta}\binom{2m}{\beta}(2m-2\beta)^{2k+1}=0. \tag{141}$$

This can be shown in the following way:

Denoting in (141) by S_β the expression under the summation sign, we may write

$$S_1=\sum_{\beta=0}^{m-1}S_\beta+\sum_{\beta=m+1}^{2m}S_\beta. \tag{142}$$

Letting in the second summation in (142) $2m-\beta=\beta'$, we obtain

$$S_1=\sum_{\beta=0}^{m-1}S_\beta-\sum_{\beta=0}^{m-1}S_\beta=0. \tag{143}$$

Then, by means of (141), we have

$$\sum_{k=0}^{n+m-1}\binom{2n+2m}{2k+1}\sum_{\alpha=0}^{q}\binom{q}{\alpha}(q-2\alpha)^{2(n+m)-2k-1}S_1=0. \tag{144}$$

Adding (144) to (140) gives

$$S=\sum_{k=0}^{2n+2m}\binom{2n+2m}{k}\sum_{\alpha=0}^{q}\binom{q}{\alpha}(q-2\alpha)^{2(n+m)-k}\sum_{\beta=0}^{2m}(-1)^{\beta}\binom{2m}{\beta}(2m-2\beta)^{k} \tag{145}$$

$$=\sum_{\alpha=0}^{q}\binom{q}{\alpha}\sum_{\beta=0}^{2m}(-1)^{\beta}\binom{2m}{\beta}(2m+q-2\alpha-2\beta)^{2n+2m}. \tag{146}$$

(*b*) If $p=2m+1$, then

$$S=\sum_{k=0}^{n}\binom{2n+2m+1}{2k+2m+1}\sum_{\alpha=0}^{q}\binom{q}{\alpha}(q-2\alpha)^{2n-2k}\sum_{\beta=0}^{2m+1}(-1)^{\beta}\binom{2m+1}{\beta}$$
$$(2m+1-2\beta)^{2k+2m+1}. \tag{147}$$

Letting $k+m=k'$, then

$$S=\sum_{k=m}^{n+m}\binom{2n+2m+1}{2k+1}\sum_{a=0}^{q}\binom{q}{a}(q-2a)^{2n+2m-2k}\sum_{\beta=0}^{2m+1}(-1)^{\beta}\binom{2m+1}{\beta}(2m+1-2\beta)^{2k+1}. \quad (148)$$

Now $$\sum_{\beta=0}^{2m+1}(-1)^{\beta}\binom{2m+1}{\beta}(2m+1-2\beta)^{2k+1}=0, \text{ if } k<m;$$

and since $$\sum_{\beta=0}^{2m+1}(-1)^{\beta}\binom{2m+1}{\beta}(2m+1-2\beta)^{2k}=0, \quad (149)$$

we obtain

$$S=\sum_{a=0}^{q}\binom{q}{a}\sum_{\beta=0}^{2m+1}(-1)^{\beta}\binom{2m+1}{\beta}(2m+1+q-2a-2\beta)^{2n+2m+1}. \quad (150)$$

Now (146) and (150) being of the same form, therefore, whether p be even or odd,

$$S=\sum_{a=0}^{q}\binom{q}{a}\sum_{\beta=0}^{p}(-1)^{\beta}\binom{p}{\beta}(p+q-2a-2\beta)^{2n+p} \quad (151)$$

and

$$\sin^p x\cos^q x=\frac{1}{2^{p+q}}\sum_{n=0}^{\infty}(-1)^n\frac{x^{2n+p}}{(2n+p)!}\sum_{k=0}^{q}\binom{q}{k}\sum_{a=0}^{p}(-1)^{a}\binom{p}{a}(p+q-2a-2\beta)^{2n+p}. \quad (152)$$

(ii) To express $$y=\sin^p x\cos^q x$$

in terms of sin and cos of multiples of x.

Now $$y=\frac{(-1)^p i^p}{2^{p+q}}(e^{ix}-e^{-ix})^p(e^{ix}+e^{-ix})^q \quad (153)$$

$$=\frac{i^p}{2^{p+q}}e^{-(p+q)ix}(1-e^{2ix})^p(1+e^{2ix})^q. \quad (154)$$

Letting $e^{ix}=r$, then

$$y=\frac{i^p}{2^{p+q}}e^{-(p+q)ix}(1-r^2)^p(1+r^2)^q. \quad (155)$$

But $$((r^{2k}))(1-r^2)^p(1+r^2)^q=\sum_{a=0}^{k}(-1)^{a}\binom{p}{a}\binom{q}{k-a}$$

and $$(1-r^2)^p(1+r^2)^q=\sum_{k=0}^{p+q}r^{2k}\sum_{a=0}^{k}(-1)^{a}\binom{p}{a}\binom{q}{k-a}. \quad (156)$$

Therefore

$$\sin^p x\cos^q x=\frac{i^p}{2^{p+q}}\sum_{k=0}^{p+q}e^{-ix(p+q-2k)}\sum_{a=0}^{k}(-1)^{a}\binom{p}{a}\binom{q}{k-a}$$

$$=\frac{i^p}{2^{p+q}}\sum_{k=0}^{p+q}\cos(p+q-2k)\sum_{a=0}^{k}(-1)^{a}\binom{p}{a}\binom{q}{k-a}$$

$$-\frac{i^{p+1}}{2^{p+q}}\sum_{k=0}^{p+q}\sin(p+q-2k)\sum_{a=0}^{k}(-1)^{a}\binom{p}{a}\binom{q}{k-a}. \quad (157)$$

Since the result must be real, therefore the second or first double summation in (157) will vanish according as p is even or odd.

Hence

$$\sin^p x\cos^q x=(-1)^{\left[\frac{p}{2}\right]}\frac{1+(-1)^p}{2^{p+q+1}}\sum_{k=0}^{p+q}\cos(p+q-2k)x\sum_{\alpha=0}^{k}(-1)^\alpha\binom{p}{\alpha}\binom{q}{k-\alpha}$$
$$-(-1)^{\left[\frac{p+1}{2}\right]}\frac{1-(-1)^p}{2^{p+q+1}}\sum_{k=0}^{p+q}\sin(p+q-2k)x\sum_{\alpha=0}^{k}(-1)^\alpha\binom{p}{\alpha}\binom{q}{k-\alpha}. \quad (158)$$

(iii) The expansion (152) can also be obtained from (157) as follows:

Let $p=2m$, then

$$y=\frac{(-1)^m}{2^{2m+q}}\sum_{k=0}^{2m+q}\sum_{\alpha=0}^{k}(-1)^\alpha\binom{2m}{\alpha}\binom{q}{k-\alpha}\cos(2m+q-2k)x. \quad (159)$$

Now $$\cos(2m+q-2k)x=\sum_{\beta=0}^{\infty}(-1)^\beta(2m+q-2k)^{2\beta}\frac{x^{2\beta}}{(2\beta)!}. \quad (160)$$

Applying (160) to (159), we have

$$y=\frac{(-1)^m}{2^{2m+q}}\sum_{\beta=0}^{\infty}(-1)^\beta\frac{x^{2\beta}}{(2\beta)!}S_{\alpha,\beta}, \quad (161)$$

where $$S_{\alpha,\beta}=\sum_{k=0}^{2m+q}\sum_{\alpha=0}^{k}(-1)^\alpha\binom{2m}{\alpha}\binom{q}{k-\alpha}(2m+q-2k)^{2\beta}. \quad (162)$$

Letting in (162) $k-\alpha=\alpha'$, then

$$S_{\alpha,\beta}=\sum_{k=0}^{2m+q}(-1)^k\sum_{\alpha=0}^{k}(-1)^\alpha\binom{2m}{k-\alpha}\binom{q}{\alpha}(2m+q-2k)^{2\beta}$$
$$=\sum_{\alpha=0}^{2m+q}(-1)^\alpha\binom{q}{\alpha}\sum_{k=\alpha}^{2m+q}(-1)^k\binom{2m}{k-\alpha}(2m+q-2k)^{2\beta},\text{ by Ch. I. (97);} \quad (163)$$

and since $\binom{q}{\alpha}=0$, if $\alpha>q$, therefore

$$S_{\alpha,\beta}=\sum_{\alpha=0}^{q}(-1)^\alpha\binom{q}{\alpha}\sum_{k=\alpha}^{2m+q}(-1)^k\binom{2m}{k-\alpha}(2m+q-2k)^{2\beta}. \quad (164)$$

Letting now $k-\alpha=k'$ in (164), then

$$S_{\alpha,\beta}=\sum_{\alpha=0}^{q}\binom{q}{\alpha}\sum_{k=0}^{2m+q-\alpha}(-1)^k\binom{2m}{k}(2m+q-2k-2\alpha)^{2\beta}; \quad (165)$$

and since $\alpha\leqq q$, $\binom{2m}{k}=0$, if $k>2m$, hence

$$S_{\alpha,\beta}=\sum_{\alpha=0}^{q}\binom{q}{\alpha}\sum_{k=0}^{2m}(-1)^k\binom{2m}{k}(2m+q-2k-2\alpha)^{2\beta}. \quad (166)$$

But by Ch. I. (136), $S_{\alpha,\beta}=0$, if $\beta<m$; therefore

$$y=\frac{(-1)^m}{2^{2m+q}}\sum_{\beta=m}^{\infty}(-1)^\beta\frac{x^{2\beta}}{(2\beta)!}\sum_{\alpha=0}^{q}\binom{q}{\alpha}\sum_{k=0}^{2m}(-1)^k\binom{2m}{k}(2m+q-2k-2\alpha)^{2\beta}. \quad (167)$$

Letting $\beta - m = n$, and interchanging k and a, gives

$$y = \frac{1}{2^{2m+q}} \sum_{n=0}^{\infty} (-1)^n \frac{x^{2m+2n}}{(2m+2n)!} \sum_{k=0}^{q} \binom{q}{k} \sum_{a=0}^{2m} (-1)^a \binom{2m}{a} (2m+q-2k-2a)^{2n+2m}. \tag{168}$$

If $p = 2m+1$, we obtain the same form as (168), except that $2m+1$ is in place of $2m$.

Therefore, whether p be even or odd,

$$\sin^p x \cos^q x = \frac{1}{2^{p+q}} \sum_{n=0}^{\infty} (-1)^n \frac{x^{2n+p}}{(2n+p)!} \sum_{k=0}^{q} \binom{q}{k} \sum_{a=0}^{p} (-1)^a \binom{p}{a} (p+q-2k-2a)^{2n+p}, \tag{169}$$

which is the same as (152).

If $q = 0$, then, by making use of the relation

$$\sum_{a=0}^{p} (-1)^a \binom{p}{a} (p-2a)^{2n+p} = 2 \sum_{a=0}^{\left[\frac{p}{2}\right]} (-1)^a \binom{p}{a} (p-2a)^{2n+p},$$

(169) reduces to (24).

If $p = 0$, then, by means of (55), (169) reduces to (56).

11. To expand in powers of x,

$$y = (a_1 \cos bx + a_2 \sin bx)^p, \tag{170}$$

where p is any real number.

Now
$$y = \frac{(a_1 i - a_2)^p}{(2i)^p} \frac{(1 + ce^{2ibx})^p}{e^{ibpx}}, \tag{171}$$

where
$$c = \frac{a_1 i + a_2}{a_1 i - a_2}. \tag{172}$$

Then, by Leibnitz's theorem,

$$\left.\frac{d^n y}{dx^n}\right]_{x=0} = \frac{(a_1 i - a_2)^p}{(2i)^p} \sum_{k=0}^{n} \binom{n}{k} \frac{d^{n-k}}{dx^{n-k}} e^{-ibpx} \left.\frac{d^k}{dx^k} (1 + ce^{2ibx})^p \right]_{x=0}. \tag{173}$$

But
$$\left.\frac{d^{n-k}}{dx^{n-k}} e^{-ibpx}\right]_{x=0} = (-1)^{n-k} i^{n-k} b^{n-k} p^{n-k} \tag{174}$$

and

$$\left.\frac{d^k}{dx^k} (1 + ce^{2ibx})^p\right]_{x=0} = 2^k i^k b^k (1+c)^p \sum_{\beta=0}^{k} (-1)^\beta \binom{p}{\beta} \sum_{\gamma=0}^{\beta} (-1)^\gamma \binom{\beta}{\gamma} \gamma^k \frac{c^\beta}{(1+c)^\beta}. \tag{175}$$

Applying (174) and (175) to (173), then, by means of

$$\begin{aligned} \frac{(a_1 i - a_2)^p}{(2i)^p} (1+c)^p \frac{c^\beta}{(1+c)^\beta} &= \frac{a_1^{\,p}}{2^\beta a_1^{\,\beta}} (a_1 - ia_2)^\beta \\ &= \frac{a_1^{\,p}}{2^\beta a_1^{\,\beta}} (N_{2\gamma_1} - iN_{2\gamma_1+1}), \end{aligned} \tag{176}$$

where
$$N_{2\gamma_1} = \sum_{\gamma_1=0}^{\left[\frac{\beta}{2}\right]} (-1)^{\gamma_1} \binom{p}{2\gamma_1} a_1^{\,p-2\gamma_1} a_2^{\,2\gamma_1}$$

and
$$N_{2\gamma_1+1} = \sum_{\gamma_1=0}^{\left[\frac{\beta-1}{2}\right]} (-1)^{\gamma_1} \binom{\beta}{2\gamma_1+1} a_1^{\,\beta-2\gamma_1-1} a_2^{\,2\gamma_1+1},$$

we obtain

$$\frac{dy^n}{dx^n}\bigg]_{x=0} = (-1)^n i^n b^n p^n a_1^{\,p} \sum_{k=0}^{n} (-1)^k \binom{n}{k} \left(\frac{2\gamma}{p}\right)^k \sum_{\beta=0}^{k} (-1)^\beta \binom{p}{\beta} \frac{1}{(2a_1)^\beta} \sum_{\gamma=0}^{\beta} (-1)^\gamma \binom{\beta}{\gamma} (N_{2\gamma_1} - iN_{2\gamma_1+1}) \quad (177)$$

$$= (-1)^n i^n b^n a_1^{\,p} \sum_{\beta=0}^{n} (-1)^\beta \binom{p}{\beta} \frac{1}{(2a_1)^\beta} \sum_{\gamma=0}^{\beta} (-1)^\gamma \binom{\beta}{\gamma} (p-2\gamma)^n (N_{2\gamma_1} - iN_{2\gamma_1+1}). \quad (178)$$

Therefore, whether n be even or odd,

$$\frac{d^n y}{dx^n}\bigg]_{x=0} = (-1)^{\left[\frac{n+1}{2}\right]} b^n a_1^{\,p} \sum_{\beta=0}^{n} (-1)^\beta \binom{p}{\beta} \frac{1}{(2a_1)^\beta} \sum_{\gamma=0}^{\beta} (-1)^\gamma \binom{\beta}{\gamma} (p-2\gamma)^n N_{2\gamma_1+\Delta}, \quad (179)$$

where

$$\Delta = \frac{1-(-1)^n}{2},$$

and

$$y = a_1^{\,p} \sum_{n=0}^{\infty} (-1)^{\left[\frac{n+1}{2}\right]} b^n \frac{x^n}{n!} \sum_{\beta=0}^{n} (-1)^\beta \binom{p}{\beta} \frac{1}{(2a_1)^\beta} \sum_{\gamma=0}^{\beta} (-1)^\gamma \binom{\beta}{\gamma} (p-2\gamma)^n N_{2\gamma_1+\Delta}. \quad (180)$$

12. In Chapter I. 12, a method was given by which the higher derivatives of functions may be obtained from their expansions.

We shall here find $\dfrac{d^n}{dx^n}\cos^p x$ from the expansion

$$\cos^p x = \frac{1}{2^p} \sum_{k=0}^{\infty} (-1)^k \frac{x^{2k}}{(2k)!} \sum_{a=0}^{p} \binom{p}{a} (p-2a)^{2k}. \quad (181)$$

Taking the nth derivative of (181), we have

$$\frac{d^n}{dx^n}\cos^p x = \frac{1}{2^p}\frac{n!}{x^n} \sum_{k=0}^{\infty} (-1)^k \binom{2k}{n} \frac{x^{2k}}{(2k)!} \sum_{a=0}^{p} \binom{p}{a} (p-2a)^{2k}; \quad (182)$$

and since

$$\sum_{a=0}^{p} \binom{p}{a} (p-2a)^{2k+1} = 0,$$

therefore

$$\frac{d^n}{dx^n}\cos^p x = \frac{1}{2^p}\frac{n!}{x^n} \sum_{k=0}^{\infty} i^k \binom{k}{n} \frac{x^k}{k!} \sum_{a=0}^{p} \binom{p}{a} (p-2a)^k \quad (183)$$

$$= \frac{i^n}{2^p} \sum_{k=n}^{\infty} \frac{i^{k-n} x^{k-n}}{(k-n)!} \sum_{a=0}^{p} \binom{p}{a} (p-2a)^k, \text{ since } \binom{k}{n} = 0, \text{ if } k<n. \quad (184)$$

Letting $k-n=k'$ in (184) gives

$$\frac{d^n}{dx^n}\cos^p x = \frac{i^n}{2^p} \sum_{a=0}^{p} \binom{p}{a} (p-2a)^n \sum_{k=0}^{\infty} \frac{i^k x^k}{k!} (p-2a)^k$$

$$= \frac{i^n}{2^p} \sum_{a=0}^{p} \binom{p}{a} (p-2a)^n e^{(p-2a)ix}. \quad (185)$$

Then, if n is even,

$$\frac{d^{2n}}{dx^{2n}}\cos^p x = \frac{(-1)^n}{2^p}\sum_{k=0}^{p}\binom{p}{k}(p-2k)^{2n}\cos(p-2k)x \tag{186}$$

$$= \frac{(-1)^n}{2^{p-1}}\sum_{k=0}^{\left[\frac{p-1}{2}\right]}\binom{p}{k}(p-2k)^{2n}\cos(p-2k)x$$

$$= \frac{(-1)^n}{2^{p-1}}\sum_{k=0}^{\left[\frac{p-1}{2}\right]}\binom{p}{k}(p-2k)^{2n}\sum_{\alpha=0}^{\left[\frac{p}{2}\right]-k}(-1)^\alpha\binom{p-2k}{2\alpha}$$
$$\cos^{p-2k-2\alpha}x\sin^{2\alpha}x, \tag{187}$$

and if n is odd,

$$\frac{d^{2n+1}}{dx^{2n+1}}\cos^p x = \frac{(-1)^{n-1}}{2^{p-1}}\sum_{k=0}^{\left[\frac{p-1}{2}\right]}\binom{p}{k}(p-2k)^{2n+1}\sin(p-2k)x \tag{188}$$

$$= \frac{(-1)^{n-1}}{2^{p-1}}\sum_{k=0}^{\left[\frac{p-1}{2}\right]}\binom{p}{k}(p-2k)^{2n+1}\sum_{\alpha=0}^{\left[\frac{p-1}{2}\right]-k}(-1)^\alpha\binom{p-2k}{2\alpha+1}$$
$$\cos^{p-2k-2\alpha-1}x\sin^{2\alpha+1}x. \tag{189}$$

Combining (187) and (189) gives (53).

CHAPTER V.

THE OPERATOR $\left(x\frac{d}{dx}\right)^n$.

THE SUM OF EQUAL POWERS OF A SERIES OF NATURAL NUMBERS.

1. LET $\left(x\frac{d}{dx}\right)^n$ denote n operations $x\frac{d}{dx}$ each on the analytic function S, x and $\frac{d}{dx}$ not being permutable, that is

$$\left(x\frac{d}{dx}\right)^n S = \overset{(1)}{\left(x\frac{d}{dx}\right)}\overset{(2)}{\left(x\frac{d}{dx}\right)}\overset{(3)}{\left(x\frac{d}{dx}\right)}\cdots\overset{(n)}{\left(x\frac{d}{dx}\right)}S. \tag{1}$$

We shall show that

$$\left(x\frac{d}{dx}\right)^n S = \sum_{k=1}^{n}\frac{(-1)^k}{k!}\sum_{a=1}^{k}(-1)^a\binom{k}{a}a^n x^k\frac{d^k}{dx^k}S. \tag{2}$$

Carrying out the indicated operations, we have

$$\left(x\frac{d}{dx}\right)S = x\frac{dS}{dx},$$

$$\left(x\frac{d}{dx}\right)^2 S = x\frac{dS}{dx} + x^2\frac{d^2S}{dx^2},$$

$$\left(x\frac{d}{dx}\right)^3 S = x\frac{dS}{dx} + 3x^2\frac{d^2S}{dx} + x^3\frac{d^3S}{dx^3},$$

$$\left(x\frac{d}{dx}\right)^4 S = x\frac{dS}{dx} + 7x^2\frac{d^2S}{dx^2} + 6x^3\frac{d^3S}{dx^3} + x^4\frac{d^4S}{dx^4}.$$

Continuing this process, we may write

$$\left(x\frac{d}{dx}\right)^n S = \sum_{k=1}^{n} a_{n,k}\, x^k\frac{d^kS}{dx^k}. \tag{3}$$

Now from the above it is evident that $a_{n,k}$ is obtained by multiplying by k the coefficient of $x^k\frac{d^kS}{dx^k}$ in the expansion of $\left(x\frac{d}{dx}\right)^{n-1}S$, and adding to it the coefficient of $x^{k-1}\frac{d^{k-1}S}{dx^{k-1}}$ in the expansion of $\left(x\frac{d}{dx}\right)^{n-1}S$.

That is,

$$a_{n,k} = ka_{n-1,k} + a_{n-1,k-1}. \tag{4}$$

Writing in (4), $n-1$, $n-2$, ..., k for n, then multiplying the resulting relations in order by k, k^2, k^3, ..., k^{n-k}, and adding the equations thus obtained, gives

$$\sum_{\alpha=0}^{n-k} k^\alpha a_{n-\alpha,k} = \sum_{\alpha=0}^{n-k} k^{\alpha+1} a_{n-\alpha-1,k} + \sum_{\alpha=0}^{n-k} k^\alpha a_{n-\alpha-1,k-1}. \tag{5}$$

Cancelling terms, we have

$$a_{n,k} = \sum_{\alpha=0}^{n-k} k^\alpha a_{n-\alpha-1,k-1}. \tag{6}$$

Now $a_{n,1}=1$, and from (6)

$$a_{n,2} = \sum_{\alpha=0}^{n-2} 2^\alpha a_{n-\alpha-1,1} = \sum_{\alpha=0}^{n-2} 2^\alpha = 2^{n-1}-1. \tag{7}$$

Next,

$$\begin{aligned} a_{n,3} &= \sum_{\alpha=0}^{n-3} 3^\alpha a_{n-\alpha-1,2} \\ &= 2^{n-2}\sum_{\alpha=0}^{n-3}\left(\frac{3}{2}\right)^\alpha - \sum_{\alpha=0}^{n-3} 3^\alpha \\ &= \frac{1}{3!}\left[3^n - \binom{3}{1}2^n + \binom{3}{2}1^n\right]; \end{aligned} \tag{8}$$

or, written symbolically,

$$a_{n,3} = \frac{1}{3!}\sum_{\alpha=0}^{2}(-1)^\alpha\binom{3}{\alpha}(3-\alpha)^n. \tag{9}$$

Letting $3-\alpha=\alpha'$,
$$a_{n,3} = \frac{(-1)^3}{3!}\sum_{\alpha=1}^{3}(-1)^\alpha\binom{3}{\alpha}\alpha^n. \tag{10}$$

Again,
$$a_{n,4} = \sum_{\beta=0}^{n-4} 4^\beta a_{n-\beta-1,3} \tag{11}$$
$$= \frac{(-1)^3}{3!}\sum_{\beta=0}^{n-4}4^\beta\sum_{\alpha=1}^{3}(-1)^\alpha\binom{3}{\alpha}\alpha^{n-\beta-1}$$
$$= \frac{(-1)^3}{4!}\sum_{\alpha=1}^{3}(-1)^\alpha\binom{4}{\alpha}(4-\alpha)\sum_{\beta=0}^{n-4}4^\beta\alpha^{n-\beta-1}.$$

But
$$\sum_{\beta=0}^{n-4}4^\beta\alpha^{n-\beta-1} = \frac{1}{4-\alpha}(4^{n-3}\alpha^3-\alpha^n),$$

$$a_{n,4} = \frac{(-1)^3}{4!}4^{n-3}\sum_{\alpha=1}^{3}(-1)^\alpha\binom{4}{\alpha}\alpha^3 - \frac{(-1)^3}{4!}\sum_{\alpha=1}^{3}(-1)^\alpha\binom{4}{\alpha}\alpha^n. \tag{12}$$

Now, since the terms in both summations corresponding to $\alpha=4$ are equal, we have

$$a_{n,4} = \frac{(-1)^3}{4!}4^{n-3}\sum_{\alpha=1}^{4}(-1)^\alpha\binom{4}{\alpha}\alpha^3 + \frac{(-1)^4}{4!}\sum_{\alpha=1}^{4}(-1)^\alpha\binom{4}{\alpha}\alpha^n. \tag{13}$$

But
$$\sum_{\alpha=1}^{4}(-1)^\alpha\binom{4}{\alpha}\alpha^3 = 0, \text{ by Ch. I. (136)};$$

hence
$$a_{n,4} = \frac{(-1)^4}{4!}\sum_{\alpha=1}^{4}(-1)^\alpha\binom{4}{\alpha}\alpha^n. \tag{14}$$

We now assume $$a_{n,k}=\frac{(-1)^k}{k!}\sum_{\alpha=1}^{k}(-1)^\alpha\binom{k}{\alpha}\alpha^n, \tag{15}$$

and shall show that this form holds also for $a_{n,k+1}$.

From (6), $$a_{n,k+1}=\sum_{\beta=0}^{n-k-1}(k+1)^\beta a_{n-\beta-1,k}, \tag{16}$$

which, by means of (15), becomes

$$a_{n,k+1}=\frac{(-1)^k}{k!}\sum_{\beta=0}^{n-k-1}(k+1)^\beta\sum_{\alpha=1}^{k}(-1)^\alpha\binom{k}{\alpha}\alpha^{n-\beta-1} \tag{17}$$

$$=\frac{(-1)^k}{(k+1)!}\sum_{\alpha=1}^{k}(-1)^\alpha\binom{k+1}{\alpha}(k+1-\alpha)\sum_{\beta=0}^{n-k-1}(k+1)^\beta\alpha^{n-\beta-1}$$

$$=\frac{(-1)^k}{(k+1)!}\sum_{\alpha=1}^{k}(-1)^\alpha\binom{k+1}{\alpha}(k+1-\alpha)\alpha^{n-1}\sum_{\beta=0}^{n-k-1}\left(\frac{k+1}{\alpha}\right)^\beta$$

$$=\frac{(-1)^k}{(k+1)!}\sum_{\alpha=1}^{k}(-1)^\alpha\binom{k+1}{\alpha}(k+1)^{n-k}\alpha^k-\frac{(-1)^k}{(k+1)!}\sum_{\alpha=1}^{k}(-1)^\alpha\binom{k+1}{\alpha}\alpha^n$$

$$=(-1)^k\frac{(k+1)^{n-k}}{(k+1)!}\sum_{\alpha=1}^{k+1}(-1)^\alpha\binom{k+1}{\alpha}\alpha^k+\frac{(-1)^{k+1}}{(k+1)!}\sum_{\alpha=1}^{k+1}(-1)^\alpha\binom{k+1}{\alpha}\alpha^n. \tag{18}$$

Now, by Ch. I. (136), the first summation in (18) is zero; therefore

$$a_{n,k+1}=\frac{(-1)^{k+1}}{(k+1)!}\sum_{\alpha=1}^{k+1}(-1)^\alpha\binom{k+1}{\alpha}\alpha^n, \tag{19}$$

which is of the same form as (15), $k+1$ appearing in place of k. Applying (15) to (3) gives (2).

2. The expression for $\frac{d^n}{dx^n}F(u)$, where u is a function of x, as given in Ch. I. (83), can also be obtained from (2) as follows:

Writing u in place of x in (2), and letting $u=e^x$, then

$$\left(u\frac{d}{du}\right)^n=\left(e^x\frac{d}{dx}\div\frac{du}{dx}\right)^n=\left(e^x\frac{d}{dx}\div e^x\right)^n=\left(\frac{d}{dx}\right)^n, \tag{20}$$

and (2) becomes

$$\frac{d^n}{dx^n}F(u)=\sum_{k=1}^{n}\frac{(-1)^k}{k!}\sum_{\alpha=1}^{k}(-1)^\alpha\binom{k}{\alpha}\alpha^n e^{kx}\frac{d^k}{du^k}F(u). \tag{21}$$

Now $$\alpha^n e^{kx}=\alpha^n e^{\alpha x}e^{(k-\alpha)x}$$

$$=e^{(k-\alpha)x}\frac{d^n}{dx^n}e^{\alpha x}=u^{k-\alpha}\frac{d^n}{dx^n}u^\alpha. \tag{22}$$

Then, by means of (22), we obtain from (21)

$$\frac{d^n}{dx^n}F(u)=\sum_{k=1}^{n}\frac{(-1)^k}{k!}\sum_{\alpha=1}^{k}(-1)^\alpha\binom{k}{\alpha}u^{k-\alpha}\frac{d^n}{dx^n}u^\alpha\frac{d^k}{du^k}F(u), \tag{23}$$

which is the same as Ch. I. (83).

And conversely, by letting $x=\log u$ in (23), the expansion (2) might be obtained.

3. The operator $\left(x\frac{d}{dx}\right)^n$ has a wide range of applications. It has enabled the author to perform operations and obtain results which he believes to be new. A few applications of the operator are given here, and further use is made of it in subsequent chapters.

(i) To find the value of

$$S=\sum_{n=1}^{\infty}\frac{n^p}{n!}r^n. \tag{24}$$

Now
$$S=\left(r\frac{d}{dr}\right)^p\sum_{n=1}^{\infty}\frac{r^n}{n!}=\left(r\frac{d}{dr}\right)^p(e^r-1)\,; \tag{25}$$

and by means of (2), we obtain

$$S=\sum_{k=1}^{p}\frac{(-1)^k}{k!}\sum_{a=1}^{k}(-1)^a\binom{k}{a}a^p r^k e^r. \tag{26}$$

If $r=1$, then
$$S=\sum_{n=1}^{\infty}\frac{n^p}{n!}=e\sum_{k=1}^{p}\frac{(-1)^k}{k!}\sum_{a=1}^{k}(-1)^a\binom{k}{a}a^p. \tag{27}$$

(ii) Show that

$$\sum_{n=1}^{\infty}(-1)^{n-1}\frac{n^p}{n!}r^n=\sum_{k=1}^{p}\frac{1}{k!}\sum_{a=1}^{k}(-1)^{a-1}\binom{k}{a}a^p r^k e^{-r}. \tag{28}$$

(iii) To express in powers of n

$$S_{n,p}=\sum_{k=1}^{n}\binom{n}{k}k^p. \tag{29}$$

Now
$$S_{n,p}=\left(r\frac{d}{dr}\right)^p\sum_{k=1}^{n}\binom{n}{k}r^k\Bigg]_{r=1} \tag{30}$$

$$=\left(r\frac{d}{dr}\right)^p\Big[(1+r)^n-1\Big]_{r=1}.$$

If $p=0$,
$$S_{n,0}=2^n-1\,; \tag{31}$$

and if $p>0$,
$$S_{n,p}=\sum_{k=1}^{p}\frac{(-1)^k}{k!}\sum_{a=1}^{k}(-1)^a\binom{k}{a}a^p r^k\frac{d^k}{dr^k}(1+r)^n\Bigg]_{r=1}$$

$$=2^n\sum_{k=1}^{p}(-1)^k\binom{n}{k}\frac{1}{2^k}\sum_{a=1}^{k}(-1)^a\binom{k}{a}a^p. \tag{32}$$

Now it follows from Ch. I. (137), (138) and (139), that if $\alpha=\gamma=p$,

$$\sum_{a=1}^{p}(-1)^a\binom{p}{a}a^p=(-1)^p p!\,((x^p))(e^x-1)^p=(-1)^p p!\,; \tag{33}$$

therefore
$$S_{n,p}=2^{n-p}\binom{n}{p}p!+2\sum_{k=1}^{p-1}(-1)^k\binom{n}{k}\frac{1}{2^k}\sum_{a=1}^{k}(-1)^a\binom{k}{a}a^p. \tag{34}$$

Thus
$$S_{n,0}=2^n-1,$$
$$S_{n,1}=2^{n-1}n,$$
$$S_{n,2}=2^{n-2}n(n+1),$$
$$S_{n,3}=2^{n-3}n^2(n+3),$$
$$S_{n,4}=2^{n-4}n(n+1)(n^2+5n-2),$$
and so on.

(iv) To find
$$S=\sum_{n=1}^{\infty}(-1)^{n-1}n^p r^n. \tag{35}$$

Then
$$S=\left(r\frac{d}{dr}\right)^p\sum_{n=1}^{\infty}(-1)^{n-1}r^n \tag{36}$$
$$=\left(r\frac{d}{dr}\right)^p\frac{r}{1+r}$$
$$=\sum_{k=1}^{p}\frac{(-1)^k}{k!}\sum_{a=1}^{k}(-1)^{a-1}\binom{k}{a}a^p r^k\frac{d^k}{dr^k}\frac{1}{1+r}$$
$$=\sum_{k=1}^{p}\frac{r^k}{(1+r)^{k+1}}\sum_{a=1}^{k}(-1)^{a-1}\binom{k}{a}a^p. \tag{37}$$

In a similar way we obtain
$$\sum_{n=1}^{\infty}n^p r^n=\sum_{k=1}^{p}\frac{(-1)^k r^k}{(1-r)^{k+1}}\sum_{a=1}^{k}(-1)^a\binom{k}{a}a^p. \tag{38}$$

(v) To find the value of
$$S=\sum_{n=1}^{\infty}(-1)^{\left[\frac{n-1}{m}\right]}n^p r^n. \tag{39}$$

Now
$$S=\left(r\frac{d}{dr}\right)^p\sum_{n=1}^{\infty}(-1)^{\left[\frac{n-1}{m}\right]}r^n \tag{40}$$
$$=\left(r\frac{d}{dr}\right)^p\left[\frac{1}{1+r^m}\sum_{k=1}^{m}r^k\right] \tag{41}$$
$$=\left(r\frac{d}{dr}\right)^p\sum_{k=1}^{m}F, \tag{42}$$
where
$$F=\frac{r^k}{1+r^m}. \tag{43}$$

But
$$\left(r\frac{d}{dr}\right)^p F=\sum_{a=1}^{p}\frac{(-1)^a}{a!}\sum_{a_1=1}^{a}(-1)^{a_1}\binom{a}{a_1}a_1{}^p r^a\frac{d^a}{dr^a}F; \tag{44}$$
then, by Ch. I. (146), we have
$$\frac{d^a}{dr^a}F=\frac{a!\,F}{r^a}\sum_{\beta=0}^{a}\frac{r^{m\beta}}{(1+r^m)^\beta}\sum_{\beta_1=0}^{\beta}(-1)^{\beta_1}\binom{\beta}{\beta_1}\binom{k+m\beta_1}{a}. \tag{45}$$

Then by means of (45) and (44) the desired result is obtained.

THE SUM OF EQUAL POWERS OF A SERIES OF NATURAL NUMBERS.

4. The operator $\left(r\frac{d}{dr}\right)^n$ enables us to find the sum of equal powers of a series of natural numbers in a manner and obtain it in a form not given heretofore.

(i) To express
$$S_{n,p}=\sum_{k=1}^{n} k^p \tag{46}$$
as a polynomial in n.

Now
$$S_{n,p}=\left(r\frac{d}{dr}\right)^p \sum_{m=1}^{n} r^m\Big]_{r=1} \tag{47}$$
$$=\sum_{k=1}^{p}\frac{(-1)^k}{k!}\sum_{\alpha=1}^{k}(-1)^\alpha\binom{k}{\alpha}\alpha^p r^k\frac{d^k}{dr^k}\sum_{m=1}^{n} r^m\Big]_{r=1} \tag{48}$$
$$=\sum_{k=1}^{p}(-1)^k\sum_{\alpha=1}^{k}(-1)^\alpha\binom{k}{\alpha}\alpha^p\sum_{m=k}^{n}\binom{m}{k}. \tag{49}$$

But
$$\sum_{m=k}^{n}\binom{m}{k}=((x^k))\sum_{m=k}^{n}(1+x)^m$$
$$=((x^{k+1}))[(1+x)^{n+1}-(1+x)]=\binom{n+1}{k+1}; \tag{50}$$

therefore
$$S_{n,p}=\sum_{k=1}^{p}(-1)^k\binom{n+1}{k+1}\sum_{\alpha=1}^{k}(-1)^\alpha\binom{k}{\alpha}\alpha^p. \tag{51}$$

If in (48) we write
$$S_1=r^k\frac{d^k}{dr^k}\sum_{m=1}^{n} r^m=r^k\frac{d^k}{dr^k}\frac{r-r^{n+1}}{1-r} \tag{52}$$
and perform the differentiation on the second member, the work is more involved, but the methods employed will be helpful in subsequent work.

From (52) we obtain
$$S_1=k!\left[\frac{r^k}{(1-r)^{k+1}}-\sum_{\beta=0}^{k}\binom{n+1}{k-\beta}\frac{r^{n+1+\beta}}{(1-r)^{\beta+1}}\right]. \tag{53}$$

To evaluate (53) for $r=1$, we bring the terms in the summation to a common denominator; we then have
$$S_1=k!\left[\frac{r^k}{(1-r)^{k+1}}-\sum_{\beta=0}^{k}\binom{n+1}{k-\beta}\frac{r^{n+1+\beta}}{(1-r)^{k+1}}\sum_{\gamma=0}^{k-\beta}(-1)^\gamma\binom{k-\beta}{\gamma}r^\gamma\right]. \tag{54}$$

Taking the $(k+1)$st derivative with respect to r of the numerator and the denominator of (54) separately, we obtain
$$S_1\Big]_{r=1}=(-1)^k k!\sum_{\beta=0}^{k}\binom{n+1}{k-\beta}\sum_{\gamma=0}^{k-\beta}(-1)^\gamma\binom{k-\beta}{\gamma}\binom{n+1+\beta+\gamma}{k+1}. \tag{55}$$

Now
$$\binom{n+1+\beta+\gamma}{k+1}=(-1)^{n-k+\beta+\gamma}\binom{-k-2}{n-k+\beta+\gamma}. \tag{56}$$

Then, by means of (56), (55) becomes

$$S_1\Big]_{r=1} = (-1)^n k! \sum_{\beta=0}^{k} (-1)^\beta \binom{n+1}{k-\beta} S_2, \tag{57}$$

where

$$S_2 = \sum_{\gamma=0}^{k-\beta} \binom{k-\beta}{k-\beta-\gamma} \binom{-k-2}{n-k+\beta+\gamma}. \tag{58}$$

But

$$S_2 = \sum_{\gamma=0}^{k-\beta} ((x^{k-\beta-\gamma}))(1+x)^{k-\beta}((x^{n-k+\beta+\gamma}))(1+x)^{-k-2}$$

$$= ((x^n))(1+x)^{-\beta-2} = (-1)^{n+\beta-1}\binom{-n-1}{\beta+1}. \tag{59}$$

Applying (59) to (57) gives

$$\frac{1}{k!}S_1\Big]_{r=1} = -\sum_{\beta=1}^{k+1}\binom{-n-1}{\beta}\binom{n+1}{k+1-\beta}$$

$$= -\sum_{\beta=0}^{k+1}\left[\binom{-n-1}{\beta}\binom{n+1}{k+1-\beta} - \binom{-n-1}{0}\binom{n+1}{k+1}\right]$$

$$= -\sum_{\beta=0}^{k+1}\left[((x^{k+1}))(1+x)^0 - \binom{n+1}{k+1}\right] = \binom{n+1}{k+1}, \tag{60}$$

which is the same as (50).

(ii) The terms in (46) obey the Law of Finite Differences.
The sum may therefore also be found in the following manner :
If d_k denotes the first term of the kth order of differences, then

$$S_{n,p} = \sum_{k=0}^{n-1}\binom{n}{k+1} d_k \tag{61}$$

and

$$d_k = \sum_{\alpha=0}^{k}(-1)^\alpha \binom{k}{\alpha}(k+1-\alpha)^p. \tag{62}$$

We may write

$$S_{n,p} = \sum_{k=0}^{n-1}\binom{n}{k+1}\sum_{\alpha=0}^{k}(-1)^\alpha\binom{k}{\alpha}(k+1-\alpha)^p. \tag{63}$$

It will now be shown that in (63) k cannot be greater than p.
From (63),

$$S_{n,p} = (-1)^p\sum_{k=0}^{n-1}\binom{n}{k+1}\sum_{\alpha=0}^{k}(-1)^\alpha\binom{k}{\alpha}\sum_{\beta=0}^{p}(-1)^\beta \alpha^{p-\beta}(k+1)^\beta$$

$$= (-1)^p\sum_{k=0}^{n-1}\binom{n}{k+1}\sum_{\beta=0}^{p}(-1)^\beta(k+1)^\beta\sum_{\alpha=0}^{k}(-1)^\alpha\binom{k}{\alpha}\alpha^{p-\beta}, \tag{64}$$

and since, by Ch. I. (136), $S_{n,p}=0$, if $k>p$, (63) becomes

$$S_{n,p} = \sum_{k=0}^{p}\binom{n}{k+1}\sum_{\alpha=0}^{k}(-1)^\alpha\binom{k}{\alpha}(k+1-\alpha)^p. \tag{65}$$

Letting $k-\alpha=\alpha'$,

$$S_{n,p} = \sum_{k=0}^{p}(-1)^k\binom{n}{k+1}\sum_{\alpha=0}^{k}(-1)^\alpha\binom{k}{\alpha}(\alpha+1)^p; \tag{66}$$

and letting next $a+1=a'$, then

$$S_{n,p}=\sum_{k=0}^{p}(-1)^k\binom{n}{k+1}\sum_{a=1}^{k+1}(-1)^{a-1}\binom{k}{a-1}a^p$$
$$=\sum_{k=1}^{p+1}(-1)^k\binom{n}{k}\sum_{a=1}^{k}(-1)^a\binom{k-1}{a-1}a^p. \tag{67}$$

5. We shall now derive a relation between the coefficients of $\binom{n}{k}$ in $S_{n,p}$ and $S_{n,p-1}$ and the coefficient of $\binom{n}{k-1}$ in $S_{n,p-1}$.

Let $a_{p,k}$ denote the coefficient of $\binom{n}{k}$ in $S_{n,p}$; then, from (67),

$$a_{p,k}=\sum_{a=1}^{k}(-1)^{k-a}\binom{k-1}{a-1}a^p. \tag{68}$$

And similarly let $a_{p-1,k}$ and $a_{p-1,k-1}$ denote the coefficients of $\binom{n}{k}$ and $\binom{n}{k-1}$ respectively in $S_{n,p-1}$.

We shall then show that

$$a_{p,k}=ka_{p-1,k}+(k-1)a_{p-1,k-1}. \tag{69}$$

Letting in (68) $k-a=a'$, then

$$a_{p,k}=\sum_{a=0}^{k-1}(-1)^a\binom{k-1}{a}(k-a)^p$$
$$=k\sum_{a=0}^{k-1}(-1)^a\binom{k-1}{a}(k-a)^{p-1}-\sum_{a=1}^{k-1}(-1)^a\binom{k-1}{a}a(k-a)^{p-1}. \tag{70}$$

But $$\sum_{a=1}^{k-1}(-1)^a\binom{k-1}{a}a(k-a)^{p-1}=-\sum_{a=0}^{k-2}(-1)^a\binom{k-1}{a+1}(a+1)(k-1-a)^{p-1}$$
$$=-(k-1)\sum_{a=0}^{k-2}(-1)^a\binom{k-2}{a}(k-1-a)^{p-1}. \tag{71}$$

Applying (71) to (70) gives (69).

By means of (69) we obtain from

$$\sum_{k=1}^{n}k=\binom{n}{1}+\binom{n}{2}$$

successively,

$$\sum_{k=1}^{n}k^2=\binom{n}{1}+3\binom{n}{2}+2\binom{n}{3},$$

$$\sum_{k=1}^{n}k^3=\binom{n}{1}+7\binom{n}{2}+12\binom{n}{3}+6\binom{n}{4},$$

$$\sum_{k=1}^{n}k^4=\binom{n}{1}+15\binom{n}{2}+50\binom{n}{3}+60\binom{n}{4}+24\binom{n}{5},$$

$$\sum_{k=1}^{n}k^5=\binom{n}{1}+31\binom{n}{2}+180\binom{n}{3}+390\binom{n}{4}+360\binom{n}{5}+120\binom{n}{6}$$

....

6. The sum of equal powers of a series of natural numbers, with the signs of the terms alternating.

To express
$$S_{n,p}=\sum_{k=1}^{n}(-1)^{k-1}k^p \tag{72}$$
as a polynomial in n.

We have
$$S_{n,p}=\sum_{k=1}^{n}k^p-2^{p+1}\sum_{k=1}^{\left[\frac{n}{2}\right]}k^p; \tag{73}$$
then, by means of (51),
$$S_{n,p}=\sum_{k=1}^{p}(-1)^k\left[\binom{n+1}{k+1}-2^{p+1}\binom{\left[\frac{n}{2}\right]+1}{k+1}\right]\sum_{a=0}^{k}(-1)^a\binom{k}{a}a^p\Big]. \tag{74}$$

7. We shall now express
$$S_{n,p}=\sum_{k=1}^{n}k^p$$
as an explicit function in n.

We have
$$S_{n,p}=S_{n-1,p}+n^p. \tag{75}$$

Now
$$S_{n-1,p}=\frac{d^p}{dx^p}\sum_{k=0}^{n-1}e^{kx}\Big]_{x=0}=\frac{d^p}{dx^p}\frac{e^{nx}-1}{e^x-1}\Big]_{x=0}. \tag{76}$$

Let
$$\frac{e^{nx}-1}{x}=f(x)\quad\text{and}\quad\frac{x}{e^x-1}=\phi(x); \tag{77}$$
then, by Leibnitz's theorem,
$$S_{n-1,p}=\sum_{k=0}^{p}\binom{p}{k}\frac{d^{p-k}}{dx^{p-k}}f(x)\frac{d^k}{dx^k}\phi(x)\Big]_{x=0} \tag{78}$$
$$=\phi(x)\frac{d^p}{dx^p}f(x)\Big]_{x=0}+p\phi'(x)\frac{d^{p-1}}{dx^{p-1}}f(x)\Big]_{x=0}$$
$$+\sum_{k=2}^{p}\binom{p}{k}\frac{d^{p-k}}{dx^{p-k}}f(x)\frac{d^k}{dx^k}\phi(x)\Big]_{x=0}. \tag{79}$$

Now
$$\frac{d^{p-k}}{dx^{p-k}}f(x)\Big]_{x=0}=\frac{d^{p-k}}{dx^{p-k}}\sum_{a=0}^{\infty}\frac{n^{a+1}}{(a+1)!}x^a\Big]_{x=0}$$
$$=\sum_{a=0}^{\infty}\frac{n^{a+1}}{(a+1)!}\binom{a}{p-k}(p-k)!\,x^{a-p+k}\Big]_{x=0}$$
$$=0,\ \text{unless } a=p-k, \tag{80}$$
in which case
$$\frac{d^{p-k}}{dx^{p-k}}f(x)\Big]_{x=0}=\frac{n^{p-k+1}}{(p-k+1)!}(p-k)!=\frac{n^{p-k+1}}{p-k+1}; \tag{81}$$
and from (81),
$$\frac{d^p}{dx^p}f(x)\Big]_{x=0}=\frac{n^{p+1}}{p+1};\quad\frac{d^{p-1}}{dx^{p-1}}f(x)\Big]_{x=0}=\frac{n^p}{p}. \tag{82}$$

The result (81) can also be obtained in the following way:

Let $\dfrac{e^{nx}-1}{x}=u$; then
$$ux=e^{nx}-1, \tag{83}$$

and
$$\frac{d^{p-k+1}}{dx^{p-k+1}}ux\Big]_{x=0}=\frac{d^{p-k+1}}{dx^{p-k+1}}(e^{nx}-1)\Big]_{x=0}$$

or
$$\sum_{\beta=0}^{p-k+1}\binom{p-k+1}{\beta}\frac{d^{p-k+1-\beta}}{dx^{p-k+1-\beta}}x\frac{d^{\beta}}{dx^{\beta}}u\Big]_{x=0}=\frac{d^{p-k+1}}{dx^{p-k+1}}(e^{nx}-1)\Big]_{x=0}. \tag{84}$$

Now the first member in (84) is equal to zero, except when $\beta=p-k$. We then have
$$\frac{d^{p-k}}{dx^{p-k}}u\Big]_{x=0}=\frac{1}{p-k+1}\frac{d^{p-k+1}}{dx^{p-k+1}}(e^{nx}-1)\Big]_{x=0}=\frac{n^{p-k+1}}{p-k+1}, \tag{85}$$
which is the same as (81).

Next
$$\frac{d^k}{dx^k}\phi(x)\Big]_{x=0}=\frac{d^k}{dx^k}\frac{x}{e^x-1}\Big]_{x=0}=-\frac{1}{2^k-1}\frac{d^k}{dx^k}\frac{x}{e^x+1}\Big]_{x=0},\ \text{by Ch. II. (103)}, \tag{86}$$
$$=-\frac{k}{2^k-1}\frac{d^{k-1}}{dx^{k-1}}\frac{1}{e^x+1}\Big]_{x=0}. \tag{87}$$

But
$$\frac{d^{k-1}}{dx^{k-1}}\frac{1}{e^x+1}\Big]_{x=0}=\sum_{\alpha=0}^{k-1}\frac{1}{2^{\alpha+1}}\sum_{\beta=0}^{\alpha}(-1)^{\beta}\binom{\alpha}{\beta}\beta^{k-1}; \tag{88}$$

therefore
$$\frac{d^k}{dx^k}\phi(x)\Big]_{x=0}=-\frac{k}{2^k-1}\sum_{\alpha=0}^{k-1}\frac{1}{2^{\alpha+1}}\sum_{\beta=0}^{\alpha}(-1)^{\beta}\binom{\alpha}{\beta}\beta^{k-1}, \tag{89}$$

from which $\phi'(x)]_{x=0}=-\frac{1}{2}$. Also $\phi(x)]_{x=0}=1$. (90)

Substituting (81), (82), (89) and (90) in (79) gives
$$S_{n-1,p}=\frac{n^{p+1}}{p+1}-\tfrac{1}{2}n^p+\sum_{k=2}^{p}\binom{p}{k}\frac{n^{p-k+1}}{p-k+1}\frac{k}{2^k-1}\sum_{\alpha=1}^{k-1}\frac{1}{2^{\alpha+1}}\sum_{\beta=1}^{\alpha}(-1)^{\beta-1}\binom{\alpha}{\beta}\beta^{k-1}. \tag{91}$$

We shall now show that
$$S_1=\sum_{\alpha=0}^{k-1}\frac{1}{2^{\alpha}}\sum_{\beta=0}^{\alpha}(-1)^{\beta}\binom{\alpha}{\beta}\beta^{k-1}=0,\ \text{if } k-1 \text{ is even}, \tag{92}$$
that is, if k is odd, except when $k=1$, in which case $S_1=1$.

Now
$$S_2=\sum_{\beta=1}^{\alpha}(-1)^{\beta}\binom{\alpha}{\beta}\beta^{k-1}=\frac{d^{k-1}}{dx^{k-1}}(1-e^x)^{\alpha}\Big]_{x=0}; \tag{93}$$
and since $S_2=0$, if $\alpha>k-1$, therefore
$$S_1=\sum_{\alpha=1}^{\infty}\frac{d^{k-1}}{dx^{k-1}}\left(\frac{1-e^x}{2}\right)^{\alpha}\Big]_{x=0}=\frac{d^{k-1}}{dx^{k-1}}\frac{1-e^x}{1+e^x}\Big]_{x=0}. \tag{94}$$

But $\frac{1-e^x}{1+e^x}$ being an odd function in x, we conclude that $S_1=0$, if $k-1$ is even, and in (91) the values of k can only be even.

We then obtain
$$S_{n-1,p}=\frac{n^{p+1}}{p+1}-\tfrac{1}{2}n^p+\sum_{k=1}^{\left[\frac{p}{2}\right]}\binom{p}{2k-1}\frac{1}{2^{2k}-1}\sum_{\alpha=1}^{2k-1}\frac{1}{2^{\alpha+1}}\sum_{\beta=1}^{\alpha}(-1)^{\beta-1}\binom{\alpha}{\beta}\beta^{2k-1}n^{p-2k+1}, \tag{95}$$
and $S_{n,p}$ by adding n^p to (95).

8. The coefficients of the powers of n in the expansion of

$$S_{n,p}=\sum_{k=1}^{n} k^p$$

can be also expressed as determinants.

Let

$$S_{n,p}=\sum_{\alpha=0}^{\infty} A_\alpha n^\alpha ; \tag{96}$$

then

$$S_{n+1,p}=\sum_{\alpha=0}^{\infty} A_\alpha (n+1)^\alpha . \tag{97}$$

But

$$S_{n+1,p}=\sum_{k=1}^{n+1} k^p = S_{n,p}+(n+1)^p$$

$$=\sum_{\alpha=0}^{\infty} A_\alpha n^\alpha +(n+1)^p . \tag{98}$$

Equating (97) and (98) gives

$$\sum_{\alpha=0}^{\infty} A_\alpha (n+1)^\alpha = \sum_{\alpha=0}^{\infty} A_\alpha n^\alpha +(n+1)^p \tag{99}$$

or

$$\sum_{\alpha=0}^{\infty} A_\alpha \sum_{\beta=0}^{\alpha} \binom{\alpha}{\beta} n^\beta = \sum_{\alpha=0}^{\infty} A_\alpha n^\alpha + \sum_{\beta=0}^{k} \binom{p}{\beta} n^\beta . \tag{100}$$

Equating in (100) the coefficients of n^k, we have

$$\sum_{\alpha=k}^{\infty} \binom{\alpha}{k} A_\alpha = A_k + \binom{p}{k}$$

or

$$\sum_{\alpha=k+1}^{\infty} \binom{\alpha}{k} A_\alpha = \binom{p}{k} . \tag{101}$$

Now, since $\binom{p}{k}=0$, if $k>p$, hence

$A_{p+\gamma}=0$, if $\gamma>1$, is one of the solutions of (101),

and

$$\sum_{\alpha=k+1}^{p+1} \binom{\alpha}{k} A_\alpha = \binom{p}{k} . \tag{102}$$

Assigning to k the values $k, k+1, k+2, \ldots, p-2, p-1, p$, we obtain the set of $p-k+1$ equations

$$\binom{p+1}{p} A_{p+1} = \binom{p}{p},$$

$$\binom{p+1}{p-1} A_{p+1} + \binom{p}{p-1} A_p = \binom{p}{p-1},$$

$$\binom{p+1}{p-2} A_{p+1} + \binom{p}{p-2} A_p + \binom{p-1}{p-2} A_{p-1} = \binom{p}{p-2},$$

$$\cdots\cdots\cdots\cdots\cdots\cdots\cdots\cdots\cdots\cdots\cdots\cdots ,$$

$$\binom{p+1}{k+1} A_{p+1} + \binom{p}{k+1} A_p + \binom{p-1}{k+1} A_{p-1} + \ldots + \binom{k+2}{k+1} A_{k+2} = \binom{p}{k+1},$$

$$\binom{p+1}{k} A_{p+1} + \binom{p}{k} A_p + \binom{p-1}{k} A_{p-1} + \ldots + \binom{k+2}{k} A_{k+2} + \binom{k+1}{k} A_{k+1} = \binom{p}{k}.$$

Solving for A_{k+1} gives

$$A_{k+1}=\begin{vmatrix} \binom{p}{k} & \binom{k+2}{k} & \binom{k+3}{k} & \cdots & \binom{p}{k} & \binom{p+1}{k} \\ \binom{p}{k+1} & \binom{k+2}{k+1} & \binom{k+3}{k+1} & \cdots & \binom{p}{k+1} & \binom{p+1}{k+1} \\ \cdots & \cdots & \cdots & \cdots & \cdots & \cdots \\ \binom{p}{p-1} & 0 & 0 & \cdots & \binom{p}{p-1} & \binom{p+1}{p-1} \\ \binom{p}{p} & 0 & 0 & \cdots & 0 & \binom{p+1}{p} \end{vmatrix} \div \begin{vmatrix} \binom{k+1}{1} & \binom{k+2}{2} & \cdots & \binom{p+1}{k} \\ 0 & \binom{k+2}{1} & \cdots & \binom{p+1}{k+1} \\ \cdots & \cdots & \cdots & \cdots \\ 0 & 0 & \cdots & \binom{p+1}{p-1} \\ 0 & 0 & \cdots & \binom{p+1}{p} \end{vmatrix}. \qquad (103)$$

Reducing (103), we obtain

$$A_{k+1}=\frac{k!}{(p+1)!}\,\frac{p!(k+2)!(k+3)!\dots p!(p+1)!}{k!(k+1)!(k+2)!\dots p!}\begin{vmatrix} \frac{1}{(p-k)!} & \frac{1}{2!} & \frac{1}{3!} & \cdots & \frac{1}{(p-k+1)!} \\ \frac{1}{(p-k-1)!} & \frac{1}{1!} & \frac{1}{2!} & \cdots & \frac{1}{(p-k)!} \\ \cdots & \cdots & \cdots & \cdots & \cdots \\ 0 & 0 & 0 & \cdots & \frac{1}{1!} \end{vmatrix}. \qquad (104)$$

Therefore

$$S_{n,p}=p!\sum_{k=1}^{p+1}\frac{1}{k!}\begin{vmatrix} \frac{1}{(p-k+1)!} & \frac{1}{2!} & \frac{1}{3!} & \cdots & \frac{1}{(p-k+2)!} \\ \frac{1}{(p-k)!} & \frac{1}{1!} & \frac{1}{2!} & \cdots & \frac{1}{(p-k+1)!} \\ \frac{1}{(p-k-1)!} & 0 & \frac{1}{1!} & \cdots & \frac{1}{(p-k)!} \\ \cdots & \cdots & \cdots & \cdots & \cdots \\ \frac{1}{1!} & 0 & 0 & \cdots & \frac{1}{2!} \\ \frac{1}{0!} & 0 & 0 & \cdots & \frac{1}{1!} \end{vmatrix} n^k. \qquad (105)$$

9. The expression (51) for $$S_{n,p}=\sum_{k=1}^{n} k^p \qquad (106)$$

can also be obtained by the following method:

Let $$S=\sum_{n=1}^{\infty} S_{n,p}x^n, \qquad x<1; \qquad (107)$$

then $$S_{n,p} \text{ is } ((x^n))S. \qquad (108)$$

Applying (106) to (107), we have

$$S=\sum_{n=1}^{\infty} x^n \sum_{k=1}^{n} k^p \qquad (109)$$

$$=\sum_{k=1}^{\infty} k^p x^k \sum_{n=k}^{\infty} x^{n-k}, \text{ by Ch. I. (97),}$$

$$=\frac{1}{1-x}\sum_{k=1}^{\infty} k^p x^k$$

$$=\frac{1}{1-x}\left(x\frac{d}{dx}\right)^p \frac{1}{1-x}. \tag{110}$$

Now $$\left(x\frac{d}{dx}\right)^p \frac{1}{1-x}=\sum_{k=1}^{p}(-1)^k \frac{x^k}{(1-x)^{k+1}}\sum_{a=1}^{k}(-1)^a\binom{k}{a}a^p;$$

therefore $$S=\sum_{k=1}^{p}(-1)^k x^k(1-x)^{-k-2}\sum_{a=1}^{k}(-1)^a\binom{k}{a}a^p. \tag{111}$$

Now, since $S_{n,p}$ is $((x^n))S$, we must find in (111)

$$((x^n))x^k(1-x)^{-k-2} \quad \text{or} \quad ((x^{n-k}))(1-x)^{-k-2}.$$

This coefficient is $(-1)^{n-k}\binom{-k-2}{n-k}=\binom{n+1}{k+1}$, and from (111) we obtain

$$S_{n,p}=\sum_{k=1}^{p}(-1)^k\binom{n+1}{k+1}\sum_{a=1}^{k}(-1)^a\binom{k}{a}a^p,$$

which is the same as (51).

10. The method of the preceding article enables us to solve problems which otherwise present considerable difficulty. A few illustrations of the method are given here, and further applications will be found in subsequent chapters.

(i) To find the value of

$$S_p=\sum_{k=0}^{\left[\frac{p}{2}\right]}\binom{n}{k}\binom{n-k}{p-2k}2^{p-2k}. \tag{112}$$

Let $$S=\sum_{p=0}^{\infty} S_p x^p, \qquad x<1; \tag{113}$$

then $$S=\sum_{p=0}^{\infty}\sum_{k=0}^{\left[\frac{p}{2}\right]}\binom{n}{k}\binom{n-k}{p-2k}2^{p-2k}x^p, \tag{114}$$

and by means of $$S_1=\sum_{p=0}^{\infty}\sum_{k=0}^{\left[\frac{p}{2}\right]}A_{p,k}=\sum_{k=0}^{\infty}\sum_{p=2k}^{\infty}A_{p,k},\text{*} \tag{115}$$

* $S_1=\sum_{k=0}^{0}A_{0,k}+\sum_{k=0}^{0}A_{1,k}+\sum_{k=0}^{1}A_{2,k}+\sum_{k=0}^{1}A_{3,k}+\sum_{k=0}^{2}A_{4,k}+\sum_{k=0}^{2}A_{5,0}+\dots$.

Writing the terms with equal indices of k in columns and adding these columns gives

$$S=\sum_{p=0}^{\infty}A_{p,0}+\sum_{p=2}^{\infty}A_{p,1}+\sum_{p=4}^{\infty}A_{p,2}+\dots+\sum_{p=2k}^{\infty}A_{p,k}+\dots=\sum_{k=0}^{\infty}\sum_{p=2k}^{\infty}A_{p,k}.$$

(114) changes to
$$S=\sum_{k=0}^{\infty}\binom{n}{k}x^{2k}\sum_{p=2k}^{\infty}\binom{n-k}{p-2k}(2x)^{p-2k}$$
$$=\sum_{k=0}^{\infty}\binom{n}{k}x^{2k}S_2, \tag{116}$$

where
$$S_2=\sum_{k=2p}^{\infty}\binom{n-k}{p-2k}(2x)^{p-2k}. \tag{117}$$

Letting $p-2k=h$, then
$$S_2=\sum_{h=0}^{\infty}\binom{n-k}{h}(2x)^h=(1+2x)^{n-k}. \tag{118}$$

Applying (118) to 116), we have
$$S=(1+2x)^n\sum_{k=0}^{\infty}\binom{n}{k}\left(\frac{x^2}{1+2x}\right)^k \tag{119}$$
$$=(1+2x)^n\left(1+\frac{x^2}{1+2x}\right)^n=(1+x)^{2n}; \tag{120}$$

and since
$$S_p=((x^p))S=((x^p))(1+x)^{2n},$$

therefore
$$S_p=\binom{2n}{p}. \tag{121}$$

In a similar manner we obtain
$$\sum_{k=0}^{\left[\frac{p}{2}\right]}\binom{n}{k}\binom{n-k}{p-2k}\frac{1}{2^{p-2k}}=\frac{1}{2^n}((x^p))(2x^2+x+2)^n, \tag{122}$$
$$\sum_{k=0}^{\left[\frac{p}{2}\right]}\binom{n}{k}\binom{n-k}{p-2k}3^{p-2k}=((x^p))(x^2+3x+1)^n. \tag{123}$$

(ii) To find
$$S_n=\sum_{k=0}^{n}\frac{1}{p-k}\binom{p-k}{n-k}, \tag{124}$$

where p is any real number, except n.

Let
$$S=\sum_{n=0}^{\infty}x^n\sum_{k=0}^{n}\frac{1}{p-k}\binom{p-k}{n-k} \tag{125}$$
$$=\sum_{k=0}^{\infty}\sum_{n=k}^{\infty}\frac{x^n}{p-k}\binom{p-k}{n-k},\ \text{by Ch. I. (97).} \tag{126}$$

Letting $n-k=n'$, then
$$S=\sum_{k=0}^{\infty}\frac{x^k}{p-k}\sum_{n=0}^{\infty}\binom{p-k}{n}x^n$$
$$=\sum_{k=0}^{\infty}\frac{x^k}{p-k}(1+x)^{p-k}=x^p\sum_{k=0}^{\infty}\frac{1}{p-k}\left(1+\frac{1}{x}\right)^{p-k}. \tag{127}$$

And letting $$1+\frac{1}{x}=r \quad\text{and}\quad \sum_{k=0}^{\infty}\frac{1}{p-k}r^{p-k}=u, \tag{128}$$

then $$\frac{du}{dr}=\sum_{k=0}^{\infty}r^{p-k-1}=-\frac{r^p}{1-r}$$

and $$\frac{du}{dx}=\frac{du}{dr}\cdot\frac{dr}{dx}=-\frac{(1+x)^p}{x^{p+1}}. \tag{129}$$

Therefore $$u=\sum_{n=0}^{\infty}\frac{1}{p-n}\binom{p}{n}x^{n-p}+C \tag{130}$$

and $$\sum_{n=0}^{\infty}S_n x^n=\sum_{n=0}^{\infty}\frac{1}{p-n}\binom{p}{n}x^n+Cx^p. \tag{131}$$

If p is negative, we multiply both sides of (131) by x^{-p}, and for $x=0$, then $C=0$.

If p is positive but not an integer, we may write

$$p=i+f, \text{ where } f<1.$$

Differentiating (131) $i+1$ times with respect to x and multiplying both sides by x^{1-f}, then C is again zero.

Hence for $p\neq 0, 1, 2, \ldots,$

$$S_n=\frac{1}{p-n}\binom{p}{n}. \tag{132}$$

Since (132) and (124) are each continuous functions of p, except when $p=n$, (132) is true for all values of p except n.

(iii) To find the value of

$$S_n=\sum_{k=0}^{n}\binom{2n-k}{k}r^k. \tag{133}$$

Let $$S=\sum_{n=0}^{\infty}S_n x^n; \tag{134}$$

then $$S=\sum_{n=0}^{\infty}x^n\sum_{k=0}^{n}\binom{2n-k}{k}r^k$$

$$=\sum_{k=0}^{\infty}(rx)^k\sum_{n=k}^{\infty}\binom{2n-k}{2n-2k}x^{n-k}. \tag{135}$$

Letting $n-k=n'$, $$S=\sum_{k=0}^{\infty}(rx)^k\sum_{n=0}^{\infty}\binom{2n+k}{2n}x^n. \tag{136}$$

Now $$\binom{2n+k}{2n}=(-1)^{2n}\binom{-k-1}{2n}=\binom{-k-1}{2n};$$

hence $$S=\sum_{k=0}^{\infty}(rx)^k\sum_{n=0}^{\infty}\binom{-k-1}{2n}(x^{\frac{1}{2}})^{2n}. \tag{137}$$

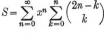

But $$\sum_{n=0}^{\infty}\binom{-k-1}{2n}(x^{\frac{1}{2}})^{2n}=\tfrac{1}{2}[(1+x^{\frac{1}{2}})^{-k-1}+(1-x^{\frac{1}{2}})^{-k-1}]; \tag{138}$$

therefore $$S=\frac{1}{2}\sum_{k=0}^{\infty}\left[\frac{1}{1+x^{\frac{1}{2}}}\left(\frac{rx}{1+x^{\frac{1}{2}}}\right)^k+\frac{1}{1-x^{\frac{1}{2}}}\left(\frac{rx}{1-x^{\frac{1}{2}}}\right)^k\right]$$

$$=\frac{1}{2}\left[\frac{1}{1+x^{\frac{1}{2}}-rx}+\frac{1}{1-x^{\frac{1}{2}}-rx}\right]$$

$$=\frac{1-rx}{1-\frac{1}{r}(2r+1)rx+(rx)^2}. \tag{139}$$

If we let $rx=y$, then, from (134) and (139),

$$\sum_{n=0}^{\infty}\frac{1}{r^n}S_ny^n=\frac{1-y}{1-\frac{1}{r}(2r+1)y+y^2}=f(y). \tag{140}$$

Now $$f(y)=\frac{A}{r_1-y}+\frac{B}{r_2-y}, \tag{141}$$

where r_1 and r_2 are the roots of

$$1-\frac{1}{r}(2r+1)y+y^2=0.$$

We then find

$$f(y)=\frac{1-r_1}{r_2-r_1}\frac{1}{r_1-y}+\frac{r_2-1}{r_2-r_1}\frac{1}{r_2-y}$$

$$=\frac{1-r_1}{r_1(r_2-r_1)}\sum_{n=0}^{\infty}\frac{y^n}{r_1{}^n}+\frac{r_2-1}{r_2(r_2-r_1)}\sum_{n=0}^{\infty}\frac{y^n}{r_2{}^n}. \tag{142}$$

Comparing (140) and (142), we obtain

$$S_n=\frac{r^n}{r_2-r_1}\left(\frac{1-r_1}{r_1{}^{n+1}}-\frac{1-r_2}{r_2{}^{n+1}}\right); \tag{143}$$

and since $r_1r_2=1$,

$$S_n=\frac{r^n}{r_1{}^n(r_1+1)}(r_1{}^{2n+1}+1). \tag{144}$$

But $$r_1=\frac{1}{2r}(2r+1\pm\sqrt{1+4r});$$

therefore $$S_n=\frac{1}{2^n}\frac{(2r+1\pm\sqrt{1+4r})^{2n+1}+(2r)^{2n+1}}{(2r+1\pm\sqrt{1+4r})^n(4r+1\pm\sqrt{1+4r})}. \tag{145}$$

If $r=1$,

$$S_n=\sum_{k=0}^{n}\binom{2n-k}{k}=\frac{1}{2^n(5\pm\sqrt{5})}[(3\pm\sqrt{5})^{n+1}+2(3\mp\sqrt{5})^n]. \tag{146}$$

If $r=-1$,

$$S_n=\sum_{k=0}^{n}(-1)^k\binom{2n-k}{k}=\frac{(-1)^{n-1}}{2^{n-1}\sqrt{-3}}[(1+\sqrt{-3})^{n-1}-(1-\sqrt{-3})^{n-1}]. \tag{147}$$

(iv) To reduce
$$S_n = \sum_{k=0}^{n} \binom{2k}{k} \binom{2\overline{n-k}}{n-k} \frac{1}{2k+1}, \tag{148}$$

we let
$$S = \sum_{n=0}^{\infty} S_n x^n, \quad x < \tfrac{1}{4}; \tag{149}$$

then
$$S = \sum_{n=0}^{\infty} x^n \sum_{k=0}^{n} \binom{2k}{k} \binom{2\overline{n-k}}{n-k} \frac{1}{2k+1}$$

$$= \sum_{k=0}^{\infty} \binom{2k}{k} \frac{x^k}{2k+1} \sum_{n=k}^{\infty} \binom{2\overline{n-k}}{n-k} x^{n-k}. \tag{150}$$

Letting $n-k=n'$,
$$S = \sum_{k=0}^{\infty} \binom{2k}{k} \frac{x^k}{2k+1} \sum_{n=0}^{\infty} \binom{2n}{n} x^n. \tag{151}$$

Now
$$S_1 = \sum_{k=0}^{\infty} \binom{2k}{k} \frac{x^k}{2k+1} \tag{152}$$

suggests the form Ch. I. (40) of the expansion of $\sin^{-1} x$.

We may write for (152),
$$S_1 = \frac{1}{2x^{\frac{1}{2}}} \sum_{k=0}^{\infty} \frac{1}{2^{2k}} \binom{2k}{k} \frac{(2x^{\frac{1}{2}})^{2k+1}}{2k+1} = \frac{1}{2x^{\frac{1}{2}}} \sin^{-1}(2x^{\frac{1}{2}}). \tag{153}$$

We shall next consider in (151),
$$S_2 = \sum_{n=0}^{\infty} \binom{2n}{n} x^n. \tag{154}$$

The expression (154) suggests the expansion of a binomial with a negative exponent.

Writing
$$\binom{2n}{n} = (-1)^n \binom{-\frac{1}{2}}{n} 2^{2n},$$

we have
$$S_2 = \sum_{n=0}^{\infty} (-1)^n \binom{-\frac{1}{2}}{n} (4x)^n = \frac{1}{(1-4x)^{\frac{1}{2}}}. \tag{155}$$

Then by means of (153) and (155), we obtain from (148)
$$S_n = ((x^n)) \frac{\sin^{-1}(2x^{\frac{1}{2}})}{2x^{\frac{1}{2}}(1-4x)^{\frac{1}{2}}}. \tag{156}$$

Show that
$$\sum_{k=0}^{n} \binom{-p}{k} = ((x^n)) \frac{1}{(1-x)(1+x)^p};$$

$$\sum_{k=0}^{n} \binom{p-k}{n-k} = \binom{p+1}{n};$$

$$\sum_{k=0}^{n} (-1)^k \binom{p-k}{n-k} = ((x^n)) \frac{(1+x)^{p+1}}{1+2x}.$$

11. (i) To express
$$S=\sum_{k=0}^{n}(2k+1)^p \tag{157}$$
as a polynomial in n.

Now
$$S=\sum_{k=0}^{n}(2k+1)^p r^{2k+1}\Big]_{r\doteq 1}$$
$$=\left(r\frac{d}{dr}\right)^p\sum_{k=0}^{n}r^{2k+1}\Big]_{r\doteq 1} \tag{158}$$
$$=\sum_{\alpha=1}^{p}\frac{(-1)^\alpha}{\alpha!}\sum_{\beta=1}^{\alpha}(-1)^\beta\binom{\alpha}{\beta}\beta^p r^\alpha\frac{d^\alpha}{dr^\alpha}\sum_{k=0}^{n}r^{2k+1}\Big]_{r\doteq 1}. \tag{159}$$

But
$$\frac{d^\alpha}{dr^\alpha}\sum_{k=0}^{n}r^{2k+1}\Big]_{r\doteq 1}=\alpha!\sum_{k=0}^{n}\binom{2k+1}{\alpha}r^{2k+1-\alpha}\Big]_{r\doteq 1}$$
$$=\alpha!\sum_{k=\left[\frac{\alpha}{2}\right]}^{n}\binom{2k+1}{\alpha} \tag{160}$$
$$=\frac{(-1)^{\alpha-1}}{2^{\alpha+2}}\alpha!\left[\sum_{\gamma=0}^{\alpha+1}(-1)^\gamma\binom{2n+3}{\gamma}2^\gamma+1\right],\text{ by Ch. III. (86).} \tag{161}$$

Then, by means of (161), we obtain from (159) the desired result.

(ii) To find the value of
$$S=\sum_{k=0}^{n}(-1)^k(2k+1)^p. \tag{162}$$

Now
$$S=\left(r\frac{d}{dr}\right)^p\sum_{k=0}^{n}(-1)^k r^{2k+1}\Big]_{r\doteq 1} \tag{163}$$
$$=\sum_{\alpha=1}^{p}\frac{(-1)^\alpha}{\alpha!}\sum_{\beta=1}^{\alpha}(-1)^\beta\binom{\alpha}{\beta}\beta^p r^\alpha\frac{d^\alpha}{dr^\alpha}\sum_{k=0}^{n}(-1)^k r^{2k+1}\Big]_{r\doteq 1} \tag{164}$$

and
$$\frac{d^\alpha}{dr^\alpha}\sum_{k=0}^{n}(-1)^k r^{2k+1}\Big]_{r\doteq 1}=\alpha!\sum_{k=\left[\frac{\alpha}{2}\right]}^{n}(-1)^k\binom{2k+1}{\alpha} \tag{165}$$
$$=(-1)^\alpha\alpha!\sum_{\beta=0}^{\alpha}(-1)^\beta\left[(-1)^{\frac{\alpha-\delta}{2}}\binom{\alpha+1-\delta}{\beta}+(-1)^n\binom{2n+\beta}{\beta}\right]$$
$$\sum_{\gamma=0}^{\left[\frac{\alpha-\beta}{2}\right]}(-1)^\gamma\binom{\alpha-\beta-\gamma}{\gamma}\frac{1}{2^{\gamma+1}},\text{ by Ch. III. (99),} \tag{166}$$

where
$$\delta=\frac{1-(-1)^\alpha}{2}.$$

Then, by means of (166), we obtain from (164) for $r=1$ the value of S.

(iii) To express
$$S=\sum_{k=0}^{n}(a+kh)^p, \tag{167}$$
where a and h, either or both, are integers or fractions, as a polynomial in n.

Then
$$S=\left(r\frac{d}{dr}\right)^p\sum_{k=0}^{n} r^{a+kh}\Big]_{r=1}$$
$$=\sum_{m=0}^{p}\frac{(-1)^m}{m!}\sum_{\beta=0}^{m}(-1)^\beta\binom{m}{\beta}\beta^p r^m\frac{d^m}{dr^m}\frac{r^{a+(n+1)h}-r^a}{r^h-1}. \tag{168}$$

But by Ch. I. (148),
$$\frac{d^m}{dr^m}\frac{r^{a+(n+1)h}-r^a}{r^h-1}=\frac{m!\,r^a}{r^m}\Bigg[r^{(n+1)h}\sum_{\gamma=0}^{m}\frac{r^{\gamma h}}{(r^h-1)^{\gamma+1}}\sum_{\gamma_1=0}^{\gamma}(-1)^{\gamma_1}\binom{\gamma}{\gamma_1}$$
$$\binom{a+\overline{n+1}\,h+\gamma_1 h}{m}-\sum_{\gamma=0}^{m}\frac{r^{\gamma h}}{(r^h-1)^{\gamma+1}}\sum_{\gamma_1=0}^{\gamma}(-1)^{\gamma_1}\binom{\gamma_1}{\gamma}\binom{a+\gamma_1 h}{m}\Bigg]. \tag{169}$$

To evaluate (169) for $r=1$, we bring the terms in the bracket to a common denominator; we then have
$$\sum_{\gamma=0}^{m} r^{(n+1+\gamma)h}\frac{(r^h-1)^{m-\gamma}}{(r^h-1)^{m+1}}\sum_{\gamma_1=0}^{\gamma}(-1)^{\gamma_1}\binom{\gamma}{\gamma_1}\binom{a+\overline{n+1+\gamma_1}h}{m}$$
$$-\sum_{\gamma=0}^{m} r^{\gamma h}\frac{(r^h-1)^{m-\gamma}}{(r^h-1)^{m+1}}\sum_{\gamma_1=0}^{\gamma}(-1)^{\gamma_1}\binom{\gamma}{\gamma_1}\binom{a+\gamma_1 h}{m}. \tag{170}$$

Then, by the method applied to (54), the desired result is obtained.

In the same way the value of $\sum_{k=0}^{n}(-1)^k(a+kh)^p$ is found.

(iv) To find
$$S=\sum_{n=0}^{\infty}(a+nh)^p r^n, \tag{171}$$
where a and b are either, or both, integers or fractions.

Letting $r_1=r^{1/h}$, then
$$S=\frac{1}{r_1{}^a}\sum_{n=0}^{\infty}(a+nh)^p r_1{}^{a+nh}=\frac{1}{r_1{}^a}S_1. \tag{172}$$

Now
$$S_1=\left(r_1\frac{d}{dr_1}\right)^p\sum_{n=0}^{\infty}r_1{}^{a+nh} \tag{173}$$
$$=-\left(r_1\frac{d}{dr_1}\right)^p\frac{r_1{}^a}{r_1{}^h-1}$$
$$=\sum_{k=1}^{p}\frac{(-1)^k}{k!}\sum_{\beta=1}^{k}(-1)^{\beta-1}\binom{k}{\beta}\beta^p r_1{}^k\frac{d^k}{dr_1{}^k}\frac{r_1{}^a}{r_1{}^h-1} \tag{174}$$

and
$$\frac{d^k}{dr_1{}^k}\frac{r_1{}^a}{r_1{}^h-1}=\frac{k!\,r_1{}^a}{r_1{}^k}\sum_{\gamma=0}^{k}\frac{r_1{}^{\gamma h}}{(r_1{}^h-1)^{\gamma+1}}\sum_{\gamma_1=0}^{\gamma}(-1)^{\gamma_1}\binom{\gamma}{\gamma_1}\binom{a+\gamma_1 h}{k}. \tag{175}$$

Applying (175) to (174) we obtain S_1, and then S from (172).

(v) If
$$S=\sum_{n=0}^{\infty}(-1)^n(a+nh)^p r^n, \tag{176}$$

then
$$S=\frac{1}{r_1{}^a}\left(r_1\frac{d}{dr_1}\right)^p\frac{r_1{}^a}{r_1{}^h+1},\quad r_1=r^{1/h}; \tag{177}$$

and continuing as in (iv), the value of S is obtained.

12. The series
$$S_{n,p}=\sum_{k=0}^{n}(-1)^k\binom{n}{k}k^p \tag{178}$$
enters frequently into the work in connection with operations with series. Its value for $p=n$ has been found in Ch. I. (140), and in this chapter (33) for $p=n$. In the following, a further discussion of this important series is given.

We shall first derive the value of $S_{n,p}$ for $p<n$ and for $p=n$, by a method different from the one used before.

(i)
$$S_{n,0}=\sum_{k=0}^{n}(-1)^k\binom{n}{k}k^0 \tag{179}$$
$$=S_{0,0}+\sum_{k=1}^{n}(-1)^k\binom{n}{k}.$$

But $S_{0,0}=1$ and $\sum_{k=1}^{n}(-1)^k\binom{n}{k}=\sum_{k=0}^{n}(-1)^k\binom{n}{k}-1, \quad =-1;$

therefore
$$S_{n,0}=0. \tag{180}$$

Next
$$S_{n,1}=\sum_{k=0}^{n}(-1)^k\binom{n}{k}k \tag{181}$$
$$=n\sum_{k=1}^{n}(-1)^k\binom{n-1}{k-1}.$$

Letting $k-1=k'$,
$$S_{n,1}=-n\sum_{k=0}^{n-1}(-1)^k\binom{n-1}{k}=-n(1-1)^{n-1}=0. \tag{182}$$

Again
$$S_{n,2}=\sum_{k=0}^{n}(-1)^k\binom{n}{k}k^2 \tag{183}$$
$$=n\sum_{k=1}^{n}(-1)^k\binom{n-1}{k-1}k=-n\sum_{k=0}^{n-1}(-1)^k\binom{n-1}{k}(k+1)$$
$$=-n\sum_{k=0}^{n-1}(-1)^k\binom{n-1}{k}k-n\sum_{k=0}^{n-1}(-1)^k\binom{n-1}{k}$$
$$=-nS_{n-1,1}-nS_{n-1,0}=0. \tag{184}$$

We now assume $\quad S_{n,p}=0,$ where p is at most $n-2$, (185)

and shall show that $S_{n,p+1}$ is then also zero.
$$S_{n,p+1}=\sum_{k=0}^{n}(-1)^k\binom{n}{k}k^{p+1} \tag{186}$$
$$=-n\sum_{k=0}^{n-1}(-1)^k\binom{n-1}{k}(k+1)^p$$
$$=-n\sum_{\alpha=0}^{p}\binom{p}{\alpha}S_{n-1,p-\alpha}. \tag{187}$$

But each of the terms in (187) vanishes, if $p<n-1$; therefore

$$S_{n,p+1}=0$$

or

$$S_{n,p}=0, \text{ if } p \text{ is at most } n-1. \tag{188}$$

We shall next consider the case when $p=n$.

Then

$$S_{n,n}=\sum_{k=0}^{n}(-1)^k\binom{n}{k}k^n \tag{189}$$

$$=-n\sum_{k=0}^{n-1}(-1)^k\binom{n-1}{k}(k+1)^{n-1}$$

$$=-n\sum_{\alpha=0}^{n-1}\binom{n-1}{\alpha}S_{n-1,n-1-\alpha}. \tag{190}$$

Now all the terms in (190) except the one corresponding to $\alpha=0$ vanish; therefore

$$S_{n,n}=-nS_{n-1,n-1}. \tag{191}$$

Substituting in (191) in succession $n-1$, $n-2$, ..., 2, 1 for n and multiplying the resulting relations, we obtain

$$S_{n,n}=(-1)^n n! \tag{192}$$

(ii) If $p=n+1$, then

$$S_{n,n+1}=\sum_{k=0}^{n}(-1)^k\binom{n}{k}k^{n+1} \tag{193}$$

$$=-n\sum_{k=0}^{n-1}(-1)^k\binom{n-1}{k}(k+1)^n$$

$$=-n\sum_{\alpha=0}^{n-1}\binom{n}{\alpha}S_{n-1,n-\alpha}; \tag{194}$$

and since

$$S_{n-1,n-\alpha}=0, \text{ if } \alpha>1,$$

therefore

$$S_{n,n+1}+nS_{n-1,n}=(-1)^n n!\, n. \tag{195}$$

Now we first write in (195) $n-1$ for n and multiply the result by $-n$. In the relation thus obtained, we again write $n-1$ for n and again multiply the result by $-n$. Continuing this process, we obtain n equations, which if added give

$$S_{n,n+1}=(-1)^n\frac{n}{2}(n+1)! \tag{196}$$

If $p=n+2$, then

$$S_{n,n+2}=-n\sum_{\alpha=0}^{n+1}\binom{n+1}{\alpha}S_{n-1,n+1-\alpha}; \tag{197}$$

and since the terms in (197) vanish except those corresponding to $\alpha=0$, $\alpha=1$ and $\alpha=2$, therefore

$$S_{n,n+2}+nS_{n-1,n+1}=-n\left[\binom{n+1}{1}S_{n-1,n}+\binom{n+1}{2}S_{n-1,n-1}\right]. \tag{198}$$

But
$$S_{n-1,n}=(-1)^{n-1}\frac{n-1}{2}n!$$
and
$$S_{n-1,n-1}=(-1)^{n-1}(n-1)!;$$
hence
$$S_{n,n+2}+nS_{n-1,n+1}=(-1)^n\frac{n^2}{2}(n+1)!. \tag{199}$$

Applying to (199) the method used in deriving (196), we obtain
$$S_{n,n+2}=(-1)^n\frac{n}{4!}(n+2)!(3n+1). \tag{200}$$

(iii) The following method for obtaining the value of $S_{n,p}$ is not as laborious as the one given above. But as p increases the work becomes also cumbersome.

By (33) we have
$$S_{n,p}=(-1)^n p!((x^p))(e^x-1)^n. \tag{201}$$

Now
$$(e^x-1)^n=x^n\left(1+\frac{x}{2!}+\frac{x^2}{3!}+\dots\right)^n. \tag{202}$$

But
$$\left(1+\frac{x}{2!}+\frac{x^2}{3!}+\dots\right)^n=1+\frac{n}{2}x+\frac{n(3n+1)}{4!}x^2+\frac{n^2(n+1)}{2.4!}x^3$$
$$+\frac{n}{10(4!)^2}(15n^3+30n^2+5n-2)x^4+\frac{n^2}{20(4!)^2}(3n^3+10n^2+5n-2)x^5$$
$$+\frac{n}{7!(4!)^2}(63n^5+315n^4+315n^3-91n^2-42n+16)x^6+\dots.$$

Therefore
$$S_{n,n}=(-1)^n n!,$$
$$S_{n,n+1}=(-1)^n(n+1)!\frac{n}{2},$$
$$S_{n,n+2}=(-1)^n(n+2)!\frac{n}{4!}(3n+1),$$
$$S_{n,n+3}=(-1)^n(n+3)!\frac{n^2}{2.4!}(n+1),$$
$$S_{n,n+4}=(-1)^n(n+4)!\frac{n}{10(4!)^2}(15n^3+30n^2+5n-2),$$
$$S_{n,n+5}=(-1)^n(n+5)!\frac{n^2}{20(4!)^2}(3n^3+10n^2+5n-2),$$
$$S_{n,n+6}=(-1)^n(n+6)!\frac{n}{7!(4!)^2}(63n^5+315n^4+315n^3-91n^2-42n+16),$$
$$S_{n,n+7}=(-1)^n(n+7)!\frac{n^2}{3!4!8!}(9n^6+65n^5+105n^4-7n^3-4074n^2+12112n-8064),$$
$$S_{n,n+8}=(-1)^n(n+8)!\frac{n}{5!9!(2!)^5}(135n^7+1260n^6+3150n^5+840n^4-2345n^3+540n^2+404n-144),$$
....

13. In the following a few examples will be given which illustrate some of the principles established above.

(i) To reduce
$$S=\sum_{m=n}^{\infty}\frac{1}{m!}\binom{m}{p}x^m\sum_{k=1}^{n}(-1)^k\binom{n}{k}k^m. \tag{203}$$

Now, since
$$\sum_{k=1}^{n}(-1)^k\binom{n}{k}k^m=0, \text{ when } m<n,$$

therefore
$$S=\sum_{m=0}^{\infty}\frac{1}{m!}\binom{m}{p}x^m\sum_{k=1}^{n}(-1)^k\binom{n}{k}k^m. \tag{204}$$

But from $\binom{m}{p}$ follows that $m\geqq p$;

hence
$$S=\sum_{m=p}^{\infty}\frac{1}{m!}\binom{m}{p}x^m\sum_{k=1}^{n}(-1)^k\binom{n}{k}k^m$$
$$=\frac{x^p}{p!}\sum_{m=p}^{\infty}\frac{x^{m-p}}{(m-p)!}\sum_{k=1}^{n}(-1)^k\binom{n}{k}k^m. \tag{205}$$

Letting $m-p=m'$,
$$S=\frac{x^p}{p!}\sum_{k=1}^{n}(-1)^k\binom{n}{k}k^p\sum_{m=0}^{\infty}\frac{x^m k^m}{m!}$$
$$=\frac{x^p}{p!}\sum_{k=1}^{n}(-1)^k\binom{n}{k}k^p e^{kx}. \tag{206}$$

(ii) To find the value of
$$S=\sum_{k=0}^{n}(-1)^k\binom{n}{k}\binom{p-kr}{n}. \tag{207}$$

Now $\binom{p-kr}{n}$ is a polynomial of the nth degree in k.

We may therefore write $\binom{p-kr}{n}=\sum_{a=0}^{n}A_a k^{n-a}$, (208)

where the A's are free of k.

Then
$$S=\sum_{k=0}^{n}(-1)^k\binom{n}{k}\sum_{a=0}^{n}A_a k^{n-a}$$
$$=\sum_{a=0}^{n}A_a\sum_{k=0}^{n}(-1)^k\binom{n}{k}k^{n-a}; \tag{209}$$

and since $\sum_{k=0}^{n}(-1)^k\binom{n}{k}k^{n-a}=0$, for $a>0$,

therefore
$$S=A_0\sum_{k=1}^{n}(-1)^k\binom{n}{k}k^n$$
$$=A_0(-1)^n n!. \tag{210}$$

But
$$A_0=\frac{(-1)^n}{n!}r^n;$$

hence
$$S=r^n. \tag{211}$$

In a similar way we obtain

$$\sum_{k=0}^{n}(-1)^k\binom{n}{k}\binom{p+kr}{n}=(-1)^n r^n. \tag{212}$$

Show that

$$\sum_{k=0}^{n}(-1)^k\binom{n}{k}\binom{p\pm kr}{q}=0, \text{ if } q<n. \tag{213}$$

(iii) To find the value of

$$S=\sum_{k=1}^{n}\binom{p}{k}k^n\sum_{\alpha=0}^{n-k}(-1)^\alpha\binom{p-k}{\alpha}. \tag{214}$$

Now

$$\binom{p}{k}\binom{p-k}{\alpha}=\binom{p}{k+\alpha}\binom{k+\alpha}{\alpha};$$

hence

$$S=\sum_{k=1}^{n}k^n\sum_{\alpha=0}^{n-k}(-1)^\alpha\binom{k+\alpha}{\alpha}\binom{p}{k+\alpha}. \tag{215}$$

Letting $k+\alpha=\alpha'$,

$$S=\sum_{k=1}^{n}(-1)^k k^n\sum_{\alpha=k}^{n}(-1)^\alpha\binom{p}{\alpha}\binom{\alpha}{k} \tag{216}$$

$$=\sum_{\alpha=1}^{n}(-1)^\alpha\binom{p}{\alpha}\sum_{k=1}^{\alpha}(-1)^\alpha\binom{\alpha}{k}k^n. \tag{217}$$

This form is similar to (2), and suggests the expansion of

$$\left(r\frac{d}{dr}\right)^\alpha r^p\Big]_{r=1}.$$

But

$$\frac{d^\alpha}{dr^\alpha}r^p=\binom{p}{\alpha}\alpha!\,r^{p-\alpha}. \tag{218}$$

We may therefore write

$$S=\sum_{\alpha=1}^{n}\frac{(-1)^\alpha}{\alpha!}\sum_{k=1}^{\alpha}(-1)^k\binom{\alpha}{k}k^n r^\alpha\frac{d^\alpha}{dr^\alpha}r^p\Big]_{r=1} \tag{219}$$

$$=\left(r\frac{d}{dr}\right)^n r^p\Big]_{r=1}=p^n r^n\Big]_{r=1}=p^n. \tag{220}$$

CHAPTER VI.

HIGHER DERIVATIVES OF A CERTAIN CLASS OF FUNCTIONS. THE CONTINUED PRODUCT $\prod_{k=1}^{n}(x+k)$.

1. The higher derivatives of functions like

$$\prod_{k=1}^{p}(1-x^k), \quad \prod_{k=1}^{p}\sin kx, \quad \text{etc.},$$

cannot be readily obtained by the methods given in the preceding chapters.

Let
$$f'(x)=f(x)S'(x), \tag{1}$$
where $f'(x)$ is the derivative of the given function $f(x)$.

Applying Leibnitz's theorem to (1), we have

$$f^{(n)}(x)=\sum_{k=0}^{n-1}\binom{n-1}{k}f^{(n-1-k)}(x)\,S^{(k+1)}(x). \tag{2}$$

Now, if to n be assigned the values 1, 2, 3, ..., n, we obtain a system of equations in the n unknowns,

$$\frac{f^{(n)}(x)}{f(x)}, \quad n=1,\,2,\,3,\,\ldots,\,n. \tag{3}$$

Solving the system gives

$$\frac{f^{(n)}(x)}{f(x)}=\frac{\begin{vmatrix} -1 & 0 & 0 & \ldots & 0 & -S' \\ S' & -1 & 0 & \ldots & 0 & -S'' \\ \binom{2}{1}S'' & \binom{2}{2}S' & -1 & \ldots & 0 & -S''' \\ \cdots & \cdots & \cdots & \cdots & \cdots & \cdots \\ \binom{n-2}{1}S^{n(-2)} & \binom{n-2}{2}S^{(n-3)} & \binom{n-2}{3}S^{(n-4)} & \ldots & -1 & -S^{(n-1)} \\ \binom{n-1}{1}S^{(n-1)} & \binom{n-1}{2}S^{(n-2)} & \binom{n-1}{3}S^{(n-3)} & \ldots & S' & -S^{(n)} \end{vmatrix}}{\begin{vmatrix} -1 & 0 & 0 & \ldots & 0 & 0 \\ S' & -1 & 0 & \ldots & 0 & 0 \\ \binom{2}{1}S'' & \binom{2}{2}S' & -1 & \ldots & 0 & 0 \\ \cdots & \cdots & \cdots & \cdots & \cdots & \cdots \\ \binom{n-2}{1}S^{(n-2)} & \binom{n-2}{2}S^{(n-3)} & \binom{n-2}{3}S^{(n-4)} & \ldots & -1 & 0 \\ \binom{n-1}{1}S^{(n-1)} & \binom{n-1}{2}S^{(n-2)} & \binom{n-1}{3}S^{(n-3)} & \ldots & S' & -1 \end{vmatrix}}$$

The determinant in the denominator reduces to $(-1)^n$. Changing in the determinant of the numerator the sign of the last column, and then moving it to the first column, multiplies the determinant by $(-1)^n$. Therefore

$$f^{(n)}(x)=f(x)\begin{vmatrix} S' & -1 & 0 & \dots & 0 \\ S'' & S' & -1 & \dots & 0 \\ S''' & \binom{2}{1}S'' & \binom{2}{2}S' & \dots & 0 \\ \dots & \dots & \dots & \dots & \dots \\ S^{(n-1)} & \binom{n-2}{1}S^{(n-2)} & \binom{n-2}{2}S^{(n-3)} & \dots & -1 \\ S^{(n)} & \binom{n-1}{1}S^{(n-1)} & \binom{n-1}{2}S^{(n-2)} & \dots & S' \end{vmatrix}^{*}. \tag{4}$$

2. We shall apply the foregoing to a few examples:

(i) To expand
$$f(x)=\prod_{k=1}^{p}(1-x^k), \tag{5}$$
in powers of x.

Now
$$f(x)=\sum_{n=1}^{\frac{1}{2}p(p+1)}\frac{f^{(n)}(0)}{n!}x^n. \tag{6}$$

To obtain $f^{(n)}(0)$ we let
$$\log f(x)=\sum_{k=1}^{p}\log(1-x^k)=S; \tag{7}$$
then
$$f'(x)=f(x)S' \tag{8}$$
and
$$S_0^{(n)}=\sum_{k=1}^{p}\frac{d^n}{dx^n}\log(1-x^k)\Big]_{x=0}$$
$$=-n!\sum_{k=1}^{p}\sum_{a=1}^{n}\frac{(-1)^a}{a}\sum_{\beta=1}^{a}(-1)^\beta\binom{a}{\beta}\binom{k\beta}{n}x^{ka-n}\frac{1}{(1-x^k)^a}\Big]_{x=0}$$
$$=0, \text{ except when } ka=n. \tag{9}$$

Now, since $ka \geqq k\beta \geqq n$, it follows that $\beta=a$.

Hence
$$S_0^{(n)}=-(n-1)!\sum_{k=1}^{p}k, \tag{10}$$
where by (9) k is a factor of n.

The result (10) may also be obtained as follows:
$$S=\sum_{k=1}^{p}\log(1-x^k)=\sum_{k=1}^{p}\sum_{a=1}^{\infty}\frac{x^{ka}}{a};$$
then
$$S_0^{(n)}=0, \text{ except when } a=\frac{n}{k};$$
hence as before
$$S_0^{(n)}=-(n-1)!\sum_{k=1}^{p}k.$$

* I am informed that Sylvester used a similar form, but I cannot find any reference to it.

Letting $$\sum_{k=1}^{p} k = N_n, \quad \text{then } S_0^{(n)} = -(n-1)!\,N_n, \tag{11}$$

where N_n denotes the sum of all values of k between 1 and p which are factors of n.

We then obtain

$$f^{(n)}(0) = (-1)^n \begin{vmatrix} 0!\,N_1 & 1 & \dots & 0 \\ 1!\,N_2 & 0!\,N_1 & \dots & 0 \\ 2!\,N_3 & \binom{2}{1}!\,N_2 & \dots & 0 \\ \dots & \dots & \dots & \dots \\ (n-2)!\,N_{n-1} & \binom{n-2}{1}(n-3)!\,N_{n-2} & \dots & 1 \\ (n-1)!\,N_n & \binom{n-1}{1}(n-2)!\,N_{n-1} & \dots & 0!\,N_1 \end{vmatrix}. \tag{12}$$

Multiplying the columns successively by $0!, 1!, 2!, \dots, (n-1)!$ and then removing from the successive rows the factors $0!, 1!, 2!, \dots, (n-1)!$, we have

$$f^{(n)}(0) = (-1)^n \begin{vmatrix} N_1 & 1 & 0 & \dots & 0 \\ N_2 & N_1 & 2 & \dots & 0 \\ N_3 & N_2 & N_1 & \dots & 0 \\ \dots & \dots & \dots & \dots & \dots \\ N_{n-1} & N_{n-2} & N_{n-3} & \dots & n-1 \\ N_n & N_{n-1} & N_{n-2} & \dots & N_1 \end{vmatrix}. \tag{13}$$

Now, since $f(x)$ is an integral expression, $f^{(n)}(0)$ must contain $n!$ as a factor. Denoting the determinant in (13) by $n!\,\Delta_n$, then

$$f^{(n)}(0) = (-1)^n n!\,\Delta_n$$

and $$f(x) = 1 + \sum_{n=1}^{\frac{1}{2}p(p+1)} (-1)^n \Delta_n x^n.* \tag{14}$$

Expanding in (13) Δ_n in minor determinants corresponding to the elements of the last column, again expanding the resulting determinants in the same manner and continuing this process, we obtain

$$f^{(n)}(0) = (-1)^{2n-1}[N_1 f^{(n-1)}(0) + (n-1)N_2 f^{(n-2)}(0) + (n-1)(n-2)N_3 f^{(n-3)}(0)$$
$$+ \dots + (n-1)(n-2)\dots 2N_{n-1}f'(0) + (n-1)!\,N_n f(0)]$$

$$= -\sum_{k=1}^{n} \frac{(n-1)!}{(n-k)!} N_k f^{(n-k)}(0) = (-1)^n n!\,\Delta_n; \tag{15}$$

therefore $$\Delta_n = \frac{1}{n} \sum_{k=1}^{n} (-1)^{k-1} N_k \Delta_{n-k}. \tag{16}$$

* The method given here for finding the expansion of $f(x)$ is believed to be more direct and the result obtained more simple than arrived at by Cayley—see his works, vol. ii. p. 243.

(ii) To expand in powers of x,

$$f(x)=\prod_{k=1}^{p} \sin kx. \tag{17}$$

We may write
$$f(x)=\frac{i^p}{2^p}e^{-\frac{1}{2}p(p+1)ix}\prod_{k=1}^{p}(1-e^{2ikx}). \tag{18}$$

Letting
$$e^{2ix}=r \quad \text{and} \quad \tfrac{1}{2}p(p+1)=m, \tag{19}$$

we have
$$f(r)=\frac{i^p}{2^p}r^{-mix}\prod_{k=1}^{p}(1-r^k). \tag{20}$$

And if we let
$$P(r)=\prod_{k=1}^{p}(1-r^k), \tag{21}$$

then
$$P(r)=\sum_{n=0}^{m}P^{(n)}(0)\frac{r^n}{n!}, \qquad P^{(0)}(0)=1,$$

$$=\sum_{n=0}^{m}(-1)^n\Delta_n r^n, \tag{22}$$

where Δ_n is the determinant in (13) divided by $n!$.

Therefore
$$f(x)=\frac{i^p}{2^p}e^{-mix}\sum_{n=0}^{m}(-1)^n\Delta_n e^{2nix} \tag{23}$$

$$=\frac{1}{2^p}\sum_{n=0}^{m}(-1)^n\Delta_n\sum_{k=0}^{\infty}\frac{i^{k+p}}{k!}(2n-m)^k x^k; \tag{24}$$

and since the lowest power of x in $f(x)$ is x^p,

$$f(x)=\frac{1}{2^p}\sum_{k=p}^{\infty}\frac{i^{k+p}}{k!}x^k\sum_{n=0}^{m}(-1)^n\Delta_n(2n-m)^k. \tag{25}$$

This can also be shown as follows:
From (24),

$$\left.\sum_{n=0}^{m}(-1)^n\Delta_n n^k r^n\right]_{r=1}=\left(r\frac{d}{dr}\right)^k\left.\prod_{a=1}^{p}(1-r^a)\right]_{r=1}$$

$$=\sum_{\beta=1}^{k}\frac{(-1)^\beta}{\beta!}\sum_{\gamma=1}^{\beta}(-1)^\gamma\binom{\beta}{\gamma}\gamma^k r^\beta\frac{d^\beta}{dr^\beta}\left.\prod_{a=1}^{p}(1-r^a)\right]_{r=1}.$$

If k is less than p, the terms of the derivative will each contain at least one factor of the form $1-r^a$, which vanishes for $r=1$; hence

$$\sum_{n=0}^{m}(-1)^n\Delta_n n^k=0, \text{ if } k<p.$$

Letting now $k-p=k'$ in (24), then

$$f(x)=(-1)^p\frac{x^p}{2^p}\sum_{k=0}^{\infty}\frac{i^k x^k}{(p+k)!}\sum_{n=0}^{m}(-1)^n\Delta_n(2n-m)^{p+k}; \tag{26}$$

and since $f(x)$ is real,

$$\prod_{k=1}^{p} \sin kx = \frac{(-1)^p}{2^p} \sum_{k=0}^{\infty} (-1)^k \frac{x^{p+2k}}{(p+2k)!} \sum_{n=0}^{m} (-1)^n \Delta_n (2n-m)^{p+2k}. \qquad (27)$$

To expand $f(x)$ in terms of sines and cosines of multiples of x, we change (23) to

$$f(x) = \frac{i^p}{2^p} \sum_{n=0}^{m} (-1)^n \Delta_n [\cos(m-2n)x - i \sin(m-2n)x];$$

then

$$f(x) = \frac{(-1)^{\frac{p}{2}}}{2^p} \sum_{n=0}^{m} (-1)^n \Delta_n \cos(m-2n), \text{ if } p \text{ is even,}$$

$$= \frac{(-1)^{\frac{p-1}{2}}}{2^p} \sum_{n=0}^{m} (-1)^n \Delta_n \sin(m-2n), \text{ if } p \text{ is odd,}$$

and

$$\prod_{k=1}^{p} \sin kx = \frac{(-1)^{\left[\frac{p}{2}\right]}}{2^p} \sum_{n=0}^{m} (-1)^n \Delta_n \cos\left[\frac{p\pi}{2} + (m-2n)x\right],$$

whether p be even or odd.

It follows that if m is even,

$$\prod_{k=1}^{p} \sin kx = \frac{(-1)^{\left[\frac{p}{2}\right]}}{2^p} \sum_{n=0}^{\frac{m-2}{2}} (-1)^n \cos\left(\frac{p\pi}{2} + \overline{m-2n}\,x\right)[\Delta_n + (-1)^{m+p}\Delta_{m-n}]$$
$$+ \frac{(-1)^{\frac{m}{2}}}{2^{p+1}} \Delta_{\frac{m}{2}} [1 + (-1)^p];$$

and if m is odd,

$$\prod_{k=1}^{p} \sin kx = \frac{(-1)^{\left[\frac{p}{2}\right]}}{2^p} \sum_{n=0}^{\frac{m-1}{2}} (-1)^n \cos\left(\frac{p\pi}{2} + \overline{m-2n}\,x\right)[\Delta_n + (-1)^{m+p}\Delta_{m-n}].$$

Therefore

$$\prod_{k=1}^{p} \sin kx = \frac{(-1)^{\left[\frac{p}{2}\right]}}{2^p} \sum_{n=0}^{\left[\frac{m-1}{2}\right]} (-1)^n \cos\left(\frac{p\pi}{2} + \overline{m-2n}\,x\right)[\Delta_n + (-1)^{m+p}\Delta_{m-n}]$$
$$+ (-1)^{\frac{m}{2}} \frac{1+(-1)^m}{2^{p+2}} \Delta_{\frac{m}{2}} [1 + (-1)^p].$$

(iii) To expand $f(x) = x^x$ in powers of $x-1$.

Let $x-1 = y$; then

$$f(y) = (1+y)^{1+y} = 1 + \sum_{n=1}^{\infty} \frac{f^{(n)}(0)}{n!} y^n. \qquad (28)$$

Now $\log f(y) = (1+y)\log(1+y)$ and $f'(y) = f(y)S'$,

where

$$S' = \frac{d}{dy}[(1+y)\log(1+y)]. \qquad (29)$$

Then $$S^{(n)} = (1+y)\frac{d^n}{dy^n}\log(1+y) + n\frac{d^{n-1}}{dy^{n-1}}\log(1+y)$$
$$= (-1)^{n-1}\frac{(n-1)!}{(1+y)^{n-1}} + n(-1)^n\frac{(n-2)!}{(1+y)^{n-1}}$$
$$= (-1)^n\frac{(n-2)!}{(1+y)^{n-1}} \tag{30}$$

and $$S_0^{(n)} = (-1)^n(n-2)!, \qquad S_0' = 1.$$

Therefore

$$f^{(n)}(0) = \begin{vmatrix} 1 & -1 & 0 & \dots & 0 \\ (-1)^2 & \binom{1}{1}1 & -1 & \dots & 0 \\ (-1)^3 1! & \binom{2}{1}(-1)^2 0! & \binom{2}{2} & \dots & 0 \\ \dots & \dots & \dots & \dots & \dots \\ (-1)^{n-1}(n-3)! & \binom{n-2}{1}(-1)^{n-2}(n-4)! & \binom{n-2}{2}(-1)^{n-3}(n-5)! & \dots & -1 \\ (-1)^n(n-2)! & \binom{n-1}{1}(-1)^{n-1}(n-3)! & \binom{n-1}{2}(-1)^{n-2}(n-4)! & \dots & \binom{n-1}{n-1} \end{vmatrix}. \quad (3$$

Removing $(\alpha-1)!$ from the αth row and $\dfrac{1}{(\beta-1)!}$ from the βth column, we finally obtain

$$x^x = 1 + \sum_{n=1}^{\infty}\frac{1}{n!}\begin{vmatrix} 1 & -1 & \dots & 0 \\ \frac{1}{1} & 1 & \dots & 0 \\ -\frac{1}{2} & \frac{1}{1} & \dots & 0 \\ \frac{1}{3} & -\frac{1}{2} & \dots & 0 \\ \dots & \dots & \dots & \dots \\ (-1)^n\frac{1}{n-1} & (-1)^{n-1}\frac{1}{n-2} & \dots & 1 \end{vmatrix}(x-1)^n. \tag{32}$$

3. (i) To find the expansion of the continued product

$$f(x) = \prod_{k=1}^{n}(x+k), \tag{33}$$

in powers of x.

Let $$f(x) = \sum_{k=0}^{n} Q_{n,k}\, x^{n-k} = \sum_{k=0}^{n} Q_{n,n-k}\, x^k, \tag{34}$$

where $Q_{n,k}$ is the sum of the products of 1, 2, 3, ..., n taken k at a time.

The Q's can then be expressed symbolically thus:

$$Q_{n,1} = \sum_{k_1=1}^{n} k_1,$$
$$Q_{n,2} = \sum_{k_1=1}^{n-1} k_1 \sum_{k_2=k_1+1}^{n} k_2,$$
$$Q_{n,3} = \sum_{k_1=1}^{n-2} k_1 \sum_{k_2=k_1+1}^{n-1} k_2 \sum_{k_3=k_2+1}^{n} k_3;$$

and in general,

$$Q_{n,k}=\sum_{a_1=1}^{n-k+1} a_1 \sum_{a_2=a_1+1}^{n-k+2} a_2 \sum_{a_3=a_2+1}^{n-k+3} a_3 \cdots \sum_{a_k=a_{k-1}+1}^{n} a_k \tag{35}$$

$$=\prod_{a=1}^{k}\left(\sum_{k_a=k_{a-1}+1}^{n-k+a} k_a\right), \text{ where } k_0=0. \tag{36}$$

From (33) we have

$$\log f(x)=\sum_{k=1}^{n}\log(x+k)=S \quad \text{and} \quad f'(x)=f(x)S'. \tag{37}$$

To find

$$f(x)=n!+\sum_{k=1}^{n} f'^{(k)}(0)\frac{x^k}{k!}, \tag{38}$$

we must first determine $S_0^{(k)}$.

Now

$$S^{(k)}=(-1)^{k-1}(k-1)!\sum_{a=1}^{n}\frac{1}{(x+a)^k}$$

and

$$S_0^{(k)}=(-1)^{k-1}(k-1)!\sum_{a=1}^{n}\frac{1}{a^k}=(k-1)!\,N_k. \tag{39}$$

Therefore, by (4),

$$f^{(k)}(0)=n!\begin{vmatrix} 0!N_1 & -1 & 0 & \cdots & 0 \\ 1!N_2 & 0!N_1 & -1 & \cdots & 0 \\ 2!N_3 & \binom{2}{1}1!N_2 & \binom{2}{2}N_1 & \cdots & 0 \\ \cdots & \cdots & \cdots & \cdots & \cdots \\ (k-2)!\,N_{k-1} & \binom{k-2}{2}(k-3)!N_{k-2} & \binom{k-2}{2}(k-4)!N_{k-3} & \cdots & -1 \\ (k-1)!\,N_k & \binom{k-1}{1}(k-2)!N_{k-1} & \binom{k-1}{2}(k-3)!N_{k-2} & \cdots & N_1 \end{vmatrix}.$$

Removing $(a-1)!$ from the ath row and $\frac{1}{(\beta-1)!}$ from the βth column, we obtain

$$f^{(k)}(0)=n!\begin{vmatrix} N_1 & -1 & 0 & \cdots & 0 \\ N_2 & N_1 & -1 & \cdots & 0 \\ N_3 & N_2 & N_1 & \cdots & 0 \\ \cdots & \cdots & \cdots & \cdots & \cdots \\ N_{k-1} & N_{k-2} & N_{k-3} & \cdots & -1 \\ N_k & N_{k-1} & N_{k-2} & \cdots & N_1 \end{vmatrix}. \tag{40}$$

Designating the determinant in (40) by Δ_n, then

$$f^{(k)}(0)=n!\Delta_k;$$

and we finally have

$$\prod_{k=1}^{n}(x+k)=n!+n!\sum_{k=1}^{n}\Delta_k\frac{x^k}{k!}$$

$$=n!+n!\sum_{k=0}^{n-1}\Delta_{n-k}\frac{x^{n-k}}{(n-k)!}. \tag{41}$$

Comparing (41) with (34), we obtain

$$Q_{n,k}=\binom{n}{k}k!\,\Delta_{n-k},\quad k=0,\ 1,\ 2,\ \ldots\ n-1. \tag{42}$$

(ii) The coefficients of the expansion in (33) can also be expressed in form of determinants, the elements of which are powers of 1, 2, 3, ... n.

Let $$\prod_{m=1}^{n}(x+m)=\sum_{k=0}^{n}Q_{n,\,n-k}\,x^k;$$

hence $$\sum_{k=0}^{n}Q_{n,\,n-k}(-m)^k=0,\quad m=1,\ 2,\ 3,\ \ldots,\ n. \tag{43}$$

Solving the system of equations resulting from (43), we obtain

$$Q_{n,\,n-k}=(-1)^{k(n-1-k)}n!\begin{vmatrix}(-1)^{k+1}\,(-1)^{k+2}\ldots(-1)^n\,(-1)^0\,(-1)^1\ldots(-1)^{k-1}\\(-2)^{k+1}\,(-2)^{k+2}\ldots(-2)^n\,(-2)^0\,(-2)^1\ldots(-2)^{k-1}\\\cdots\cdots\cdots\cdots\cdots\cdots\\(-n)^{k+1}\,(-n)^{k+2}\ldots(-n)^n\,(-n)^0\,(-n)^1\ldots(-n)^{k-1}\end{vmatrix}\div\begin{vmatrix}(-1)^1\,(-1)^2\ldots(-1)^n\\(-2)^1\,(-2)^2\ldots(-2)^n\\\cdots\cdots\cdots\\(-n)^1\,(-n)^2\ldots(-n)^n\end{vmatrix}$$

or $$Q_{n,\,n-k}=n!\begin{vmatrix}1&1&1^2&\ldots&1^{k-1}&1^{k+1}&\ldots&1^n\\1&2&2^2&\ldots&2^{k-1}&2^{k+1}&\ldots&2^n\\\cdots&&&&&&&\cdots\\1&n&n^2&\ldots&n^{k-1}&n^{k+1}&\ldots&n^n\end{vmatrix}\div\begin{vmatrix}1&1^2&\ldots&1^n\\2&2^2&\ldots&2^n\\\cdots&&&\cdots\\n&n^2&\ldots&n^n\end{vmatrix}. \tag{44}$$

4. We shall next express $Q_{n,k}$ as a double summation.
For that purpose we shall first derive the expansion

$$\log^p(x+1)=Q_{p-1,0}\,x^p+p!\sum_{k=1}^{\infty}\frac{(-1)^k}{(p+k)!}Q_{p+k-1,k}\,x^{p+k},^{*}\quad -1<x<1, \tag{45}$$

where, as it will be shown, the Q's have the same meaning here as in (34).
By successive differentiations, we obtain

$$\frac{d^n}{dx^n}f(lx)=\frac{1}{x^n}\sum_{k=0}^{n-1}(-1)^kQ_kf^{(n-k)}(lx), \tag{46}$$

where $$f^{(k)}(lx)=\frac{d^k}{d(lx)^k}f(lx).$$

* Cauchy, *Analyse Algèbrique*, obtains by induction (see also Chrystal, *Text-Book of Algebra*, part ii. p. 215),

$$\log^p(x+1)=p!\sum_{k=0}^{\infty}(-1)^k{}_{p-1+k}P_{p-1}\frac{x^{p+k}}{p+k},$$

where ${}_nP_m$ is the sum of the products of $\frac{1}{1},\ \frac{1}{2},\ \frac{1}{3},\ \ldots\ \frac{1}{n}$, taken m at a time.

Now, to find Q_k, we assume

$$f(lx)=e^{-vlx}=x^{-v}; \tag{47}$$

then

$$\frac{d^n}{dx^n}f(lx)=(-1)^n\binom{v+n-1}{n}n!\,x^{-v-n} \tag{48}$$

and

$$f^{(n-k)}(lx)=f^{(n-k)}(e^{-vlx})=(-1)^{n-k}v^{n-k}e^{-vlx}$$
$$=(-1)^{n-k}v^{n-k}x^{-v}. \tag{49}$$

Substituting (48) and (49) in (46) gives

$$\sum_{k=0}^{n-1}Q_kv^{n-k}=n!\binom{v+n-1}{n},$$

which shows that Q_k (we shall designate it by $Q_{n-1,k}$) has the same meaning in (46) as it has in (34).

Letting in (46) $n-1-k=k'$, we have

$$\frac{d^n}{dx^n}f(lx)=\frac{(-1)^{n-1}}{x^n}\sum_{k=0}^{n-1}(-1)^kQ_{n-1,n-1-k}f^{(k+1)}(lx). \tag{50}$$

Letting now $f(lx)=(lx)^p$, then

$$f^{(k+1)}(lx)=(k+1)!\binom{p}{k+1}(lx)^{p-k-1} \tag{51}$$

and

$$\frac{d^n}{dx^n}(lx)^p=\frac{(-1)^{n-1}}{x^n}\sum_{k=1}^{n}(-1)^{k-1}\binom{p}{k}k!\,Q_{n-1,n-k}(lx)^{p-k}. \tag{52}$$

If $x=1$,

$$\frac{d^n}{dx^n}(lx)^p=(-1)^{n+p}p!\,Q_{n-1,n-p},\ \text{if } n\geqq p. \tag{53}$$

Now, by Taylor's theorem,

$$\log^p(x+1)=\sum_{k=p}^{\infty}\frac{f^{(k)}(1)}{k!}x^k, \tag{54}$$

which, by means of (53), becomes

$$\log^p(x+1)=p!\sum_{k=p}^{\infty}(-1)^{k+p}Q_{k-1,k-p}\frac{x^k}{k!}$$
$$=Q_{p-1,0}x^p+p!\sum_{k=p+1}^{\infty}(-1)^{k+p}Q_{k-1,k-p}\frac{x^k}{k!}. \tag{55}$$

Letting $k-p=k'$, we have

$$\log^p(x+1)=Q_{p-1,0}x^p+\sum_{k=1}^{\infty}\frac{(-1)^k}{(p+k)!}Q_{p+k-1,k}x^{p+k},$$

which is the same as (45).

5. Lagrange* obtains from the relation

$$y=x\phi(y) \tag{56}$$

the expansion $u=f(y)=u_0+\sum_{k=1}^{\infty}\frac{d^{k-1}}{dy^{k-1}}[\{\phi(y)\}^kf'(y)]_{y=0}\frac{x^k}{k!}$. (57)

* Edwards, *Treatise on Differential Calculus*, p. 451.

Letting in (57)

$$u = \log^p (x+1), \quad y = \log (x+1), \quad \phi(y) = \frac{y}{x} = \frac{y}{e^y - 1}$$

and

$$f'(y) = py^{p-1}, \quad u_0 = 0,$$

we have

$$\log^p (x+1) = \sum_{k=1}^{\infty} \frac{d^{k-1}}{dy^{k-1}} \left[\left(\frac{y}{e^y - 1} \right)^k py^{p-1} \right]_{y=0} \frac{x^k}{k!}. \tag{58}$$

Comparing coefficients of equal powers of x in (58) and (45), we obtain

$$Q_{p+k-1,\,k} = \frac{(-1)^k}{p!} \frac{d^{p+k-1}}{dy^{p+k-1}} \left[\left(\frac{y}{e^y - 1} \right)^{p+k} py^{p-1} \right]_{y=0}$$

$$= \frac{(-1)^k}{(p-1)!} \sum_{a=0}^{p+k-1} \binom{p+k-1}{a} \frac{d^{p+k-1-a}}{dy^{p+k-1-a}} y^{p-1} \frac{d^a}{dy^a} \left(\frac{y}{e^y - 1} \right)^{p+k} \Bigg]_{y=0}$$

$$= 0, \text{ except when } a = k, \tag{59}$$

in which case

$$Q_{p+k-1,\,k} = (-1)^k \binom{p+k-1}{k} \frac{d^k}{dy^k} \left(\frac{y}{e^y - 1} \right)^{p+k} \Bigg]_{y=0}. \tag{60}$$

Now, by Ch. I. (169),

$$\frac{d^k}{dy^k} \left(\frac{e^y - 1}{y} \right)^{-p-k} \Bigg]_{y=0} = (p+k) \binom{p+2k}{k} \sum_{a=0}^{k} \frac{(-1)^a}{p+k+a} \binom{k}{a} \left(\frac{e^y - 1}{y} \right)^{-p-2k} \frac{d^k}{dy^k} \left(\frac{e^y - 1}{y} \right)^a \Bigg]_{y=0}$$

$$= (p+k) \binom{p+2k}{k} \sum_{a=0}^{k} \frac{(-1)^a}{p+k+a} \binom{k}{a} \frac{d^k}{dy^k} \left(\frac{e^y - 1}{y} \right)^a \Bigg]_{y=0}. \tag{61}$$

To find

$$N = \frac{d^k}{dy^k} \left(\frac{e^y - 1}{y} \right)^a \Bigg]_{y=0}, \tag{62}$$

we write

$$y^a \left(\frac{e^y - 1}{y} \right)^a = (e^y - 1)^a. \tag{63}$$

Taking the $(k+a)$th derivative of (63), we have

$$\sum_{\beta=0}^{k+a} \binom{k+a}{\beta} \frac{d^{k+a-\beta}}{dy^{k+a-\beta}} y^a \frac{d^\beta}{dy^\beta} \left(\frac{e^y - 1}{y} \right)^a \Bigg]_{y=0} = \frac{d^{k+a}}{dy^{k+a}} (e^y - 1)^a \Bigg]_{y=0}. \tag{64}$$

Now the first member of (64) is zero, except when $\beta = k$; we then obtain

$$N = \frac{k!}{(k+a)!} \frac{d^{k+a}}{dy^{k+a}} (e^y - 1)^a \Bigg]_{y=0}$$

$$= \frac{(-1)^a k!}{(k+a)!} \sum_{\gamma=1}^{a} (-1)^\gamma \binom{a}{\gamma} \gamma^{k+a}; \tag{65}$$

and (61) becomes

$$\frac{d^k}{dy^k} \left(\frac{e^y - 1}{y} \right)^{-p-k} \Bigg]_{y=0} = \frac{(p+2k)!}{(p+k-1)!} \sum_{a=1}^{k} \frac{1}{p+k+a} \frac{1}{(k+a)!} \binom{k}{a} \sum_{\gamma=1}^{a} (-1)^\gamma \binom{a}{\gamma} \gamma^{k+a}. \tag{66}$$

Applying (66) to (60), we obtain,

$$Q_{p+k-1,\,k}=\frac{(-1)^k}{(p+k-1)!}\binom{p+k-1}{k}(p+2k)!\sum_{a=1}^{k}\frac{1}{(p+k+a)(k+a)!}\binom{k}{a}\sum_{\gamma=1}^{a}(-1)^\gamma\binom{a}{\gamma}\gamma^{k+a}. \quad (67)$$

Writing $n+1$ for $p+k$, then

$$Q_{n,\,k}=\frac{(-1)^k}{n!}\binom{n}{k}(n+1+k)!\sum_{a=1}^{k}\frac{1}{(n+1+a)(k+a)!}\binom{k}{a}\sum_{\gamma=1}^{a}(-1)^\gamma\binom{a}{\gamma}\gamma^{k+a}, \quad (68)$$

and we have

$$Q_{n,n} \quad =(-1)^n\sum_{a=1}^{n}\frac{1}{a!}\binom{2n+1}{n-a}\sum_{\gamma=1}^{a}(-1)^\gamma\binom{a}{\gamma}\gamma^{n+a}=n!,$$

$$Q_{n,\,n-1}=(-1)^{n-1}\sum_{a=1}^{n-1}\frac{n+a}{a!}\binom{2n}{n-a-1}\sum_{\gamma=1}^{a}(-1)^\gamma\binom{a}{\gamma}\gamma^{n-1+a}=n!\sum_{k=1}^{n}\frac{1}{k},$$

$$Q_{n,\,n-2}=\frac{(-1)^n}{2}\sum_{a=1}^{n-2}\frac{(n+a)(n+a-1)}{a!}\binom{2n-1}{n-a-2}\sum_{\gamma=1}^{a}(-1)^\gamma\binom{a}{\gamma}\gamma^{n-2+a}$$
$$=n!\sum_{k=1}^{n-1}\frac{1}{k+1}\sum_{a=1}^{k}\frac{1}{a},$$

$$Q_{n,\,n-3}=n!\sum_{k_1=1}^{n-2}\frac{1}{k_1+2}\sum_{k_2=1}^{k_1}\frac{1}{k_2+1}\sum_{k_3=1}^{k_2}\frac{1}{k_3};$$

and in general

$$Q_{n,\,k}=n!\sum_{a_1=1}^{k+1}\frac{1}{a_1+n-k-1}\sum_{a_2=1}^{a_1}\frac{1}{a_2+n-k-2}\sum_{a_3=1}^{a_2}\frac{1}{a_3+n-k-3}\cdots\sum_{a_{n-k}=1}^{a_{n-k-1}}\frac{1}{a_{n-k}}. \quad (69)$$

Letting in (69) $k=n-n$, we have

$$Q_{n,0}=n!\sum_{k_1=1}^{1}\frac{1}{k_1+n-1}\sum_{k_2=1}^{k_1}\frac{1}{k_2+n-2}\cdots\sum_{k_{n-1}=1}^{k_{n-2}}\frac{1}{k_{n-1}+1}\sum_{k_n=1}^{k_{n-1}}\frac{1}{k_n}$$
$$=n!\frac{1}{n!}=1.$$

Another form for $Q_{n,\,k}$ is derived thus:

$$Q_{n,1}=\binom{n+1}{2},$$

$$Q_{n,\,2}=\sum_{k=0}^{n-2}(k+2)Q_{k+1,1}=\sum_{k=0}^{n-2}(k+2)\binom{k+2}{2}=\tfrac{1}{4}(3n+2)\binom{n+1}{3},$$

$$Q_{n,\,3}=\sum_{k=0}^{n-3}(k+3)Q_{k+2,\,2}=\sum_{k_1=0}^{n-3}(k_1+3)\sum_{k_2=0}^{k_1}(k_2+2)\binom{k_2+2}{2}$$
$$=\tfrac{1}{4}n(n+1)\binom{n+1}{4}.$$

We further obtain

$$Q_{n,4}=\tfrac{1}{48}(15n^3+15n^2-10n-8)\binom{n+1}{5},$$

$$Q_{n,5}=\tfrac{1}{16}(3n^4+2n^3-17n^2+104n-300)\binom{n+1}{6},$$

$$Q_{n,6}=\tfrac{1}{576}(63n^5-315n^3-224n^2+140n+96)\binom{n+1}{7}.$$

6. We shall now express $Q_{n,k}$ as a function of the Q's preceding it.

Let, as before, $$f(x)=\prod_{k=1}^{n}(x+k)=\sum_{k=0}^{n}Q_{n,k}x^{n-k}; \tag{70}$$

then $$f(x+1)=\sum_{k=0}^{n}Q_{n,k}\sum_{a=0}^{n-k}\binom{n-k}{a}x^{n-k-a}.$$

Letting $k+a=a'$,

$$f(x+1)=\sum_{k=0}^{n}Q_{n,k}\sum_{a=k}^{n}\binom{n-k}{a-k}x^{n-a}$$

$$=\sum_{a=0}^{n}x^{n-a}\sum_{k=0}^{a}\binom{n-k}{a-k}Q_{n,k},\ \text{by Ch. I. (58).} \tag{71}$$

Applying (70) and (71) to

$$(x+1)f(x+1)=(x+n+1)f(x)$$

gives $$(x+1)\sum_{a=0}^{n}x^{n-a}\sum_{k=0}^{a}\binom{n-k}{a-k}Q_{n,k}=(x+n+1)\sum_{a=0}^{n}Q_{n,a}x^{n-a}. \tag{72}$$

Equating coefficients of like powers of x, we have

$$\sum_{k=0}^{a+1}\binom{n-k}{a+1-k}Q_{n,k}+\sum_{k=0}^{a}\binom{n-k}{a-k}Q_{n,k}=(n+1)Q_{n,a}+Q_{n,a+1} \tag{73}$$

or $$\sum_{k=0}^{a}\left[\binom{n-k}{a+1-k}+\binom{n-k}{a-k}\right]Q_{n,k}=(n+1)Q_{n,a}. \tag{74}$$

But $$\binom{n-k}{a+1-k}+\binom{n-k}{a-k}=\binom{n-k+1}{a-k+1}=\binom{n-k+1}{n-a}; \tag{75}$$

therefore $$\sum_{k=0}^{a}\binom{n-k+1}{n-a}Q_{n,k}=(n+1)Q_{n,a}$$

or $$aQ_{n,a}=\sum_{k=0}^{a-1}\binom{n-k+1}{n-a}Q_{n,k}.$$

Changing a into k and k into a,

$$Q_{n,k}=\frac{1}{k}\sum_{a=0}^{k-1}\binom{n-a+1}{n-k}Q_{n,a}. \tag{76}$$

7. The higher derivatives of certain functions may also be obtained by special devices. Such methods, however, often present considerable difficulty, and the results are, as a rule, in a form not convenient for practical application. As an example we shall find here the nth derivative of

$$y = e^{cx^p}.$$

By actual differentiation we have

$$y' = ycpx^{p-1},$$
$$y'' = y[(cp)^2x^{2p-2} + cp(p-1)x^{p-2}],$$
$$y''' = y[(cp)^3x^{3p-3} + 3(cp)^2(p-1)x^{2p-3} + cp(p-1)(p-2)x^{p-3}],$$
$$\dots\dots\dots\dots\dots\dots\dots\dots\dots$$

We shall now assume

$$y^{(n)} = y\sum_{h=1}^{n}(cp)^{n+1-h}A_{n,h}x^{(n+1-h)p-n}, \tag{77}$$

where $A_{n,h}$ is free of x.

To find $A_{n,h}$ we differentiate (77) with respect to x; we then have

$$y^{(n+1)} = y\Big[\sum_{h=1}^{n}(cp)^{n+1-h}A_{n,h}(\overline{n+1-h}\,p-n)x^{(n+1-h)p-(n+1)}$$
$$+\sum_{h=1}^{n}(cp)^{(n+1)+1-h}A_{n,h}x^{(n+2-h)p-(n+1)}\Big]$$
$$= y\Big[\sum_{h=1}^{n-1}(cp)^{n+1-h}A_{n,h}(\overline{n+1-h}\,p-n)x^{(n+1-h)p-(n+1)}$$
$$+\sum_{h=1}^{n-1}(cp)^{n+1-h}A_{n,h+1}x^{(n+1-h)p-(n+1)}$$
$$+(cp)^{n+1}A_{n,1}x^{(n+1)p-(n+1)} + cpA_{n,n}(p-n)x^{p-(n+1)}\Big]$$
$$= y\Big[(cp)^{n+1}A_{n,1}x^{(n+1)p-(n+1)} + \sum_{h=1}^{n-1}(cp)^{n+1-h}x^{(n+1-h)p-(n+1)}$$
$$\cdot\{(\overline{n+1-h}\,p-n)A_{n,h} + A_{n,h+1}\} + cpA_{n,n}(p-n)x^{p-(n+1)}\Big]; \tag{78}$$

and since $A_{n,0} = 0 = A_{n,n+1}$, we may write

$$y^{(n+1)} = y\sum_{h=0}^{n}(cp)^{n+1-h}x^{(n+1-h)p-(n+1)}\{(\overline{n+1-h}\,p-n)A_{n,h} + A_{n,h+1}\}$$
$$= y\sum_{h=1}^{n+1}(cp)^{n+2-h}x^{(n+2-h)p-(n+1)}\{(\overline{n+2-h}\,p-n)A_{n,h-1} + A_{n,h}\}. \tag{79}$$

But from (77)

$$y^{(n+1)} = y\sum_{h=1}^{n+1}(cp)^{n+2-h}A_{n+1,h}x^{(n+2-h)p-(n+1)}. \tag{80}$$

Comparing (79) and (80), we obtain

$$A_{n+1,h}=A_{n,h}+(\overline{n+2-h}\,p-n)A_{n,h-1}, \tag{81}$$

from which $$\sum_{k=1}^{n}A_{k+1,h}=\sum_{k=1}^{n}A_{k,h}+\sum_{k=1}^{n}(\overline{k+2-h}\,p-k)A_{k,h-1}.$$

But $$\sum_{k=1}^{n}(A_{k+1,h}-A_{k,h})=A_{n+1,h}-A_{1,h};$$

and since if $h>1$, $A_{1,h}=0$,

$$A_{n+1,h}=\sum_{k=h-1}^{n}(\overline{k+2-h}\,p-k)A_{k,h-1} \tag{82}$$

and $$A_{k,h-1}=\sum_{m=h-2}^{k-1}(\overline{m+3-h}\,p-m)A_{m,h-2}.$$

Therefore

$$A_{n+1,h}=\sum_{k=h-1}^{n}\sum_{m=h-2}^{k-1}(\overline{k+2-h}\,p-k)(\overline{m+3-h}\,p-m)A_{m,h-2}$$

$$=\sum_{m=h-2}^{n-1}(\overline{m+3-h}\,p-m)A_{m,h-2}\sum_{k=m+1}^{n}(\overline{k+2-h}\,p-k). \tag{83}$$

In a similar way

$$A_{n+1,h}=\sum_{m_1=h-3}^{n-2}(\overline{m_1+4-h}\,p-m_1)A_{m_1,h-3}\sum_{m_2=m_1+1}^{n-1}(\overline{m_2+3-h}\,p-m_2)$$

$$\sum_{m_3=m_2+1}^{n}(\overline{m_3+2-h}\,p-m_3). \tag{84}$$

Continuing this process, we obtain

$$A_{n+1,h}=\sum_{m_1=1}^{n-h+2}A_{m_1,1}(m_1p-m_1)\prod_{k=2}^{h-1}\left(\sum_{m_k=m_{k-1}+1}^{n-h+1+k}(\overline{m_k-k}\,p-m_k)\right); \tag{85}$$

and since $A_{m_1,1}=1$,

$$A_{n,h}=\sum_{m_1=1}^{n-h+1}(m_1p-m_1)\prod_{k=2}^{h-1}\left(\sum_{m_k=m_{k-1}+1}^{n-h+k}(\overline{m_k-k}\,p-m_k)\right). \tag{86}$$

Applying (86) to (77) gives the required derivative, a much simpler form of which has been obtained in Ch. I. (167).

CHAPTER VII.

EXPANSION OF POWERS OF SERIES.

In extending the methods given in Ch. I. 4 and 5, we shall treat of the two cases:

1. When the sum of the series to be expanded to a given power can be expressed in terms of known functions and the general derivative of the power of the sum can be readily obtained.

2. When the sum of the series cannot be expressed in terms of elementary functions, or when the general derivative of the power of the sum cannot conveniently be found.

The methods will be illustrated by a few examples:

1. (i) To find the expansion in powers of x of

$$y=(1+x+x^2+\dots+x^{m-1})^p, \quad p \text{ any real number.} \tag{1}$$

Now
$$y=\left(\frac{1-x^m}{1-x}\right)^p \tag{2}$$

and
$$\frac{d^ny}{dx^n}=\sum_{k=0}^{n}\binom{n}{k}\frac{d^{n-k}}{dx^{n-k}}\frac{1}{(1-x)^p}\frac{d^k}{dx^k}(1-x^m)^p. \tag{3}$$

But
$$\frac{d^{n-k}}{dx^{n-k}}\frac{1}{(1-x)^p}=(-1)^{n-k}\binom{-p}{n-k}(n-k)!\frac{1}{(1-x)^{p+n-k}} \tag{4}$$

and
$$\frac{d^k}{dx^k}(1-x^m)^p=k!\sum_{\alpha=0}^{k}\binom{p}{\alpha}\sum_{\beta=0}^{\alpha}(-1)^\beta\binom{\alpha}{\beta}\binom{m\beta}{k}x^{m\alpha-k}(1-x^m)^{p-\alpha}. \tag{5}$$

Applying (4) and (5) to (3) gives

$$\left.\frac{d^ny}{dx^n}\right]_{x=0}=(-1)^n n!\sum_{k=0}^{n}(-1)^k\binom{-p}{n-k}\sum_{\alpha=0}^{k}\binom{p}{\alpha}$$
$$\sum_{\beta=0}^{\alpha}(-1)^\beta\binom{\alpha}{\beta}\binom{m\beta}{k}\left.\frac{x^{m\alpha-k}(1-x^m)^{p-\alpha}}{(1-x)^{p+n-k}}\right]_{x=0} \tag{6}$$

$=0$, unless $m\alpha=k$.

Now, from $\binom{\alpha}{\beta}$, $\alpha \geqq \beta$, and from $\binom{m\beta}{k}$, $m\beta \geqq k$. It then follows that $m\alpha \geqq m\beta \geqq k$. But $m\alpha=k$; hence $\beta=\alpha$, and

$$\left.\frac{d^ny}{dx^n}\right]_{x=0}=(-1)^n n!\sum_{k=0}^{n}(-1)^k\binom{-p}{n-k}\sum_{\alpha=0}^{k}(-1)^\alpha\binom{p}{\alpha}. \tag{7}$$

Since $a=\frac{k}{m}$, k can only have values which are multiples of m. Letting $k=mh$, then $a=h$.

Therefore $$\left.\frac{d^n y}{dx^n}\right]_{x=0}=n!\sum_{k=0}^{\left[\frac{n}{m}\right]}(-1)^k\binom{n-mk+p-1}{n-mk}\binom{p}{k} \tag{8}$$

and $$y=1+\sum_{n=1}^{\infty}\sum_{k=0}^{\left[\frac{n}{m}\right]}(-1)^k\binom{n-mk+p-1}{p-1}\binom{p}{k}x^n. \tag{9}$$

In a similar way we find

$$(1-x+x^2-\dots+(-1)^{m-1}x^{m-1})^p$$

$$=1+\sum_{n=1}^{\infty}(-1)^n\sum_{k=0}^{\left[\frac{n}{m}\right]}(-1)^{(m-1)k}\binom{n-mk+p-1}{p-1}\binom{p}{k}x^n, \tag{10}$$

when m is even,

$$=1+\sum_{n=1}^{\infty}(-1)^n\sum_{k=0}^{\left[\frac{n}{m}\right]}(-1)^{mk}\binom{n-mk+p-1}{p-1}\binom{p}{k}x^n, \tag{11}$$

when m is odd.

(ii) Given $$y=\sum_{n=1}^{\infty}(n^2+2n+3)x^n, \quad |x|<1, \tag{12}$$

to find the expansion of y^p, p any real number, in powers of x.

Now $$y=\left[\left(x\frac{d}{dx}\right)^2+2\left(x\frac{d}{dx}\right)+3\right]\frac{x}{1-x}$$

$$=\frac{x(3x^2-7x+6)}{(1-x)^3}=xy_1. \tag{13}$$

To expand y^p we first find

$$\left.\frac{d^n}{dx^n}y_1{}^p\right]_{x=0}=\sum_{k=0}^{n}\binom{n}{k}\frac{d^{n-k}}{dx^{n-k}}(1-x)^{-3p}\left.\frac{d^k}{dx^k}(3x^2-7x+6)^p\right]_{x=0}$$

$$=(-1)^n 6^p n!\sum_{k=0}^{n}\binom{-3p}{n-k}\left(\frac{7}{6}\right)^k\sum_{a=0}^{\left[\frac{k}{2}\right]}\binom{p}{k-a}\binom{k-a}{a}\left(\frac{18}{49}\right)^a; \tag{14}$$

then $$y^p=6^p\sum_{n=0}^{\infty}(-1)^n x^{n+p}\sum_{k=0}^{n}\binom{-3p}{n-k}\left(\frac{7}{6}\right)^k\sum_{a=0}^{\left[\frac{k}{2}\right]}\binom{p}{a}\binom{p-a}{k-2a}\left(\frac{18}{49}\right)^a, \tag{15}$$

by Ch. I. (207).

(iii) To find the expansion of y^p in powers of x, if

$$y=\sum_{n=0}^{\infty}(3n+1)x^{3n}, \quad |x|<1, \tag{16}$$

we have
$$\int_0^x y\,dx = \frac{x}{1-x^3}, \tag{17}$$

from which
$$y^p = \frac{(1+2x^3)^p}{(1-x^3)^{2p}}. \tag{18}$$

Now
$$\frac{d^n y^p}{dx^n} = \sum_{k=0}^{n} \binom{n}{k} \frac{d^{n-k}}{dx^{n-k}} (1+2x^3)^p \frac{d^k}{dx^k} (1-x^3)^{-2p}. \tag{19}$$

But
$$\frac{d^{n-k}}{dx^{n-k}}(1+2x^3)^p = (n-k)! \sum_{\alpha=0}^{n-k} (-1)^\alpha \binom{p}{\alpha} 2^\alpha \sum_{\beta=0}^{\alpha} (-1)^\beta \binom{\alpha}{\beta}\binom{3\beta}{n-k} x^{3\alpha-n+k}(1+2x^3)^{p-\alpha} \tag{20}$$

and
$$\frac{d^k}{dx^k}(1-x^3)^{-2p} = k! \sum_{\alpha_1=0}^{k} \binom{-2p}{\alpha_1} \sum_{\beta_1=0}^{\alpha_1} (-1)^{\beta_1} \binom{\alpha_1}{\beta_1}\binom{3\beta_1}{k} \frac{x^{3\alpha_1-k}}{(1-x^3)^{2p+\alpha_1}}. \tag{21}$$

Applying (19) and (20) to (18), we have
$$\left.\frac{d^n y^p}{dx^n}\right]_{x=0} = 0, \text{ except when } 3\alpha - n + k + 3\alpha_1 - k = 0. \tag{22}$$

We shall now show that
$$3\alpha - n + k = 0 \quad \text{and} \quad 3\alpha_1 - k = 0. \tag{23}$$

Let $3\alpha - n + k > 0$; then from (22) $3\alpha_1 - k < 0$ and $3\alpha_1 < k$, and since from $\binom{\alpha_1}{\beta_1}$, $\alpha_1 \geqq \beta_1$, $3\beta_1 < k$, which is not tenable, since from $\binom{3\beta_1}{k}$, $3\beta_1 \geqq k$.

In a similar way it can be shown that the assumption $3\alpha - n + k < 0$ is not valid, and the equations (23) hold.

Now, from $\binom{\alpha}{\beta}$, $\alpha \geqq \beta$, and from $\binom{3\beta}{n-k}$, $3\beta \geqq n-k$; hence $3\alpha \geqq 3\beta \geqq n-k$. But $3\alpha = n-k$; therefore $\beta = \alpha$. Similarly $\beta_1 = \alpha_1$.

And we obtain
$$\left.\frac{d^n y^p}{dx^n}\right]_{x=0} = n! \sum_{k=0}^{n} \sum_{\alpha=0}^{n-k} 2^\alpha \binom{p}{\alpha} \sum_{\alpha_1=0}^{k} (-1)^{\alpha_1} \binom{-2p}{\alpha_1}. \tag{24}$$

But $\alpha = \dfrac{n-k}{3}$ and $\alpha_1 = \dfrac{k}{3}$; n and k must therefore be multiples of 3, and (24) becomes
$$\left.\frac{d^n y^p}{dx^n}\right]_{x=0} = (3n)! \sum_{k=0}^{n} (-1)^k 2^{n-k} \binom{p}{n-k}\binom{-p}{2k}, \tag{25}$$

and we finally obtain
$$y^p = \sum_{n=0}^{\infty} x^{3n} \sum_{k=0}^{n} (-1)^k 2^{n-k} \binom{p}{n-k}\binom{-2p}{k}. \tag{26}$$

The above result can also be obtained by means of the Binomial Theorem.

(iv) To find the expansion of y^p in powers of x, if

$$y=\sum_{n=0}^{\infty}(-1)^{n-1}\frac{x^{2n+1}}{(2n+1)!}2^{2n+1}\sum_{k=1}^{2n+1}\frac{1}{2^k}\sum_{a=1}^{k}(-1)^a\binom{k}{a}a^{2n+1}. \tag{27}$$

Let $$S=\sum_{k=1}^{2n+1}\frac{1}{2^k}S_1, \tag{28}$$

where $$S_1=\sum_{a=1}^{k}(-1)^a\binom{k}{a}a^{2n+1}=\frac{d^{2n+1}}{dx^{2n+1}}(1-e^x)^k\Big]_{x=0};$$

and since $S_1=0$, if $k>2n+1$ by Ch. I. (136), therefore

$$S=\sum_{k=1}^{\infty}\frac{d^{2n+1}}{dx^{2n+1}}\left(\frac{1-e^x}{2}\right)^k\Big]_{x=0}=\frac{d^{2n+1}}{dx^{2n+1}}\frac{1-e^x}{1+e^x}\Big]_{x=0}$$

$$=\frac{d^{2n+1}}{dx^{2n+1}}\frac{e^{-\frac{x}{2}}-e^{\frac{x}{2}}}{e^{-\frac{x}{2}}+e^{\frac{x}{2}}}\Big]_{x=0}=-\frac{1}{2^{2n+1}}\frac{d^{2n+1}}{dx^{2n+1}}\frac{e^x-e^{-x}}{e^x+e^{-x}}\Big]_{x=0}. \tag{29}$$

Then, by means of (28) and (29), we obtain from (27),

$$y=\sum_{n=0}^{\infty}-i^{2n+2}\frac{d^{2n+1}}{dx^{2n+1}}\frac{e^x-e^{-x}}{e^x+e^{-x}}\Big]_{x=0}\frac{x^{2n+1}}{(2n+1)!} \tag{30}$$

$$=\sum_{n=0}^{\infty}\frac{d^{2n+1}}{dx^{2n+1}}\frac{e^{ix}-e^{-ix}}{i(e^{ix}+e^{-ix})}\Big]_{x=0}\frac{x^{2n+1}}{(2n+1)!}$$

$$=\sum_{n=0}^{\infty}\frac{d^{2n+1}}{dx^{2n+1}}\tan x\Big]_{x=0}\frac{x^{2n+1}}{(2n+1)!}=\tan x, \tag{31}$$

and from Ch. IV. 5 the expansion of $\tan^p x$ in powers of x.

2. Let $$y=\sum_{n=0}^{\infty}A_{1,n}x^n, \tag{32}$$

where the A's are free of x, be a series which converges for certain values of x.

To find the expansion of y^p in powers of x, p being a positive integer.

Now $$y^2=\sum_{n_1=0}^{\infty}A_{1,n_1}x^{n_1}\sum_{n=0}^{\infty}A_{1,n}x^n. \tag{33}$$

Letting $n+n_1=n'$, then

$$y^2=\sum_{n_1=0}^{\infty}A_{1,n_1}\sum_{n=n_1}^{\infty}A_{1,n-n_1}x^n \tag{34}$$

$$=\sum_{n=0}^{\infty}x^n\sum_{n_1=0}^{n}A_{1,n_1}A_{1,n-n_1}, \text{ by Ch. I. (97)},$$

$$=\sum_{n=0}^{\infty}A_{2,n}x^n, \text{ where } A_{2,n}=\sum_{n_1=0}^{n}A_{1,n-n_1}A_{1,n_1}. \tag{35}$$

Next $$y^3=\sum_{n_1=0}^{\infty} A_{2,n_1}x^{n_1}\sum_{n=0}^{\infty} A_{1,n}x^n \tag{36}$$

$$=\sum_{n_1=0}^{\infty} A_{2,n_1}\sum_{n=n_1}^{\infty} A_{1,n-n_1}x^n$$

$$=\sum_{n=0}^{\infty} x^n\sum_{n_1=0}^{n} A_{1,n-n_1}A_{2,n_1}$$

$$=\sum_{n=0}^{\infty} A_{3,n}x^n, \text{ where } A_{3,n}=\sum_{n_1=0}^{n} A_{1,n-n_1}A_{2,n_1}. \tag{37}$$

We now assume

$$y^p=\sum_{n=0}^{\infty} A_{p,n}x^n, \text{ where } A_{p,n}=\sum_{n_1=0}^{n} A_{1,n-n_1}A_{p-1,n_1}, \tag{38}$$

and shall show that this form holds also for the expansion of y^{p+1}.

From (38) we have

$$y^{p+1}=\sum_{n_1=0}^{\infty} A_{p,n_1}x^{n_1}\sum_{n=0}^{\infty} A_{1,n}x^n \tag{39}$$

$$=\sum_{n_1=0}^{\infty} A_{p,n_1}\sum_{n=n_1}^{\infty} A_{1,n-n_1}x^n$$

$$=\sum_{n=0}^{\infty} x^n\sum_{n_1=0}^{n} A_{1,n-n_1}A_{p,n_1}$$

$$=\sum_{n=0}^{\infty} A_{p+1,n}x^n, \text{ where } A_{p+1,n}=\sum_{n_1=0}^{n} A_{1,n-n_1}A_{p,n_1}, \tag{40}$$

which shows that $A_{p+1,n}$ is of the same form as $A_{p,n}$.

We shall now express A_p in terms of A_1's.

Using (38) as a recurring formula, we have

$$A_{p,n}=\sum_{n_1=0}^{n} A_{1,n-n_1}\sum_{n_2=0}^{n_1} A_{1,n_1-n_2}A_{p-2,n_1} \tag{41}$$

$$=\sum_{n_1=0}^{n} A_{1,n-n_1}\sum_{n_2=0}^{n_1} A_{1,n_1-n_2}\sum_{n_3=0}^{n_2} A_{1,n_2-n_3}A_{p-3,n_3}$$

$$=\sum_{n_1=0}^{n} A_{1,n-n_1}\sum_{n_2=0}^{n_1} A_{1,n_1-n_2}\cdots\sum_{n_{p-1}=0}^{n_{p-2}} A_{1,n_{p-2}-n_{p-1}}A_{1,n_{p-1}}$$

$$=\prod_{k=1}^{p-1}\left(\sum_{n_k=0}^{n_{k-1}} A_{1,n_{k-1}-n_k}\right)A_{1,p-1},\quad n_0=n. \tag{42}$$

By means of (42), we find

$$(2-3x+5x^2-4x^3+7x^4)^5=32-240x+1120x^2-3800x^3+\dots.$$

(i) To find the expansion of $(\tan^{-1}x)^p$ in powers of x.

Now $$\tan^{-1}x=\sum_{n=0}^{\infty}(-1)^n\frac{x^{2n+1}}{2n+1}=x\sum_{n=0}^{\infty}(-1)^n\frac{(x^2)^n}{2n+1} \tag{43}$$

and $$A_{1,m}=\frac{(-1)^m}{2m+1}.$$

Therefore

$$(\tan^{-1}x)^p = x^p \sum_{n=0}^{\infty} x^{2n} \prod_{k=1}^{p-1} \left(\sum_{n_k=0}^{n_{k-1}} \frac{(-1)^{n_{k-1}-n_k}}{2n_{k-1}-2n_k+1} \right) \frac{(-1)^{n_{p-1}}}{2n_{p-1}+1}$$

$$= \sum_{n=0}^{\infty} (-1)^n x^{2n+p} \prod_{k=1}^{p-1} \left(\sum_{n_k=0}^{n_{k-1}} \frac{1}{2n_{k-1}-2n_k+1} \right) \frac{1}{2n_{p-1}+1}. \tag{44}$$

Ex. $$(\tan^{-1}x)^5 = x^5 - \tfrac{5}{3}x^7 + \tfrac{19}{9}x^9 - \tfrac{457}{189}x^{11} + \dots .$$

(ii) To expand $(\sin^{-1}x)^p$ in powers of x.

Now $$\sin^{-1}x = \sum_{n=0}^{\infty} (-1)^n \binom{-\frac{1}{2}}{n} \frac{x^{2n+1}}{2n+1}$$

$$= x \sum_{n=0}^{\infty} \frac{1}{4^n(2n+1)} \binom{2n}{n} (x^2)^n ; \tag{45}$$

then $$A_{1,m} = \frac{1}{4^m(2m+1)} \binom{2m}{m}$$

and $$(\sin^{-1}x)^p = \sum_{n=0}^{\infty} x^{2n+p} \prod_{k=1}^{p-1} \left[\sum_{n_k=0}^{n_{k-1}} \frac{1}{2^{2(n_{k-1}-n_k)}(2n_{k-1}-2n_k+1)} \binom{2n_{k-1}-n_k}{n_{k-1}-n_k} \right.$$

$$\left. \frac{1}{2^{2n_{p-1}}(2n_{p-1}+1)} \binom{2n_{p-1}}{n_{p-1}} \right]. \tag{46}$$

The following method for obtaining the expansion of $(\sin^{-1}x)^p$ is due to Cauchy.

Expanding $\sin mx$ and $\cos mx$ in powers of $\sin x$*, we have

$$\sin mx = m \sum_{n=0}^{\infty} (-1)^n \prod_{k=1}^{n} (m^2 - \overline{2k-1}^2) \frac{\sin^{2n+1}x}{(2n+1)!}, \tag{47}$$

where $$\left. \prod_{k=1}^{n} (m^2 - \overline{2k-1}^2) \right]_{n=0} = 1,$$

and $$\cos mx = \sum_{n=0}^{\infty} (-1)^n \prod_{k=0}^{n-1} (m^2 - \overline{2k}^2) \frac{\sin^{2n}x}{(2n)!}, \tag{48}$$

where $$\left. \prod_{k=0}^{n-1} (m^2 - \overline{2k}^2) \right]_{n=0} = 1.$$

$$-\tfrac{1}{2}\pi < x < \tfrac{1}{2}\pi \text{ for all values of } m.$$

The results (47) and (48) can also be obtained by means of some of the methods given before.

To derive (48), we have

$$\cos m\theta = \sum_{k=0}^{[\frac{m}{2}]} (-1)^k \binom{m}{2k} \cos^{m-2k}\theta \sin^{2k}\theta.$$

Now, if m is even,

$$\cos^{m-2k}\theta = (1-\sin^2\theta)^{\frac{m}{2}-k} = \sum_{a=0}^{\frac{m}{2}-k} (-1)^a \binom{\frac{m}{2}-k}{a} \sin^{2a}\theta ;$$

therefore $$\cos m\theta = \sum_{k=0}^{\frac{m}{2}} (-1)^k \binom{m}{2k} \sum_{a=0}^{\frac{m}{2}-k} (-1)^a \binom{\frac{m}{2}-k}{a} \sin^{2k+2a}\theta.$$

* Hobson, *A Treatise on Plane Trigonometry*, p. 105 and p. 265.

But
$$\sin mx = \sum_{n=0}^{\infty} (-1)^n \frac{(mx)^{2n+1}}{(2n+1)!} \tag{49}$$

and
$$\cos mx = \sum_{n=0}^{\infty} (-1)^n \frac{(mx)^{2n}}{(2n)!}. \tag{50}$$

Equating coefficients of equal powers of m in (42) and (49) and in (48) and (50), we obtain

$$\sin^{-1}x = \sum_{n=0}^{\infty} \frac{\prod_{k=1}^{n-1}(2k+1)}{2^n n!} \frac{x^{2n+1}}{2n+1}, \tag{51}$$

Letting $k+\alpha=n$, then

$$\cos m\theta = \sum_{k=0}^{\frac{m}{2}} \binom{m}{2k} \sum_{n=k}^{\frac{m}{2}} (-1)^n \binom{\frac{m}{2}-k}{n-k} \sin^{2n}\theta$$

$$= \sum_{n=0}^{\frac{m}{2}} (-1)^n \sum_{k=0}^{n} \binom{m}{2k} \binom{\frac{m}{2}-k}{n-k} \sin^{2n}\theta. \tag{a}$$

Denoting the coefficient of $\sin^{2n}\theta$ by S, then

$$S = (-1)^n \sum_{k=0}^{n} \binom{m}{2k} \binom{\frac{m}{2}-k}{n-k}.$$

Now $\binom{m}{2k} = \frac{1}{2^k k!} \frac{\prod_{\alpha=0}^{2k-1}(m-\alpha)}{\prod_{\alpha=0}^{k-1}(2\alpha+1)} = \frac{1}{2^k k!} \frac{\prod_{\alpha=0}^{k-1}(m-2\alpha)\prod_{\alpha=0}^{k-1}(m-2\alpha-1)}{\prod_{\alpha=0}^{k-1}(2\alpha+1)}$, $(2k)! = 2^k k! \prod_{\alpha=0}^{k-1}(2\alpha+1)$.

Also
$$\binom{\frac{m}{2}-k}{n-k} = \frac{1}{(n-k)!} \prod_{\alpha=0}^{n-k-1} \left(\frac{m}{2}-k-\alpha\right)$$

$$= \frac{1}{2^{n-k}(n-k)!} \prod_{\alpha=k}^{n-1} (m-2\alpha), \text{ after letting } k+\alpha=\alpha'.$$

Denoting $\binom{m}{2k}\binom{\frac{m}{2}-k}{n-k}$ by P, then $P = \frac{\prod_{\alpha=0}^{n-1}(m-2\alpha)\prod_{\alpha=0}^{k-1}(m-2\alpha+1)}{2^n k!(n-k)!\prod_{\alpha=0}^{k-1}(2\alpha+1)}$.

Multiplying the numerator and the denominator of P by $\prod_{\alpha=k}^{n-1}(2\alpha+1)$, we have

$$P = \prod_{\alpha=0}^{n-1} \frac{m-2\alpha}{2\alpha+1} \frac{\prod_{\alpha=0}^{k-1}(m-2\alpha-1)\prod_{\alpha=k}^{n-1}(2\alpha+1)}{2^n k!(n-k)!}.$$

But $\frac{1}{k!}\prod_{\alpha=0}^{k-1}(m-2\alpha-1) = 2^k \binom{\frac{m-1}{2}}{k}$ and $\frac{1}{2^n(n-k)!}\prod_{\alpha=k}^{n-1}(2\alpha+1) = \frac{1}{2^k}\binom{\frac{2n-1}{2}}{n-k}$.

Hence
$$P = \left(\prod_{\alpha=0}^{n-1} \frac{m-2\alpha}{2\alpha+1}\right) \binom{\frac{2n-1}{2}}{n-k} \binom{\frac{m-1}{2}}{k},$$

and
$$S = (-1)^n \left(\prod_{\alpha=0}^{n-1} \frac{m-2\alpha}{2\alpha+1}\right) \sum_{k=0}^{n} \binom{\frac{2n-1}{2}}{n-k} \binom{\frac{m-1}{2}}{k}.$$

where for $n=0$ and $n=1$, $\prod_{k=1}^{n-1}(2k+1)=1$;

$$(\sin^{-1}x)^2=2!\sum_{n=1}^{\infty}\frac{2^{n-1}(n-1)!}{\prod_{k=0}^{n-1}(2k+1)}\frac{x^{2n}}{2n}; \tag{52}$$

$$(\sin^{-1}x)^3=3!\sum_{n=1}^{\infty}\frac{\prod_{k=1}^{n-1}(2k+1)}{2^n n!}\sum_{a=1}^{n}\frac{1}{(2a-1)^2}\frac{x^{2n+1}}{2n+1}, \tag{53}$$

Denoting the summation on the right by S_1,

then
$$S_1=\sum_{k=0}^{n}((x^{n-k}))(1+x)^{\frac{2n-1}{2}}((x^k))(1+x)^{\frac{m-1}{2}}$$
$$=((x^n))(1+x)^{\frac{m+2n-2}{2}}=\binom{\frac{m+2n-2}{2}}{n}=\frac{1}{2^n n!}\prod_{k=0}^{n-1}(m+2k),$$

and
$$S=\frac{(-1)^n}{(2n)!}\prod_{k=0}^{n-1}(m-2k)\prod_{k=0}^{n-1}(m+2k)=\frac{(-1)^n}{(2n)!}\prod_{k=0}^{n-1}(m^2-\overline{2k}^2). \tag{b}$$

Similarly when m is odd, etc.
The result (b) can also be obtained in the following way.
Letting $n-k=k'$ in the coefficient of $(-1)^n\sin^{2n}\theta$ in (a), then

$$S_2=\sum_{k=0}^{n}\binom{m}{2n-2k}\binom{\frac{m}{2}-n+k}{k}$$
$$=\sum_{k=0}^{n}((x^{2n-2k}))(1+x)^m((x^{2k}))(1-x^2)^{-\left(\frac{m}{2}-n+1\right)}$$
$$=((x^{2n}))(1+x)^{\frac{m}{2}+n-1}(1-x)^{-\left(\frac{m}{2}-n+1\right)}=((x^{2n}))S_3.$$

We then have
$$S_3=\sum_{\alpha=0}^{\frac{m}{2}+n-1}\binom{\frac{m}{2}+n-1}{\alpha}x^\alpha\sum_{\beta=0}^{\infty}\binom{\frac{m}{2}-n+\beta}{\beta}x^\beta.$$

Letting $\alpha+\beta=\beta'$,
$$S_3=\sum_{\alpha=0}^{\frac{m}{2}+n-1}\binom{\frac{m}{2}+n-1}{\alpha}\sum_{\beta=\alpha}^{\infty}\binom{\frac{m}{2}-n+\beta-\alpha}{\beta-\alpha}x^\beta$$
$$=\sum_{\beta=0}^{\frac{m}{2}+n-1}x^\beta\sum_{\alpha=0}^{\beta}\binom{\frac{m}{2}+n-1}{\alpha}\binom{\frac{m}{2}-n+\beta-\alpha}{\beta-\alpha},$$

and
$$((x^{2n}))S_3=\sum_{\alpha=0}^{2n}\binom{\frac{m}{2}+n-1}{\alpha}\binom{\frac{m}{2}+n-\alpha}{2n-\alpha}=\sum_{\alpha=0}^{2n}P_1P_2.$$

Now $P_1=\frac{1}{\alpha!}\prod_{k=0}^{\alpha-1}\left(\frac{m}{2}+n-1-k\right)$ and $P_2=\frac{1}{\left(\frac{m}{2}-n\right)!}\prod_{k=0}^{\frac{m}{2}-n-1}\left(\frac{m}{2}+n-\alpha-k\right)$;

hence
$$P_1P_2=\frac{\frac{m}{2}+n-\alpha}{\left(\frac{m}{2}-n\right)!\,\alpha!\left(\frac{m}{2}+n\right)}\prod_{k=0}^{\frac{m}{2}-n+\alpha-1}\left(\frac{m}{2}+n-k\right)=\frac{\left(\frac{m}{2}+n\right)!\,\frac{m}{2}+n-\alpha}{\left(\frac{m}{2}-n\right)!\,\alpha!\,(2n-\alpha)!\left(\frac{m}{2}+n\right)}.$$

where $$\prod_{k=1}^{n-1}(2k+1)\Big]_{n=1}=1;$$

$$(\sin^{-1}x)^4=4!\sum_{n=2}^{\infty}\frac{2^{n-2}(n-1)!}{\prod\limits_{k=1}^{n-1}(2k+1)}\sum_{\alpha=1}^{n-1}\frac{1}{\alpha^2}\frac{x^{2n}}{4n};\tag{54}$$

$$(\sin^{-1}x)^5=5!\sum_{n=2}^{\infty}\frac{\prod\limits_{k=1}^{n-1}(2k+1)}{2^n n!}S_2\frac{x^{2n+1}}{2n+1},\tag{55}$$

where S_2 denotes the sum of the products of $\frac{1}{1^2}, \frac{1}{3^2}, \cdots \frac{1}{(2n-1)^2}$ taken two at a time.

And since $$\frac{\left(\frac{m}{2}+n\right)!}{\left(\frac{m}{2}-n\right)!}=\binom{\frac{m}{2}+n}{2n}(2n)! \quad\text{and}\quad \frac{(2n)!}{\alpha!(2n-\alpha)!}=\binom{2n}{\alpha},$$

therefore $$P_1P_2=\binom{\frac{m}{2}+n}{2n}\binom{2n}{\alpha}\left(1-\frac{2\alpha}{m+2n}\right),$$

and $$((x^{2n}))S_3=\binom{\frac{m}{2}+n}{2n}\sum_{\alpha=0}^{2n}\binom{2n}{\alpha}\left(1-\frac{2\alpha}{m+2n}\right)=\binom{\frac{m}{2}+n}{2n}\left[2^{2n}-\frac{4n}{m+2n}2^{2n-1}\right]$$

$$=2^{2n}\frac{m}{m+2n}\binom{\frac{m}{2}+n}{2n}=\frac{m}{(2n)!}\prod_{k=1}^{2n-1}(m+2n-2k)$$

$$=\frac{m}{(2n)!}\prod_{k=1}^{n-1}(m+2n-2k)\Big[(m+2n-2k)\Big]_{k=n}\prod_{k=n+1}^{2n-1}(m+2n-2k).$$

Letting $2n-k=k'$ in the second product, then

$$((x^{2n}))S_3=\frac{m^2}{(2n)!}\prod_{k=1}^{n-1}[(m+2n-2k)(m-2n+2k)];$$

and letting $n-k=k'$, we obtain

$$((x^{2n}))S_3=\frac{m^2}{(2n)!}\prod_{k=1}^{n-1}(m^2-\overline{2k}^2)=\frac{1}{(2n)!}\prod_{k=0}^{n-1}(m^2-\overline{2k}^2).$$

In connection with the above we shall show that

$$\sin m\theta=\sum_{k=0}^{\left[\frac{m-1}{2}\right]}(-1)^k\binom{m-k-1}{k}2^{m-2k-1}\cos^{m-2k-1}\theta.$$

Now $$\sin m\theta=\sum_{n=0}^{\left[\frac{m-1}{2}\right]}(-1)^n\binom{m}{2n+1}\cos^{m-2n-1}\theta\sin^{2n+1}\theta$$

$$=\sin\theta\sum_{n=0}^{\left[\frac{m-1}{2}\right]}(-1)^n\binom{m}{2n+1}\sum_{k=0}^{n}(-1)^k\binom{n}{k}\cos^{m-2n+2k-1}\theta, \text{ letting } n-k=k',$$

$$=\sin\theta\sum_{n=0}^{\left[\frac{m-1}{2}\right]}\binom{m}{2n+1}\sum_{k=0}^{n}(-1)^k\binom{n}{k}\cos^{m-2k-1}\theta$$

$$=\sin\theta\sum_{k=0}^{\left[\frac{m-1}{2}\right]}(-1)^k\cos^{m-2k-1}\theta\sum_{n=k}^{\left[\frac{m-1}{2}\right]}\binom{m}{2n+1}\binom{n}{k}.$$

(iii) To expand $(\sec^{-1}x)^p$ in powers of $\frac{1}{x}$.

Now
$$\sec^{-1}x=\sum_{n=0}^{\infty}(-1)^{n+1}\binom{-\frac{1}{2}}{n}\frac{1}{2n+1}\frac{1}{x^{2n+1}}$$

$$=-\frac{1}{x}\sum_{n=0}^{\infty}\frac{1}{2^{2n}(2n+1)}\binom{2n}{n}\frac{1}{(x^2)^n}; \tag{56}$$

then
$$(\sec^{-1}x)^p=(-1)^p\sum_{n=0}^{\infty}\frac{1}{x^{2n+p}}\prod_{k=1}^{p-1}P_{n_k}, \tag{57}$$

where P_{n_k} is the expression following the product sign in (46).

If in $S=\sum_{n=k}^{\left[\frac{m-1}{2}\right]}\binom{m}{2n+1}\binom{n}{k}$ we let $n-k=n'$, then

$$S=\sum_{n=0}^{\left[\frac{m-1}{2}\right]-k}\binom{m}{2n+2k+1}\binom{n+k}{k}=\sum_{n=0}^{\left[\frac{m-1}{2}\right]-k}((x^{2n+2k+1}))(1+x)^m((x^{-2k}))(1-x^{-2})^{-(k+1)}$$
$$=((x^k))(1+x)^{m-k-1}(1-x^{-1})^{-(k+1)}=((x^k))P.$$

Now $P=\sum_{n=0}^{m-k-1}\binom{m-k-1}{n}x^{m-k-1-n}\sum_{a=0}^{\infty}\binom{k+a}{a}x^{-a}$, letting $n+a=a'$,

$$=\sum_{n=0}^{m-k-1}\binom{m-k-1}{n}\sum_{a=n}^{\infty}\binom{k+a-n}{a-n}x^{m-k-1-a}$$
$$=\sum_{a=0}^{m-k-1}\sum_{n=0}^{a}\binom{m-k-1}{n}\binom{k+a-n}{a-n}x^{m-k-1-a};$$

and if we let $a=m-2k-1$, we have

$$((x^k))P=\sum_{n=0}^{m-2k-1}\binom{m-k-1}{n}\binom{m-k-n-1}{k}=\sum_{n=0}^{m-2k-1}\binom{m-k-1}{n+k}\binom{n+k}{k}$$
$$=\binom{m-k-1}{k}\sum_{n=0}^{m-2k-1}\binom{m-2k-1}{n}=\binom{m-k-1}{k}2^{m-2k-1}, \text{ by Ch. I. (207).}$$

In this way the desired result is obtained. In a similar manner

$$\cos m\theta=\sum_{k=0}^{\left[\frac{m}{2}\right]}(-1)^k\binom{m-k-1}{k}\frac{m}{m-2k}2^{m-2k-1}\cos^{m-2k}\theta.$$

CHAPTER VIII.

SEPARATION OF FRACTIONS INTO PARTIAL FRACTIONS.

We shall in this chapter consider the separation of certain fractions into partial fractions. As a rule the coefficients are obtained in form of determinants, while the methods used here render them as single or double summations.

1. (i) To separate

$$F(x)=\frac{f_1(x)}{f_2(x)}=\frac{\sum\limits_{a=0}^{n} m_a x^{n-a}}{\prod\limits_{k=0}^{p}(x+kh)}, \quad p>n, \tag{1}$$

into partial fractions.

Let

$$F(x)=\sum_{k=0}^{p}\frac{A_k}{x+kh}; \tag{2}$$

then

$$A_k=(x+kh)\frac{f_1(x)}{f_2(x)}\Bigg]_{x=-kh}$$

$$=\frac{f_1(x)}{\prod\limits_{a_1=0}^{k-1}(x+a_1h)\prod\limits_{a_2=k+1}^{p}(x+a_2h)}\Bigg]_{x=-kh}, \tag{3}$$

where, when $k=0$, the first product in the denominator is 1, and when $k=p$, the second product is 1.

We then obtain

$$A_k=\frac{(-1)^k f_1(-kh)}{k!\,h^p(p-k)!}, \tag{4}$$

and

$$F(x)=\frac{m_n}{p!\,h^p}\frac{1}{x}+\frac{(-1)^n}{p!\,h^{p-n}}\sum_{k=1}^{p}(-1)^k\binom{p}{k}k^n\sum_{a=0}^{n}(-1)^a\frac{m_a}{(kh)^a}\frac{1}{x+kh}$$

$$=\frac{1}{p!\,h^p}\left[\frac{m_n}{x}+\sum_{k=0}^{p}(-1)^k\binom{p}{k}\sum_{a=0}^{n}(-1)^a m_{n-a}(kh)^a\frac{1}{x+kh}\right]. \tag{5}$$

In a similar way we find

(ii)
$$\frac{1}{\prod\limits_{k=1}^{n}(x+k)}=\frac{1}{(n-1)!}\sum_{k=1}^{n}(-1)^{k-1}\binom{n-1}{k-1}\frac{1}{x+k}$$

and

$$\frac{1}{\prod\limits_{k=0}^{n}(x+k)}=\frac{1}{n!}\sum_{k=0}^{n}(-1)^k\binom{n}{k}\frac{1}{x+k}. \tag{6}$$

$$\text{(iii)}\quad \frac{\prod_{k=1}^{p_1}(x+kg)}{\prod_{k=1}^{p_2}(x+kh)}=\frac{1}{(p_2-1)!\,h^{p_2-1}}\sum_{n=1}^{p_2}(-1)^{n-1}\binom{p_2-1}{n-1}\prod_{k=1}^{p_1}(kg-nh)\frac{1}{x+nh},\qquad p_2>p_1. \quad (7)$$

$$\text{(iv)}\quad \frac{\sum_{a=0}^{n} m_a x^{n-a}}{\prod_{k=1}^{p}(x+h_k)}=(-1)^n\sum_{k=1}^{p}\frac{\sum_{a=0}^{n}(-1)^a m_a h_k{}^{n-a}}{\prod_{a_1=1}^{k-1}(-h_k+h_{a_1})\prod_{a_2=k+1}^{p}(-h_k+h_{a_2})}\frac{1}{x+h_k},\qquad p>n. \quad (8)$$

2. To separate into partial fractions

$$F(x)=\frac{\sum_{k=0}^{n} m_k x^{n-k}}{(x+a)^p}. \quad (9)$$

(i) By division.

Dividing the numerator and the denominator of $F(x)$ by $x+a$, we obtain

$$F(x)=\frac{\sum_{k=0}^{n-1} Q_{1,k}x^{n-1-k}}{(x+a)^{p-1}}+\frac{R_1}{(x+a)^p}=F_1(x)+\frac{R_1}{(x+a)^p}. \quad (10)$$

Clearing (10) of fractions and equating in the result coefficients of like powers of x, we have

$$m_k=Q_{1,k}+aQ_{1,k-1},\quad k=1,2,3,\ldots,\quad n-1. \quad (11)$$

$$Q_{1,0}=m_0,$$

$$R_1=m_n-aQ_{1,n-1}. \quad (12)$$

If we now write in $\qquad Q_{1,k}=m_k-aQ_{1,k-1}, \qquad$ (13)

$k-1,\ k-2,\ldots,2,\ 1$ for k, multiplying the resulting relations by

$$-a,\quad (-a)^2,\ \ldots,\ (-a)^{k-2},\quad (-a)^{k-1}$$

and add the equations thus obtained, we have

$$\sum_{\beta=0}^{k-1}(-1)^\beta a^\beta Q_{1,k-\beta}=\sum_{\beta=0}^{k-1}(-1)^\beta a^\beta m_{k-\beta}+\sum_{\beta=1}^{k}(-1)^\beta a^\beta Q_{1,k-\beta}. \quad (14)$$

Cancelling terms gives

$$Q_{1,k}=\sum_{\beta=0}^{k}(-1)^{k-\beta}a^{k-\beta}m_\beta=\sum_{\beta=0}^{k}(-1)^\beta a^\beta m_{k-\beta}, \quad (15)$$

and

$$R_1=\sum_{\beta=0}^{n}(-1)^{n-\beta}a^{n-\beta}m_\beta=\sum_{\beta=0}^{n}(-1)^\beta a^\beta m_{n-\beta}. \quad (16)$$

Dividing now the numerator and the denominator of

$$F_1(x)=\frac{\sum_{k=0}^{n-1} Q_{1,k}x^{n-1-k}}{(x+a)^{p-1}}$$

by $x+a$, we obtain

$$F_1(x)=\frac{\sum_{k=0}^{n-2} Q_{2,k}x^{n-2-k}}{(x+a)^{p-2}}+\frac{R_2}{(x+a)^{p-1}}=F_2(x)+\frac{R_2}{(x+a)^{p-1}}, \tag{17}$$

from which

$$\begin{aligned} Q_{2,k}&=Q_{1,k}-aQ_{2,k-1}\\ &=\sum_{\beta=0}^{k}(-1)^{k-\beta}a^{k-\beta}Q_{1,\beta}\\ &=\sum_{\beta=0}^{k}(-1)^{\beta}a^{\beta}Q_{1,k-\beta}. \end{aligned} \tag{18}$$

It is evident that R_2 is formed in the same manner as $Q_{2,n-1}$, if it existed, and

$$R_2=Q_{2,n-1}. \tag{19}$$

Applying (15) to (18), we obtain

$$\begin{aligned} Q_{2,k}&=\sum_{\beta=0}^{k}(-1)^{k-\beta}a^{k-\beta}\sum_{\gamma=0}^{\beta}(-1)^{\beta-\gamma}a^{\beta-\gamma}m_\gamma\\ &=\sum_{\gamma=0}^{k}(-1)^{k-\gamma}a^{k-\gamma}m_\gamma(k-\gamma+1)\\ &=\sum_{\beta=0}^{k}(-1)^{k-\beta}a^{k-\beta}\binom{k-\beta+1}{1}m_\beta\\ &=\sum_{\beta=0}^{k}(-1)^{\beta}a^{\beta}\binom{\beta+1}{1}m_{k-\beta} \end{aligned} \tag{20}$$

and

$$\begin{aligned} R_2&=(-1)^{n-1}\sum_{\beta=0}^{n-1}(-1)^{\beta}a^{n-1-\beta}\binom{\beta+1}{1}m_\beta\\ &=\sum_{\beta=0}^{n-1}(-1)^{\beta}a^{\beta}\binom{n-\beta}{1}m_{n-1-\beta}. \end{aligned} \tag{21}$$

Dividing next numerator and denominator of

$$F_2(x)=\frac{\sum_{k=0}^{n-2} Q_{2,k}x^{n-2-k}}{(x+a)^{p-2}}$$

by $x+a$, we have

$$F_2(x)=\frac{\sum_{k=0}^{n-3} Q_{3,k}x^{n-3-k}}{(x+a)^{p-3}}+\frac{R_3}{(x+a)^{p-2}}=F_3(x)+\frac{R_3}{(x+a)^{p-2}}, \tag{22}$$

from which we obtain

$$\begin{aligned} Q_{3,k}&=\sum_{\beta=0}^{k}(-1)^{k-\beta}a^{k-\beta}\binom{k-\beta+2}{2}m_\beta\\ &=\sum_{\beta=0}^{k}(-1)^{\beta}a^{\beta}\binom{\beta+2}{2}m_{k-\beta} \end{aligned} \tag{23}$$

and
$$R_3 = Q_{3,\,n-2} = (-1)^{n-2} \sum_{\beta=0}^{n-2} (-1)^\beta a^{n-2-\beta} \binom{\beta+2}{2} m_\beta$$
$$= \sum_{\beta=0}^{n-2} (-1)^\beta a^\beta \binom{n-\beta}{2} m_{n-2-\beta}. \tag{24}$$

We now assume
$$Q_{h,\,k} = \sum_{\beta=0}^{k} (-1)^{k-\beta} a^{k-\beta} \binom{k-\beta+h-1}{h-1} m_\beta$$
$$= \sum_{\beta=0}^{k} (-1)^\beta a^\beta \binom{\beta+h-1}{h-1} m^{k-\beta}, \tag{25}$$
and shall show that this form holds also for $Q_{h+1,\,k}$.

Now
$$Q_{h+1,\,k} = \sum_{\beta=0}^{k} (-1)^{k-\beta} a^{k-\beta} Q_{h,\,\beta}$$
$$= \sum_{\beta=0}^{k} (-1)^{k-\beta} a^{k-\beta} \sum_{\gamma=0}^{\beta} (-1)^{\beta-\gamma} a^{\beta-\gamma} \binom{\beta-\gamma+h-1}{h-1} m_\gamma$$
$$= \sum_{\gamma=0}^{k} (-1)^{k-\gamma} a^{k-\gamma} m_\gamma \sum_{\beta=\gamma}^{k} \binom{\beta-\gamma+h-1}{h-1}. \tag{26}$$

But
$$\sum_{\beta=\gamma}^{k} \binom{\beta-\gamma+h-1}{h-1} = ((x^{h-1})) \sum_{\beta=\gamma}^{k} (1+x)^{\beta-\gamma+h-1}$$
$$= ((x^h))\{(1+x)^{k-\gamma+h} - (1+x)^{h-1}\}$$
$$= \binom{k-\gamma+h}{h}. \tag{27}$$

Therefore
$$Q_{h+1,\,k} = \sum_{\beta=0}^{k} (-1)^{k-\beta} a^{k-\beta} \binom{k-\beta+h}{h} m_\beta$$
$$= \sum_{\beta=0}^{k} (-1)^\beta a^\beta \binom{\beta+h}{h} m_{k-\beta} \tag{28}$$

and
$$R_{h+1,\,k} = Q_{h+1,\,n-h} = \sum_{\beta=0}^{n-k} (-1)^{n-h-\beta} a^{n-h-\beta} \binom{\beta+h}{h} m_\beta$$
$$= \sum_{\beta=0}^{n-h} (-1)^\beta a^\beta \binom{n-\beta}{h} m_{n-h-\beta}. \tag{29}$$

Hence
$$F(x) = \sum_{k=0}^{n} \frac{\sum_{\beta=0}^{n-k} (-a)^{n-k-\beta} \binom{n-\beta}{k} m_\beta}{(x+a)^{p-k}}. \tag{30}$$

Letting $n-k-\beta=\beta'$, gives
$$F(x) = \sum_{k=0}^{n} \frac{\sum_{\beta=0}^{n-k} (-a)^\beta \binom{k+\beta}{\beta} m_{n-k-\beta}}{(x+a)^{p-k}}. \tag{31}$$

If $n \gtreqless p$, then the last division will be of the form

$$\sum_{k=0}^{n-p} Q_{p,k} x^{n-p-k} + \frac{R_p}{x+a},$$

where
$$Q_{p,k} = \sum_{\beta=0}^{k} (-a)^{k-\beta} \binom{k-\beta+p-1}{p-1} m_\beta$$

$$= \sum_{\beta=0}^{k} (-a)^{\beta} \binom{\beta+p-1}{\beta} m_{k-\beta}. \tag{32}$$

Therefore
$$F(x) = \sum_{k=0}^{n-p} \sum_{\beta=0}^{k} (-a)^{\beta} \binom{\beta+p-1}{\beta} m_{k-\beta} x^{n-p-k}$$

$$+ \sum_{k=0}^{p-1} \frac{\sum_{\beta=0}^{n-k} (-a)^{\beta} \binom{k+\beta}{\beta} m_{n-k-\beta}}{(x+a)^{p-k}}. \tag{33}$$

(ii) By differentiation.

Let
$$F(x) = \sum_{k=0}^{n} \frac{A_k}{(x+a)^{p-k}}; \tag{34}$$

then clearing (34) of fractions, we have

$$\sum_{k=0}^{n} m_k x^{n-k} = \sum_{k=0}^{n} A_k (x+a)^k$$

$$= \sum_{k=0}^{h-1} A_k (x+a)^k + A_h (x+a)^h + \sum_{k=h+1}^{n} A_k (x+a)^k. \tag{35}$$

Taking the hth derivative of (35) and then letting $x = -a$, we obtain

$$A_h = \frac{1}{h!} \frac{d^h}{dx^h} \sum_{k=0}^{n} m_k x^{n-k} \Big]_{x=-a} \tag{36}$$

$$= \sum_{k=0}^{n-h} (-a)^{n-k-h} \binom{n-k}{h} m_k.$$

Letting $n-k-h = \beta$, gives

$$A_h = \sum_{\beta=0}^{n-h} (-a)^{\beta} \binom{\beta+h}{\beta} m_{n-h-\beta}, \tag{37}$$

which is the same as (28).

(iii) Another method of effecting the separation of $F(x)$ into Partial Fractions is as follows:

Let $x = y - a$; then from (9),

$$F(y-a) = \frac{\sum_{k=0}^{n} m_k (y-a)^{n-k}}{y^p}$$

$$= y^{-p} \sum_{k=0}^{n} m_k \sum_{\beta=0}^{n-k} (-1)^{\beta} \binom{n-k}{\beta} a^{\beta} y^{n-k-\beta}. \tag{38}$$

Letting $k+\beta=\beta'$, (38) becomes

$$F(y-a)=\sum_{k=0}^{n} m_k \sum_{\beta=k}^{n} (-1)^{\beta-k}\binom{n-k}{\beta-k} a^{\beta-k} y^{n-p-\beta}$$

$$=\sum_{\beta=0}^{n} y^{n-p-\beta} \sum_{k=0}^{\beta} (-1)^{\beta-k} a^{\beta-k}\binom{n-k}{\beta-k} m_k. \tag{39}$$

Now if $n<p$, we may write for (39)

$$F(y-a)=\sum_{\beta=0}^{n} \frac{\sum_{k=0}^{\beta} (-1)^{\beta-k} a^{\beta-k}\binom{n-k}{\beta-k} m_k}{y^{p-(n-\beta)}}. \tag{40}$$

Letting $n-k=\beta$ and $\beta-k=\beta'$, we have

$$F(y-a)=\sum_{k=0}^{n} \frac{\sum_{\beta=0}^{n-k} (-a)^{\beta}\binom{k+\beta}{\beta} m_{n-k-\beta}}{y^{p-k}}. \tag{41}$$

Substituting $x+a$ for y gives (31).

If $n \overline{\gtrless} p$, the integral part of (9) is the quotient of

$$F_1(x)=\frac{\sum_{k=0}^{n-p} m_k x^{n-k}}{(x+a)^p}=\sum_{k=0}^{n-p} m_k \sum_{\beta=0}^{n-k} (-1)^{\beta}\binom{n-k}{\beta} a^{\beta} y^{n-p-k-\beta}. \tag{42}$$

Now the exponent of y can only be positive; therefore

$$F_1(x)=\sum_{k=0}^{n-p} m_k \sum_{\beta=0}^{n-p-k} (-1)^{\beta}\binom{n-k}{\beta} a^{\beta} y^{n-p-k-\beta}. \tag{43}$$

Denoting the second of the double summation in (43) by $F_2(x)$, and letting in it $y=x+a$, we have

$$F_2(x)=\sum_{\beta=0}^{n-p-k} (-1)^{\beta}\binom{n-k}{\beta} \sum_{\gamma=0}^{n-p-k-\beta} \binom{n-p-k-\beta}{\gamma} a^{n-p-k-\gamma} x^{\gamma};$$

and since

$$\sum_{g=0}^{m} \sum_{h=0}^{m-g} A_{g,h}=\sum_{h=0}^{m} \sum_{g=0}^{m-h} A_{g,h},$$

therefore

$$F_2(x)=\sum_{\gamma=0}^{n-p-k} a^{n-p-k-\gamma} x^{\gamma} \sum_{\beta=0}^{n-p-k-\gamma} (-1)^{\beta}\binom{n-k}{\beta}\binom{n-p-k-\beta}{\gamma}.$$

Letting $n-p-k-\gamma=\gamma'$, then

$$F_2(x)=\sum_{\gamma=0}^{n-p-k} a^{\gamma} x^{n-p-k-\gamma} \sum_{\beta=0}^{\gamma} (-1)^{\beta}\binom{n-k}{\beta}\binom{n-p-k-\beta}{n-p-k-\gamma}.$$

But

$$\binom{n-p-k-\beta}{n-p-k-\gamma}=\binom{n-p-k-\beta}{\gamma-\beta}=(-1)^{\gamma-\beta}\binom{p-n+k+\gamma-1}{\gamma-\beta};$$

hence

$$F_2(x)=\sum_{\gamma=0}^{n-p-k} (-1)^{\gamma} a^{\gamma} x^{n-p-k-\gamma} \sum_{\beta=0}^{\gamma} \binom{n-k}{\beta}\binom{p-n+k+\gamma-1}{\gamma-\beta};$$

and the value of the second of the double summation being $\binom{p+\gamma-1}{\gamma}$, we obtain

$$F_2(x)=\sum_{\gamma=0}^{n-p-k} (-1)^{\gamma}\binom{p+\gamma-1}{\gamma} a^{\gamma} x^{n-p-k-\gamma}.$$

Letting $k+\gamma=\gamma'$,

$$F_2(x)=\sum_{\gamma=k}^{n-p}(-1)^{\gamma-k}\binom{\gamma-k+p-1}{\gamma-k}a^{\gamma-k}x^{n-p-\gamma}, \tag{44}$$

and

$$F_1(x)=\sum_{k=0}^{n-p}m_k\sum_{\gamma=k}^{n-p}(-1)^{\gamma-k}\binom{\gamma-k+p-1}{\gamma-k}a^{\gamma-k}x^{n-p-\gamma}$$

$$=\sum_{\gamma=0}^{n-p}\sum_{k=0}^{\gamma}(-a)^{\gamma-k}\binom{\gamma-k+p-1}{\gamma-k}m_kx^{n-p-\gamma}. \tag{45}$$

Letting $\gamma-k=k'$,

$$F_1(x)=\sum_{\gamma=0}^{n-p}\sum_{k=0}^{\gamma}(-a)^k\binom{k+p-1}{k}m_{\gamma-k}x^{n-p-\gamma}. \tag{46}$$

Interchanging γ and k and writing β for γ, we obtain the same result as the integral part of (33).

3. To separate into Partial Fractions

$$F(x)=\frac{f(x)}{(x+a)^p}, \tag{47}$$

where $f(x)$ is a polynomial in x of higher degree than p.

Let $\phi(x)$ be the integral part of $F(x)$; we shall then show that

$$F(x)=\phi(x)+\sum_{k=0}^{p-1}\frac{f^{(k)}(-a)}{k!}\frac{1}{(x+a)^{p-k}}. \tag{48}$$

We may write

$$\frac{f(x)}{(x+a)^p}=\phi(x)+\frac{f(x)-(x+a)^p\phi(x)}{(x+a)^p}$$

$$=\phi(x)+\frac{R}{(x+a)^p}, \tag{49}$$

where R is a polynomial in x of lower degree than p.

Now

$$\frac{R}{(x+a)^p}=\sum_{k=0}^{p-1}\frac{A_k}{(x+a)^{p-k}}. \tag{50}$$

from which

$$A_k=\frac{1}{k!}\frac{d^k}{dx^k}[f(x)-(x+a)^p\phi(x)]_{x=-a}. \tag{51}$$

But

$$\frac{d^k}{dx^k}(x+a)^p\phi(x)]_{x=-a}=0,\ \text{for } k=0,\ 1,\ 2,\ \dots,\ p-1;$$

therefore

$$A_k=\frac{1}{k!}\frac{d^k}{dx^k}f(x)\Big]_{x=-a}, \tag{52}$$

which proves the principle.

To separate an improper fraction into partial fractions it is not necessary to find first the remainder, but the coefficients of the partial fractions may be obtained directly from the given fraction in the same way as if it were a proper fraction. The integral part can be written without carrying out the actual division.

4. To separate into Partial Fractions

$$\frac{f(x)}{F(x)}=\frac{\sum_{a=0}^{n}m_ax^{n-a}}{\prod_{k=0}^{r}(x+h_k)^{p_k}},\quad n<\sum_{k=0}^{r}p_k. \tag{53}$$

Let
$$\frac{f(x)}{F(x)}=\sum_{k=0}^{r}\sum_{v=0}^{p_k-1}\frac{A_{k,v}}{(x+h_k)^{p_k-v}}$$
$$=\sum_{v=0}^{p_k-1}\frac{A_{k,v}}{(x+h_k)^{p_k-v}}+\theta_k(x)\phi_k(x), \tag{54}$$

where $\theta_k(x)$ is a polynomial of degree less than $\sum_{k=0}^{r} p_k-1$, and

$$\phi_k(x)=\frac{1}{\prod_{k_1=0}^{k-1}(x+h_{k_1})^{p_{k_1}}\prod_{k_2=k+1}^{r}(x+h_{k_2})^{p_{k_2}}}. \tag{55}$$

Clearing (54) of fractions, we have

$$f(x)\phi_k(x)=\sum_{\nu=0}^{p_k-1}A_{k,v}(x+h_k)^v+(x+h_k)^{p_k}\theta_k(x)\phi_k(x). \tag{56}$$

Taking the νth derivative of (56) and letting then $x=-h_k$, we obtain

$$A_{k,v}=\frac{1}{v!}\sum_{t=0}^{v}\binom{v}{t}\frac{d^{v-t}}{dx^{v-t}}f(x)\frac{d^t}{dx^t}\phi_k(x)\Big]_{x=-h_k} \tag{57}$$
$$=\sum_{t=0}^{v}\frac{1}{t!}\sum_{a=0}^{n-v+t}m_a\binom{n-a}{v-t}x^{n-a-v+t}\phi_k^{(t)}(x)\Big]_{x=-h_k}$$
$$=\sum_{t=0}^{v}\frac{1}{t!}\sum_{a=0}^{n-v+t}m_{n-v+t-a}\binom{n-a}{a}x^{a}\phi_k^{(t)}(x)\Big]_{x=-h_k}. \tag{58}$$

We shall next find $\phi_k^{(t)}(x)\Big]_{x=-h_k}$.

From (55), we have

$$\log\phi_k(x)=-\sum_{k_1=0}^{k-1}p_{k_1}\log(x+h_{k_1})-\sum_{k_2=k+1}^{r}p_{k_2}\log(x+h_{k_2}). \tag{59}$$

Differentiating (59) gives

$$\phi_k'(x)=-\phi_k(x)\left[\sum_{k_1=0}^{k-1}\frac{p_{k_1}}{x+h_{k_1}}+\sum_{k_2=k+1}^{r}\frac{p_{k_2}}{x+h_{k_2}}\right]. \tag{60}$$

Denoting the expression within the brackets by S, we have by Ch. VI. (4) (notice that for S' there, we write S here)

$$\phi_k^{(t)}(x)\Big]_{x=-h_k}=-\phi_k(x)\Big]_{x=-h_k}\begin{vmatrix} S & -1 & 0 & \cdots & 0 & 0\\ S' & S & -1 & \cdots & 0 & 0\\ S'' & 2S' & S & \cdots & 0 & 0\\ \cdots & \cdots & \cdots & \cdots & \cdots & \cdots\\ S^{(t-2)}\binom{t-2}{1} & S^{(t-3)}\binom{t-2}{2} & S^{(t-4)} & \cdots & S & -1\\ S^{(t-1)}\binom{t-1}{1} & S^{(t-2)}\binom{t-1}{1} & S^{(t-3)} & \cdots\binom{t-1}{1}S' & & S \end{vmatrix}_{x=-h_k}$$

An expression for $\phi_k^{(t)}(x)$ can also be obtained in the following way:

Let
$$(-1)^{ab}\left[\sum_{k_1=0}^{k-1}\frac{p_{k_1}}{(x+h_{k_1})^a}+\sum_{k_2=k+1}^{r}\frac{p_{k_2}}{(x+h_{k_2})^a}\right]^b=\left(\frac{1}{S_k{}^a}\right)^b; \tag{62}$$
then
$$\frac{d}{dx}\left(\frac{1}{S_k{}^a}\right)^b=(-1)^{ab}b\left[\sum_{k_1=0}^{k-1}\frac{p_{k_1}}{(x+h_{k_1})^a}+\sum_{k_2=k+1}^{r}\frac{p_{k_2}}{(x+h_{k_2})^a}\right]^{b-1}$$
$$\times a(-1)\left[\sum_{k_1=0}^{k-1}\frac{p_{k_1}}{(x+h_{k_1})^{a+1}}+\sum_{k_2=k+1}^{r}\frac{p_{k_2}}{(x+h_{k_2})^{a+1}}\right] \tag{63}$$
$$=(-1)^{a(b-1)}\left[\sum_{k_1=0}^{k-1}\frac{p_{k_1}}{(x+h_{k_1})^a}+\sum_{k_2=k+1}^{r}\frac{p_{k_2}}{(x+h_{k_2})^a}\right]^{b-1}$$
$$\times(-1)^{a+1}ab\left[\sum_{k_1=0}^{p_{k_1}}\frac{p_{k_1}}{(x+h_{k_1})^{a+1}}+\sum_{k_2=k+1}^{r}\frac{p_{k_2}}{(x+h_{k_2})^{a+1}}\right], \tag{64}$$
for which, in accordance with the notation in (62), we may write
$$\frac{d}{dx}\left(\frac{1}{S_k{}^a}\right)^b=ab\left(\frac{1}{S_k{}^a}\right)^{b-1}\left(\frac{1}{S_k{}^{a+1}}\right), \tag{65}$$
and for (60)
$$\phi_k'(x)=\phi_k(x)\left(\frac{1}{S_k}\right). \tag{66}$$

Differentiating (66) gives
$$\phi_k''(x)=\phi_k(x)\left(\frac{1}{S_k{}^2}\right)+\phi'_k(x)\left(\frac{1}{S_k}\right)$$
$$=\phi_k(x)\left(\frac{1}{S_k{}^2}\right)+\phi_k(x)\left(\frac{1}{S_k}\right)^2$$
$$=2!\,\phi_k(x)\left[\frac{1}{2!\,1^2}\left(\frac{1}{S_k}\right)^2+\frac{1}{2\,.\,1!}\left(\frac{1}{S_k{}^2}\right)\right], \tag{67}$$
$$\phi_k'''(x)=3!\,\phi_k(x)\left[\frac{1}{3!\,1^3}\left(\frac{1}{S_k}\right)^3+\frac{1}{1!\,1!\,1\,.\,2}\left(\frac{1}{S_k}\right)\left(\frac{1}{S_k{}^2}\right)+\frac{1}{3\,.\,1!}\left(\frac{1}{S_k{}^3}\right)\right], \tag{68}$$
$$\phi_k^{(\mathrm{iv})}(x)=4!\,\phi_k(x)\left[\frac{1}{4!\,1^4}\left(\frac{1}{S_k}\right)^4+\frac{1}{2!\,1!\,1^2.\,2}\left(\frac{1}{S_k}\right)^2\left(\frac{1}{S_k{}^2}\right)\right.$$
$$\left.+\frac{1}{1!\,1!\,1\,.\,3}\left(\frac{1}{S_k}\right)\left(\frac{1}{S_k{}^3}\right)+\frac{1}{2!\,2^2}\left(\frac{1}{S_k{}^2}\right)^2+\frac{1}{1!\,4}\left(\frac{1}{S_k{}^4}\right)\right], \tag{69}$$
and in general
$$\phi_k^{(t)}(x)=t!\,\phi_k(x)\sum\frac{1}{b_0!\,b_1!\,b_2!\dots b_q!\,a^{b_0}(a+1)^{b_1}\dots(a+q)^{b_q}}$$
$$\left(\frac{1}{S_k{}^a}\right)^{b_0}\left(\frac{1}{S_k{}^{a+1}}\right)^{b_1}\left(\frac{1}{S_k{}^{a+2}}\right)^{b_2}\cdots\left(\frac{1}{S_k{}^{a+q}}\right)^{b_q}, \tag{70}$$
the summation extending to all terms for which $\sum_{\gamma=0}^{q}(a+\gamma)^{b_\gamma}=t$, neither b nor a being greater than t, while a may not be zero.

Writing (70) in an abbreviated form, we have

$$\phi_k^{(t)}(x) = t!\,\phi_k(x)\sum\prod_{\gamma=0}^{q}\frac{1}{b_\gamma!\,(a+\gamma)^{b_\gamma}}\left(\frac{1}{S_k^{a+\gamma}}\right)^{b_\gamma}, \tag{71}$$

therefore

$$A_{k,\nu} = \phi_k(x)\sum_{t=0}^{v}\sum_{a=0}^{n-v+t} m_{n-v+t-a}\binom{n-a}{a}x^a\sum\prod_{\gamma=0}^{q}\frac{1}{b_\gamma!\,(a+\gamma)^{b_\gamma}}$$
$$\left(\frac{1}{S_k^{a+\gamma}}\right)^{b_\gamma}\Bigg]_{x=-h_k}. \tag{72}$$

5. To separate into Partial Fractions

$$F(x) = \frac{\sum_{k=0}^{n} m_k x^{n-k}}{(x^2+a^2)^p}, \quad n<2p. \tag{73}$$

We may write
$$F(x) = \sum_{k=0}^{p-1}\frac{A_k x + B_k}{(x^2+a^2)^{p-k}}. \tag{74}$$

Clearing (74) of fractions gives

$$\sum_{k=0}^{n} m_k x^{n-k} = \sum_{k=0}^{p-1}(A_k x + B_k)(x^2+a^2)^k. \tag{75}$$

Equating in (75) the odd powers of x and then the even powers, we have

$$\sum_{k=0}^{\left[\frac{n-1}{2}\right]} m_{n-2k-1}x^{2k} = \sum_{k=0}^{p-1} A_k(x^2+a^2)^k \tag{76}$$

and
$$\sum_{k=0}^{\left[\frac{n}{2}\right]} m_{n-2k}x^{2k} = \sum_{k=0}^{p-1} B_k(x^2+a^2)^k. \tag{77}$$

Taking the hth derivative with respect to x^2 of (76) and (77) and then letting $x^2 = -a^2$, we obtain

$$A_h = \sum_{\beta=h}^{\left[\frac{n-1}{2}\right]}(-1)^{\beta-h}\binom{\beta}{h}a^{2(\beta-h)}m_{n-2\beta-1}$$
$$= \sum_{\beta=0}^{\left[\frac{n-1}{2}\right]-h}(-1)^{\beta}\binom{h+\beta}{h}a^{2\beta}m_{n-2h-1-2\beta}, \tag{78}$$

and
$$B_h = \sum_{\beta=0}^{\left[\frac{n}{2}\right]-h}(-1)^{\beta}\binom{h+\beta}{h}a^{2\beta}m_{n-2h-2\beta}. \tag{79}$$

Therefore

$$F(x) = \sum_{k=0}^{p}\Bigg[\Bigg\{\sum_{\beta=0}^{\left[\frac{n-1}{2}\right]-k}(-1)^{\beta}\binom{k+\beta}{k}a^{2\beta}m_{n-2k-1-2\beta}\Bigg\}x$$
$$+\sum_{\beta=0}^{\left[\frac{n}{2}\right]-k}(-1)^{\beta}\binom{k+\beta}{k}a^{2\beta}m_{n-2k-2\beta}\Bigg]\frac{1}{(x^2+a^2)^{p-k}}. \tag{80}$$

6. To separate into Partial Fractions

$$F(x)=\frac{\sum_{k=0}^{n} m_k x^{n-k}}{\prod_{\beta=1}^{p}(x^2+a_\beta^2)}, \quad n<2p. \tag{81}$$

We may write $$F(x)=\sum_{\beta=1}^{p}\frac{A_\beta x+B_\beta}{x^2+a_\beta^2}=\frac{A_k x+B_k}{x^2+a_k^2}+\frac{\Theta_k(x)}{\phi_k(x)}, \tag{82}$$

where $$\phi_k(x)=\prod_{k_1=1}^{k-1}(x^2+a_{k_1}^2)\prod_{k_2=k+1}^{p}(x^2+a_{k_2}^2). \tag{83}$$

Now, from (82), we have

$$\sum_{\beta=0}^{n} m_\beta x^{n-\beta}=(A_k x+B_k)\phi_k(x)+(x^2+a_k^2)\Theta_k(x). \tag{84}$$

Letting in (84) $x=ia_k$, then

$$\sum_{\beta=0}^{n} m_{n-\beta} i^\beta a_k^\beta=(A_k ia_k+B_k)\phi_k(ia_k). \tag{85}$$

But

$$\sum_{\beta=0}^{n} m_{n-\beta} i^\beta a^\beta=\sum_{\beta=0}^{\left[\frac{n}{2}\right]}(-1)^\beta a_k^{2\beta} m_{n-2\beta}+i\sum_{\beta=0}^{\left[\frac{n-1}{2}\right]}(-1)^\beta a_k^{2\beta+1} m_{n-2\beta-1}; \tag{86}$$

therefore $$A_k=\frac{\sum_{\beta=0}^{\left[\frac{n-1}{2}\right]}(-1)^\beta a_k^{2\beta} m_{n-2\beta-1}}{\prod_{k_1=1}^{k-1}(a_{k_1}^2-a_k^2)\prod_{k_2=k+1}^{p}(a_{k_2}^2-a_k^2)} \tag{87}$$

and $$B_k=\frac{\sum_{\beta=0}^{\left[\frac{n}{2}\right]}(-1)^\beta a_k^{2\beta} m_{n-2\beta}}{\prod_{k_1=1}^{k-1}(a_{k_1}^2-a_k^2)\prod_{k_2=k+1}^{p}(a_{k_2}^2-a_k^2)}. \tag{88}$$

Denoting the denominator of A_k and B_k by P_k, we obtain

$$F(x)=\sum_{k=1}^{p}\frac{1}{P_k}\left[\sum_{\beta=0}^{\left[\frac{n-1}{2}\right]}(-1)^\beta a_k^{2\beta} m_{n-2\beta-1}x+\sum_{\beta=0}^{\left[\frac{n}{2}\right]}(-1)^\beta a_k^{2\beta} m_{n-2\beta}\right]\frac{1}{x^2+a_k^2}. \tag{89}$$

7. To separate into Partial Fractions

$$F(x)=\frac{\sum_{k=0}^{n} m_k x^{n-k}}{(x^2+ax+b)^p}, \tag{90}$$

$n\gtreqless 2p$ and $4b-a^2>0$.

Letting $x+\frac{a}{2}=y$ and $b-\frac{1}{4}a^2=c^2$, we may write for (97),

$$F(x)=\frac{\sum_{k=0}^{n} m_k\left(y-\frac{a}{2}\right)^{n-k}}{(y^2+c^2)^p}. \tag{91}$$

Now $$\sum_{k=0}^{n} m_k\left(y-\frac{a}{2}\right)^{n-k}=\sum_{k=0}^{n}\sum_{\beta=0}^{n-k} m_k\binom{n-k}{\beta}\left(-\frac{a}{2}\right)^{n-k-\beta} y^\beta\,; \tag{92}$$

and since $$\sum_{k=0}^{n}\sum_{\beta=0}^{n-k} A_{k,\beta}=\sum_{\beta=0}^{n}\sum_{k=0}^{n-\beta} A_{k,\beta}, \tag{93}$$

the second member of (99) becomes

$$\sum_{\beta=0}^{n}\left[\sum_{k=0}^{n-\beta} m_k\binom{n-k}{\beta}\left(-\frac{a}{2}\right)^{n-k-\beta}\right]y^\beta=\sum_{\beta=0}^{n} N_\beta y^\beta$$

$$=\sum_{\beta=0}^{\left[\frac{n}{2}\right]} N_{2\beta}y^{2\beta}+y\sum_{\beta=0}^{\left[\frac{n-1}{2}\right]} N_{2\beta+1}y^{2\beta}. \tag{94}$$

Letting $y^2=z$, we have

$$F(x)=\frac{\sum_{\beta=0}^{\left[\frac{n}{2}\right]} N_{2\beta}z^\beta}{(z+c^2)^p}+y\,\frac{\sum_{\beta=0}^{\left[\frac{n-1}{2}\right]} N_{2\beta+1}z^\beta}{(z+c^2)^p}. \tag{95}$$

Applying to (95) the methods of 2, leads to the required separation.

8. The separation into Partial Fractions of

$$\frac{f(x)}{F(x)}=\frac{\sum_{k=0}^{n} m_k x^{n-k}}{(x^2+ax+b)^p} \tag{96}$$

can also be obtained by division.

Let first $n<2p$, and, without loss of generality, we may write

$$(x^2-ax-b)^p \text{ for } F(x), \quad \text{where } a^2+4b<0. \tag{97}$$

Now $$\frac{f(x)}{F(x)}=\sum_{k=0}^{\left[\frac{n}{2}\right]}\frac{A_k x+B_k}{(x^2-ax-b)^{p-k}}. \tag{98}$$

To find the values of A_k and B_k we proceed as follows :

Dividing $f(x)$ by x^2-ax-b, we obtain

$$\frac{f(x)}{x^2-ax-b}=\sum_{k=0}^{n-2} Q_{1,k}x^{n-2-k}+\frac{A_0x+B_0}{x^2-ax-b}. \tag{99}$$

Clearing (105) of fractions and equating then equal powers of x, we have

$$Q_{1,0}=m_0, \tag{100}$$

$$Q_{1,1}-aQ_{1,0}=m_1,$$

$$Q_{1,2}-aQ_{1,1}-bQ_{1,0}=m_2,$$

$$\cdots\cdots\cdots\cdots\cdots\cdots$$

$$Q_{1,k}-aQ_{1,k-1}-bQ_{1,k-2}=m_k, \tag{101}$$

$$\cdots\cdots\cdots\cdots\cdots\cdots$$

$$A_0-aQ_{1,n-2}-bQ_{1,n-3}=m_{n-1}, \tag{102}$$

$$B_0-bQ_{1,n-2}=m_n. \tag{103}$$

The last two relations give

$$A_0=m_{n-1}+aQ_{1,n-2}+bQ_{1,n-3} \tag{104}$$

and

$$B_0=m_n+bQ_{1,n-2}. \tag{105}$$

It is evident that A_0 is formed in the same manner as $Q_{1,n-1}$, if it existed. We then would have

$$Q_{1,n-1}-aQ_{1,n-2}-bQ_{1,n-3}=Q_{0,n-1}=m_{n-1}. \tag{106}$$

We shall now express the Q's in terms of the m's.

$$Q_{1,0}=m_0,$$

$$Q_{1,1}=m_1+am_0,$$

$$Q_{1,2}=m_2+am_1+a^2m_0+bm_0,$$

$$Q_{1,3}=m_3+am_2+a^2m_1+a^3m_0+b(m_1+2am_0),$$

$$Q_{1,4}=m_4+am_3+a^2m_2+a^3m_1+a^4m_0+b(m_2+2am_1+3a^2m_0)+b^2m_0$$

$$=\sum_{\gamma=0}^{4}a^\gamma m_{4-\gamma}+b\sum_{\gamma=0}^{2}\binom{1+\gamma}{1}a^\gamma m_{4-2-\gamma}+b^2\sum_{\gamma=0}^{0}\binom{2+\gamma}{2}a^\gamma m_{4-4-\gamma} \tag{107}$$

$$=\sum_{\beta=0}^{\frac{4}{2}}b^\beta\sum_{\gamma=0}^{4-2\beta}a^\gamma\binom{\beta+\gamma}{\gamma}m_{4-2\beta-\gamma}, \tag{108}$$

$$Q_{1,5}=m_5+am_4+a^2m_3+a^3m_2+a^4m_1+a^5m_0$$
$$+b(m_3+2am_2+3a^2m_1+4a^3m_0)+b^2(m_1+3am_0)$$

$$=\sum_{\gamma=0}^{5}a^\gamma m_{5-\gamma}+b\sum_{\gamma=0}^{3}a^\gamma\binom{1+\gamma}{1}m_{5-2-\gamma}+b^2\sum_{\gamma=0}^{1}a^\gamma\binom{2+\gamma}{2}a_{5-4-\gamma} \tag{109}$$

$$=\sum_{\beta=0}^{\left[\frac{5}{2}\right]}b^\beta\sum_{\gamma=0}^{5-2\beta}a^\gamma\binom{\beta+\gamma}{\beta}m_{5-2\beta-\gamma}. \tag{110}$$

We now assume

$$Q_{1,k}=\sum_{\beta=0}^{\left[\frac{k}{2}\right]}b^\beta\sum_{\gamma=0}^{k-2\beta}a^\gamma\binom{\beta+\gamma}{\beta}m_{k-2\beta-\gamma}, \tag{111}$$

and shall show that this form holds true for $Q_{1,k+1}$.

Now $Q_{1,k+1}=m_{k+1}+aQ_{1,k}+bQ_{1,k-1}$ (112)

$$=m_{k+1}+a\sum_{\beta=0}^{\left[\frac{k}{2}\right]}b^{\beta}\sum_{\gamma=0}^{k-2\beta}a^{\gamma}\binom{\beta+\gamma}{\beta}m_{k-2\beta-\gamma}$$

$$+b\sum_{\beta=0}^{\left[\frac{k-1}{2}\right]}b^{\beta}\sum_{\gamma=0}^{k-1-2\beta}a^{\gamma}\binom{\beta+\gamma}{\beta}m_{k-1-2\beta-\gamma}$$

$$=m_{k+1}+\sum_{\beta=0}^{\left[\frac{k}{2}\right]}b^{\beta}\sum_{\gamma=1}^{k+1-2\beta}a^{\gamma}\binom{\beta+\gamma-1}{\beta}m_{k+1-2\beta-\gamma}$$

$$+\sum_{\beta=1}^{\left[\frac{k+1}{2}\right]}b^{\beta}\sum_{\gamma=0}^{k+1-2\beta}a^{\gamma}\binom{\beta+\gamma-1}{\beta-1}m_{k+1-2\beta-\gamma};$$

and since
$$\binom{\beta+\gamma-1}{\beta}+\binom{\beta+\gamma-1}{\beta-1}=\binom{\beta+\gamma}{\beta},$$

therefore
$$Q_{1,k+1}=\sum_{\beta=0}^{\left[\frac{k+1}{2}\right]}b^{\beta}\sum_{\gamma=0}^{k+1-2\beta}a^{\gamma}\binom{\beta+\gamma}{\beta}m_{k+1-2\beta-\gamma}. \tag{113}$$

The value (111) is therefore true for all values of k (the highest value of k being $n-2$).

We next divide

$$f_1(x)=\sum_{k=0}^{n-2}Q_{1,k}x^{n-2-k} \text{ by } x^2-ax-b. \tag{114}$$

We then have

$$\frac{f_1(x)}{x^2-ax-b}=\sum_{k=0}^{n-4}Q_{2,k}x^{n-4-k}+\frac{A_1x+B_1}{x^2-ax-b}, \tag{115}$$

and find

$$Q_{2,k}=Q_{1,k}+aQ_{2,k-1}+bQ_{2,k-2}, \tag{116}$$

$$A_1=Q_{1,n-3}+aQ_{2,n-4}+bQ_{2,n-5}, \tag{117}$$

$$B_1=Q_{1,n-2}+bQ_{2,n-4}. \tag{118}$$

It follows that A_1 is formed in the same way as $Q_{2,n-3}$, if it existed. We would then have

$$Q_{2,n-3}=Q_{1,n-3}+aQ_{2,n-4}+bQ_{2,n-5}. \tag{119}$$

Similar to the above, we obtain

$$Q_{2,k}=\sum_{\beta=0}^{\left[\frac{k}{2}\right]}b^{\beta}\binom{\beta+1}{\beta}\sum_{\gamma=0}^{k-2\beta}a^{\gamma}\binom{\beta+\gamma-1}{\gamma}m_{k-2\beta-\gamma}, \tag{120}$$

$$A_1=\sum_{\beta=0}^{\left[\frac{n-3}{2}\right]}b^{\beta}\binom{\beta+1}{\beta}\sum_{\gamma=0}^{n-2\beta-3}a^{\gamma}\binom{\beta+\gamma+1}{\gamma}m_{n-2\beta-3-\gamma}, \tag{121}$$

$$B_1 = \sum_{\beta=0}^{\left[\frac{n}{2}\right]-1} b^\beta \sum_{\gamma=0}^{n-2\beta-2} a^\gamma \binom{\beta+\gamma}{\gamma} m_{n-2\beta-2-\gamma}$$

$$+b \sum_{\beta=0}^{\left[\frac{n}{2}\right]-2} b^\beta \binom{\beta+1}{\beta} \sum_{\gamma=0}^{n-2\beta-4} a^\gamma \binom{\beta+\gamma+1}{\gamma} m_{n-2\beta-4-\gamma}. \quad (122)$$

It is evident from (119) that the Q_2's are the same functions of the Q_1's as the Q_1's are of the m's. Hence if $Q_{t,k}$, $k=0, 1, 2, \ldots, n-2t$, are the coefficients in the quotient of the tth division, we have from (111),

$$Q_{t,k} = \sum_{\beta=0}^{\left[\frac{k}{2}\right]} b^\beta \sum_{\gamma=0}^{k-2\beta} a^\gamma \binom{\beta+\gamma}{\beta} Q_{t-1,k-2\beta-\gamma}. \quad (123)$$

We now assume

$$Q_{t,k} = \sum_{\beta=0}^{\left[\frac{k}{2}\right]} b^\beta \binom{\beta+t-1}{\beta} \sum_{\gamma=0}^{k-2\beta} a^\gamma \binom{\beta+\gamma+t-1}{\gamma} m_{k-2\beta-\gamma}; \quad (124)$$

and shall show that this form holds true for $Q_{t,k+1}$.

Now $$Q_{t,k+1} = Q_{t-1,k+1} + aQ_{t,k} + bQ_{t,k-1}. \quad (125)$$

Writing in turn $t-1$, $t-2$, $t-3, \ldots, 2, 1$ for t and adding the resulting equations, we obtain

$$\sum_{\beta=0}^{t-1} Q_{t-\beta,k+1} = \sum_{\beta=1}^{t} Q_{t-\beta,k+1} + a\sum_{\beta=0}^{t-1} Q_{t-\beta,k} + b\sum_{\beta=0}^{t-1} Q_{t-\beta,k-1}. \quad (126)$$

Cancelling terms and since $Q_{0,k+1} = m_{k+1}$, we have

$$Q_{t,k+1} = m_{k+1} + a\sum_{\alpha=1}^{t} Q_{\alpha,k} + b\sum_{\alpha=1}^{t} Q_{\alpha,k-1} \quad (127)$$

$$= m_{k+1} + a\sum_{\alpha=1}^{t} \sum_{\beta=0}^{\left[\frac{k}{2}\right]} b^\beta \sum_{\gamma=0}^{k-2\beta} a^\gamma \binom{\alpha+\beta-1}{\beta}\binom{\alpha+\beta+\gamma-1}{\gamma} m_{k-2\beta-\gamma}$$

$$+ b\sum_{\alpha=1}^{t} \sum_{\beta=0}^{\left[\frac{k-1}{2}\right]} b^\beta \sum_{\gamma=0}^{k-1-2\beta} a^\gamma \binom{\alpha+\beta-1}{\beta}\binom{\alpha+\beta+\gamma-1}{\gamma} m_{k-1-2\beta-\gamma}$$

$$= m_{k+1} + a\sum_{\beta=0}^{\left[\frac{k}{2}\right]} b^\beta \sum_{\gamma=0}^{k-2\beta} a^\gamma m_{k-2\beta-\gamma} \sum_{\alpha=1}^{t} \binom{\alpha+\beta-1}{\beta}\binom{\alpha+\beta+\gamma-1}{\gamma}$$

$$+ b\sum_{\beta=0}^{\left[\frac{k-1}{2}\right]} b^\beta \sum_{\gamma=0}^{k-1-2\beta} a^\gamma m_{k-1-2\beta-\gamma} \sum_{\alpha=1}^{t} \binom{\alpha+\beta-1}{\beta}\binom{\alpha+\beta+\gamma-1}{\gamma}. \quad (128)$$

Now $$\binom{\alpha+\beta-1}{\beta}\binom{\alpha+\beta+\gamma-1}{\gamma} = \binom{\beta+\gamma}{\beta}\binom{\alpha+\beta+\gamma-1}{\beta+\gamma} \quad (129)$$

and $$\sum_{\alpha=1}^{t} \binom{\alpha+\beta-1}{\beta}\binom{\alpha+\beta+\gamma-1}{\gamma} = \binom{\beta+\gamma}{\beta} \sum_{\alpha=1}^{t} \binom{\alpha+\beta+\gamma-1}{\beta+\gamma}. \quad (130)$$

But
$$\sum_{\alpha=1}^{t}\binom{\alpha+\beta+\gamma-1}{\beta+\gamma}=((x^{\beta+\gamma}))\sum_{\alpha=1}^{t}(1+x)^{\alpha+\beta+\gamma-1} \tag{131}$$
$$=((x^{\beta+\gamma+1}))[(1+x)^{\beta+\gamma+t}-(1+x)^{\beta+\gamma}]$$
$$=\binom{\beta+\gamma+t}{\beta+\gamma+1}=\binom{\beta+\gamma+t}{t-1}; \tag{132}$$

therefore
$$Q_{t,k+1}=m_{k+1}+\sum_{\beta=0}^{\left[\frac{k}{2}\right]}b^{\beta}\sum_{\gamma=1}^{k+1-2\beta}a^{\gamma}\binom{\beta+\gamma-1}{\beta}\binom{\beta+\gamma+t-1}{t-1}m_{k+1-2\beta-\gamma}$$
$$+\sum_{\beta=1}^{\left[\frac{k+1}{2}\right]}b^{\beta}\sum_{\gamma=0}^{k+1-2\beta}a^{\gamma}\binom{\beta+\gamma-1}{\gamma}\binom{\beta+\gamma+t-1}{t-1}m_{k+1-2\beta-\gamma}. \tag{133}$$

Now
$$\binom{\beta+\gamma-1}{\beta}+\binom{\beta+\gamma-1}{\gamma}=\binom{\beta+\gamma}{\beta} \tag{134}$$

and
$$\binom{\beta+\gamma}{\beta}\binom{\beta+\gamma+t-1}{t-1}=\binom{\beta+t-1}{\beta}\binom{\beta+\gamma+t-1}{\gamma}. \tag{135}$$

Then, by means of (134) and (135), we obtain from (133),
$$Q_{t,k+1}=\sum_{\beta=0}^{\left[\frac{k+1}{2}\right]}b^{\beta}\binom{\beta+t-1}{\beta}\sum_{\gamma=0}^{k+1-2\beta}a^{\gamma}\binom{\beta+\gamma+t-1}{\gamma}m_{k+1-2\beta-\gamma}, \tag{136}$$
which is of the same form as (123).

To find the values for A_t and B_t, we proceed as follows:

We have
$$Q_{t,k}=Q_{t-1,k}+aQ_{t,k-1}+bQ_{t,k-2}, \tag{137}$$
so
$$A_t=Q_{t,n-1-2t}+aQ_{t+1,n-2-2t}+bQ_{t+1,n-3-2t} \tag{138}$$
$$=Q_{t+1,n-2t-1} \tag{139}$$
$$=\sum_{\beta=0}^{\left[\frac{n-1}{2}\right]-t}b^{\beta}\binom{\beta+t}{\beta}\sum_{\gamma=0}^{n-2t-2\beta-1}a^{\gamma}\binom{\beta+\gamma+t}{\gamma}m_{n-2t-2\beta-\gamma-1}$$
$$=\frac{1}{b^{t}}\sum_{\beta=t}^{\left[\frac{n-1}{2}\right]}b^{\beta}\binom{\beta}{t}\sum_{\gamma=0}^{n-2\beta-1}a^{\gamma}\binom{\beta+\gamma}{\gamma}m_{n-2\beta-\gamma-1} \tag{140}$$

and
$$B_t=Q_{t,n-2t}+bQ_{t+1,n-2t-2} \tag{141}$$
$$=\sum_{\beta=0}^{\left[\frac{n}{2}\right]-t}b^{\beta}\binom{\beta+t-1}{\beta}\sum_{\gamma=0}^{n-2t-2\beta}a^{\gamma}\binom{\beta+\gamma+t-1}{\gamma}m_{n-2t-2\beta-\gamma}$$
$$+b\sum_{\beta=0}^{\left[\frac{n}{2}\right]-t-1}b^{\beta}\binom{\beta+t}{\beta}\sum_{\gamma=0}^{n-2t-2\beta-2}a^{\gamma}\binom{\beta+\gamma+t}{\gamma}m_{n-2t-2\beta-2-\gamma}$$

$$=\frac{1}{b^t}\sum_{\beta=t}^{\left[\frac{n}{2}\right]} b^\beta \binom{\beta-1}{t-1} \sum_{\gamma=0}^{n-2\beta} a^\gamma \binom{\beta+\gamma-1}{\gamma} m_{n-2\beta-\gamma}$$

$$+\frac{1}{b^t}\sum_{\beta=t+1}^{\left[\frac{n}{2}\right]} b^\beta \binom{\beta-1}{t} \sum_{\gamma=0}^{n-2\beta} a^\gamma \binom{\beta+\gamma-1}{\gamma} m_{n-2\beta-\gamma}. \tag{142}$$

If $n \gtreqless 2p$, then

$$\frac{f(x)}{F(x)}=\sum_{k=0}^{n-2p} Q_{p,k}x^{n-2p-k}+\sum_{t=0}^{p-1}\frac{A_t x+B_t}{(x^2-ax-b)^{p-t}}, \tag{143}$$

where $Q_{p,k}$, A_t and B_t have the values obtained above.

9. Cayley (*Collected Works*, Vol. II.) has shown that

$$\sum_{n=1}^{p}(-1)^{n-1}x^{\frac{1}{2}n(n-1)}\prod_{k=1}^{p-n}\frac{1-x^{n+k}}{1-x^k}=1. \tag{144}$$

The method of proof given here involves Partial Fractions, and is believed to be more direct than the proof given by Cayley.

Now
$$\frac{1}{\prod\limits_{n=1}^{p}(y-a_n)}=\sum_{n=1}^{p}\frac{1}{\prod\limits_{k=1}^{n-1}(a_n-a_k)\prod\limits_{k=n+1}^{p}(a_n-a_k)}\frac{1}{y-a_n}. \tag{145}$$

If we let $y=1$ and $a_k=x^k$, then

$$\frac{1}{\prod\limits_{k=1}^{p}(1-x^k)}=\sum_{n=1}^{p}\frac{1}{\prod\limits_{k=1}^{n-1}(x^n-x^k)\prod\limits_{k=n+1}^{p}(x^n-x^k)}\frac{1}{1-x^n} \tag{146}$$

$$=\sum_{n=1}^{p}\frac{1}{x^{n(p-n)}\prod\limits_{\beta=1}^{n-1}x^\beta\prod\limits_{k=1}^{n-1}(x^k-1)\prod\limits_{k=1}^{p-n}(1-x^k)}\frac{1}{1-x^n}$$

$$=\sum_{n=1}^{p}\frac{(-1)^{n-1}\prod\limits_{k=n+1}^{p}(1-x^k)}{x^{\frac{1}{2}n(n-1)}x^{n(p-n)}\prod\limits_{k=1}^{p-n}(1-x^k)\prod\limits_{k=1}^{p}(1-x^k)}. \tag{147}$$

Cancelling $\dfrac{1}{\prod\limits_{n=1}^{p}(1-x^k)}$, we have

$$1=\sum_{n=1}^{p}\frac{(-1)^{n-1}}{x^{\frac{1}{2}n(n-1)}x^{n(p-n)}}\prod_{k=1}^{p-n}\frac{1-x^{k+n}}{1-x^k}. \tag{148}$$

Replacing in (145) x by $\dfrac{1}{x}$, we obtain

$$\sum_{n=1}^{p}(-1)^{n-1}x^{\frac{1}{2}n(n-1)}x^{n(p-n)}\prod_{k=1}^{p-n}\frac{1}{x^n}\frac{1-x^{k+n}}{1-x^k}=1\ ; \tag{149}$$

and since
$$\prod_{k=1}^{p-n} \frac{1}{x^n} \frac{1-x^{k+n}}{1-x^k} = \frac{1}{x^{n(p-n)}} \prod_{k=1}^{p-n} \frac{1-x^{x+n}}{1-x^k}, \tag{150}$$

therefore
$$\sum_{n=1}^{p} (-1)^{n-1} x^{\frac{1}{2}n(n-1)} \prod_{k=1}^{p-n} \frac{1-x^{k+n}}{1-x^k} = 1,$$

which is the same as (144).

10. To separate
$$S = \sum_{n=1}^{p} \prod_{m=1}^{n} (a_m + ib_m) \tag{151}$$

into its real and imaginary parts.

The a's and the b's being restricted to the condition $a_\beta b_\gamma - a_\gamma b_\beta \neq 0$, where β and γ may have any value between 1 and p.

Now
$$\prod_{m=1}^{n} (a_m + ib_m) = \prod_{m=1}^{n} (a_m^2 + b_m^2) \frac{1}{\prod\limits_{m=1}^{n} (a_m - ib_m)}. \tag{152}$$

Letting
$$\frac{1}{\prod\limits_{m=1}^{n} (a_m - xb_m)} = \frac{A_k}{a_k - xb_k} + \frac{\phi_k(x)}{\prod\limits_{k_1=1}^{k-1} (a_{k_1} - xb_{k_1}) \prod\limits_{k_2=k+1}^{n} (a_{k_2} - xb_{k_2})}, \tag{153}$$

from which
$$A_k = \frac{1}{\prod\limits_{k_1=1}^{k-1} \left(a_{k_1} - \frac{a_k}{b_k} b_{k_1}\right) \prod\limits_{k_2=k+1}^{n} \left(a_{k_2} - \frac{a_k}{b_k} b_{k_2}\right)}$$
$$= \frac{b_k^{\,n-1}}{\prod\limits_{k_1=1}^{k-1} (a_{k_1} b_k - a_k b_{k_1}) \prod\limits_{k_2=k+1}^{n} (a_{k_2} b_k - a_k a_{k_2})}, \tag{154}$$

where, if $k=1$, the first product is unity, and if $k=n$, the last product is unity.

Therefore
$$\frac{1}{\prod\limits_{m=1}^{n} (a_m - xb_m)} = \sum_{k=1}^{n} \frac{b_k^{\,n-1}}{\prod\limits_{k_1=1}^{k-1} (a_{k_1} b_k - a_k b_{k_1}) \prod\limits_{k_2=k+1}^{n} (a_{k_2} b_k - a_k b_{k_2})} \frac{1}{a_k - xb_k} \tag{155}$$
$$= \sum_{k=1}^{n} \frac{b_k^{\,n-1}(a_k + ib_k)}{(a_k^2 + b_k^2) \prod\limits_{k_1=1}^{k-1} (a_{k_1} b_k - a_k b_{k_1}) \prod\limits_{k_2=k+1}^{n} (a_{k_2} b_k - a_k b_{k_2})} \tag{156}$$

and
$$\sum_{n=1}^{p} \prod_{m=1}^{n} (a_m + ib_m) = \sum_{n=1}^{p} \sum_{k=1}^{n} a_k b_k^{\,n-1} F_{n,k} + i \sum_{n=1}^{p} \sum_{k=1}^{n} b_k^{\,n} F_{n,k}, \tag{157}$$

where
$$F_{n,k} = \prod_{k_1=1}^{k-1} \frac{a_{k_1}^2 + b_{k_1}^2}{a_{k_1} b_k - a_k b_{k_1}} \prod_{k_2=k+1}^{n} \frac{a_{k_2}^2 + b_{k_2}^2}{a_{k_2} b_k - a_k b_{k_2}}.$$

CHAPTER IX.

EVALUATION OF INTEGRALS. APPLICATIONS TO THE SUMMATION OF SERIES.

WE shall in this chapter evaluate integrals of the form

$$I = \int \frac{x^{\frac{s}{t}}}{x^{\frac{p}{q}} + 1}\, dx, \quad \text{for } x = 1,$$

where $\frac{s}{t}$ and $\frac{p}{q}$ may either or both be positive or negative, and apply the results to the summation of certain types of series.

The integral I may be reduced to the forms

$$I_1 = \int \frac{x^m dx}{x^n + 1} \quad \text{or} \quad I_2 = \int \frac{x^m dx}{x^n - 1}, \tag{1}$$

where n and m are integers, n positive and m either positive or negative.

1. (i) To find I_1 we shall first separate

$$F_1(x) = \frac{x^m}{x^n + 1}, \quad m \text{ positive and less than } n, \tag{2}$$

into partial fractions. The results obtained here are in a form more convenient for purposes of application than those generally given.

We may write
$$F_1(x) = \frac{x^m}{\prod\limits_{k=1}^{n} (x - r_k)}, \tag{3}$$

where r_k is one of the n nth roots of -1, $r_k = e^{\frac{2k+1}{n}\pi i}$.

Let
$$F_1(x) = \sum_{k=1}^{n} \frac{A_k}{x - r_k}, \tag{4}$$

then
$$A_k = \frac{x^m (x - r_k)}{x^n + 1}\Big]_{x=r_k} = -\frac{1}{n} x^{m+1}\Big]_{x=r_k}; \tag{5}$$

therefore
$$F_1(x) = -\frac{1}{n} \sum_{k=1}^{n} \frac{r_k^{m+1}}{x - r_k} = -\frac{1}{n} \sum_{k=0}^{n-1} \frac{r_k^{m+1}}{x - r_k}, \tag{6}$$

since in the first summation in (6) the terms corresponding to $k = 0$ and $k = n$ are equal.

If now in $r_k = e^{\frac{2k+1}{n}\pi i}$ we let

$$k = 0,\ -1;\ 1,\ -2;\ 2,\ -3;\ \dots;\ \frac{n-2}{2},\ -\frac{n}{2},\quad \text{when } n \text{ is even,}$$

$$= 0,\ -1;\ 1,\ -2;\ 2,\ -3;\ \dots;\ \frac{n-3}{2},\ -\frac{n-1}{2};\ \frac{n-1}{2},\quad \text{when } n \text{ is odd,}$$

we obtain the sets of conjugate roots in order.

Therefore

$$F_1(x) = -\frac{1}{n}\sum_{k=0}^{\left[\frac{n-2}{2}\right]}\left(\frac{r_k^{m+1}}{x-r_k} + \frac{r_{-(k+1)}^{m+1}}{x-r_{-(k+1)}}\right) + (-1)^m\frac{1-(-1)^n}{2n(x+1)} \tag{7}$$

$$= -\frac{1}{n}\sum_{k=0}^{\left[\frac{n-2}{2}\right]}\frac{2x\cos\frac{2k+1}{n}(m+1)\pi - 2\cos\frac{2k+1}{n}m\pi}{x^2 - 2x\cos\frac{2k+1}{n}\pi + 1} + (-1)^m\frac{1-(-1)^n}{2n(x+1)}. \tag{8}$$

By means of (8) we find

$$\frac{x}{x^3+1} = -\frac{1}{3(x+1)} + \frac{x+1}{3(x^2-x+1)}, \tag{9}$$

$$\frac{x^2}{x^4+1} = \tfrac{1}{4}\sqrt{2}\left(\frac{x}{x^2-x\sqrt{2}+1} - \frac{x}{x^2+x\sqrt{2}+1}\right), \tag{10}$$

$$\frac{1}{x^5+1} = \tfrac{1}{10}(\sqrt{5}-1)\frac{x+\sqrt{5}+1}{x^2+\frac{1}{2}(\sqrt{5}-1)x+1} - \tfrac{1}{10}(\sqrt{5}+1)\frac{x-\sqrt{5}+1}{x^2-\frac{1}{2}(\sqrt{5}+1)x+1} + \frac{1}{5(x+1)}, \tag{11}$$

$$\frac{1}{x^8+1} = \tfrac{1}{8}\sqrt{2-\sqrt{2}}\left(\frac{x+\sqrt{2}\sqrt{2+\sqrt{2}}}{x^2+\sqrt{2-\sqrt{2}}x+1} - \frac{x-\sqrt{2}\sqrt{2+\sqrt{2}}}{x^2-\sqrt{2-\sqrt{2}}x+1}\right) + \tfrac{1}{8}\sqrt{2+\sqrt{2}}\left(\frac{x+\sqrt{2}\sqrt{2-\sqrt{2}}}{x^2+\sqrt{2+\sqrt{2}}x+1} - \frac{x-\sqrt{2}\sqrt{2-\sqrt{2}}}{x^2-\sqrt{2+\sqrt{2}}x+1}\right). \tag{12}$$

(ii) We shall next separate

$$F_2(x) = \frac{x^m}{x^n-1},\quad m \text{ positive and less than } n, \tag{13}$$

into partial fractions.

Similar to (6),

$$F_2(x) = \frac{1}{n}\sum_{k=1}^{n}\frac{r_k^{m+1}}{x-r_k},\quad r_k = e^{\frac{2k\pi i}{n}}, \tag{14}$$

where $k = 0;\ 1,\ -1;\ 2,\ -2;\ \dots;\ \frac{n}{2}$, when n is even,

$= 0;\ 1,\ -1;\ 2,\ -2;\ \dots;\ \frac{n-1}{2},\ -\frac{n-1}{2}$, when n is odd.

We then obtain

$$F_2(x)=\frac{1}{n}\sum_{k=1}^{\left[\frac{n-1}{2}\right]}\left(\frac{r_k{}^{m+1}}{x-r_k}+\frac{r_{-k}{}^{m+1}}{x-r_{-k}}\right)+\frac{1}{n(x-1)}+(-1)^{m-1}\frac{1+(-1)^n}{2n(x+1)}$$

$$=\frac{1}{n}\sum_{k=1}^{\left[\frac{n-1}{2}\right]}\frac{2x\cos\frac{2k}{n}(m+1)-2\cos\frac{2k}{n}m\pi}{x^2-2x\cos\frac{2k}{n}\pi+1}+\frac{1}{n(x-1)}$$

$$+(-1)^{m-1}\frac{1+(-1)^n}{2n(x+1)}. \quad (15)$$

By means of (15), we find

$$\frac{x}{x^3-1}=\frac{1}{3(x-1)}-\frac{x-1}{3(x^2+x+1)}, \quad (16)$$

$$\frac{1}{x^5-1}=\tfrac{1}{10}(\sqrt{5}-1)\frac{x-\sqrt{5}-1}{x^2-\frac{1}{2}(\sqrt{5}-1)x+1}-\tfrac{1}{10}(\sqrt{5}+1)\frac{x+\sqrt{5}-1}{x^2+\frac{1}{2}(\sqrt{5}+1)x+1}$$

$$+\frac{1}{5(x-1)}, \quad (17)$$

$$\frac{x^5}{x^6-1}=\tfrac{1}{6}\left(\frac{2x-1}{x^2-x+1}+\frac{2x+1}{x^2+x+1}+\frac{1}{x-1}+\frac{1}{x+1}\right). \quad (18)$$

(iii) If in $F_1(x)=\dfrac{x^m}{x^n+1}$, $m>n$,

we let $m=np+a$, $a<n$,

then
$$F_1(x)=\sum_{k=1}^{\left[\frac{m}{n}\right]}(-1)^{k-1}x^{m-kn}+(-1)^p\frac{x^a}{x^n+1}. \quad (19)$$

But $(-1)^p\dfrac{x^a}{x^n+1}=\dfrac{(-1)^{p-1}}{n}\displaystyle\sum_{k=1}^{n}\frac{r_k{}^{a+1}}{x-r_k}$, and $r^{np}=(-1)^p$;

therefore
$$F_1(x)=\sum_{k=1}^{\left[\frac{m}{n}\right]}(-1)^{k-1}x^{m-kn}-\frac{1}{n}\sum_{k=1}^{n}\frac{r_k{}^{m+1}}{x-r_k}, \quad r_k=e^{\frac{2k+1}{n}\pi i}. \quad (20)$$

Similarly, if $m>n$,

$$\frac{x^m}{x^n-1}=\sum_{k=1}^{\left[\frac{m}{n}\right]}x^{m-kn}+\frac{1}{n}\sum_{k=1}^{n}\frac{r_k{}^{m+1}}{x-r_k}, \quad r_k=e^{\frac{2k}{n}\pi i}. \quad (21)$$

Applying (8) to (20) and (15) to (21) gives the required separation.

(iv) If in $\dfrac{x^m}{x^n+1}$, m is negative,

we proceed with the separation as follows:

Let
$$F(x)=\frac{1}{x^m(x^n+1)}=\sum_{k=1}^{n}\frac{A_k}{x-r_k}+\sum_{k=0}^{m-1}\frac{B_k}{x^{m-k}}. \quad (22)$$

Multiplying both sides by $x-r_k$ and then letting $x=r_k$, we have

$$A_k=\frac{1}{x^m}\frac{x-r_k}{x^n+1}\Big]_{x=r_k}=-\frac{1}{n}r_k{}^{-m+1}. \tag{23}$$

Now, from (22), $$\frac{1}{x^n+1}=\sum_{k=1}^{n}\frac{A_kx^m}{x-r_k}+\sum_{k=0}^{m-1}B_kx^k. \tag{24}$$

Taking the hth derivative of (24) and then letting $x=0$, we obtain

$$B_h=\frac{1}{h!}\frac{d^h}{dx^h}\frac{1}{x^n+1}\Big]_{x=0}=\sum_{a=0}^{\infty}(-1)^a\binom{na}{h}x^{na-h}, \tag{25}$$

and $B_h=0$, if $h\neq na$,

$=1$, or -1, if $h=na$; then $B_{np}=(-1)^p$.

Therefore

$$\frac{1}{x^m(x^n+1)}=-\frac{1}{n}\sum_{k=1}^{n}\frac{r_k{}^{-m+1}}{x-r_k}+\sum_{k=0}^{\left[\frac{m-1}{n}\right]}\frac{(-1)^k}{x^{m-nk}},\quad r_k=e^{\frac{2k+1}{n}\pi i}, \tag{26}$$

$$=-\frac{1}{n}\sum_{k=0}^{\left[\frac{n-2}{2}\right]}\frac{2x\cos\frac{2k+1}{n}(m-1)\pi-2\cos\frac{2k+1}{n}m\pi}{x^2-2x\cos\frac{2k+1}{n}\pi+1}$$

$$+\sum_{k=0}^{\left[\frac{m-1}{n}\right]}\frac{(-1)^k}{x^{m-nk}}+(-1)^m\frac{1-(-1)^n}{2n(x+1)}. \tag{27}$$

A similar form is obtained for

$$\frac{1}{x^m(x^n-1)}=\frac{1}{n}\sum_{k=1}^{n}\frac{r_k{}^{-m+1}}{x-r_k}-\sum_{k=0}^{\left[\frac{m-1}{n}\right]}\frac{1}{x^{m-nk}},\quad r_k=e^{\frac{2k}{n}\pi i}. \tag{28}$$

2. The integrals I_1 and I_2 may be obtained by integrating (8) and (15) respectively. But to illustrate certain operations with series, we shall find

$$I_1=\int_0^x\frac{x^m dx}{x^n+1}, \tag{29}$$

directly from (6).

From (6) we have $$I_1=-\frac{1}{n}\int_0^x\sum_{k=1}^{n}\frac{r_k{}^{m+1}}{x-r_k}dx$$

$$=-\frac{1}{n}\sum_{k=1}^{n}r_k{}^{m+1}\log\frac{r_k-x}{r_k}. \tag{30}$$

But $$r_k{}^{m+1}=\cos\frac{2k+1}{n}(m+1)\pi+i\sin\frac{2k+1}{n}(m+1)\pi \tag{31}$$

and $$\log\frac{r_k-x}{r_k}=\log\left(1-x\cos\frac{2k+1}{n}\pi+ix\sin\frac{2k+1}{n}\pi\right). \tag{32}$$

To separate the second member of (32) into its real and imaginary parts, we make use of the relation

$$\log(u+iv)=\tfrac{1}{2}\log(u^2+v^2)+i\tan^{-1}\frac{v}{u}, \quad |v|\leqq|u|, \tag{33}$$

which can be proved as follows:

$$\log(u+iv)=\log u+\log\left(1+i\frac{v}{u}\right), \tag{34}$$

but

$$\log\left(1+i\frac{v}{u}\right)=i\sum_{k=1}^{\infty}\frac{(-1)^{k-1}}{2k-1}\left(\frac{v}{u}\right)^{2k-1}+\sum_{k=1}^{\infty}\frac{(-1)^{k-1}}{2k}\left(\frac{v}{u}\right)^{2k}$$

$$=i\tan^{-1}\frac{v}{u}+\tfrac{1}{2}\log\left(1+\frac{v^2}{u^2}\right)$$

$$=i\tan^{-1}\frac{v}{u}+\tfrac{1}{2}\log(u^2+v^2)-\log u. \tag{35}$$

Substituting (35) into (34) gives (33).

Then, by means of (33), (32) becomes

$$\log\frac{r_k-x}{r_k}=\tfrac{1}{2}\log\left(1-2x\cos\frac{2k+1}{n}\pi+x^2\right)+i\tan^{-1}\frac{x\sin\frac{2k+1}{n}\pi}{1-x\cos\frac{2k+1}{n}\pi}. \tag{36}$$

Applying (31) and (36) to (30), and, since I_1 is real, we obtain

$$I_1=\frac{1}{n}\sum_{k=1}^{n}\sin\frac{2k+1}{n}(m+1)\pi\tan^{-1}\frac{x\sin\frac{2k+1}{n}\pi}{1-x\cos\frac{2k+1}{n}\pi}$$

$$-\frac{1}{2n}\sum_{k=1}^{n}\cos\frac{2k+1}{n}(m+1)\pi\log\left(1-2x\cos\frac{2k+1}{n}\pi+x^2\right). \tag{37}$$

To reduce the upper limit in the first and the second summation in (37), we denote them by P_k and Q_k respectively; then

$$I_1=\frac{1}{n}\sum_{k=1}^{n}P_k-\frac{1}{2n}\sum_{k=1}^{n}Q_k; \tag{38}$$

and since $P_0=P_n$ and $Q_0=Q_n$,

$$I_1=\frac{1}{n}\sum_{k=0}^{n-1}P_k-\frac{1}{2n}\sum_{k=0}^{n-1}Q_k. \tag{39}$$

Now

$$\sum_{k=0}^{n-1}P_k=\sum_{k=0}^{\frac{n-2}{2}}P_k+\sum_{k=\frac{n}{2}}^{n-1}P_k, \quad \text{when } n \text{ is even.} \tag{40}$$

Letting in the second summation in the right of (40), $n-1-k=k'$; then

$$\sum_{k=0}^{n-1} P_k = 2\sum_{k=0}^{\frac{n-2}{2}} P_k. \tag{41}$$

Also, since $P_k=0$, for $k=\dfrac{n-1}{2}$, when n is odd, we find

$$\sum_{k=0}^{n-1} P_k = 2\sum_{k=0}^{\frac{n-3}{2}} P_k. \tag{42}$$

Therefore $$\sum_{k=0}^{n-1} P_k = 2\sum_{k=0}^{\left[\frac{n-2}{2}\right]} P_k, \quad \text{whether } n \text{ be even or odd.} \tag{43}$$

Next $$\sum_{k=0}^{n-1} Q_k = 2\sum_{k=0}^{\frac{n-2}{2}} Q_k, \quad \text{when } n \text{ is even,} \tag{44}$$

$$= 2\sum_{k=0}^{\frac{n-3}{2}} Q_k + Q_{\frac{n-1}{2}}, \quad \text{when } n \text{ is odd.} \tag{45}$$

But $$Q_{\frac{n-1}{2}} = 2(-1)^{m-1}\log(1+x);$$

hence $$\sum_{k=0}^{n-1} Q_k = 2\sum_{k=0}^{\left[\frac{n-2}{2}\right]} Q_k + (-1)^{m-1}[1-(-1)^n]\log(1+x), \tag{46}$$

whether n be even or odd.

Applying (43) and (46) to (38), we obtain

$$I_1 = \frac{2}{n}\sum_{k=0}^{\left[\frac{n-2}{2}\right]} \sin\frac{2k+1}{n}(m+1)\pi \tan^{-1}\frac{x\sin\dfrac{2k+1}{n}\pi}{1-x\cos\dfrac{2k+1}{n}\pi}$$

$$-\frac{1}{n}\sum_{k=0}^{\left[\frac{n-2}{2}\right]} \cos\frac{2k+1}{n}(m+1)\pi \log\left(x^2-2x\cos\frac{2k+1}{n}\pi+1\right)$$

$$+(-1)^m\frac{1-(-1)^n}{2}\log(1+x). \tag{47}$$

In a similar way we find

$$I_2 = \int_0^x \frac{x^m\,dx}{x^n-1} = -\frac{2}{n}\sum_{k=1}^{\left[\frac{n-1}{2}\right]} \sin\frac{2k}{n}(m+1)\pi \tan^{-1}\frac{x\sin\dfrac{2k}{n}\pi}{1-x\cos\dfrac{2k}{n}\pi}$$

$$+\frac{1}{n}\sum_{k=1}^{\left[\frac{n-1}{2}\right]} \cos\frac{2k}{n}(m+1)\pi\log\left(x^2-2x\cos\frac{2k}{n}\pi+1\right)+\frac{1}{n}\log(1-x)$$

$$+(-1)^{m-1}\frac{1+(-1)^n}{2n}\log(1+x). \tag{48}$$

We also find

$$\int \frac{dx}{x^m(x^n+1)} = -\frac{2}{n}\sum_{k=0}^{\left[\frac{n-2}{2}\right]} \sin\frac{2k+1}{n}(m+1)\pi \tan^{-1}\frac{x\sin\frac{2k+1}{n}}{1-x\cos\frac{2k+1}{n}}$$

$$-\frac{1}{n}\sum_{k=0}^{\left[\frac{n-2}{2}\right]} \cos\frac{2k+1}{n}(m+1)\pi \log\left(x^2-2x\cos\frac{2k+1}{n}\pi+1\right)$$

$$+(-1)^m\frac{1-(-1)^n}{2n}\log(1+x) - \sum_{k=0}^{\left[\frac{m-1}{n}\right]}\frac{1}{(m-nk-1)x^{m-nk-1}}, \tag{49}$$

and a similar form for $\displaystyle\int\frac{dx}{x^m(x^n-1)}$.

By means of the above we find

$$\int_0^x \frac{dx}{x^5+1} = \tfrac{1}{20}(\sqrt{5}-1)\log(x^2+\tfrac{1}{2}\sqrt{5-1}\,x+1)$$

$$-\tfrac{1}{20}(\sqrt{5}+1)\log(x^2-\tfrac{1}{2}\sqrt{5+1}\,x+1)$$

$$+\tfrac{1}{10}\sqrt{10+2\sqrt{5}}\tan^{-1}\frac{4x+\sqrt{5}-1}{\sqrt{10+2\sqrt{5}}} + \tfrac{1}{10}\sqrt{10-2\sqrt{5}}\tan^{-1}\frac{4x-\sqrt{5}-1}{\sqrt{10-2\sqrt{5}}}$$

$$+\tfrac{1}{5}\log(1+x), \tag{50}$$

$$\int_0^x \frac{dx}{x^6+1} = \tfrac{1}{12}\sqrt{3}\log\frac{x^2+x\sqrt{3}+1}{x^2-x\sqrt{3}+1} + \tfrac{1}{6}\tan^{-1}\frac{x}{1-x^2} + \tfrac{1}{3}\tan^{-1}x, \tag{51}$$

$$\int_0^x \frac{x^6\,dx}{x^8+1} = \tfrac{1}{16}\sqrt{2-\sqrt{2}}\log\frac{x^2-\sqrt{2-\sqrt{2}}\,x+1}{x^2+\sqrt{2-\sqrt{2}}\,x+1} + \tfrac{1}{16}\sqrt{2+\sqrt{2}}\log\frac{x^2-\sqrt{2+\sqrt{2}}\,x+1}{x^2+\sqrt{2+\sqrt{2}}\,x+1}$$

$$+\tfrac{1}{8}\sqrt{2+\sqrt{2}}\tan^{-1}\frac{\sqrt{2+\sqrt{2}}\,x}{1-x^2} + \tfrac{1}{8}\sqrt{2-\sqrt{2}}\tan^{-1}\frac{\sqrt{2-\sqrt{2}}\,x}{1-x^2}, \tag{52}$$

$$\int \frac{dx}{x^2(x^3+1)} = \tfrac{1}{6}\log\frac{x^2+2x+1}{x^2-x+1} - \tfrac{1}{3}\sqrt{3}\tan^{-1}\frac{x\sqrt{3}}{2-x} - \frac{1}{x}. \tag{53}$$

3. We shall give here a few applications of the results in the preceding articles.

(i) To find the value of $\displaystyle S=\sum_{n=0}^{\infty}(-1)^n\frac{r^n}{5n+1}$. (54)

Let $r=x^5$; then $\displaystyle S=\frac{1}{x}\sum_{n=0}^{\infty}(-1)^n\frac{x^{5n+1}}{5n+1}=\frac{1}{x}S_1.$ (55)

Now $\displaystyle \frac{dS_1}{dx}=\sum_{n=0}^{\infty}(-1)^n x^{5n}=\frac{1}{x^5+1};$

hence $\displaystyle S_1=\int_0^x\frac{dx}{x^5+1}.$ (56)

Then, by means of (50) and letting $x=r^{1/5}$, we obtain from (55),

$$S=\frac{1}{20r^{1/5}}(\sqrt{5}-1)\log(r^{2/5}+\tfrac{1}{2}\sqrt{5-1}\,r^{1/5}+1)$$

$$-\frac{1}{20r^{1/5}}(\sqrt{5}+1)\log(r^{2/5}-\tfrac{1}{2}\sqrt{5+1}\,r^{1/5}+1)$$

$$+\frac{1}{10r^{1/5}}\sqrt{10+2\sqrt{5}}\tan^{-1}\frac{4r^{1/5}+\sqrt{5}-1}{\sqrt{10+2\sqrt{5}}}+\frac{1}{10r^{1/5}}\sqrt{10-2\sqrt{5}}\tan^{-1}\frac{4r^{1/5}-\sqrt{5}-1}{\sqrt{10-2\sqrt{5}}}$$

$$+\frac{1}{5r^{1/5}}\log(r^{1/5}+1). \qquad (57)$$

To find $$S=\sum_{n=0}^{\infty}\frac{(-1)^n}{5n+1}, \qquad (58)$$

we must evaluate (57) for $r=1$.

Denoting in (57) the terms in order, for $r=1$, by T_1, T_2, T_3, T_4 and T_5, we find

$$T_1+T_3=\tfrac{1}{20}(\sqrt{5}-1)\log\tfrac{1}{3}(3+\sqrt{5})+\tfrac{1}{10}\sqrt{10+2\sqrt{5}}\tan^{-1}\sqrt{5-2\sqrt{5}}.$$

But $\tan^{-1}\sqrt{5-2\sqrt{5}}=\frac{\pi}{5}$ (see table at the end of this chapter) ; hence

$$T_1+T_3=\tfrac{1}{10}(\sqrt{5}-1)\log\tfrac{1}{2}(\sqrt{5}+1)+\frac{\pi}{50}\sqrt{10+2\sqrt{5}}. \qquad (59)$$

Similarly

$$-T_2+T_4=-\tfrac{1}{10}(\sqrt{5}+1)\log\tfrac{1}{2}(\sqrt{5}-1)+\frac{2\pi}{50}\sqrt{10-2\sqrt{5}} \qquad (60)$$

and $$T_5=\tfrac{1}{5}\log 2. \qquad (61)$$

Then, by means of (59)–(61), we obtain from (57),

$$S=\tfrac{1}{10}\sqrt{5}\log\frac{\sqrt{5}+1}{\sqrt{5}-1}+\frac{\pi}{50}(\sqrt{10+2\sqrt{5}}+2\sqrt{10-2\sqrt{5}})+\tfrac{1}{5}\log 2.$$

But $$(\sqrt{10+2\sqrt{5}}+2\sqrt{10-2\sqrt{5}})^2=5(10+2\sqrt{5});$$

therefore $$\sum_{n=0}^{\infty}\frac{(-1)^n}{5n+1}=\tfrac{1}{5}\sqrt{5}\log\tfrac{1}{2}(\sqrt{5}+1)+\frac{\pi}{50}\sqrt{5}\sqrt{10+2\sqrt{5}}+\tfrac{1}{5}\log 2. \qquad (62)$$

(ii) To find the value of

$$S=\sum_{n=0}^{\infty}\frac{r^n}{\prod_{k=1}^{3}(4n+2k-1)}. \qquad (63)$$

Now

$$\frac{1}{\prod_{k=1}^{3}(4n+2k-1)}=\frac{1}{2^3}\sum_{k=1}^{3}(-1)^{k-1}\binom{2}{k-1}\frac{1}{4n+2k-1}, \text{ by Ch. VIII. (6),} \qquad (64)$$

and letting $r=x^4$, then

$$S=\frac{1}{8}\sum_{k=1}^{3}(-1)^{k-1}\binom{2}{k-1}\frac{1}{x^{2k-1}}\sum_{n=0}^{\infty}\frac{x^{4n+2k-1}}{4n+2k-1}. \qquad (65)$$

Denoting $$\sum_{n=0}^{\infty}\frac{x^{4n+2k-1}}{4n+2k-1} \text{ by } S_k, \tag{66}$$

we have $$\frac{dS_k}{dx}=x^{2k-2}\sum_{n=0}^{\infty}x^{4n}=-\frac{x^{2k-2}}{x^4-1}$$

and $$S_k=-\int_0^x\frac{x^{2k-2}\,dx}{x^4-1}, \tag{67}$$

the constant being zero.

Then, from (65), $$S=\frac{1}{8}\left(\frac{1}{x}S_1-\frac{2}{x^3}S_2+\frac{1}{x^5}S_3\right). \tag{68}$$

Now $$S_1=\tfrac{1}{4}\log\frac{1+x}{1-x}+\tfrac{1}{2}\tan^{-1}x, \tag{69}$$

$$S_2=\tfrac{1}{4}\log\frac{1+x}{1-x}-\tfrac{1}{2}\tan^{-1}x, \tag{70}$$

$$S_3=-x+\tfrac{1}{4}\log\frac{1+x}{1-x}+\tfrac{1}{2}\tan^{-1}x. \tag{71}$$

Applying (69)–(71) to (68), and letting $x=r^{1/5}$, we obtain

$$S=\frac{1}{32r^{5/4}}(1-r^{1/2})^2\log\frac{1+r^{1/4}}{1-r^{1/4}}+\frac{1}{16r^{5/4}}(1+r^{1/2})^2\tan^{-1}r^{1/4}-\frac{1}{8r}. \tag{72}$$

If $r=1$, $$S=\sum_{n=0}^{\infty}\frac{1}{\prod_{k=1}^{3}(4n+2k-1)}=\frac{\pi}{16}-\frac{1}{8}. \tag{73}$$

(iii) If $$S=\sum_{n=0}^{\infty}\frac{(-1)^n r^n}{\prod_{k=1}^{3}(4n+2k-1)}, \tag{74}$$

then $$S=\frac{1}{8}\left(\frac{1}{x}S_1-\frac{2}{x^3}S_2+\frac{1}{x^5}S_3\right),\quad x=r^{1/4}, \tag{75}$$

and we find

$$S_1=\int_0^x\frac{dx}{x^4+1}=\tfrac{1}{8}\surd 2\log\frac{x^2+x\surd 2+1}{x^2-x\surd 2+1}+\tfrac{1}{4}\surd 2\tan^{-1}\frac{x\surd 2}{1-x^2}, \tag{76}$$

$$S_2=\int_0^x\frac{x^2\,dx}{x^4+1}=-\tfrac{1}{8}\surd 2\log\frac{x^2+x\surd 2+1}{x^2-x\surd 2+1}+\tfrac{1}{4}\surd 2\tan^{-1}\frac{x\surd 2}{1-x^2}, \tag{77}$$

$$S_3=\int_0^x\frac{x^4\,dx}{x^4+1}=x-\tfrac{1}{8}\surd 2\log\frac{x^2+x\surd 2+1}{x^2-x\surd 2+1}-\tfrac{1}{4}\surd 2\tan^{-1}\frac{x\surd 2}{1-x^2}. \tag{78}$$

Then, by means of (76)–(78), we have from (75),

$$S=\frac{\surd 2}{64r^{5/4}}(r+2r^{1/2}-1)\log\frac{r^{1/2}+r^{1/4}\surd 2+1}{r^{1/2}-r^{1/4}\surd 2+1}$$

$$+\frac{\surd 2}{32r^{5/4}}(r-2r^{1/2}-1)\tan^{-1}\frac{r^{1/4}\surd 2}{1-r^2}+\frac{1}{8r}. \tag{79}$$

This result can also be obtained by writing in (72), $-r$ for r. In this way the laborious operations of integration are avoided.

Denoting in (72)

$$\frac{1}{r^{5/4}}(1-r^{1/2})^2 \text{ by } F_1(r),\ \log\frac{1+r^{1/4}}{1-r^{1/4}} \text{ by } F_2(r) \text{ and } \frac{1}{r^{5/4}}(1+r^{1/2})^2 \text{ by } F_3(r), \quad (80)$$

and since the principal value of $(-1)^{1/4}=\frac{1}{2}(1+i)\sqrt{2}$; we have

$$F_1(-r)=-\frac{\sqrt{2}}{2r^{5/4}}(1-i)(1-r-2ir^{1/2})$$

$$=-\frac{\sqrt{2}}{2r^{5/4}}[(1-r-2r^{1/2})-i(1-r+2r^{1/2})]. \quad (81)$$

Similarly $$F_3(-r)=-\frac{\sqrt{2}}{2r^{5/4}}[(1-r+2r^{1/2})-i(1-r-2r^{1/2})]. \quad (82)$$

Now $$F_2(-r)=\log\frac{1+\frac{1}{2}r^{1/4}\sqrt{2}+\frac{1}{2}ir^{1/4}\sqrt{2}}{1-\frac{1}{2}r^{1/4}\sqrt{2}-\frac{1}{2}ir^{1/4}\sqrt{2}}; \quad (83)$$

then, by means of (33),

$$F_2(-r)=\frac{1}{2}\log\frac{1+r^{1/4}\sqrt{2}+r^{1/2}}{1-r^{1/4}\sqrt{2}+r^{1/2}}+i\tan^{-1}\frac{r^{1/4}\sqrt{2}}{1-r^2}. \quad (84)$$

To separate $$\tan^{-1}(-r)^{1/4}=\tan^{-1}(\tfrac{1}{2}r^{1/4}\sqrt{2}+\tfrac{1}{2}ir^{1/4}\sqrt{2}) \quad (85)$$

into its real and imaginary parts, we shall first show that for $|v|\leqq|u|$,

$$\tan^{-1}(u+iv)=-\frac{i}{4}\log\frac{(1-v)^2+u^2}{(1+v)^2+u^2}+\frac{1}{2}\tan^{-1}\frac{2u}{1-v^2-u^2}. \quad (86)$$

Now $$\log(1+iu)=i\sum_{k=1}^{\infty}\frac{(-1)^{k-1}}{2k-1}u^{2k-1}+\sum_{k=1}^{\infty}\frac{(-1)^{k-1}}{2k}u^{2k} \quad (87)$$

and $\log(1-iu)$ is of the same form as (87), except that i is negative.

Therefore $$\log\frac{1+iu}{1-iu}=2i\sum_{k=1}^{\infty}\frac{(-1)^{k-1}}{2k-1}u^{2k-1}=2i\tan^{-1}u. \quad (88)$$

Writing in (88) $u+iv$ for u, we have

$$\tan^{-1}(u+iv)=\frac{1}{2i}\log\frac{1-v+iu}{1+v-iu}=\frac{1}{2i}\left[\log\frac{1-v}{1+v}+\log\left(1+i\frac{u}{1-v}\right)-\log\left(1-i\frac{u}{1+v}\right)\right]. \quad (89)$$

But $$\log\left(1+i\frac{u}{1-v}\right)=i\tan^{-1}\frac{u}{1-v}+\frac{1}{2}\log\left[1+\left(\frac{u}{1-v}\right)^2\right] \quad (90)$$

and $$\log\left(1-i\frac{u}{1+v}\right)=-i\tan^{-1}\frac{u}{1+v}+\frac{1}{2}\log\left[1+\left(\frac{u}{1+v}\right)^2\right]. \quad (91)$$

Substituting (90) and (91) in (89) gives (86), by means of which (85) becomes

$$\tan^{-1}(-r)^{1/4}=-\frac{i}{4}\log\frac{1-r^{1/4}\sqrt{2}+r^{1/2}}{1+r^{1/4}\sqrt{2}+r^{1/2}}+\frac{1}{2}\tan^{-1}\frac{r^{1/4}\sqrt{2}}{1-r^2}. \quad (92)$$

Applying (81), (82), (84) and (92) to (72), (79) is obtained.

If $r=1$,

$$S=\sum_{n=0}^{\infty}\frac{(-1)^n}{\prod_{k=1}^{3}(4n+2k-1)}=\tfrac{1}{16}\sqrt{2}[\sqrt{2}+\log(1+\sqrt{2})-\tfrac{1}{2}\pi]. \quad (93)$$

(iv) Show that

$$\sum_{n=0}^{\infty}\frac{r^n}{\prod_{k=1}^{5}(4n+k)}=\frac{1}{4!}\left[\frac{r-6r^{1/2}+1}{2r^{5/4}}\tan^{-1}r^{1/4}\right.$$

$$\left.+\frac{r+6r^{1/2}+1}{4r^{5/4}}\log\frac{1+r^{1/4}}{1-r^{1/4}}+\frac{1+r^{1/2}}{r}\log(1+r^{1/2})+\frac{1+r^{1/2}}{r}\log(1-r^{1/2})-\frac{1}{r}\right] \tag{94}$$

and

$$\sum_{n=0}^{\infty}\frac{1}{\prod_{k=1}^{5}(4n+k)}=\frac{1}{4!}\left(4\log 2-\frac{\pi}{2}-1\right). \tag{95}$$

Also

$$\sum_{n=0}^{\infty}\frac{(-1)^n r^n}{\prod_{k=1}^{5}(4n+k)}=\frac{1}{4!}\left[\frac{\sqrt{2}}{4r^{5/4}}(r+6r^{1/2}-1)\tan^{-1}\frac{r^{1/4}\sqrt{2}}{1-r^{1/2}}\right.$$

$$\left.-2\tan^{-1}r^{1/2}+\frac{\sqrt{2}}{8r^{5/4}}(r-6r^{1/2}-1)\log\frac{r^{1/2}+r^{1/4}\sqrt{2}+1}{r^{1/2}-r^{1/4}\sqrt{2}+1}-\frac{1}{r}\log(1+r)+\frac{1}{r}\right] \tag{96}$$

and

$$\sum_{n=0}^{\infty}\frac{(-1)^n}{\prod_{k=1}^{5}(4n+k)}=\frac{1}{4!}\left(\tfrac{3}{4}\pi\sqrt{2}-\frac{\pi}{2}-\tfrac{3}{4}\sqrt{2}\log\frac{\sqrt{2}+1}{\sqrt{2}-1}+1-\log 2\right). \tag{97}$$

(v) Show that

$$\sum_{n=0}^{\infty}\frac{r^n}{\prod_{k=1}^{3}(6n+3k-2)}=\frac{(1-r^{1/2})^2}{216r^{7/6}}\log\frac{r^{1/3}+r^{1/6}+1}{(1-r^{1/6})^2}$$

$$+\frac{(1+r^{1/2})^2}{216r^{7/6}}\log\frac{1+2r^{1/6}+r^{1/3}}{1-r^{1/6}+r^{1/3}}+\frac{\sqrt{3}(1+r^{1/2})^2}{108r^{7/6}}\tan^{-1}\frac{r^{1/6}\sqrt{3}}{1-r^{1/3}}$$

$$-\frac{\sqrt{3}}{27r^{2/3}}\tan^{-1}\frac{r^{1/6}\sqrt{3}}{2+r^{1/6}}-\frac{1}{18r}, \tag{98}$$

and by writing in (98) $-r$ for r, find the value of

$$\sum_{n=0}^{\infty}\frac{(-1)^n r^n}{\prod_{k=1}^{3}(6n+3k-2)}.$$

4. The integrals I_1 and I_2 are involved in the process of obtaining the sum of many types of series. We shall here evaluate these integrals for $x=1$. Letting $x=1$ in (20) and (47), we have

$$I_1\Big]_{x=1}=\sum_{k=1}^{\left[\frac{m}{n}\right]}(-1)^{k-1}\frac{1}{m-kn+1}+\frac{\pi}{n}\sum_{k=0}^{\left[\frac{n-2}{2}\right]}\sin\frac{2k+1}{n}(m+1)\pi$$

$$-\frac{2}{n}\sum_{k=0}^{\left[\frac{n-2}{2}\right]}\frac{2k+1}{2n}\sin\frac{2k+1}{n}(m+1)\pi-\frac{2}{n}\log 2\sum_{k=0}^{\left[\frac{n-2}{2}\right]}\cos\frac{2k+1}{n}(m+1)\pi$$

$$-\frac{2}{n}\sum_{k=0}^{\left[\frac{n-2}{2}\right]}\cos\frac{2k+1}{n}(m+1)\pi\log\sin\frac{2k+1}{2n}\pi+(-1)^m\frac{1-(-1)^n}{2n}\log 2, \tag{99}$$

where the first summation is zero if $m<n$.

The result (99) will be reduced by evaluating the several summations in it.

(i) To reduce
$$S_1=\sum_{k=1}^{\left[\frac{n-2}{2}\right]} \sin\frac{2k+1}{n}a\pi, \quad a=m+1. \tag{100}$$

If in
$$\sum_{k=0}^{n} \sin(b+kg)=\sin\left(b+\frac{n}{2}g\right)\sin\frac{n+1}{2}g\operatorname{cosec}\frac{g}{2},$$

we let $b=\frac{a\pi}{n}$, $g=\frac{2a\pi}{n}$, and write $\frac{n-2}{2}$ for the upper limit n, when n is even, and $\frac{n-3}{2}$ for n, when n is odd, we obtain

$$S_1=\sin^2\frac{a\pi}{2}\operatorname{cosec}\frac{a\pi}{n}=\frac{1-(-1)^a}{2}\operatorname{cosec}\frac{a\pi}{n}, \quad \text{when } n \text{ is even,} \tag{101}$$

and
$$=\sin^2\left(\frac{a\pi}{2}-\frac{a\pi}{2n}\right)\operatorname{cosec}\frac{a\pi}{n}$$
$$=\left(\frac{1-(-1)^a}{2}\cos^2\frac{a\pi}{2n}+\frac{1+(-1)^a}{2}\sin^2\frac{a\pi}{2n}\right)\operatorname{cosec}\frac{a\pi}{n}$$
$$=\tfrac{1}{2}\left(\operatorname{cosec}\frac{a\pi}{n}-(-1)^a\cot\frac{a\pi}{n}\right), \quad \text{when } n \text{ is odd.} \tag{102}$$

Therefore, whether n be even or odd,

$$S_1=\tfrac{1}{2}\operatorname{cosec}\frac{a\pi}{n}-(-1)^a\frac{1+(-1)^n}{4}\operatorname{cosec}\frac{a\pi}{n}-(-1)^a\frac{1-(-1)^n}{4}\cot\frac{a\pi}{n}$$
$$=\tfrac{1}{2}\operatorname{cosec}\frac{a\pi}{n}-\frac{(-1)^a}{4}\left(\cot\frac{a\pi}{2n}+(-1)^n\tan\frac{a\pi}{2n}\right), \tag{103}$$

if a is not a multiple of n.

And $$S_1=0, \quad \text{if } a \text{ is a multiple of } n. \tag{104}$$

(ii) We shall next simplify
$$S_2=\sum_{k=o}^{\left[\frac{n-2}{2}\right]} \cos\frac{2k+1}{n}a\pi \tag{105}$$

by letting in
$$\sum_{k=0}^{n}\cos(b+kg)=\cos\left(b+\frac{n}{2}g\right)\sin\frac{n+1}{2}g\operatorname{cosec}\frac{g}{2},$$

$b=\frac{a\pi}{n}$, $g=\frac{2a\pi}{n}$, and by writing for the upper limit n, first $\frac{n-2}{2}$ and then $\frac{n-3}{2}$. We then find, if a is not a multiple of n,

$$\sum_{k=0}^{\left[\frac{n-2}{2}\right]}\cos\frac{2k+1}{n}a\pi=0 \quad\text{and}\quad \sum_{k=0}^{\left[\frac{n-3}{2}\right]}\cos\frac{2k+1}{n}a\pi=(-1)^{a-1}\tfrac{1}{2}. \tag{106}$$

Therefore, whether n be even or odd,

$$S_2=(-1)^{a-1}\frac{1-(-1)^n}{4}, \quad \text{if } a \text{ is not a multiple of } n, \tag{107}$$
$$=(-1)^{\frac{a}{n}}\left[\frac{n}{2}\right], \quad \text{if } a \text{ is a multiple of } n. \tag{108}$$

(iii) To find the value of

$$S_3 = \sum_{k=0}^{\left[\frac{n-2}{2}\right]} (2k+1)\sin\frac{2k+1}{n}a\pi. \tag{109}$$

Then, when n is even,

$$S_3 = \frac{1}{2i}\sum_{k=0}^{\left[\frac{n-2}{2}\right]} (2k+1)(r_1^{2k+1} - r_2^{2k+1}),$$

where $$r_1 = e^{\frac{a\pi i}{n}} \quad \text{and} \quad r_2 = e^{-\frac{a\pi i}{n}}.$$

Therefore $$S_3 = \frac{1}{2i}\left[\left(r_1\frac{d}{dr_1}\right)\sum_{k=0}^{\frac{n-2}{2}} r_1^{2k+1} - \left(r_2\frac{d}{dr_2}\right)\sum_{k=0}^{\frac{n-2}{2}} r_2^{2k+1}\right] \tag{110}$$

$$= \frac{r_1[1-(-1)^a(n+1)] + r_1^3[1+(-1)^a(n-1)]}{2i(1-r_1)^2}$$

$$- \frac{r_2[1-(-1)^a(n+1)] + r_2^3[1+(-1)^a(n-1)]}{2i(1-r_2)^2}$$

$$= (-1)^{a-1}\frac{n}{2}\operatorname{cosec}\frac{a\pi}{n}, \text{ if } a \text{ is not a multiple of } n. \tag{111}$$

And when n is odd, $$S_3 = (-1)^{a-1}\frac{n}{2}\cot\frac{a\pi}{n}. \tag{112}$$

Hence, whether n be even or odd,

$$S_3 = (-1)^{a-1}\frac{n}{4}\left(\cot\frac{a\pi}{2n} + (-1)^n\tan\frac{a\pi}{2n}\right), \tag{113}$$

when a is not a multiple of n, and

$$S_3 = 0, \quad \text{when } a \text{ is a multiple of } n. \tag{114}$$

Substituting (103), (107) and (113) in (99), we obtain

$$I_1 = \sum_{k=1}^{\left[\frac{m}{n}\right]} (-1)^{k-1}\frac{1}{m-kn+1} + \frac{\pi}{2n}\operatorname{cosec}\frac{m+1}{n}\pi$$

$$-\frac{2}{n}\sum_{k=0}^{\left[\frac{n-2}{2}\right]} \cos\frac{2k+1}{n}(m+1)\pi\log\sin\frac{2k+1}{2n}\pi, \tag{115}$$

when $m+1$ is not a multiple of n.

If n is even, the second summation in (115) reduces to

$$\sum_{k=0}^{\left[\frac{n}{4}\right]-1} \cos\frac{2k+1}{n}(m+1)\pi\log\tan\frac{2k+1}{2n}\pi, \quad \text{when } m \text{ is even}, \tag{116}$$

and to

$$\sum_{k=0}^{\left[\frac{n}{4}\right]-1} \cos\frac{2k+1}{n}(m+1)\pi\log\left(\tfrac{1}{2}\sin\frac{2k+1}{n}\pi\right)-\frac{(-1)^{\frac{m+1}{2}}}{4}\left[1-(-1)^{\frac{m}{2}}\right]\log 2,$$

when m is odd. (117)

When $n=2$, the summations in (116) and (117) are defined as zero.

If $m+1$ is a multiple of n, then

$$I_1\Big]_{x=1}=\sum_{k=1}^{\left[\frac{m}{n}\right]}\frac{(-1)^{k-1}}{m-kn+1}+N, \tag{118}$$

where $N=-\frac{1}{n}\log 2$, when $m+1$ is an even multiple of n,

and $N=\frac{1}{n}\log 2$, when $m+1$ is an odd multiple of n.

The result (118) can also be obtained from (99) as follows. This method is given because of the principles in the operation with series which it involves. Applying (104), (108) and (114) to (99), we have

$$I_1\Big]_{x=1}=\sum_{k=1}^{\left[\frac{m}{n}\right]}\frac{(-1)^{k-1}}{m-kn+1}+\frac{2}{n}\left[(-1)^m\frac{1-(-1)^m}{4}-(-1)^{\frac{m+1}{n}}\left[\frac{n}{2}\right]\right]\log 2$$

$$-(-1)^{\frac{m+1}{n}}\sum_{k=0}^{\left[\frac{n-2}{2}\right]}\log\sin\frac{2k+1}{2n}\pi. \tag{119}$$

Now $$S_4=\sum_{k=0}^{\left[\frac{n-2}{2}\right]}\log\sin\frac{2k+1}{2n}\pi \text{ in (119)} \tag{120}$$

can be reduced in the following way:

Whether n be even or odd,

$$S_4=\tfrac{1}{2}\sum_{k=0}^{n-1}\log\sin\frac{2k+1}{2n}\pi \tag{121}$$

$$=\tfrac{1}{2}\log\prod_{k=0}^{n-1}\frac{i}{2}\left(e^{-\frac{2k+1}{2n}\pi i}-e^{\frac{2k+1}{2n}\pi i}\right)$$

$$=\tfrac{1}{2}\log\prod_{k=0}^{n-1}\frac{i}{2}e^{\frac{1-2k}{2n}\pi i}\left(e^{-\frac{\pi i}{n}}-e^{\frac{2k}{n}\pi i}\right). \tag{122}$$

But $e^{-\frac{\pi i}{n}}-e^{\frac{2k}{n}\pi i}$ is a factor of x^n-1, when $x=e^{-\frac{\pi i}{n}}$; therefore

$$\prod_{k=0}^{n-1}\left(e^{-\frac{\pi i}{n}}-e^{\frac{2k}{n}\pi i}\right)=\left(e^{-\frac{\pi i}{n}}\right)^n-1=e^{-\pi i}-1=-2, \tag{123}$$

and $$S_4=\tfrac{1}{2}\log\left(\frac{-i^n}{2^{n-1}}\prod_{k=0}^{n-1}e^{\frac{1-2k}{2n}\pi i}\right)$$

$$=\tfrac{1}{2}\log\left(\frac{-i^n}{2^{n-1}}e^{\frac{2-n}{2}\pi i}\right)=-\frac{n-1}{2}\log 2. \tag{124}$$

Applying (124) to (119), we obtain

$$I_1\Big]_{x=1}=\sum_{k=1}^{\left[\frac{m}{n}\right]}\frac{(-1)^{k-1}}{m-kn+1}+\frac{2}{n}\left[(-1)^{\frac{m+1}{2}}\left\{\frac{n-1}{2}-\left[\frac{n}{2}\right]\right\}+(-1)^m\frac{1-(-1)^n}{4}\right]\log 2;$$

and since $$\frac{2}{n}\left(\frac{n-1}{2}-\left[\frac{n}{2}\right]\right)=-\frac{1+(-1)^n}{2},$$

$$I_1\Big]_{x=1}=\sum_{k=1}^{\left[\frac{m}{n}\right]}\frac{(-1)^{k-1}}{m-kn+1}+\frac{1}{2n}\left[(-1)^m(1-(-1)^n)\right.$$

$$\left.-(-1)^{\frac{m+1}{n}}(1+(-1)^n)\right]\log 2. \qquad (125)$$

Denoting the expression within the brackets of (125) by M, then, when n is even and $m+1$ is an even multiple of n, $M=-2$, and when $m+1$ is an odd multiple of n, $M=2$.

When n is odd and $m+1$ is an even multiple of n, $m+1$ is even; therefore m is odd and $M=-2$. And if $m+1$ is an odd multiple of n, $m+1$ is odd; therefore m is even and $M=2$. Applying the values of M to (125), we obtain (118).

Although I_2 is infinite for $x=1$ we shall nevertheless find it to our advantage to evaluate the finite terms that are involved.

5. To find the value of I_2 for $x=1$, we let $x=1$ in (21) and (48), which gives

$$I_2\Big]_{x=1}=\sum_{k=1}^{\left[\frac{m}{n}\right]}\frac{1}{m-kn+1}-\frac{\pi}{n}\sum_{k=1}^{\left[\frac{n-1}{2}\right]}\sin\frac{2k}{n}(m+1)\pi+\frac{1}{n}\sum_{k=1}^{\left[\frac{n-1}{2}\right]}\frac{2k\pi}{n}$$

$$\sin\frac{2k}{n}(m+1)\pi+\frac{2}{n}\log 2\sum_{k=1}^{\left[\frac{n-1}{2}\right]}\cos\frac{2k}{n}(m+1)\pi$$

$$+\frac{2}{n}\sum_{k=1}^{\left[\frac{n-1}{2}\right]}\cos\frac{2k}{n}(m+1)\pi\log\sin\frac{k\pi}{n}+(-1)^{m-1}\frac{1+(-1)^n}{2n}\log 2+\frac{1}{n}\log(1-x)\Big]_{x=1}. \qquad (126)$$

(i) To find the sum

$$S_5=\sum_{k=1}^{\left[\frac{n-1}{2}\right]}\sin\frac{2k}{n}a\pi, \quad a=m+1. \qquad (127)$$

Then $$S_5=\frac{1-(-1)^a}{2}\cot\frac{a\pi}{n}, \quad \text{when } n \text{ is even,}$$

$$=\tfrac{1}{2}\cot\frac{a\pi}{n}-(-1)^a\tfrac{1}{2}\operatorname{cosec}\frac{a\pi}{n}, \quad \text{when } n \text{ is odd,}$$

$$=\tfrac{1}{2}\cot\frac{a\pi}{n}-(-1)^a\tfrac{1}{4}\left(\cot\frac{a\pi}{2n}-(-1)^n\tan\frac{a\pi}{2n}\right), \qquad (128)$$

whether n be even or odd, and if a is not a multiple of n.

Also $$S_5=0, \quad \text{if } a \text{ is a multiple of } n. \qquad (129)$$

(ii) $$S_6 = \sum_{k=1}^{\left[\frac{n-1}{2}\right]} \frac{2k\pi}{n} \sin \frac{2k}{n} a\pi. \tag{130}$$

Now $$S_6 = (-1)^{a-1} \frac{\pi}{2} \cot \frac{a\pi}{n}, \quad \text{when } n \text{ is even,}$$

$$= (-1)^{a-1} \frac{\pi}{2} \operatorname{cosec} \frac{a\pi}{n}, \quad \text{when } n \text{ is odd,}$$

$$= (-1)^{a-1} \frac{\pi}{4} \left(\cot \frac{a\pi}{2n} - (-1)^n \tan \frac{a\pi}{2n} \right), \tag{131}$$

whether n be even or odd, and if a is not a multiple of n.

And $$S_6 = 0, \quad \text{if } a \text{ is a multiple of } n. \tag{132}$$

(iii) Let $$S_7 = \sum_{k=1}^{\left[\frac{n-1}{2}\right]} \cos \frac{2k}{n} a\pi. \tag{133}$$

Then $$S_7 = -\frac{1+(-1)^a}{2}, \quad \text{when } n \text{ is even,}$$

$$= -\tfrac{1}{2}, \quad \text{when } n \text{ is odd,}$$

$$= -\tfrac{1}{4}[2 + (-1)^a(1 + (-1)^n)], \tag{134}$$

whether n be even or odd, and if a is not a multiple of n.

And $$S_7 = \left[\frac{n-1}{2}\right], \quad \text{if } a \text{ is a multiple of } n. \tag{135}$$

Then, by means of (128), 131) and (134), we obtain from (126)

$$I_2\Big]_{x=1} = \sum_{k=1}^{\left[\frac{m}{n}\right]} \frac{1}{m-kn+1} - \frac{\pi}{2n} \cot \frac{m+1}{n} \pi - \frac{1}{n} \log 2$$

$$+ \frac{2}{n} \sum_{k=1}^{\left[\frac{n-1}{2}\right]} \cos \frac{2k}{n}(m+1)\pi \log \sin \frac{k\pi}{n} + \frac{1}{n} \log(1-x)\Big]_{x=1}, \tag{136}$$

if $m+1$ is not a multiple of n.

If n is even, the second summation in (136) reduces to

$$\sum_{k=1}^{\left[\frac{n-2}{4}\right]} \cos \frac{2k}{n}(m+1) \log \tan \frac{k\pi}{n}, \quad \text{when } m \text{ is even,} \tag{137}$$

and to $$\sum_{k=1}^{\left[\frac{n-1}{2}\right]} \cos \frac{2k}{n}(m+1)\pi \log\left(\tfrac{1}{2} \sin \frac{2k\pi}{n}\right) - \frac{(-1)^{\frac{m+1}{2}}}{4} \left[1 + (-1)^{\frac{n}{2}}\right] \log 2,$$

$$\text{when } m \text{ is odd.} \tag{138}$$

When $n=2$ and $n=4$, the summations in (137) and (138) are defined as zero.

If $m+1$ is a multiple of n,

$$I_2 = \sum_{k=1}^{\left[\frac{m}{n}\right]} \frac{1}{m-kn+1} + \frac{1}{n}\log n + \frac{1}{n}\log(1-x)\Big]_{x \doteq 1}. \tag{139}$$

This result can also be obtained from (126) as follows:
Applying (129), (132) and (135) to (126), we have

$$I_2\Big]_{x\doteq 1} = \sum_{k=1}^{\left[\frac{m}{n}\right]} \frac{1}{m-kn+1} + \frac{2}{n}\left[\frac{n-1}{2}\right]\log 2 + \frac{2}{n}\sum_{k=1}^{\left[\frac{n-1}{2}\right]} \log\sin\frac{k\pi}{n}$$

$$+(-1)^{m-1}\frac{1+(-1)^n}{2n}\log 2 + \frac{1}{n}\log(1-x)\Big]_{x\doteq 1}. \tag{140}$$

To reduce (140), we shall find the value of

$$S_8 = \sum_{k=1}^{\left[\frac{n-1}{2}\right]} \log\sin\frac{k\pi}{n}. \tag{141}$$

Now

$$S_8 = \tfrac{1}{2}\sum_{k=1}^{n-1} \log\sin\frac{k\pi}{n} \tag{142}$$

$$= \tfrac{1}{2}\sum_{k=1}^{n-1}\left[\log\left(1-e^{\frac{2k}{n}\pi i}\right) - \log\left(-2ie^{\frac{k}{n}\pi i}\right)\right]$$

$$= \tfrac{1}{2}\log\prod_{k=1}^{n-1}\left(1-e^{\frac{2k}{n}\pi i}\right) - \tfrac{1}{2}\log\prod_{k=1}^{n-1}\left(-2ie^{\frac{k}{n}\pi i}\right). \tag{143}$$

But $1-e^{\frac{2k}{n}\pi i}$ is a factor of $1-x^n]_{x\doteq 1}$.

Therefore

$$\prod_{k=1}^{n-1}\left(1-e^{\frac{2k}{n}\pi i}\right) = \frac{1-x^n}{1-x}\Big]_{x\doteq 1} = n. \tag{144}$$

Also

$$\log\prod_{k=1}^{n-1}\left(-2ie^{\frac{k}{n}\pi i}\right) = (n-1)\log 2. \tag{145}$$

Applying (144) and (145) to (143) gives

$$S_8 = \tfrac{1}{2}\log\frac{2n}{2^n}. \tag{146}$$

Then, by means of (146), we obtain from (140)

$$I_2\Big]_{x\doteq 1} = \sum_{k=1}^{\left[\frac{m}{n}\right]} \frac{1}{m-kn+1} + \frac{2}{n}\left[\frac{n-1}{2}\right]\log 2 + \frac{1}{n}\log 2$$

$$+\frac{1}{n}\log n - \log 2 - (-1)^m\frac{1+(-1)^m}{2n}\log 2 + \frac{1}{n}\log(1-x)\Big]_{x\doteq 1} \tag{147}$$

and since

$$\frac{2}{n}\left[\frac{n-1}{2}\right] - \frac{n-1}{n} = -\frac{1+(-1)^n}{2n},$$

therefore

$$I_2\Big]_{x\doteq 1}=\sum_{k=1}^{\left[\frac{m}{n}\right]}\frac{1}{m-kn+1}+\frac{1}{n}\log n-[1+(-1)^m]\frac{1+(-1)^n}{2n}\log 2$$

$$+\frac{1}{n}\log(1-x)\Big]_{x\doteq 1}. \tag{148}$$

Now, if n is odd, the term

$$[1+(-1)^m]\frac{1+(-1)^n}{2n}\log 2 \tag{149}$$

vanishes. If n is even, and since $m+1$ is a multiple of n, m must be odd, and (149) is again zero.

We then obtain

$$I_2\Big]_{x\doteq 1}=\sum_{k=1}^{\left[\frac{m}{n}\right]}\frac{1}{m-kn+1}+\frac{1}{n}\log n+\frac{1}{n}\log(1-x)\Big]_{x\doteq 1},$$

which is the same as (139).

6. (i) As an application of I_1 and I_2 for $x=1$, we shall obtain (73) without first finding the integrals (69), (70) and (71) and the result (72).

Applying (126) to (67), we have

$$S_1\Big]_{x=1}=\frac{\pi}{8}+\tfrac{1}{4}\log 2-\tfrac{1}{4}\log(1-x)\Big]_{x\doteq 1}, \tag{150}$$

$$S_2\Big]_{x=1}=-\frac{\pi}{8}+\tfrac{1}{4}\log 2-\tfrac{1}{4}\log(1-x)\Big]_{x\doteq 1}, \tag{151}$$

$$S_3\Big]_{x=1}=-1+S_1\Big]_{x\doteq 1}. \tag{152}$$

Substituting (150)–(152) in (68) gives, by evaluating the resulting indeterminate form,

$$\frac{1}{8}\left(\frac{\pi}{2}-1\right),$$

which is the same as (73).

(ii) To obtain (62) from (115) without finding (57).

Then $$\int_0^1\frac{dx}{x^5+1}=\pi\operatorname{cosec}\frac{\pi}{5}-\frac{2}{5}\left(\cos\frac{\pi}{5}\log\sin\frac{\pi}{10}-\sin\frac{\pi}{10}\log\cos\frac{\pi}{5}\right)$$

$$=\frac{\pi}{50}\sqrt{5}\sqrt{10+2\sqrt{5}}+\tfrac{1}{5}\sqrt{5}\log\frac{\sqrt{5}+1}{2}+\tfrac{1}{5}\log 2,$$

which is the same as (62).

7. To find the sum of $$S=\sum_{n=0}^{\infty}\frac{(-1)^n r^n}{a+nh}. \tag{153}$$

Letting $r=x^h$, then $$S=\frac{1}{x^a}\sum_{n=0}^{\infty}(-1)^n\frac{x^{a+nh}}{a+nh}$$

$$=\frac{1}{x^a}\int_0^x\frac{x^{a-1}dx}{x^h+1}. \tag{154}$$

By means of (47) we obtain

$$S=\frac{1}{r^{a/h}}\left[\sum_{k=1}^{\left[\frac{a-1}{2}\right]}(-1)^{k-1}\frac{r^{\frac{a-kh}{h}}}{a-kh}+\frac{2}{h}\sum_{k=0}^{\left[\frac{h-2}{2}\right]}\sin\frac{2k+1}{h}a\pi\tan^{-1}\frac{r^{1/h}\sin\frac{2k+1}{h}\pi}{1-r^{1/h}\cos\frac{2k+1}{h}\pi}\right.$$

$$-\frac{1}{h}\sum_{k=0}^{\left[\frac{h-2}{2}\right]}\cos\frac{2k+1}{h}a\pi\log\left(r^{2/h}-2r^{1/h}\cos\frac{2k+1}{h}\pi+1\right)$$

$$\left.+(-1)^{a-1}\frac{1-(-1)^h}{2h}\log(1+r^{1/h})\right]. \qquad (155)$$

Letting in (153) $r=1$, (155) gives

$$\sum_{n=0}^{\infty}\frac{(-1)^n}{a+nh}=\sum_{k=1}^{\left[\frac{a-1}{h}\right]}\frac{(-1)^{k-1}}{a-kh}+\frac{\pi}{2h}\operatorname{cosec}\frac{a\pi}{h}-\frac{2}{h}\sum_{k=0}^{\left[\frac{h-2}{2}\right]}\cos\frac{2k+1}{h}a\pi$$

$$\log\sin\frac{2k+1}{2h}\pi, \qquad (156)$$

if a is not a multiple of h. But if a is a multiple of h, we let $a=a_1h$; then

$$\sum_{n=0}^{\infty}\frac{(-1)^n}{a+nh}=\frac{1}{h}\sum_{n=0}^{\infty}\frac{(-1)^n}{a_1+n}$$

$$=\frac{1}{h}\sum_{k=1}^{a_1-1}\frac{(-1)^{k-1}}{a_1-k}+\frac{1}{h}(-1)^{a_1-1}\log 2, \text{ by (118).} \qquad (157)$$

8. To find the value of

$$S=\frac{1}{a}+\frac{1}{a+h}+\frac{1}{a+2h}+\ldots+\frac{1}{a+(p-1)h}-\frac{1}{a+ph}-\frac{1}{a+(p+1)h}$$

$$-\frac{1}{a+(p+2)h}-\ldots-\frac{1}{a+(2p-1)h}+\frac{1}{a+2ph}+\frac{1}{a+(2p+1)h}+\ldots. \qquad (158)$$

This may be written thus:

$$S=\sum_{n=0}^{\infty}\frac{(-1)^{\left[\frac{n}{p}\right]}}{a+nh}. \qquad (159)$$

Let $$S_1=\sum_{n=0}^{\infty}(-1)^{\left[\frac{n}{p}\right]}\frac{r^{a+nh}}{a+nh}, \quad \text{then } S=S_1\Big]_{r=1}. \qquad (160)$$

Now $$\frac{dS_1}{dr}=\sum_{n=0}^{\infty}(-1)^{\left[\frac{n}{p}\right]}r^{a-1+nh}$$

and $$S_1=\int_0^1\frac{1}{1+r^{ph}}\sum_{n_1=0}^{p-1}r^{a-1+n_1h}\,dr. \qquad (161)$$

Therefore, by (115),

$$S=\sum_{n_1=0}^{p-1}\sum_{k=1}^{\left[\frac{a-1+n_1h}{ph}\right]}(-1)^{k-1}\frac{1}{a+(n_1-kp)h}+\frac{\pi}{2ph}\sum_{n_1=0}^{p-1}\operatorname{cosec}\frac{a+n_1h}{ph}\pi$$

$$-\frac{2}{ph}\sum_{n_1=0}^{p-1}\sum_{k=0}^{\left[\frac{ph-2}{2}\right]}\cos(2k+1)\frac{a+n_1h}{ph}\pi\log\sin\frac{2k+1}{2ph}\pi. \quad (162)$$

Letting in $\sum_{a=0}^{q}\cos(b+ag)=\cos\left(b+\frac{q}{2}g\right)\sin\frac{q+1}{2}g\operatorname{cosec}\tfrac{1}{2}g,$

$$p-1=q,\quad \frac{2k+1}{ph}a\pi=b \quad\text{and}\quad \frac{2k+1}{p}\pi=g,$$

and applying the result to (162), we obtain

$$S=\sum_{n_1=0}^{p-1}\sum_{k=1}^{\left[\frac{a-1+n_1h}{ph}\right]}(-1)^{k-1}\frac{1}{a+(n_1-kp)h}+\frac{\pi}{2ph}\sum_{n_1=0}^{p-1}\operatorname{cosec}\frac{a+n_1h}{ph}\pi$$

$$-\frac{2}{ph}\sum_{k=0}^{\left[\frac{ph-2}{2}\right]}(-1)^k\cos\frac{2a+(p-1)h}{2ph}(2k+1)\pi\operatorname{cosec}\frac{2k+1}{2p}\pi$$

$$\log\sin\frac{2k+1}{2ph}\pi. \quad (163)$$

If $a=1$, $h=2$ and $p=3$, then from (163)

$$S=\frac{\pi}{12}\sum_{n_1=0}^{2}\operatorname{cosec}(2n_1+1)\frac{\pi}{6}-\frac{1}{3}\sum_{k=0}^{2}(-1)^k\cos(2k+1)\frac{\pi}{2}$$

$$\operatorname{cosec}(2k+1)\frac{\pi}{6}\log\sin(2k+1)\frac{\pi}{12}$$

$$=\tfrac{5}{12}\pi; \quad (164)$$

and indeed, since from (161)

$$S_1=\int_0^1\frac{1+r^2+r^4}{r^6+1}dr, \quad (165)$$

then by (116) $$\int_0^1\frac{dr}{r^6+1}=\frac{\pi}{12}\operatorname{cosec}\frac{\pi}{6}-\cos\frac{\pi}{6}\log\tan\frac{\pi}{12}, \quad (166)$$

$$\int_0^1\frac{r^2dr}{r^6+1}=\frac{\pi}{12}\operatorname{cosec}\frac{\pi}{2}-\cos\frac{\pi}{2}\log\tan\frac{\pi}{12}, \quad (167)$$

$$\int_0^1\frac{r^4dr}{r^6+1}=\frac{\pi}{12}\operatorname{cosec}\frac{5\pi}{12}+\cos\frac{\pi}{6}\log\tan\frac{\pi}{12}, \quad (168)$$

and $S=\frac{5\pi}{12}$, the same as (164).

If, however, the integrations are carried out, we obtain

$$\int_0^r \frac{dr}{r^6+1} = \frac{1}{4\sqrt{3}} \log \frac{r^2+r\sqrt{3}+1}{r^2-r\sqrt{3}+1} + \tfrac{1}{6}\tan^{-1}\frac{r}{1-r^2} + \tfrac{1}{3}\tan^{-1} r, \tag{169}$$

$$\int_0^r \frac{r^2\,dr}{r^6+1} = \tfrac{1}{3}\tan^{-1} r^3, \tag{170}$$

$$\int_0^r \frac{r^4\,dr}{r^6+1} = -\frac{1}{4\sqrt{3}} \log \frac{r^2+r\sqrt{3}+1}{r^2-r\sqrt{3}+1} + \tfrac{1}{6}\tan^{-1}\frac{r}{1-r^2} + \tfrac{1}{3}\tan^{-1} r. \tag{171}$$

Then $$S_1 = \tfrac{1}{3}\tan^{-1}\frac{r}{1-r^2} + \tfrac{2}{3}\tan^{-1} r + \tfrac{1}{3}\tan^{-1} r^3,$$

and $S = \frac{5\pi}{12}$, as before.

9. To find the value of

$$S = \sum_{n=0}^{\infty} \frac{r^n}{\prod_{k=1}^{p} (na+k)}. \tag{172}$$

Now $$\frac{1}{\prod_{k=1}^{p} (na+k)} = \frac{1}{(p-1)!} \sum_{m=0}^{p-1} (-1)^m \binom{p-1}{m} \frac{1}{na+m+1}; \tag{173}$$

therefore $$S = \frac{1}{(p-1)!} \sum_{m=0}^{p-1} (-1)^m \binom{p-1}{m} \frac{1}{x^{m+1}} S_m, \tag{174}$$

where $$S_m = -\int_0^x \frac{x^m\,dx}{x^a-1} = -\sum_{k=1}^{\left[\frac{m}{a}\right]} \frac{x^{m-ka+1}}{m-ka+1} - I_2, \quad x = r^{1/a}. \tag{175}$$

And by means of (48) we obtain S in terms of r.

If $r=1$, we have by (136)

$$\sum_{n=0}^{\infty} \frac{1}{\prod_{k=1}^{p} (na+k)} = \frac{1}{a(p-1)!} \left\{ -a \sum_{m=0}^{p-1} (-1)^m \binom{p-1}{m} \sum_{k=1}^{\left[\frac{m}{a}\right]} \frac{1}{m-ka+1} \right.$$

$$+ \frac{\pi}{2} \sum_{m=0}^{p-1} (-1)^m \binom{p-1}{m} \cot \frac{m+1}{a}\pi + \log 2 \sum_{m=0}^{p-1} (-1)^m \binom{p-1}{m}$$

$$-2 \sum_{m=0}^{p-1} (-1)^m \binom{p-1}{m} \sum_{k=1}^{\left[\frac{a-1}{2}\right]} \cos \frac{2k}{a}(m+1)\pi \log \sin \frac{k\pi}{a}$$

$$\left. - \sum_{m=0}^{p-1} (-1)^m \binom{p-1}{m} \frac{1}{x^{m+1}} \log(1-x) \Big]_{x=1} \right\}. \tag{176}$$

Reducing the summations in (176), we find

$$\sum_{m=0}^{p-1}(-1)^m\binom{p-1}{m}=0\,; \tag{177}$$

$$\sum_{m=0}^{p-1}(-1)^m\binom{p-1}{m}\sum_{k=1}^{\left[\frac{a-1}{2}\right]}\cos\frac{2k}{a}(m+1)\pi\log\sin\frac{k\pi}{a}$$

$$=\frac{1}{2}\left[\sum_{k=1}^{\left[\frac{a-1}{2}\right]}e^{\frac{2k\pi}{a}}\sum_{m=0}^{p-1}(-1)^m\binom{p-1}{m}e^{\frac{2km\pi}{a}}\right.$$

$$\left.+\sum_{k=1}^{\left[\frac{a-1}{2}\right]}e^{-\frac{2k\pi}{a}}\sum_{m=0}^{p-1}(-1)^m\binom{p-1}{m}e^{-\frac{2km\pi}{a}}\right]\log\sin\frac{k\pi}{a}$$

$$=\frac{1}{2}\left[\sum_{k=1}^{\left[\frac{a-1}{2}\right]}e^{\frac{2k\pi}{a}}\left(1-e^{\frac{2k\pi}{a}}\right)^{p-1}+\sum_{k=1}^{\left[\frac{a-1}{2}\right]}e^{-\frac{2k\pi}{a}}\left(1-e^{-\frac{2k\pi}{a}}\right)^{p-1}\right]\log\sin\frac{k\pi}{a}$$

$$=(-1)^{\frac{p-2}{2}}2^{p-1}\sum_{k=1}^{\left[\frac{a-1}{2}\right]}\sin\frac{k}{a}(p+1)\pi\sin\frac{k\pi}{a}\log\sin\frac{k\pi}{a},\ \text{when } p \text{ is even,} \tag{178}$$

$$=(-1)^{\frac{p-1}{2}}2^{p-1}\sum_{k=1}^{\left[\frac{a-1}{2}\right]}\cos\frac{k}{a}(p+1)\pi\sin\frac{k\pi}{a}\log\sin\frac{k\pi}{a},\ \text{when } p \text{ is odd.} \tag{179}$$

Also

$$\sum_{m=0}^{p-1}(-1)^m\binom{p-1}{m}\frac{1}{x^{m+1}}\log(1-x)\Big]_{x\doteq 1}=\frac{1}{x^p}(1-x)^{p-1}\log(1-x)\Big]_{x\doteq 1}. \tag{180}$$

Applying (177), (178) and (180) to (176), we obtain, when p is even,

$$\sum_{n=0}^{\infty}\frac{1}{\prod_{k=1}^{p}(na+k)}=\frac{1}{a(p-1)!}\left[-a\sum_{m=0}^{p-1}(-1)^m\binom{p-1}{m}\sum_{k=1}^{\left[\frac{m}{a}\right]}\frac{1}{m-ak+1}\right.$$

$$\left.+\frac{\pi}{2}\sum_{m=0}^{p-1}(-1)^m\binom{p-1}{m}\cot\frac{m+1}{a}\pi+(-1)^{\frac{p}{2}}2^p\sum_{k=1}^{\left[\frac{a-1}{2}\right]}\sin\frac{k}{a}(p+1)\pi\sin\frac{k\pi}{a}\log\sin\frac{k\pi}{a}\right]. \tag{181}$$

If $p\geqq a$ the sum of these terms arising in finding the sum of (172), in which $m+1$ is not a multiple of a, can be found by the same method.

If p is odd, the last summation in (181) is replaced by

$$(-1)^{\frac{p+1}{2}}2^p\sum_{k=1}^{\left[\frac{a-1}{2}\right]}\cos\frac{k}{a}(p+1)\pi\sin\frac{k\pi}{a}\log\sin\frac{k\pi}{a}. \tag{182}$$

The sum of the terms in which $m+1$ is a multiple of a is obtained from (148).

If $a=1$, then from (148)

$$V=\sum_{n=0}^{\infty}\frac{1}{\prod\limits_{k=1}^{p}(n+k)}=-\frac{1}{(p-1)!}\sum_{m=1}^{p-1}(-1)^m\binom{p-1}{m}\sum_{k=1}^{m}\frac{1}{m-k+1}. \tag{183}$$

Letting $m-k+1=k'$, then

$$V=\frac{1}{(p-1)!}\sum_{m=1}^{p-1}(-1)^{m-1}\binom{p-1}{m}\sum_{k=1}^{m}\frac{1}{k}; \tag{184}$$

and since the summation in (185) is, by Ch. III. (136), equal to $\frac{1}{p-1}$, therefore

$$V=\frac{1}{(p-1)(p-1)!}. \tag{185}$$

10. It may be noted here that

$$\sum_{n=0}^{\infty}\frac{r^n}{\prod\limits_{k=1}^{n}(ak+1)} \quad\text{and}\quad \sum_{n=0}^{\infty}\frac{(-1)^n r^n}{\prod\limits_{k=1}^{n}(ak+1)}, \tag{186}$$

which are similar to (172), lead to integrals which cannot be expressed in terms of elementary functions.

Operating on the second summation in (186), we have

$$\frac{1}{\prod\limits_{k=1}^{n}(ak+1)}=\frac{1}{a^{n-1}}\sum_{k=1}^{n}\frac{(-1)^{k-1}}{(n-1)!}\binom{n-1}{k-1}\frac{1}{ak+1}. \tag{187}$$

Then $$S-1=S_1=a\sum_{n=1}^{\infty}(-1)^n\frac{r^n}{a^n}\sum_{k=1}^{n}\frac{(-1)^{k-1}}{(n-1)!}\binom{n-1}{k-1}\frac{1}{ak+1}. \tag{188}$$

Letting $\frac{r}{a}=t$, we have

$$S_1=-a\sum_{k=1}^{\infty}\frac{1}{(k-1)!}\frac{t^k}{ak+1}\sum_{n=k}^{\infty}(-1)^{n-k}\frac{t^{n-k}}{(n-k)!} \tag{189}$$

$$=-ae^{-t}\sum_{k=1}^{\infty}\frac{1}{(k-1)!}\frac{t^k}{ak+1}. \tag{190}$$

Writing x^a for t, then

$$S_1=-\frac{a}{x}e^{-\frac{x}{a}}\sum_{k=1}^{\infty}\frac{1}{(k-1)!}\frac{x^{ak+1}}{ak+1}=-\frac{a}{x}e^{-\frac{x}{a}}S_2 \tag{191}$$

and $$\frac{dS_2}{dx}=\sum_{k=1}^{\infty}\frac{1}{(k-1)!}x^{ak}=x^a\sum_{k=1}^{\infty}\frac{(x^a)^{k-1}}{(k-1)!}=x^ae^{x^a}$$

or $$S_2=\frac{x}{a}e^{\frac{x}{a}}-\frac{1}{a}\int_0^x e^{x^a}dx. \tag{192}$$

Therefore $$S_1=-1+\frac{1}{x}e^{-x^a}\int_0^x e^{x^a}dx \tag{193}$$

and $$S=\frac{1}{x}e^{-x^a}\int_0^x e^{x^a}dx,\quad x=\left(\frac{r}{a}\right)^{1/a}. \tag{194}$$

If $a>1$, the integral in (194) cannot be expressed in terms of elementary functions.

We also find
$$\sum_{n=0}^{\infty} \frac{r^n}{\prod_{k=1}^{n}(ak+1)} = \frac{1}{x} e^{x^a} \int_0^x e^{-x^a} dx. \tag{195}$$

11. To find the value of
$$S = \sum_{n=0}^{\infty} \prod_{k=0}^{n} \left(\frac{a+k}{b+k}\right) r^n, \tag{196}$$

where a and b are positive integers.

Let
$$\prod_{k=0}^{n} \left(\frac{a+k}{b+k}\right) = Q_n; \tag{197}$$

then
$$Q_n = \frac{(b-1)!\,(a+n)!}{(a-1)!\,(b+n)!} = \frac{(b-1)!}{(a-1)!} \frac{1}{\prod_{k=1}^{b-a}(n+a+k)}. \tag{198}$$

Now
$$\frac{1}{\prod_{k=1}^{b-a}(n+a+k)} = \frac{1}{(b-a-1)!} \sum_{k=1}^{b-a} (-1)^{k-1} \binom{b-a-1}{k-1} \frac{1}{n+a+k};$$

hence
$$Q_n = a\binom{b-1}{a} \sum_{k=1}^{b-a} (-1)^{k-1} \binom{b-a-1}{k-1} \frac{1}{n+a+k} \tag{199}$$

and
$$S = a\binom{b-1}{a} \sum_{k=1}^{b-a} (-1)^{k-1} \binom{b-a-1}{k-1} \sum_{n=0}^{\infty} \frac{r^n}{n+a+k}$$
$$= a\binom{b-1}{a} \sum_{k=1}^{b-a} (-1)^{k-1} \binom{b-a-1}{k-1} \frac{1}{r^{a+k}} \sum_{n=0}^{\infty} \frac{r^{n+a+k}}{n+a+k}. \tag{200}$$

Letting
$$\sum_{n=0}^{\infty} \frac{r^{n+a+k}}{n+a+k} = S_k, \tag{201}$$

then
$$S_k = \sum_{n=a+k}^{\infty} \frac{r^n}{n} = \sum_{n=1}^{\infty} \frac{r^n}{n} - \sum_{n=1}^{a+k-1} \frac{r^n}{n}$$
$$= -\log(1-r) - \sum_{n=1}^{a+k-1} \frac{r^n}{n}. \tag{202}$$

Applying (202) to (201) gives
$$S = a\binom{b-1}{a} \left[-\frac{1}{r^{a+1}} \log(1-r) \sum_{k=0}^{b-a-1} (-1)^k \binom{b-a-1}{k} \frac{1}{r^k} \right.$$
$$\left. + \frac{1}{r^a} \sum_{k=1}^{b-a} (-1)^k \binom{b-a-1}{k-1} \sum_{n=1}^{a+k-1} \frac{r^{n-k}}{n} \right]; \tag{203}$$

and since
$$\sum_{k=0}^{b-a-1} (-1)^k \binom{b-a-1}{k} \frac{1}{r^k} = \left(1-\frac{1}{r}\right)^{b-a-1} = \frac{(r-1)^{b-a-1}}{r^{b-a-1}},$$

therefore

$$S=a\binom{b-1}{a}\left[\frac{(-1)^{b-a}}{r^b}(1-r)^{b-a-1}\log(1-r)\right.$$
$$\left.+\frac{1}{r^a}\sum_{k=1}^{b-a}(-1)^k\binom{b-a-1}{k-1}\sum_{n=1}^{a+k-1}\frac{r^{n-k}}{n}\right]. \tag{204}$$

To find
$$S=\sum_{n=0}^{\infty}\prod_{k=0}^{n}\left(\frac{a+k}{b+k}\right), \tag{205}$$

we evaluate (204) for $r=1$.

Now
$$(1-r)^{b-a-1}\log(1-r)\Big]_{r=1}=\frac{\log(1-r)}{(1-r)^{a-b+1}}\Big]_{r=1}=0 \text{ if } a<b-1. \tag{206}$$

We shall next reduce

$$S_1=\sum_{k=1}^{b-a}(-1)^k\binom{b-a-1}{k-1}\sum_{n=1}^{a+k-1}\frac{1}{n}. \tag{207}$$

Since
$$\sum_{n=1}^{a+k-1}\frac{1}{n}=\sum_{n=1}^{a-1}\frac{1}{n}+\sum_{n=a}^{a+k-1}\frac{1}{n}, \tag{208}$$

$$S_1=\sum_{n=1}^{a-1}\frac{1}{n}\sum_{k=1}^{b-a}(-1)^k\binom{b-a-1}{k-1}+\sum_{k=1}^{b-a}(-1)^k\binom{b-a-1}{k-1}\sum_{n=a}^{a+k-1}\frac{1}{n}. \tag{209}$$

But
$$\sum_{k=1}^{b-a}(-1)^k\binom{b-a-1}{k-1}=-(1-1)^{b-a}=0;$$

therefore
$$S_1=\sum_{k=1}^{b-a}(-1)^k\binom{b-a-1}{k-1}\sum_{n=a}^{a+k-1}\frac{1}{n}. \tag{210}$$

Letting
$$S_{1,x}=\sum_{k=1}^{b-a}(-1)^k\binom{b-a-1}{k-1}\sum_{n=a}^{a+k-1}\frac{x^n}{n} \tag{211}$$

and
$$n-a+1=n' \text{ in (211)},$$

then
$$\frac{dS_{1,x}}{dx}=x^{a-1}\sum_{k=0}^{b-a-1}(-1)^{k-1}\binom{b-a-1}{k}\sum_{n=0}^{k}x^n. \tag{212}$$

Writing m for $b-a-1$, n for k and k for n, we have from (212)

$$\frac{dS_{1,x}}{dx}=x^{a-1}\sum_{n=0}^{m}(-1)^{n-1}\binom{m}{n}\sum_{k=0}^{n}x^k$$
$$=x^{a-1}\sum_{n=0}^{m}(-1)^{n-1}\binom{m}{n}+\frac{x^{a-1}}{1-x}\sum_{n=0}^{m}(-1)^n\binom{m}{n}x^{n+1}$$
$$=\frac{x^a}{1-x}\sum_{n=0}^{m}(-1)^n\binom{m}{n}x^n=x^a(1-x)^{m-1}, \tag{213}$$

and
$$S_{1,x}=\int x^a(1-x)^{m-1}dx+C. \tag{214}$$

But when $x=0$, $S_{1,x}=0$ and $C=0$,

therefore
$$S_1=\int_0^1 x^a(1-x)^{m-1}dx=\frac{a!\,(m-1)!}{(m+a)!}$$
$$=\frac{a!\,(b-a-2)!}{(b-1)!}. \tag{215}$$

Applying (206) and (215) to (204), we obtain for $a<b-1$
$$S=\sum_{n=0}^{\infty}\prod_{k=1}^{n}\left(\frac{a+k}{b+k}\right)=a\binom{b-1}{a}S_1=\frac{a}{b-a-1}. \tag{216}$$

12. To find the value of
$$S=\sum_{n=0}^{\infty}\sum_{k=0}^{\infty}(-1)^k\frac{1}{\binom{n+k+1}{k}}r^n. \tag{217}$$

Letting
$$\sum_{k=0}^{\infty}(-1)^k\frac{1}{\binom{n+k+1}{k}}=S_{n,1}, \tag{218}$$

then
$$S_{n,1}=(n+1)!\sum_{k=0}^{\infty}(-1)^k\frac{k!}{(n+k+1)!}$$
$$=(n+1)!\sum_{k=0}^{\infty}(-1)^k\frac{1}{\prod\limits_{a=1}^{n+1}(k+a)}. \tag{219}$$

Now
$$\frac{1}{\prod\limits_{a=1}^{n+1}(k+a)}=\frac{1}{n!}\sum_{a=1}^{n+1}(-1)^{a-1}\binom{n}{a-1}\frac{1}{k+a};$$

therefore
$$S_{n,1}=(n+1)\sum_{a=1}^{n+1}(-1)^{a-1}\binom{n}{a-1}\sum_{k=0}^{\infty}\frac{(-1)^k}{k+a} \tag{220}$$
$$=S_{n,x}\Big]_{x=1}=(n+1)\sum_{a=1}^{n+1}(-1)^{a-1}\binom{n}{a-1}\sum_{k=0}^{\infty}(-1)^k\frac{x^{k+a}}{k+a}\Big]_{x=1}. \tag{221}$$

Now
$$\frac{dS_{n,x}}{dx}=\frac{n+1}{1+x}\sum_{a=0}^{n}(-1)^a\binom{n}{a}x^a \tag{222}$$
$$=\frac{n+1}{1+x}(1-x)^n;$$

hence
$$S_{n,x}=(n+1)\int_0^x\frac{(1-x)^n}{1+x}dx. \tag{223}$$

Letting in (223), $1+x=y$, we have
$$S_{n,x}=(n+1)\int_1^{1+x}\sum_{k=0}^{n}(-1)^k\binom{n}{k}2^{n-k}y^{k-1}dy$$
$$=(n+1)2^n\int_1^{1+x}\frac{dy}{y}+(n+1)\int_1^{1+x}\sum_{k=1}^{n}(-1)^k\binom{n}{k}2^{n-k}y^{k-1}dy. \tag{224}$$

Therefore

$$S_{n,1}=(n+1)2^n\log 2+(n+1)\sum_{k=1}^{n}\frac{(-1)^k}{k}\binom{n}{k}2^n$$
$$-(n+1)\sum_{k=1}^{n}\frac{(-1)^k}{k}\binom{n}{k}2^{n-k} \qquad (225)$$

and

$$S=\log 2\sum_{n=0}^{\infty}(n+1)(2r)^n+\sum_{n=1}^{\infty}(n+1)\sum_{k=1}^{n}\frac{(-1)^k}{k}\binom{n}{k}(2r)^n$$
$$-\sum_{n=1}^{\infty}(n+1)\sum_{k=1}^{n}\frac{(-1)^k}{k}\binom{n}{k}\frac{1}{2^k}(2r)^n. \qquad (226)$$

Denoting in (226) the first summation by S_1 and the double summations in order by S_2 and S_3, we have

$$S=S_1\log 2+S_2-S_3. \qquad (227)$$

Now $$S_1=\frac{d}{d(2r)}\sum_{n=0}^{\infty}(2r)^n=\frac{d}{d(2r)}\frac{1}{1-2r}=\frac{1}{(1-2r)^2}, \quad -\tfrac{1}{2}<r<\tfrac{1}{2}. \qquad (228)$$

Next $$S_2=\sum_{k=1}^{\infty}\frac{(-1)^k}{k}\sum_{n=k}^{\infty}\binom{n}{k}(n+1)(2r)^n, \text{ by Ch. I. (97)},$$
$$=\sum_{k=1}^{\infty}(-1)^k\frac{k+1}{k}\sum_{n=k}^{\infty}\binom{n+1}{k+1}(2r)^n. \qquad (229)$$

Denoting by S_4 the second summation of the double summation in (229), and letting in it $n-k=n'$, then

$$S_4=\sum_{n=0}^{\infty}\binom{n+k+1}{k+1}(2r)^{n+k} \qquad (230)$$
$$=(2r)^k\sum_{n=0}^{\infty}(-1)^n\binom{-k-2}{n}(2r)^n$$
$$=\frac{(2r)^k}{(1-2r)^{k+2}}, \quad -\tfrac{1}{2}<r<\tfrac{1}{2}. \qquad (231)$$

Applying (231) to (229), we obtain

$$S_2=\frac{1}{(1-2r)^2}\left[\sum_{k=1}^{\infty}(-1)^k\left(\frac{2r}{1-2r}\right)^k+\sum_{k=1}^{\infty}\frac{(-1)^k}{k}\left(\frac{2r}{1-2r}\right)^k\right]$$
$$=\frac{1}{(1-2r)^2}[-2r+\log(1-2r)], \quad r<\tfrac{1}{4}. \qquad (232)$$

Similarly $$S_3=\sum_{k=1}^{\infty}\frac{(-1)^k}{2^k}\frac{k+1}{k}\sum_{n=k}^{\infty}\binom{n+1}{k+1}(2r)^n \qquad (233)$$
$$=\sum_{k=1}^{\infty}(-1)^k\frac{k+1}{k}\frac{r^k}{(1-2r)^{k+2}}, \quad -\tfrac{1}{2}<r<\tfrac{1}{3},$$
$$=\frac{1}{(1-2r)^2}\left[-\frac{r}{1-r}+\log(1-2r)-\log(1-r)\right]. \qquad (234)$$

Applying (228), (232) and (234) to (226), we obtain

$$S=\frac{1}{(1-2r)^2}\left[\log 2+\log(1-r)-\frac{r(1-2r)}{1-r}\right], \quad -\tfrac{1}{2}<r<\tfrac{1}{4}. \tag{235}$$

It can be shown that (235) is valid for $-1<r<1$ except when $r=\frac{1}{2}$, in which case $S=\frac{3}{2}$.

If $r=0$,
$$S=\log 2. \tag{236}$$

The result (236) can be obtained from (217) directly.

If $r=0$ in (217), n can have the value zero only, and

$$S=\sum_{k=0}^{\infty}(-1)^k\frac{1}{k+1}=\log 2.$$

The expression (221) might also be reduced by first finding the value of

$$S_a\Big]_{x=1}=\sum_{k=0}^{\infty}(-1)^k\frac{x^{k+a}}{k+a}\Big]_{x=1}. \tag{237}$$

Now
$$\frac{dS_a}{dx}=\sum_{k=0}^{\infty}(-1)^k x^{k+a-1}=\frac{x^{a-1}}{1+x}$$

and
$$S_a=\int_0^x\frac{x^{a-1}}{1+x}\,dx. \tag{238}$$

But
$$\frac{x^{a-1}}{1+x}=\sum_{\beta=0}^{a-2}(-1)^{a-\beta}x^{\beta}+\frac{(-1)^{a-1}}{1+x};$$

therefore
$$S_a=\sum_{\beta=0}^{a-2}(-1)^{a-\beta}\frac{x^{\beta+1}}{\beta+1}+(-1)^{a-1}\log(1+x) \tag{239}$$

and
$$S_a\Big]_{x=1}=\sum_{\beta=0}^{a-2}\frac{(-1)^{a-\beta}}{\beta+1}+(-1)^{a-1}\log 2. \tag{240}$$

Then, by means of (240), (221) becomes

$$S_{n,x}\Big]_{x=1}=(n+1)\log 2\sum_{a=1}^{n+1}\binom{n}{a-1}+(n+1)\sum_{a=1}^{n+1}\binom{n}{a-1}\sum_{\beta=0}^{a-2}\frac{(-1)^{\beta+1}}{\beta+1}$$
$$=(n+1)2^n\log 2+(n+1)\sum_{k=1}^{n}\binom{n}{k}\sum_{a=1}^{k}\frac{(-1)^a}{a}. \tag{241}$$

To reduce the double summation in (241), we let

$$S_4\Big]_{x=1}=\sum_{k=1}^{n}\binom{n}{k}\sum_{a=1}^{k}\frac{(-1)^a}{a}x^a\Big]_{x=1}; \tag{242}$$

then
$$\frac{dS_4}{dx}=\sum_{k=1}^{n}\binom{n}{k}\sum_{a=1}^{k}(-1)^a x^{a-1} \tag{243}$$

$$=\frac{1}{1+x}\sum_{k=1}^{n}(-1)^k\binom{n}{k}x^k-\frac{1}{1+x}\sum_{k=1}^{n}\binom{n}{k}$$

$$=\frac{1}{1+x}\sum_{k=0}^{n}(-1)^k\binom{n}{k}x^k-\frac{1}{1+x}\sum_{k=0}^{n}\binom{n}{k}$$

$$=\frac{(1-x)^n}{1+x}-\frac{2^n}{1+x}. \tag{244}$$

Letting in (244) $1+x=y$, then

$$\frac{dS_4}{dx}=\frac{dS_4}{dy}=\frac{(2-y)^n}{y}-\frac{2^n}{y} \tag{245}$$

$$=(-1)^n\frac{(y-2)^n}{y}-\frac{2^n}{y}$$

$$=(-1)^n\sum_{k=0}^{n}(-1)^k\binom{n}{k}2^k y^{n-k-1}-\frac{2^n}{y}$$

$$=(-1)^n\sum_{k=0}^{n-1}(-1)^k\binom{n}{k}2^k y^{n-k-1}. \tag{246}$$

Therefore $$S_4\Big]_{x=1}=(-1)^n\sum_{k=0}^{n-1}(-1)^k\binom{n}{k}\frac{2^n-2^k}{n-k}. \tag{247}$$

Letting $n-k=k'$, $$S_4=\sum_{k=0}^{n}(-1)^k\binom{n}{k}\frac{2^n-2^k}{k}. \tag{248}$$

Applying (248) to (241) gives (225).

Show that

$$\sum_{k=0}^{\infty}\frac{1}{\binom{n+k+1}{k}}=\frac{n+1}{n},\ n \text{ a positive integer.} \tag{249}$$

$$\sum_{n=1}^{\infty}\sum_{k=0}^{\infty}\frac{r^n}{\binom{n+k+1}{k}}=\frac{r}{1-r}-\log(1-r), \tag{250}$$

$$\sum_{n=0}^{\infty}(-1)^n r^n\sum_{k=0}^{\infty}\frac{(-1)^k}{\binom{n+k+1}{k}}=\frac{1}{(1+2r)^2}\left[\log(1+r)+\log 2+\frac{r(1+2r)}{1+r}\right]. \tag{251}$$

13. The separation into Partial Fractions of

$$F(x)=\frac{\sum_{k=0}^{m}a_{m-k}x^k}{(x^n+1)^p}=\frac{\sum_{k=0}^{m}a_{m-k}x^k}{\prod_{a=1}^{n}(x-r_a)^p}, \tag{252}$$

where m, n and p ($p>1$) are positive integers and $r_a=e^{\frac{2a+1}{n}\pi}$.

If it be required to find $$I=\int_0^x F(x)\,dx, \tag{253}$$

the following method reduces I to (29).

Let $$I_{k,p}=\int_0^x\frac{x^k\,dx}{(x^n+1)^p}; \tag{254}$$

then $$I=\sum_{k=0}^{m}a_{m-k}I_{k,p}. \tag{255}$$

Integrating by parts, we have

$$I_{k,p} = -\frac{1}{n(p-1)}\frac{x^{k+1-n}}{(x^n+1)^{p-1}} + \frac{k+1-n}{n(p-1)} I_{k-n,\,p-1}, \tag{256_{p-1}}$$

where

$$I_{k-n,\,p-1} = \int_0^x \frac{x^{k-n}\,dx}{(x^n+1)^{p-1}}.$$

Using (256_{p-1}) as a recurring formula, we obtain

$$\frac{k+1-n}{n(p-1)} I_{k-n,\,p-1} = -\frac{k+1-n}{n^2(p-1)(p-2)}\frac{x^{k+1-2n}}{(x^n+1)^{p-2}} + \frac{(k+1-n)(k+1-2n)}{n^2(p-1)(p-2)} I_{k-2n,\,p-2}, \tag{256_{p-2}}$$

. . . .

$$\frac{\prod\limits_{\alpha=1}^{p-2}(k+1-\alpha n)}{n^{p-2}p!} I_{k-(p-2)n,\,2} = -\frac{\prod\limits_{\alpha=1}^{p-2}(k+1-\alpha n)}{n^{p-1}(p-1)!}\frac{x^{k+1-(p-1)n}}{x^n+1} + \frac{\prod\limits_{\alpha=1}^{p-1}(k+1-\alpha n)}{n^{p-1}(p-1)!} I_{k-(p-1)n,\,1}. \tag{256_1}$$

Adding (256_{p-1})–(256_1) gives

$$I_{k,p} = \frac{\prod\limits_{\alpha=1}^{p-1}(k+1-\alpha n)}{n^{p-1}(p-1)!}\int_0^x \frac{x^{k-(p+1)n}\,dx}{x^n+1} - \sum_{h=1}^{p-1}\frac{\prod\limits_{\alpha=1}^{h-1}(k+1-\alpha n)}{n^h\prod\limits_{\alpha=1}^{h}(p-\alpha)}\frac{x^{k+1-hn}}{(x^n+1)^{p-h}}, \tag{257}$$

where

$$\prod_{\alpha=1}^{0}(k+1-\alpha n) = 1.$$

Now

$$\prod_{\alpha=1}^{p-1}(k+1-\alpha n) = n^{p-1}\prod_{\alpha=1}^{p-1}\left(\frac{k+1}{n}-\alpha\right); \tag{258}$$

hence

$$\frac{\prod\limits_{\alpha=1}^{p-1}(k+1-\alpha n)}{n^{p-1}(p-1)!} = \frac{np}{k+1}\binom{\frac{k+1}{n}}{p}. \tag{259}$$

Similarly

$$\frac{\prod\limits_{\alpha=1}^{h-1}(k+1-\alpha n)}{n^h\prod\limits_{\alpha=1}^{h}(p-\alpha)} = \frac{1}{(k+1)\binom{p-1}{h}}\binom{\frac{k+1}{n}}{h}. \tag{260}$$

Therefore

$$I_{k,p} = \frac{np}{k+1}\binom{\frac{k+1}{n}}{p}\int_0^x \frac{x^{k-(p-1)n}\,dx}{x^n+1} - \frac{1}{k+1}\sum_{h=1}^{p-1}\binom{\frac{k+1}{n}}{h}\frac{1}{\binom{p-1}{h}}\frac{x^{k+1-hn}}{(x^n+1)^{p-h}}. \tag{261}$$

VALUES OF TRIGONOMETRICAL FUNCTIONS OF CERTAIN ANGLES.

1. $\sin \frac{7}{30}\pi = \frac{1}{8}[-(\sqrt{5}-1)+\sqrt{3}\sqrt{10+2\sqrt{5}}]$,

$\cos \frac{7}{30}\pi = \frac{1}{8}[\sqrt{3}(\sqrt{5}-1)+\sqrt{10+2\sqrt{5}}]$,

$\tan \frac{7}{30}\pi = \frac{1}{4}(\sqrt{5}+1)(2\sqrt{3}-\sqrt{10-2\sqrt{5}})$,

$\cot \frac{7}{30}\pi = \frac{1}{4}(3-\sqrt{5})(2\sqrt{3}+\sqrt{10-2\sqrt{5}})$.

2. $\sin \frac{5}{24}\pi = \frac{1}{4}(\sqrt{3}\sqrt{2+\sqrt{2}}-\sqrt{2-\sqrt{2}}) = \frac{1}{2}2\sqrt{2-\sqrt{2-\sqrt{3}}}$,

$\cos \frac{5}{24}\pi = \frac{1}{4}(\sqrt{2+\sqrt{2}}+\sqrt{3}\sqrt{2-\sqrt{2}}) = \frac{1}{2}\sqrt{2+\sqrt{2-\sqrt{3}}}$,

$\tan \frac{5}{24}\pi = (\sqrt{2}+1)(\sqrt{3}-\sqrt{2})$, $\cot \frac{5}{24}\pi = (\sqrt{2}-1)(\sqrt{3}+\sqrt{2})$.

3. $\sin \frac{\pi}{5} = \frac{1}{4}\sqrt{10-2\sqrt{5}}$, $\cos \frac{\pi}{5} = \frac{1}{4}(1+\sqrt{5})$,

$\tan \frac{\pi}{5} = \sqrt{5-2\sqrt{5}}$, $\cot \frac{\pi}{5} = \frac{1}{\sqrt{5}}\sqrt{5+2\sqrt{5}}$.

4. $\sin \frac{3\pi}{16} = \frac{1}{2}\sqrt{2-\sqrt{2-\sqrt{2}}}$,

$\cos \frac{3}{16}\pi = \frac{1}{2}\sqrt{2+\sqrt{2-\sqrt{2}}}$,

$\tan \frac{3}{16}\pi = \sqrt{2}\sqrt{2-\sqrt{2}}-(\sqrt{2}-1)$,

$\cot \frac{3}{16}\pi = \sqrt{2}\sqrt{2-\sqrt{2}}+\sqrt{2}-1$.

5. $\sin \frac{3}{20}\pi = \frac{1}{8}\sqrt{2}[\sqrt{10+2\sqrt{5}}-(\sqrt{5}-1)]$,

$\cos \frac{3}{20}\pi = \frac{1}{8}\sqrt{2}[\sqrt{10+2\sqrt{5}}+\sqrt{5}+1]$,

$\tan \frac{3}{20}\pi = \sqrt{5}-1-\sqrt{5-2\sqrt{5}}$, $\cot \frac{3}{20}\pi = \sqrt{5}-1+\sqrt{5-2\sqrt{5}}$.

6. $\sin \frac{2}{15}\pi = \frac{1}{8}[\sqrt{3}(\sqrt{5}+1)-\sqrt{10-2\sqrt{5}}]$,

$\cos \frac{2}{15}\pi = \frac{1}{8}[\sqrt{5}+1+\sqrt{3}\sqrt{10-2\sqrt{5}}]$,

$\tan \frac{2}{15}\pi = \frac{1}{4}(3+\sqrt{5})(-2\sqrt{3}+\sqrt{10+2\sqrt{5}})$,

$\cot \frac{2}{15}\pi = \frac{1}{4}(\sqrt{5}-1)(2\sqrt{3}+\sqrt{10+2\sqrt{5}})$.

7. $\sin \frac{\pi}{8} = \frac{1}{2}\sqrt{2-\sqrt{2}}$, $\cos \frac{\pi}{8} = \frac{1}{2}\sqrt{2+\sqrt{2}}$,

$\tan \frac{\pi}{8} = \sqrt{2}-1$, $\cot \frac{\pi}{8} = \sqrt{2}+1$.

8. $\sin \frac{\pi}{10} = \frac{1}{4}(\sqrt{5}-1)$, $\cos \frac{\pi}{10} = \frac{1}{4}\sqrt{10+2\sqrt{5}}$,

$\tan \frac{\pi}{10} = \frac{1}{\sqrt{5}}\sqrt{5-2\sqrt{5}}$, $\cot \frac{\pi}{10} = \sqrt{5+2\sqrt{5}}$.

9. $\sin\frac{\pi}{12}=\frac{1}{4}(\sqrt{6}-\sqrt{2}),\quad \cos\frac{\pi}{12}=\frac{1}{4}(\sqrt{6}+\sqrt{2}),$

$\tan\frac{\pi}{12}=2-\sqrt{3},\quad \cot\frac{\pi}{12}=2+\sqrt{3}.$

10. $\sin\frac{3}{40}\pi=\frac{1}{8}[\sqrt{2+\sqrt{2}}\sqrt{10-2\sqrt{5}}-\sqrt{2-\sqrt{2}}(1+\sqrt{5})],$

$\cos\frac{3}{40}\pi=\frac{1}{8}[\sqrt{2-\sqrt{2}}\sqrt{10-2\sqrt{5}}+\sqrt{2+\sqrt{2}}(1+\sqrt{5})],$

$\tan\frac{3}{40}\pi=\frac{1}{4}(1-\sqrt{5}+2\sqrt{2})[\sqrt{10-2\sqrt{5}}-\sqrt{2}(\sqrt{5}-1)],$

$\cot\frac{3}{40}\pi=\frac{1}{4}(-1+\sqrt{5}+2\sqrt{2})[\sqrt{10-2\sqrt{5}}+\sqrt{2}(\sqrt{5}-1)].$

11. $\sin\frac{\pi}{15}=\frac{1}{8}[-\sqrt{3}(\sqrt{5}-1)+\sqrt{10+2\sqrt{5}}],$

$\cos\frac{\pi}{15}=\frac{1}{8}[\sqrt{5}-1+\sqrt{3}\sqrt{10+2\sqrt{5}}],$

$\tan\frac{\pi}{15}=\frac{1}{4}(3-\sqrt{5})(2\sqrt{3}-\sqrt{10-2\sqrt{5}}),$

$\cot\frac{\pi}{15}=\frac{1}{4}(1+\sqrt{5})(2\sqrt{3}+\sqrt{10-2\sqrt{5}}).$

12. $\sin\frac{\pi}{16}=\frac{1}{2}\sqrt{2-\sqrt{2+\sqrt{2}}},\quad \cos\frac{\pi}{16}=\frac{1}{2}\sqrt{2+\sqrt{2+\sqrt{2}}},$

$\tan\frac{\pi}{16}=\sqrt{2}\sqrt{2+\sqrt{2}}-(\sqrt{2}+1),$

$\cot\frac{\pi}{16}=\sqrt{2}\sqrt{2+\sqrt{2}}+\sqrt{2}+1.$

13 $\sin\frac{\pi}{20}=\frac{1}{8}\sqrt{2}(\sqrt{5}+1-\sqrt{10-2\sqrt{5}}),$

$\cos\frac{\pi}{20}=\frac{1}{8}\sqrt{2}(\sqrt{5}+1+\sqrt{10-2\sqrt{5}}),$

$\tan\frac{\pi}{20}=\sqrt{5}+1-\sqrt{5+2\sqrt{5}},\quad \cot\frac{\pi}{20}=\sqrt{5}+1+\sqrt{5+2\sqrt{5}}.$

14. $\sin\frac{\pi}{24}=\frac{1}{4}(\sqrt{2+\sqrt{2}}-\sqrt{3}\sqrt{2-\sqrt{2}})=\frac{1}{2}\sqrt{2-\sqrt{2+\sqrt{3}}},$

$\cos\frac{\pi}{24}=\frac{1}{4}(\sqrt{2-\sqrt{2}}+\sqrt{3}\sqrt{2+\sqrt{2}})=\frac{1}{2}\sqrt{2+\sqrt{2+\sqrt{3}}}.$

$\tan\frac{\pi}{24}=\surd(2-1)(\sqrt{3}-\sqrt{2}),\quad \cot\frac{\pi}{24}=(\sqrt{2}+1)(\sqrt{3}+\sqrt{2}).$

15. $\sin\frac{\pi}{30}=\frac{1}{8}[-(\sqrt{5}+1)+\sqrt{3}\sqrt{10-2\sqrt{5}}],$

$\cos\frac{\pi}{30}=\frac{1}{8}[\sqrt{3}(\sqrt{5}+1)+\sqrt{10-2\sqrt{5}}],$

$$\tan\frac{\pi}{30}=\tfrac{1}{4}(\sqrt{5}-1)(\sqrt{10+2\sqrt{5}}-2\sqrt{3}),$$

$$\cot\frac{\pi}{30}=\tfrac{1}{4}(3+\sqrt{5})(\sqrt{10+2\sqrt{5}}+2\sqrt{3}).$$

16. $$\sin\frac{\pi}{60}=\tfrac{1}{8}\sqrt{2}[\sqrt{(2+\sqrt{3})(3-\sqrt{5})}-\sqrt{(2-\sqrt{3})(5+\sqrt{5})}],$$

$$\cos\frac{\pi}{60}=\tfrac{1}{8}\sqrt{2}[\sqrt{(2-\sqrt{3})(3-\sqrt{5})}+\sqrt{(2+\sqrt{3})(5+\sqrt{5})}],$$

$$\tan\frac{\pi}{60}=\tfrac{1}{4}(2-\sqrt{3})(1+2\sqrt{3}-\sqrt{5})(\sqrt{10-2\sqrt{5}}-2),$$

$$\cot\frac{\pi}{60}=\tfrac{1}{4}(2+\sqrt{3})(-1+2\sqrt{3}+\sqrt{5})(\sqrt{10-2\sqrt{5}}+2).$$

17. $$\sin\frac{n\pi}{2}=(-1)^{\left[\frac{n}{2}\right]}\frac{1-(-1)^n}{2},$$

$$\cos\frac{n\pi}{2}=(-1)^{\left[\frac{n}{2}\right]}\frac{1+(-1)^n}{2},$$

$$\tan\frac{n\pi}{2}=\frac{1-(-1)^n}{1+(-1)^n}.$$

18. $$\sin\frac{n\pi}{3}=(-1)^{\left[\frac{n}{3}\right]}\frac{\sqrt{3}}{4}\left[1-(-1)^{\left[\frac{n+1}{3}\right]}\right],\quad \text{if } n \text{ is even},$$

$$=(-1)^{\left[\frac{n}{3}\right]}\frac{\sqrt{3}}{4}\left[1+(-1)^{\left[\frac{n+1}{3}\right]}\right],\quad \text{if } n \text{ is odd};$$

$$\cos\frac{n\pi}{3}=(-1)^{\left[\frac{n+1}{3}\right]}\frac{3+(-1)^{\left[\frac{n+1}{3}\right]}}{4},\quad \text{if } n \text{ is even},$$

$$=(-1)^{\left[\frac{n+1}{3}\right]}\frac{3-(-1)^{\left[\frac{n+1}{3}\right]}}{4},\quad \text{if } n \text{ is odd};$$

$$\tan\frac{n\pi}{3}=(-1)^{\left[\frac{n+2}{3}\right]}\frac{\sqrt{3}}{2}\left[1-(-1)^{\left[\frac{n+1}{3}\right]}\right],\quad \text{if } n \text{ is even},$$

$$=(-1)^{\left[\frac{n}{3}\right]}\frac{\sqrt{3}}{2}\left[1+(-1)^{\left[\frac{n+1}{3}\right]}\right],\quad \text{if } n \text{ is odd}.$$

19. $$\sin\frac{n\pi}{4}=(-1)^{\left[\frac{n}{4}\right]}\frac{1-(-1)^{\left[\frac{n}{2}\right]}}{2},\quad \text{if } n \text{ is even},$$

$$=(-1)^{\left[\frac{n-1}{4}\right]}\frac{1}{\sqrt{2}},\quad \text{if } n \text{ is odd};$$

$$\cos\frac{n\pi}{4}=(-1)^{\left[\frac{n}{4}\right]}\frac{1+(-1)^{\left[\frac{n}{2}\right]}}{2},\quad \text{if } n \text{ is even,}$$

$$=(-1)^{\left[\frac{n+1}{4}\right]}\frac{1}{\sqrt{2}},\quad \text{if } n \text{ is odd;}$$

$$\tan\frac{n\pi}{4}=(-1)^{\left[\frac{n}{4}\right]}\frac{1-(-1)^{\left[\frac{n}{2}\right]}}{1+(-1)^{\left[\frac{n}{2}\right]}},\quad \text{if } n \text{ is even,}$$

$$=(-1)^{\left[\frac{2n+1}{4}\right]},\quad \text{if } n \text{ is odd.}$$

20. $$\sin\frac{n\pi}{6}=(-1)^{\left[\frac{n}{6}\right]}\frac{\sqrt{3}}{4}\left[1-(-1)^{\left[\frac{n+1}{3}\right]}\right],\quad \text{if } n \text{ is even,}$$

$$=(-1)^{\left[\frac{n}{6}\right]}\frac{3-(-1)^{\left[\frac{n+1}{3}\right]}}{4},\quad \text{if } n \text{ is odd;}$$

$$\cos\frac{n\pi}{6}=(-1)^{\left[\frac{n+2}{6}\right]}\frac{3+(-1)^{\left[\frac{n+1}{3}\right]}}{4},\quad \text{if } n \text{ is even,}$$

$$=(-1)^{\left[\frac{n+1}{6}\right]}\frac{\sqrt{3}}{2}\left[1-(-1)^{\left[\frac{n+1}{3}\right]}\right],\quad \text{if } n \text{ is odd;}$$

$$\tan\frac{n\pi}{6}=(-1)^{\left[\frac{n}{3}\right]}\frac{\sqrt{3}}{2}\left[1-(-1)^{\left[\frac{n+1}{3}\right]}\right],\quad \text{if } n \text{ is even,}$$

$$=(-1)^{\left[\frac{n}{3}\right]}\frac{2}{\sqrt{3}\left[1+(-1)^{\left[\frac{n+1}{3}\right]}\right]},\quad \text{if } n \text{ is odd.}$$

21. $$\sin\frac{n\pi}{8}=(-1)^{\left[\frac{n+1}{8}\right]}\frac{1}{2}\sqrt{2-(-1)^{\left[\frac{n}{4}\right]}-(-1)^{\left[\frac{3n+1}{4}\right]}},\quad \text{if } n \text{ is even,}$$

$$=(-1)^{\left[\frac{n}{8}\right]}\frac{1}{2}\sqrt{2-(-1)^{\left[\frac{n+1}{4}\right]}\sqrt{2}},\quad \text{if } n \text{ is odd;}$$

$$\cos\frac{n\pi}{8}=(-1)^{\left[\frac{n+5}{8}\right]}\frac{1}{2}\sqrt{2+(-1)^{\left[\frac{n}{4}\right]}+(-1)^{\left[\frac{3n+1}{4}\right]}},\quad \text{if } n \text{ is even,}$$

$$=(-1)^{\left[\frac{n+3}{8}\right]}\frac{1}{2}\sqrt{2+(-1)^{\left[\frac{n+1}{4}\right]}\sqrt{2}},\quad \text{if } n \text{ is odd;}$$

$$\tan\frac{n\pi}{8}=(-1)^{\left[\frac{2n+1}{8}\right]}\frac{2-(-1)^{\left[\frac{n}{4}\right]}-(-1)^{\left[\frac{3n+1}{4}\right]}}{(-1)^{\left[\frac{n}{4}\right]}-(-1)^{\left[\frac{3n+1}{4}\right]}},\quad \text{if } n \text{ is even,}$$

$$=(-1)^{\left[\frac{2n+1}{8}\right]}\left[\sqrt{2}-(-1)^{\left[\frac{n+1}{4}\right]}\right],\quad \text{if } n \text{ is odd.}$$

CHAPTER X.

THE SUM OF A SERIES AS THE SOLUTION OF A DIFFERENTIAL EQUATION.

BOOLE* obtains the sum of a special type of series as the solution of a differential equation.

A method is developed here which applies to a more general class of series.

1. Every finite or infinite power series in a single variable in which the coefficients are rational functions of the number of the term of the series can be expressed as the solution of a linear differential equation in which the coefficients are rational functions of the variable.

Let
$$S=\sum_{n=0}^{t}\frac{f(n)}{F(n)}r^n \tag{1}$$
be the given series in which $f(n)$ and $F(n)$ are polynomials.

Let u_n denote the $(n+1)$st term of (1); then
$$\frac{u_n}{u_{n-1}}=r\frac{f(n)F(n-1)}{F(n)f(n-1)}=r\frac{\theta(n)}{\phi(n)}, \tag{2}$$
where $\theta(n)$ and $\phi(n)$ are relatively prime.

We then have
$$\sum_{n=1}^{t}\phi(n)u_n=r\sum_{n=1}^{t}\theta(n)u_{n-1}$$
$$=r\sum_{n=0}^{t}\theta(n+1)u_n-r\theta(t+1)u_t. \tag{3}$$

Adding $\phi(0)u_0$ to both sides of (3) gives
$$\sum_{n=0}^{t}\phi(n)u_n=r\sum_{n=0}^{t}\theta(n+1)u_n-r\theta(t+1)u_t+\phi(0)\frac{f(0)}{F(0)}. \tag{4}$$

Letting
$$\phi(n)=\sum_{k=0}^{m}a_kn^k$$
and
$$\theta(n+1)=\sum_{k=0}^{m}b_kn^k,$$
then (4) becomes
$$\sum_{n=0}^{t}\sum_{k=0}^{m}a_kn^ku_n=r\sum_{n=0}^{t}\sum_{k=0}^{m}b_kn^ku_n-r\theta(t+1)u_t-\phi(0)\frac{f(0)}{F(0)}. \tag{5}$$

* *A Treatise on Differential Equations*, third edition, pp. 441–450.

Letting $$\sum_{n=0}^{t} u_n = S;$$

then
$$\sum_{n=0}^{t} n^k u_n = \left(r\frac{d}{dr}\right)^k S$$
$$= \sum_{\beta=1}^{k} \frac{(-1)^\beta}{\beta!} \sum_{\gamma=1}^{\beta} (-1)^\gamma \binom{\beta}{\gamma} \gamma^k r^\beta \frac{d^\beta}{dr^\beta} S$$
$$= \sum_{\beta=1}^{k} G_\beta r^\beta \frac{d^\beta}{dr^\beta} S, \tag{6}$$

where
$$G_\beta = \frac{(-1)^\beta}{\beta!} \sum_{\gamma=1}^{\beta} (-1)^\gamma \binom{\beta}{\gamma} \gamma^k.$$

Then, by means of (6) we obtain from (5) the differential equation

$$(a_0 - rb_0) S + \sum_{k=0}^{m} (a_k - rb_k) \sum_{\beta=1}^{k} G_\beta r^\beta \frac{d^\beta}{dr^\beta} S = \phi(0) \frac{f(0)}{F(0)} - r\theta(t+1) u_t, \tag{7}$$

the solution of which is the required sum.

If the series is infinite, that is if $u_t = 0$, then

$$(a_0 - rb_0) S + \sum_{k=0}^{m} (a_k - rb_k) \sum_{\beta=1}^{k} G_\beta r^\beta \frac{d^\beta}{dr^\beta} S = \phi(0) \frac{f(0)}{F(0)}. \tag{8}$$

We shall now establish the following principles:

(i) If $\theta(n+1)$ and $\phi(n)$ have a common factor, say $n-p$, then $S = r^p$ is a particular integral of the differential equation.

(ii) If n is a common factor of $\theta(n+1)$ and $\phi(n)$, the substitution $r\frac{d}{dr} S = y$ reduces the order of the differential equation by one.

To prove (i) we write

$$\prod_{h=1}^{m} (n - v_h) \text{ for } \phi(n) \quad \text{and} \quad \prod_{h=1}^{m} (n+1-w_h) \text{ for } \theta(n+1); \tag{9}$$

then for $t = \infty$, (4) becomes

$$\sum_{n=0}^{\infty} \prod_{h=1}^{m} (n - v_h) u_n = r \sum_{n=0}^{\infty} \prod_{h=1}^{m} (n - w_h') u_n + \Pi(0), \tag{10}$$

where
$$w_h' = w_h - 1 \quad \text{and} \quad \Pi(0) = \prod_{h=1}^{m} (-v_h) \frac{f(0)}{F(0)}.$$

Let $v_h = w_h' = p$, that is, let the two products in (9) have a common factor $n-p$; then r^p is a particular integral of the differential equation.

For, if $S = r^p$, the first member of

$$\sum_{n=0}^{\infty} \left[\prod_{h=1}^{m} \left(r\frac{d}{dr} - v_h\right) - r \prod_{h=1}^{m} \left(r\frac{d}{dr} - w_h'\right) \right] S = \Pi(0) \tag{11}$$

becomes
$$\sum_{n=0}^{\infty} \left[\prod_{h=1}^{m} (p - v_h) - r \prod_{h=1}^{m} (p - w_h') \right] r^p, \tag{12}$$

which is equal to zero, since each of the products have a vanishing factor.

In general, if $\theta(n+1)$ and $\phi(n)$ have j common factors, $n-p_1$, $n-p_2$, ..., $n-p_j$, the differential equation has j particular integrals, r^{p_1}, r^{p_2}, ..., r^{p_j}, by means of which the order of the equation can be reduced from m to $m-j$.

The above includes the proof also of the second principle.

2. In the preceding the differential equation is derived from the ratio of the $(n+1)$st term to the nth term of the given series. If the series is infinite and if $f(n)$ and $F(n)$ are finite polynomials, the differential equation can be written directly from the series.

If $t=\infty$, we may write for (1)

$$F\left(r\frac{d}{dr}\right)S=f\left(r\frac{d}{dr}\right)\sum_{n=0}^{\infty}r^n=f\left(r\frac{d}{dr}\right)\frac{1}{1-r}. \tag{13}$$

Let
$$F(n)=\prod_{k=1}^{p}(n-a_k);$$

then
$$\prod_{k=1}^{p}\left(r\frac{d}{dr}-a_k\right)S=f\left(r\frac{d}{dr}\right)\frac{1}{1-r}. \tag{14}$$

Now, since
$$\left(r\frac{d}{dr}-a_p\right)r^{a_p}=(a_p-a_p)r^{a_p}=0,$$

r^{a_p} is a particular integral of (11), which by means of $S=r^{a/p}S_1$ reduces to

$$\prod_{k=1}^{p-1}\left(r\frac{d}{dr}-a_k\right)r^{a_p+1}\frac{dS_1}{dr}=f\left(r\frac{d}{dr}\right)\frac{1}{1-r}. \tag{15}$$

Let next
$$r^{a_p+1}\frac{dS_1}{dr}=r^{a_{p-1}}S_2;$$

then (15) reduces to

$$\prod_{k=1}^{p-2}\left(r\frac{d}{dr}-a_k\right)r^{a_{p-1}+1}\frac{dS_2}{dr}=f\left(r\frac{d}{dr}\right)\frac{1}{1-r}. \tag{16}$$

Continuing this process we arrive at

$$\left(r\frac{d}{dr}-a_1\right)r^{a_2+1}\frac{dS_{p-1}}{dr}=f\left(r\frac{d}{dr}\right)\frac{1}{1-r}, \tag{17}$$

where
$$r^{a_2}S_{p-1}=r^{a_3+1}\frac{dS_{p-2}}{dr}.$$

Letting
$$r^{a_2+1}\frac{dS_{p-1}}{dr}=r^{a_1}S_p,$$

we finally obtain
$$r^{a_1+1}\frac{dS_p}{dr}=f\left(r\frac{d}{dr}\right)\frac{1}{1-r}. \tag{18}$$

If the steps are retraced S may be expressed as a multiple integral, the constant of integration being determined at each step.

3. The following examples will illustrate the above methods.

(i) To find the value of

$$S=\sum_{n=0}^{\infty}(-1)^n\binom{p+n-1}{n}r^n,\quad |r|<1. \tag{19}$$

Let u_n denote the $(n+1)$st term of S; then

$$\frac{u_n}{u_{n-1}} = -r\frac{p+n-1}{n}, \tag{20}$$

and
$$\sum_{n=1}^{\infty} nu_n = -r\sum_{n=1}^{\infty}(p+n-1)\,u_{n-1}$$

or
$$\sum_{n=0}^{\infty} nu_n = -r\sum_{n=0}^{\infty}(p+n)\,u_n. \tag{21}$$

Now
$$\sum_{n=0}^{\infty} nu_n = r\frac{dS}{dr};$$

then (21) becomes
$$\frac{dS}{dr}+\frac{p}{1+r}S=0, \tag{22}$$

whence
$$\log S + p\log(1+r) + C = 0$$

or
$$S = C(1+r)^{-p}.$$

If $r=0$,
$$S=1 \quad \text{and} \quad C=1;$$

therefore
$$S=(1+r)^{-p}. \tag{23}$$

(ii) To find the value of

$$S=\sum_{n=0}^{\infty}\frac{\prod_{k=0}^{n-1}(2k+1)}{2^n n!}\frac{x^{2n+1}}{2n+1}, \qquad \prod_{k=0}^{n-1}(2k+1)\Big]_{n=0}=1. \tag{24}$$

Then
$$\frac{dS}{dx}=S'=\sum_{n=0}^{\infty}\frac{\prod_{k=0}^{n-1}(2k+1)}{2^n n!}x^{2n}. \tag{25}$$

Denoting the nth term of S' by u_n and letting $x^2=y$, then

$$\frac{u_n}{u_{n-1}}=\frac{2n-1}{n}y, \tag{26}$$

and
$$\sum_{n=1}^{\infty}2nu_n = y\sum_{n=1}^{\infty}(2n-1)\,u_{n-1}$$

or
$$\sum_{n=0}^{\infty}2nu_n = y\sum_{n=0}^{\infty}(2n+1)\,u_n;$$

whence
$$2\frac{dS'}{dy}=S'+2y\frac{dS'}{dy}, \tag{27}$$

from which
$$\log S' = \log\frac{1}{\sqrt{1-y}}+C. \tag{28}$$

Now, if $y=0$,
$$S'=1 \quad \text{and} \quad C=0;$$

hence
$$S'=\frac{1}{\sqrt{1-y}}=\frac{1}{\sqrt{1-x^2}}$$

and
$$S=\sin^{-1}x. \tag{29}$$

This result can also be obtained more directly from (25) thus:

$$\frac{\prod_{k=0}^{n-1}(2k+1)}{2^n n!}=\frac{1.3.5\ldots(2n-1)}{2^n n!}=\frac{(-1)^n}{n!}\left(-\frac{1}{2}\right)\left(-\frac{3}{2}\right)\cdots\left(-\frac{2n-1}{2}\right)$$

$$=(-1)^n\binom{-\frac{1}{2}}{n}.$$

Then $$\frac{dS}{dx}=\sum_{n=0}^{\infty}(-1)^n\binom{-\frac{1}{2}}{n}x^{2n}=(1-x^2)^{-\frac{1}{2}}$$

and $$S=\sin^{-1}x.$$

(iii) Show that

$$\sum_{n=0}^{\infty}(-1)^n\frac{\prod_{k=0}^{n-1}(2k+1)}{2^n n!}\frac{x^{2n+1}}{2n+1}=\log(x+\sqrt{1+x^2}). \tag{30}$$

(iv) To find the value of

$$S=\sum_{n=0}^{\infty}(-1)^n\frac{x^{2n+1}}{(2n+1)!}. \tag{31}$$

We may write $$\frac{S}{x}=S_1=\sum_{n=0}^{\infty}(-1)^n\frac{x^{2n}}{(2n+1)!}. \tag{32}$$

If again u_n denotes the $(n+1)$st term of S_1, then

$$\frac{u_n}{u_{n-1}}=-\frac{y}{(2n+1)2n},\quad \text{where } y=x^2, \tag{33}$$

from which $$2\sum_{n=0}^{\infty}(2n+1)nu_n=-r\sum_{n=0}^{\infty}u_n; \tag{34}$$

whence $$4y^2\frac{d^2S_1}{dy^2}+6y\frac{dS_1}{dy}+yS_1=0. \tag{35}$$

Now $$\frac{dS_1}{dy}=\frac{dS_1}{dx}\cdot\frac{dx}{dy}=\frac{dS_1}{dx}\frac{1}{2x} \tag{36}$$

and $$\frac{d^2S_1}{dy^2}=\frac{1}{4x^2}\frac{d^2S_1}{dx^2}-\frac{1}{4x^3}\frac{dS_1}{dx}. \tag{37}$$

Applying (36) and (37) to (35), we obtain

$$x\frac{d^2S_1}{dx^2}+2\frac{dS_1}{dx}+xS_1=0$$

or $$\frac{d^2}{dx^2}(xS_1)+xS_1=0. \tag{38}$$

Letting $x_1S_1=v$ and multiplying both sides of (38) by $2dv$, we have

$$2dv\frac{d^2v}{dx^2}=-2v\,dv$$

or $$\left(\frac{dv}{dx}\right)^2=-v^2+C_1^2.$$

Hence
$$\frac{dv}{\sqrt{C_1^2 - v^2}} = dx,$$
from which
$$\sin^{-1}\frac{v}{C_1} = x + C_2$$
or
$$v = xS_1 = C_1 \sin(x + C_2),$$
and
$$\frac{d(xS_1)}{dx} = C_1 \cos(x + C_2).$$

Now, if $x = 0$,
$$S_1 = 1 \quad \text{and} \quad \frac{d(xS_1)}{dx} = 1;$$
therefore
$$C_1 \sin C_2 = 0 \quad \text{and} \quad C_1 \cos C_2 = 1.$$
It follows that
$$C_2 = 0 \quad \text{and} \quad C_1 = 1,$$
and
$$xS_1 = S = \sin x.$$

(v) Show that
$$\sum_{n=0}^{\infty} \frac{x^{2n}}{(2n)!} = \tfrac{1}{2}(e^x + e^{-x}). \tag{39}$$

(vi) To find
$$S = \sum_{n=0}^{\infty} (-1)^n \frac{r^n}{8n+1}. \tag{40}$$

If as before u_n denotes the $(n+1)$st term of S,—which notation will be used hereafter,—we have
$$\frac{u_n}{u_{n-1}} = -\frac{8n-7}{8n+1}r$$
and
$$\sum_{n=0}^{\infty} (8n+1)u_n = -r\sum_{n=0}^{\infty} (8n+1)u_n + 1, \tag{41}$$
from which
$$\frac{dS}{dr} + \frac{1}{8r}S = \frac{1}{8r(1+r)}. \tag{42}$$

Letting in (42)
$$\frac{1}{8r} = P \quad \text{and} \quad \frac{1}{8r(1+r)} = Q,$$
then
$$S = e^{-\int P\,dr}\left(c + \int e^{\int P\,dr}\,dr\right) \tag{43}$$
$$= \frac{1}{8r^{1/8}}\int_0^r \frac{r^{1/8}\,dr}{r(1+r)} = \frac{1}{r^{1/8}}\int_0^x \frac{dx}{x^8+1}, \quad x = r^{1/8}. \tag{44}$$

Now
$$\frac{1}{x^8+1} = \tfrac{1}{4}\sqrt{2}\left(\frac{x(2-\sqrt{2})^{1/2}+2}{x^2+x(2-\sqrt{2})^{1/2}+1} - \frac{x(2-\sqrt{2})^{1/2}-2}{x^2-x(2-\sqrt{2})^{1/2}+1}\right.$$
$$\left. + \frac{x(2+\sqrt{2})^{1/2}+2}{x^2+x(2+\sqrt{2})^{1/2}+1} - \frac{x(2+\sqrt{2})^{1/2}-2}{x^2-x(2+\sqrt{2})^{1/2}+1}\right), \tag{45}$$
by means of which we obtain
$$S = \frac{1}{16r^{1/8}}[(2+2^{1/2})^{1/2}(2\theta + \log v) + (2-2^{1/2})^{1/2}(2\phi + \log u)], \tag{46}$$
where
$$u = \frac{r^{1/4} + r^{1/8}(2-2^{1/2})^{1/2}+1}{r^{1/4} - r^{1/8}(2-2^{1/2})^{1/2}+1}; \quad v = \frac{r^{1/4} + r^{1/8}(2+2^{1/2})^{1/2}+1}{r^{1/4} - r^{1/8}(2+2^{1/2})^{1/2}+1};$$
$$\theta = \tan^{-1}\frac{r^{1/8}(2+2^{1/2})^{1/2}}{1-r^{1/4}}; \quad \phi = \tan^{-1}\frac{r^{1/8}(2-2^{1/2})^{1/2}}{1-r^{1/4}}.$$

If $r=1$,

$$\sum_{n=0}^{\infty}\frac{(-1)^n}{8n+1}=\frac{1}{8}\Big[(2-2^{1/2})^{1/2}\log\frac{2+(2-2^{1/2})^{1/2}}{(2+2^{1/2})^{1/2}}$$

$$+(2+2^{1/2})^{1/2}\log\frac{2+(2+2^{1/2})^{1/2}}{(2-2^{1/2})^2}+\frac{\pi}{2}(4+2\,.\,2^{1/2})^{1/2}\Big]. \qquad (47)$$

This result can also be obtained from Ch. IX. (115) and (116) directly. Then

$$S=\frac{\pi}{16}\operatorname{cosec}\frac{\pi}{8}+\frac{1}{4}\left(\cos\frac{\pi}{8}\log\cot\frac{\pi}{16}+\sin\frac{\pi}{8}\log\cot\frac{3\pi}{16}\right)$$

$$=\frac{\pi}{16}2^{1/2}(2+2^{1/2})^{1/2}+\tfrac{1}{8}[(2+2^{1/2})^{1/2}\log\{2^{1/2}(2+2^{1/2})^{1/2}+2^{1/2}+1\}$$

$$+(2-2^{1/2})^{1/2}\log\{2^{1/2}(2-2^{1/2})^{1/2}+2^{1/2}-1\}],$$

which is the same as (47).

The differential equation (42) can be written from (40) thus :

$$\left(8r\frac{d}{dr}+1\right)S=\sum_{n=0}^{\infty}(-1)^n r^n=\frac{1}{1+r}. \qquad (48)$$

(vii) To find the value of

$$S=\sum_{n=0}^{\infty}\frac{r^n}{(2n+1)(2n+2)(2n+3)}. \qquad (49)$$

Then

$$\frac{u_n}{u_{n-1}}=r\frac{n(2n-1)}{(n+1)(2n+3)} \qquad (50)$$

and

$$\sum_{n=1}^{\infty}(n+1)(2n+3)u_n=r\sum_{n=1}^{\infty}n(2n-1)u_{n-1};$$

and since

$$(n+1)(2n+3)u_n]_{n=0}=\tfrac{1}{2},$$

therefore

$$\sum_{n=0}^{\infty}(n+1)(2n+3)u_n=r\sum_{n=0}^{\infty}(n+1)(2n+1)u_n+\tfrac{1}{2}. \qquad (51)$$

The resulting differential equation is then

$$\left(r\frac{d}{dr}+1\right)\left[2(1-r)r\frac{d}{dr}+3-r\right]S=\frac{1}{2}. \qquad (52)$$

Letting now

$$S=r^{-1}S_1,$$

then

$$\left[2(1-r)r\frac{d}{dr}+3-r\right]\frac{dS_1}{dr}=\frac{1}{2}; \qquad (53)$$

and letting

$$\frac{dS_1}{dr}=S_2,$$

gives the differential equation

$$\frac{dS_2}{dr}+\frac{3-r}{2r(1-r)}S_2=\frac{1}{4r(1-r)}. \qquad (54)$$

By means of (43) we obtain

$$S_2=\frac{1-r}{4r^{1/3}}\left[\frac{1}{r}-\frac{1-r}{2r^{3/2}}\log\frac{1+r^{1/2}}{1-r^{1/2}}\right], \tag{55}$$

from which
$$S_1=\frac{1}{4}\left[\frac{1+r}{r^{1/2}}\log\frac{1+r^{1/2}}{1-r^{1/2}}+2\log(1-r)-2\right], \tag{56}$$

and finally
$$S=\frac{1}{4r}\left[\frac{1+r}{r^{1/2}}\log\frac{1+r^{1/2}}{1-r^{1/2}}+2\log(1-r)-2\right]. \tag{57}$$

This result can also be obtained as follows:
Letting $r=x^2$ in (49), we have

$$x^3S=S_1=\sum_{n=0}^{\infty}\frac{x^{2n+3}}{(2n+1)(2n+2)(2n+3)}. \tag{58}$$

Now
$$\frac{d^3S}{dx^3}=\sum_{n=0}^{\infty}x^{2n}=\frac{1}{1-x^2}. \tag{59}$$

from which
$$\frac{d^2S_1}{dx^2}=\frac{1}{2}\log\frac{1+x}{1-x}, \tag{60}$$

$$\frac{dS_1}{dx}=\frac{1}{2}[(1+x)\log(1+x)+(1-x)\log(1-x)]. \tag{61}$$

Hence
$$S_1=\frac{1+x^2}{4}\log\frac{1+x}{1-x}+\frac{x}{2}\log(1-x^2)-\frac{x}{2} \tag{62}$$

and
$$S=\frac{1}{4r}\left(\frac{1+r}{r^{1/2}}\log\frac{1+r^{1/2}}{1-r^{1/2}}+2\log(1-r)-2\right),$$

which is the same as (57).

The following is another method for finding the value of

$$S=\sum_{n=0}^{\infty}\frac{x^{2n}}{(2n+1)(2n+2)(2n+3)},\quad r=x^2.$$

We then have

$$\left(x\frac{d}{dx}+1\right)\left(x\frac{d}{dx}+2\right)\left(x\frac{d}{dx}+3\right)=\sum_{n=0}^{\infty}x^{2n}=\frac{1}{1-x^2}. \tag{63}$$

Letting
$$\left(x\frac{d}{dx}+2\right)\left(x\frac{d}{dx}+3\right)S=S_1, \tag{64}$$

then, from (63),
$$\left(x\frac{d}{dx}+1\right)S_1=\frac{1}{1-x^2}$$

and
$$S_1=\frac{1}{x}\int_0^x\frac{dx}{1-x^2}=\frac{1}{2x}\log\frac{1+x}{1-x}. \tag{65}$$

Substituting (65) in (64) and letting

$$\left(x\frac{d}{dx}+3\right)S=S_2, \tag{66}$$

we have
$$\left(x\frac{d}{dx}+2\right)S_2=\frac{1}{2x}\log\frac{1+x}{1-x},$$

from which
$$S_2=\frac{1}{2x^2}\int_0^x \log\frac{1+x}{1-x}\,dx$$

$$=\frac{1}{2x^2}\left(x\log\frac{1+x}{1-x}+\log(1-x^2)\right). \tag{67}$$

Finally
$$S=\frac{1}{2x^2}\int_0^x\left[x\log\frac{1+x}{1-x}+\log(1-x^2)\right]dx. \tag{68}$$

Integrating by parts we obtain

$$S=\frac{1}{2x^3}\left[\frac{1+x^2}{2}\log\frac{1+x}{1-x}+x\log(1-x^2)-x\right]. \tag{69}$$

Letting $x=r^{1/2}$ in (69) gives (57).

We shall now find the value of (49) without the use of integration.

Since
$$\frac{1}{(2n+1)(2n+2)(2n+3)}=\frac{1}{2}\left(\frac{1}{2n+1}-\frac{1}{n+1}+\frac{1}{2n+3}\right),$$

we may write for (49)

$$S=\frac{1}{2}\left(\sum_{n=0}^{\infty}\frac{r^n}{2n+1}-\sum_{n=0}^{\infty}\frac{r^n}{n+1}+\sum_{n=0}^{\infty}\frac{r^n}{2n+3}\right). \tag{70}$$

Now
$$\sum_{n=0}^{\infty}\frac{r^n}{n+1}=-\log(1-r)$$

and
$$\sum_{n=0}^{\infty}\frac{r^n}{2n+3}=\frac{1}{r}\sum_{n=0}^{\infty}\frac{r^n}{2n+1}-\frac{1}{r};$$

therefore
$$S=\frac{1}{2}\left[\frac{1+r}{r}\sum_{n=0}^{\infty}\frac{r^n}{2n+1}-\frac{1}{r}+\log(1-r)\right]. \tag{71}$$

But
$$S_1=\sum_{n=0}^{\infty}\frac{r^n}{2n+1}=\frac{1}{r^{1/2}}\sum_{n=0}^{\infty}\frac{r^{1/2(2n+1)}}{2n+1}; \tag{72}$$

and since
$$\sum_{n=0}^{\infty}\frac{1}{2n+1}=\frac{1}{2}\sum_{n=0}^{\infty}\frac{1+(-1)^n}{n+1},$$

therefore
$$S_1=\frac{1}{2r^{1/2}}\left[\sum_{n=0}^{\infty}\frac{r^{1/2(n+1)}}{n+1}+\sum_{n=0}^{\infty}(-1)^n\frac{r^{1/2(n+1)}}{n+1}\right] \tag{73}$$

$$=\frac{1}{2r^{1/2}}[-\log(1-r^{1/2})+\log(1+r^{1/2})]$$

$$=\frac{1}{2r^{1/2}}\log\frac{1+r^{1/2}}{1-r^{1/2}}. \tag{74}$$

Applying (74) to (71) gives (57).

(viii) To find the value of

$$S=\sum_{n=0}^{\infty}\frac{(-1)^n r^n}{(2n+1)(2n+2)(2n+3)}. \tag{75}$$

Following the last method of (vii), we have

$$S=\frac{1}{2}\left[\sum_{n=0}^{\infty}\frac{(-1)^n r^n}{2n+1}+\sum_{n=0}^{\infty}\frac{(-1)^n r^n}{2n+3}-\sum_{n=0}^{\infty}\frac{(-1)^n r^n}{n+1}\right] \tag{76}$$

$$=\frac{1}{2}\left[\sum_{n=0}^{\infty}\frac{(-1)^n r^n}{2n+1}-\frac{1}{r}\sum_{n=0}^{\infty}\frac{(-1)^n r^n}{2n+1}+\frac{1}{r}-\frac{1}{r}\log(1+r)\right] \tag{77}$$

$$=\frac{1}{2}\left[-\frac{1-r}{r^{3/2}}\sum_{n=0}^{\infty}\frac{(-1)^n r^{1/2(2n+1)}}{2n+1}+\frac{1}{r}-\frac{1}{r}\log(1+r)\right]$$

$$=\frac{1}{2r}\left[1-\log(1+r)-\frac{1-r}{r^{3/2}}\tan^{-1}r^{1/2}\right]. \tag{78}$$

4. We shall next find the value of the finite series

$$S=\sum_{n=1}^{p}(-1)^{n-1}\frac{\prod_{k=1}^{n}(p-k+1)}{\prod_{k=1}^{n}(k-h)}, \tag{79}$$

where h may have any value, positive or negative, integral or fractional, except the positive integral values from 1 to p.

Let
$$S_1=\sum_{n=1}^{p}(-1)^{n-1}\frac{\prod_{k=1}^{n}(p-k+1)}{\prod_{k=1}^{n}(k-h)}r^{n-1}; \tag{80}$$

then
$$S=S_1]_{r=1}.$$

Now, from S_1,
$$\frac{u_n}{u_{n-1}}=-\frac{p-n+1}{n-h}r, \tag{81}$$

and
$$\sum_{n=2}^{p}(n-h)u_n=-r\sum_{n=2}^{p}(p-n+1)u_{n-1}$$

or
$$\sum_{n=1}^{p}(n-h)u_n=-r\sum_{n=1}^{p}(p-n)u_n+p; \tag{82}$$

therefore
$$\frac{dS_1}{dr}-\frac{h-pr}{r(1-r)}S_1=\frac{p}{r(1-r)}. \tag{83}$$

Solving (83), we obtain

$$S_1=\frac{pr^h}{(1-r)^{h-p}}\left[-\frac{(1-r)^{h-p}}{(h-p)r^{h+1}}+\frac{(1-r)^{h-p+1}}{(h+1)(h-p)(h-p+1)r^{h+2}}+\dots\right] \tag{84}$$

$$=\frac{p}{p-h}\frac{1}{r}+A_1(1-r)\frac{1}{r^2}+A_2(1-r)^2\frac{1}{r^3}+\dots,$$

where A_1, A_2, A_3, ... are free of r.

If $r=1$,
$$S=\frac{p}{p-h}. \tag{85}$$

5. To find the value of $$S=\sum_{n=0}^{\infty}\frac{n!}{\prod_{k=0}^{n}(p+k)}. \qquad (86)$$

We may write $$S=\frac{1}{p}\sum_{n=0}^{\infty}\frac{1}{\binom{p+n}{n}}.$$

Letting $$S_1=\sum_{n=0}^{\infty}\frac{r^n}{\binom{p+n}{n}}, \quad \text{then } S=S_1]_{r=1}. \qquad (87)$$

Now, from S_1 we have $$\frac{u_n}{u_{n-1}}=r\frac{n}{p+n},$$

which gives $$\frac{dS_1}{dr}+\frac{n-r}{r(1-r)}S_1=\frac{p}{r(1-r)}. \qquad (88)$$

Therefore $$S_1=\frac{p(1-r)^{p-1}}{r^p}\left[C+\int_0^r\frac{r^{p-1}\,dr}{(1-r)^p}\right]. \qquad (89)$$

But $$\int_0^r\frac{r^{p-1}\,dr}{(1-r)^p}=\sum_{k=0}^{p-2}(-1)^k\frac{r^{p-k-1}}{(p-k-1)(1-r)^{p-k-1}}+(-1)^p\log(1-r). \qquad (90)$$

Then, by means of (90), we obtain from (89)

$$S_1=p\left[\sum_{k=0}^{p-2}(-1)^k\frac{(1-r)^k}{(p-k-1)r^{k+1}}+(-1)^p\frac{(1-r)^{p-1}}{r^p}\log(1-r)+\frac{C(1-r)^{p-1}}{r^p}\right]. \qquad (91)$$

Multiplying both sides of (91) by r^p, then, if $r=0$, $C=0$.

Therefore $$S=\frac{1}{p-1}. \qquad (92)$$

6. To find the value of $$S=\sum_{n=0}^{\infty}\frac{r^n}{\prod_{k=1}^{n}(p+k)}. \qquad (93)$$

Now $$\frac{u_n}{u_{n-1}}=r\frac{n}{n+p}$$

and $$\sum_{n=0}^{\infty}(n+p)u_n=r\sum_{n=0}^{\infty}(n+1)u_n+\frac{1}{(p-1)!}. \qquad (94)$$

Whence $$\frac{dS}{dr}+\frac{p-r}{r(1-r)}S=\frac{1}{(p-1)!\,r(1-r)} \qquad (95)$$

and $$S=\frac{1}{(p-1)!}\,\frac{(1-r)^{p-1}}{r^p}\int_0^r\frac{r^{p-1}dr}{(1-r)^{p-1}}. \qquad (96)$$

Denoting the integral in (96) by I_p, then

$$I_p=\frac{1}{p-1}\,\frac{r^{p-1}}{(1-r)^{p-1}}-I_{p-1}. \qquad (97)$$

Using (97) as a recurring formula, we obtain

$$I_p = (-1)^p \sum_{k=1}^{p-1} \frac{(-1)^{k-1}}{k} \frac{r^k}{(1-r)^k} + (-1)^p \log(1-r). \tag{98}$$

Hence

$$S = \frac{1}{(p-1)!}\left[(-1)^p \frac{(1-r)^{p-1}}{r^p} \log(1-r) + \frac{(-1)^p}{r^p} \sum_{k=1}^{p-1} \frac{(-1)^{k-1}}{k} r^k (1-r)^{p-k-1}\right]. \tag{99}$$

But $$S_1 = \frac{(-1)^p}{r^p} \sum_{k=1}^{p-1} \frac{(-1)^{k-1}}{k} r^k (1-r)^{p-k-1}$$

$$= (-1)^p \sum_{k=1}^{p-1} \frac{(-1)^{k-1}}{k} \sum_{a=0}^{p-k-1} (-1)^a \binom{p-k-1}{a} \frac{1}{r^{p-k-a}}. \tag{100}$$

Letting $$p-k-a-1 = a',$$

$$S_1 = \frac{1}{r} \sum_{k=1}^{p-1} \frac{1}{k}\left(1-\frac{1}{r}\right)^{p-k-1}.$$

Therefore

$$S = \frac{1}{(p-1)!}\left[\frac{(-1)^p}{r^p}(1-r)^{p-1} \log(1-r) + \frac{1}{r} \sum_{k=1}^{p-1} \frac{1}{k}\left(1-\frac{1}{r}\right)^{p-k-1}\right]. \tag{101}$$

If $r=1$, k must be equal to $p-1$ and

$$S = \frac{1}{(p-1)(p-1)!},$$

which is the same as Ch. IX. (186).

7. To find the value of $$S = \sum_{n=0}^{\infty} \prod_{k=0}^{n} \left(\frac{a+k}{b+k}\right) r^n, \tag{102}$$

where a and b are positive integers.

Then $$\frac{u_n}{u_{n-1}} = r\frac{a+n}{b+n},$$

and $$\sum_{n=1}^{\infty} (b+n) u_n = r \sum_{n=1}^{\infty} (a+n) u_{n-1}$$

or $$\sum_{n=0}^{\infty} (b+n) u_n = r \sum_{n=0}^{\infty} (a+n+1) u_n + a, \tag{103}$$

from which $$\frac{dS}{dr} + \frac{b-(a+1)r}{r(1-r)} S = \frac{a}{r(1-r)}. \tag{104}$$

We then have $$\frac{r^b}{(1-r)^{b-a-1}} S = a\int_0^r \frac{r^{b-1}dr}{(1-r)^{b-a}}. \tag{105}$$

We shall distinguish between the cases when

$$b \leqq a, \quad b = a+1 \quad \text{and} \quad b > a+1.$$

(i) If $b \leqq a$, then

$$\frac{r^b}{(1-r)^{b-a-1}} S = a \int_0^r r^{b-1}(1-r)^{a-b} dr$$

$$= a \sum_{k=0}^{a-b} (-1)^k \binom{a-b}{k} \frac{r^{b+k}}{b+k}$$

and
$$S = \frac{a}{(1-r)^{a-b+1}} \sum_{k=0}^{a-b} (-1)^k \binom{a-b}{k} \frac{r^k}{b+k}. \tag{106}$$

If $r = 0$, then k can have the value zero only, and

$$S(0) = \frac{a}{b}, \tag{107}$$

which is evident from (102).

Also
$$S(1) = \infty. \tag{108}$$

(ii) If $b = a + 1$, then

$$r^b S = a \int_0^r \frac{r^a dr}{1-r} \tag{109}$$

$$= a \left[-\log(1-r) - \sum_{k=1}^{a} \frac{r^k}{k} \right]$$

and
$$S = \frac{a}{r^{a+1}} \left[-\log(1-r) - \sum_{k=1}^{a} \frac{r^k}{k} \right]. \tag{110}$$

We then have
$$S(0) = a\left[-\frac{1}{r^{a+1}} \log(1-r) - \sum_{k=1}^{a} \frac{r^k}{k} \right]_{r=0}$$

$$= a \frac{a!}{(a+1)!} \frac{1}{(1-r)^a} \Bigg]_{r=0} = \frac{a}{a+1} = \frac{a}{b}. \tag{111}$$

$$S(1) = \infty \tag{112}$$

and
$$S(-1) = a\left[-\log 2 - \sum_{k=1}^{a} \frac{(-1)^k}{k} \right]. \tag{113}$$

(iii) If $b > a + 1$, then

$$\frac{r^b}{(1-r)^{b-a-1}} S = -a \int_1^{1-r} \frac{(1-x)^{b-1}}{x^{b-a}} dx \tag{114}$$

$$= (-1)^b a \int_1^{1-r} \sum_{k=0}^{b-1} (-1)^k \binom{b-1}{k} x^{a-1-k} dx$$

$$= (-1)^b a \left[\sum_{k=0}^{a-1} (-1)^k \binom{b-1}{k} \frac{(1-r)^{a-k} - 1}{a-k} \right.$$

$$\left. + (-1)^a \binom{b-1}{a} \log(1-r) + \sum_{k=a+1}^{b-1} (-1)^k \binom{b-1}{k} \frac{(1-r)^{a-k} - 1}{a-k} \right]; \tag{115}$$

whence
$$S=(-1)^b\frac{a}{r^b}\Bigg[(-1)^a\binom{b-1}{a}(1-r)^{b-a-1}\log(1-r)$$
$$+\sum_{k=0}^{a-1}(-1)^k\binom{b-1}{k}\frac{(1-r)^{b-k-1}-(1-r)^{b-a-1}}{a-k}$$
$$+\sum_{k=a+1}^{b-1}(-1)^k\binom{b-1}{k}\frac{(1-r)^{b-k-1}-(1-r)^{b-a-1}}{a-k}\Bigg]. \qquad (116)$$

It follows at once from (102) that $S=\frac{a}{b}$, if $r=0$. We shall, however, evaluate (116) for $r=0$, since the work involves useful applications of the operations with series.

Now
$$\frac{S}{(1-r)^{b-a-1}}\Bigg]_{r\doteq 0}=\Bigg[(-1)^b\frac{a}{r^b}\Bigg\{(-1)^a\binom{b-1}{a}\log(1-r)$$
$$+\left(\sum_{k=0}^{a-1}+\sum_{k=a+1}^{b-1}\right)(-1)^k\binom{b-1}{k}\frac{(1-r)^{a-k}-1}{a-k}\Bigg\}\Bigg]_{r\doteq 0}. \qquad (117)$$

But
$$N_1=\frac{1}{r^b}\log(1-r)\Bigg]_{r\doteq 0}=-\frac{1}{r^b}\sum_{m=1}^{\infty}\frac{r^m}{m}\Bigg]_{r\doteq 0} \qquad (118)$$
$$=-\frac{d^b}{dr^b}\sum_{m=1}^{\infty}\frac{r^m}{m}\div\frac{d^b}{dr^b}r^b\Bigg]_{r\doteq 0}$$
$$=-\sum_{m=1}^{\infty}\binom{m}{b}b!\frac{r^{m-b}}{m}\div b!\Bigg]_{r\doteq 0};$$
and since m can have the value b only, therefore
$$N_1=-\frac{1}{b}. \qquad (119)$$

Next
$$N_2=\frac{(1-r)^{a-k}-1}{(a-k)r^b}\Bigg]_{r\doteq 0}=\frac{1}{a-k}\frac{d^b}{dr^b}(1-r)^{a-k}\div\frac{d^b}{dr^b}r^b\Bigg]_{r\doteq 0} \qquad (120)$$
$$=\frac{(-1)^b}{(a-k)b!}\binom{a-k}{b}b!=\frac{(-1)^b}{b}\binom{a-k-1}{b-1}$$
$$=-\frac{1}{b}\binom{b-a+k-1}{b-1}. \qquad (121)$$

Applying (119) and (121) to (117) gives
$$S(0)=(-1)^b\frac{a}{b}\Bigg[(-1)^{a-1}\binom{b-1}{a}+\left(\sum_{k=0}^{a-1}+\sum_{k=a+1}^{b-1}\right)$$
$$\left\{(-1)^{k-1}\binom{b-1}{k}\binom{b-a+k-1}{b-1}\right\}\Bigg]; \qquad (122)$$
and since $b>a+1$, the first summation is zero; therefore
$$S(0)=(-1)^b\frac{a}{b}\Bigg[(-1)^{a-1}\binom{b-1}{a}+\sum_{k=a+1}^{b-1}(-1)^{k-1}\binom{b-1}{k}\binom{b-a+k-1}{b-1}\Bigg]. \qquad (123)$$

But $(-1)^{a-1}\binom{b-1}{a}$ is the term of the summation corresponding to $k=a$; hence
$$S(0)=(-1)^{b-1}\frac{a}{b}\sum_{k=a}^{b-1}(-1)^k\binom{b-1}{k}\binom{b-a+k-1}{b-1}. \qquad (124)$$

Now if $k<a$, $\binom{b-a+k-1}{b-1}=0$, and we may write for (124)

$$S(0)=(-1)^{b-1}\frac{a}{b}\sum_{k=0}^{b-1}(-1)^k\binom{b-1}{k}\binom{b-a+k-1}{b-1}. \tag{125}$$

But $\binom{b-a+k-1}{b-1}=\frac{k^{b-1}}{(b-1)!}+$ terms in k of lower degree than $b-1$; and since

$$\sum_{k=0}^{b-1}(-1)^k\binom{b-1}{k}k^p=0, \text{ if } p<b-1, \text{ by Ch. I. (136),}$$

$$=(-1)^{b-1}(b-1)!, \text{ if } p=b-1, \text{ by Ch. V. (192),}$$

therefore $$S(0)=\frac{a}{b}.$$

If $r=1$, $$S(1)=\frac{a}{b-a-1},$$

the same result as in Ch. IX. (216).

We shall finally obtain S for $r=-1$.

From (116),

$$S(-1)=a\Bigg[(-1)^a\binom{b-1}{a}2^{b-a-1}\log 2$$

$$+\left(\sum_{k=0}^{a-1}+\sum_{k=a+1}^{b-1}\right)(-1)^k\binom{b-1}{k}\frac{2^{b-1-k}-2^{b-a-1}}{a-k}\Bigg]. \tag{126}$$

But $$\left.\frac{2^{b-1-k}-2^{b-a-1}}{a-k}\right]_{k=a}=2^{b-a-1}\log 2;$$

therefore $$S(-1)=a\sum_{k=0}^{b-1}(-1)^k\binom{b-1}{k}\frac{2^{b-1-k}-2^{b-a-1}}{a-k} \tag{127}$$

$$=2^{b-a-1}a\sum_{k=0}^{b-1}(-1)^k\binom{b-1}{k}\frac{2^{a-k}-1}{a-k}. \tag{128}$$

8. (i) To find the value of

$$S=\sum_{n=0}^{\infty}\frac{n!}{\prod_{k=0}^{n}(2k+5)}\,\frac{n+2}{n+3}r^n. \tag{129}$$

Then $$\frac{u_n}{u_{n-1}}=\frac{n(n+2)^2}{(n+1)(n+3)(2n+5)}, \tag{130}$$

and $$\sum_{n=1}^{\infty}(n+1)(n+3)(2n+5)u_n=r\sum_{n=1}^{\infty}n(n+2)^2u_{n-1}$$

$$=r\sum_{n=0}^{\infty}(n+1)(n+3)^2u_n$$

or $$\sum_{n=0}^{\infty}(n+1)(n+3)(2n+5)u_n=r\sum_{n=0}^{\infty}(n+1)(n+3)^2u_n+2. \tag{131}$$

We may now write (131) in the form

$$\sum_{n=0}^{\infty}(n+1)(n+3)[2n+5-r(n+3)]u_n=2,$$

from which
$$\left(r\frac{d}{dr}+1\right)\left(r\frac{d}{dr}+3\right)\left[2r\frac{d}{dr}+5-r^2\frac{d}{dr}-3r\right]S=2. \tag{132}$$

Since the indicated operations may be performed in any order, we let

$$S=r^{-3}S_1;$$

then
$$\left(r\frac{d}{dr}+3\right)S=-3r^{-3}S_1+3r^{-3}S_1+r^{-2}\frac{dS_1}{dr}=r^{-2}\frac{dS_2}{dr},$$

and (132) becomes

$$\left[(2-r)r\frac{d}{dr}+5-3r\right]\left(r\frac{d}{dr}+1\right)r^{-2}\frac{dS_1}{dr}=2. \tag{133}$$

Let now
$$r^{-2}\frac{dS_1}{dr}=r^{-1}S_2;$$

then (133) changes to
$$\left[(2-r)r\frac{d}{dr}+5-3r\right]\frac{dS_2}{dr}=2. \tag{134}$$

And again, if we let
$$\frac{dS_2}{dr}=S_3,$$

we obtain
$$(2-r)r\frac{dS_3}{dr}+(5-3r)S_3=2. \tag{135}$$

Solving the differential equation gives

$$S_3=\frac{1}{r^{5/2}(2-r)^{1/2}}\left[C_3+2\int\frac{r^{3/2}}{(2-r)^{1/2}}\,dr\right]. \tag{136}$$

Letting in (136) $r=\sin^2\theta$, then

$$S_3=\frac{1}{4\sin^5\theta\cos\theta}(3\theta-2\sin 2\theta+\tfrac{1}{4}\sin 4\theta),\qquad C_3=0,$$

$$=\frac{1}{r^{5/2}(2-r)^{1/2}}\left[3\sin^{-1}\left(\frac{r}{2}\right)^{1/2}-\frac{r+3}{2}r^{1/2}(2-r)^{1/2}\right]. \tag{137}$$

Now
$$S_3=\frac{dS_2}{dr}=\frac{dS_2}{d\theta}\frac{d\theta}{dr};$$

hence
$$S_2=\tfrac{3}{2}\operatorname{cosec}^2\theta-\tfrac{1}{2}\cot^2\theta-\theta(\cot^3\theta+3\cot\theta)+C_2; \tag{138}$$

and since
$$C_2=\tfrac{7}{6},$$

$$S_2=\tfrac{8}{3}-\theta\cot^3\theta+\cot^2\theta-3\theta\cot\theta$$

$$=\frac{5}{3}+\frac{2}{r}-\frac{2(r+1)}{r^{3/2}}(2-r)^{1/2}\sin^{-1}\left(\frac{r}{2}\right)^{1/2}. \tag{139}$$

Again
$$S_2=r^{-1}\frac{dS_1}{dr}=r^{-1}\frac{dS_1}{d\theta}\frac{d\theta}{dr};$$

therefore
$$S_1=8(\tfrac{2}{3}\sin^4\theta-\tfrac{1}{4}\cos^4\theta-\tfrac{3}{8}\theta^2+\tfrac{1}{16}\theta\sin 4\theta$$
$$+\tfrac{1}{64}\cos 4\theta-\tfrac{1}{4}\theta\sin 2\theta-\tfrac{1}{8}\cos 2\theta)+C_1. \tag{140}$$

We find $C_1 = \frac{23}{8}$ and

$$S_1 = -3\left[\sin^{-1}\left(\frac{r}{2}\right)^{1/2}\right]^2 - (1+r)r^{1/2}(2-r)^{1/2}\sin^{-1}\left(\frac{r}{2}\right)^{1/2} + \frac{13}{12}r^2 + \frac{5}{2}r; \quad (141)$$

therefore

$$S = -\frac{3}{r^3}\left[\sin^{-1}\left(\frac{r}{2}\right)^{1/2}\right]^2 - \frac{1+r}{r^{3/2}}r^{1/2}(2-r)^{1/2}\sin^{-1}\left(\frac{r}{2}\right)^{1/2} + \frac{13}{12r} + \frac{5}{2r^2}. \quad (142)$$

If $r=1$,

$$S = \frac{1}{4}\left(\frac{43}{3} - \frac{3\pi^2}{4} - 2\pi\right). \quad (143)$$

(ii) We shall now obtain the value of (129) from

$$(2-r)r^3\frac{d^3S}{dr^3} + (19-10r)r^2\frac{d^2S}{dr^2} + (41-23r)r\frac{dS}{dr} + (15-9r)S = 2, \quad (144)$$

which is the explicit form of (131). The work involved is somewhat simpler than in the preceding method.

Since $n+1$ and $n+3$ are common factors of the two summations in (131), r^{-1} and r^{-3} are particular integrals of (144).

Let therefore $S = r^{-1}y$ and $\frac{dy}{dr} = z$;

then (144) becomes

$$(2-r)r^2\frac{d^2z}{dr^2} + (13-7r)r\frac{dz}{dr} + (15-9r)z = 2. \quad (145)$$

Letting now $z = r^{-3}u$ and $\frac{du}{dr} = v$,

we have

$$(2-r)r\frac{dv}{dr} + (1-r)v = 2r^2; \quad (146)$$

hence

$$v = \frac{1}{r^{1/2}(2-r)^{1/2}}\left(C_1 + 2\int_0^r \frac{r^{3/2}\,dr}{(2-r)^{1/2}}\right). \quad (147)$$

Letting $r = 2\sin^2\theta$, then

$$v = \frac{1}{\sin\theta\cos\theta}(3\theta - 2\sin 2\theta + \tfrac{1}{4}\sin 4\theta)$$

$$= \frac{2}{r^{1/2}(2-r)^{1/2}}\left[3\sin^{-1}\left(\frac{r}{2}\right)^{1/2} - \frac{r+3}{2}r^{1/2}(2-r)^{1/2}\right] \quad (148)$$

and

$$u = 6\theta^2 + 4\cos 2\theta - \tfrac{1}{4}\cos 4\theta + C_2, \quad C_2 = -\tfrac{15}{4},$$

$$= 6\left[\sin^{-1}\left(\frac{r}{2}\right)^{1/2}\right]^2 - 3r - \frac{r^2}{2}. \quad (149)$$

We then find

$$z = \frac{6}{r^3}\left[\sin^{-1}\left(\frac{r}{2}\right)^{1/2}\right]^2 - \frac{3}{r^2} - \frac{1}{2r}, \quad (150)$$

$$y = -\frac{3}{r^2}\left[\sin^{-1}\left(\frac{r}{2}\right)^{1/2}\right]^2 - \frac{r+1}{r}r^{1/2}(2-r)^{1/2}\sin^{-1}\left(\frac{r}{2}\right)^{1/2} + \frac{5}{2r} + C_3, \quad C_3 = \frac{13}{12}, \quad (151)$$

and finally

$$S = -\frac{3}{r^3}\left[\sin^{-1}\left(\frac{r}{2}\right)^{1/2}\right]^2 - \frac{r+1}{r^3}r^{1/2}(2-r)^{1/2}\sin^{-1}\left(\frac{r}{2}\right)^{1/2} + \frac{5}{2r^2} + \frac{13}{12r}, \quad (152)$$

which is the same as (142).

Show by both methods that

$$S=\sum_{n=0}^{\infty}\frac{(-1)^n n!}{\prod_{k=0}^{n}(2k+5)}\frac{n+2}{n+3}r^n$$

$$=-\frac{3}{r^3}\left[\log\frac{r^{1/2}+(2+r)^{1/2}}{2^{1/2}}\right]^2+\frac{(r-1)(2+r)^{1/2}}{r^{5/2}}\log\frac{r^{1/2}+(2+r)^{1/2}}{2^{1/2}}+\frac{5}{2r^2}-\frac{13}{12r}. \quad (153)$$

If $r=1$, $\qquad S=\frac{17}{12}-\frac{3}{2}\log(2+\sqrt{3}).$

The result (153) can also be obtained by substituting $-r$ for r in (152). Let $f(r)$ denote the first two terms of (152); then

$$f(-r)=\frac{3}{r^3}\left[\sin^{-1}i\left(\frac{r}{2}\right)^{1/2}\right]+\frac{1-r}{r^3}r^{1/2}(2+r)^{1/2}i\sin^{-1}i\left(\frac{r}{2}\right)^{\frac{1}{2}}. \quad (154)$$

Now
$$\sin^{-1}u=\sum_{k=0}^{\infty}(-1)^k\binom{-\frac{1}{2}}{k}\frac{u^{2k+1}}{2k+1}$$

and
$$\sin^{-1}iu=i\sum_{k=0}^{\infty}\binom{-\frac{1}{2}}{k}\frac{u^{2k+1}}{2k+1}$$

$$=i\int_0^u\sum_{k=0}^{\infty}\binom{-\frac{1}{2}}{k}u^{2k}\,du$$

$$=i\int_0^u\frac{du}{(1+u^2)^{1/2}}$$

$$=i\log\left[u+(1+u^2)^{1/2}\right]. \quad (155)$$

Applying (155) to (154) gives the first two terms of (153).
Show that

$$\sum_{n=0}^{\infty}\frac{2^n n!}{(n+1)\prod_{k=0}^{n}(2k+1)}\frac{1}{2n+3}x^n=\frac{2(1-x)^{1/2}}{x^{3/2}}\sin^{-1}x^{1/2}+\frac{(\sin^{-1}x^{1/2})^2}{x}-\frac{2}{x}. \quad (156)$$

9. To show that

$$S_n=\frac{2^{4n}}{(2n+1)\binom{2n}{n}}=((x^n))\frac{\sin(2x^{1/2})}{2x^{1/2}(1-4x)^{1/2}}. \quad (157)$$

Let
$$S=\sum_{n=0}^{\infty}S_n x^n;$$

then
$$\frac{u_n}{u_{n-1}}=\frac{8x}{2n+1}$$

and
$$\sum_{n=0}^{\infty}(2n+1)u_n=8x\sum_{n=0}^{\infty}(n+1)u_n+1;$$

whence
$$\frac{dS}{dx}+\frac{1-8x}{2(1-4x)}S=\frac{1}{2x(1-4x)}. \quad (158)$$

Therefore $$S=\frac{1}{2x^{1/2}(1-4x)^{1/2}}\int_0^x \frac{dx}{x^{1/2}(1-4x)^{1/2}}$$

$$=\frac{\sin^{-1}(2x^{1/2})}{2x^{1/2}(1-4x)^{1/2}} \tag{159}$$

and $$S_n=((x^n))\frac{\sin^{-1}(2x^{1/2})}{2x^{1/2}(1-4x)^{1/2}}. \tag{160}$$

From Ch. V. (156) we conclude that

$$\sum_{k=0}^{n}\binom{2k}{k}\binom{2\overline{n-k}}{n-k}\frac{1}{2k+1}=\frac{2^{4n}}{(2n+1)\binom{2n}{n}}. \tag{161}$$

In Ch. II. (108) we have found the expansion of $x\cot x$.

We are now prepared to find another form of the expansion.

Let $x=\sin^{-1}\theta$; then

$$x\cot x=\frac{1}{\theta}(1-\theta^2)(1-\theta^2)^{-\frac{1}{2}}\sin^{-1}\theta\Big]_{\theta=\sin x}=\frac{1}{\theta}(1-\theta^2)f(\theta)\Big]_{\theta=\sin x}, \tag{162}$$

where $f(\theta)=(1-\theta^2)^{-\frac{1}{2}}\sin^{-1}\theta$.

Now $$\sin^{-1}\theta=\sum_{k=0}^{\infty}(-1)^k\binom{-\frac{1}{2}}{k}\frac{\theta^{2k+1}}{2k+1}$$

and $$(1-\theta^2)^{-\frac{1}{2}}=\sum_{n=0}^{\infty}(-1)^n\binom{-\frac{1}{2}}{k}\theta^{2n};$$

therefore $$f(\theta)=\sum_{k=0}^{\infty}(-1)^k\binom{-\frac{1}{2}}{n}\frac{1}{2k+1}\sum_{n=0}^{\infty}(-1)^n\binom{-\frac{1}{2}}{n}\theta^{2k+2n+1}. \tag{163}$$

Letting $k+n=n'$, then

$$f(\theta)=\sum_{k=0}^{\infty}\binom{-\frac{1}{2}}{k}\frac{1}{2k+1}\sum_{n=k}^{\infty}(-1)^n\binom{-\frac{1}{2}}{n-k}\theta^{2n+1}$$

$$=\sum_{n=0}^{\infty}(-1)^n\theta^{2n+1}\sum_{k=0}^{n}\binom{-\frac{1}{2}}{k}\binom{-\frac{1}{2}}{n-k}\frac{1}{2k+1},\text{ by Ch. I. (68),} \tag{164}$$

and (162) becomes

$$x\cot x=(1-\theta^2)\sum_{n=0}^{\infty}(-1)^n\theta^{2n}\sum_{k=0}^{n}\binom{-\frac{1}{2}}{k}\binom{-\frac{1}{2}}{n-k}\frac{1}{2k+1}\Big]_{\theta=\sin x}. \tag{165}$$

But

$$\sum_{k=0}^{n}\binom{-\frac{1}{2}}{k}\binom{-\frac{1}{2}}{n-k}\frac{1}{2k+1}=\frac{(-1)^n}{2^{2n}}\sum_{k=0}^{n}\binom{2k}{n}\binom{2\overline{n-k}}{n-k}\frac{1}{2k+1}=\frac{(-1)^n2^{2n}}{(2n+1)\binom{2n}{n}}; \tag{166}$$

hence $$x\cot x=(1-\theta^2)\sum_{n=0}^{\infty}\frac{2^{2n}}{(2n+1)\binom{2n}{n}}\theta^{2n}\Big]_{\theta=\sin x}. \tag{167}$$

Substituting in (167) the value of $\theta^{2n}=\sin^{2n}x$ from Ch. II. (85), we obtain (after interchanging the letters k and n)

$$x\cot x=1-\sum_{n=1}^{\infty}(-1)^n 2^{2n}\frac{x^{2n}}{(2n)!}\sum_{k=1}^{n}\frac{k!\,(k-1)!}{(2k+1)!}\sum_{a=1}^{k}(-1)^a\binom{2k}{k-a}a^{2n}. \quad (168)$$

10. To find an expression for

$$S=\sum_{n=0}^{\infty}\frac{r^n}{\prod_{k=1}^{n}(ka+1)}, \qquad \prod_{k=1}^{0}(ka+1)=1. \quad (169)$$

Now

$$\frac{u_n}{u_{n-1}}=\frac{r}{an+1},$$

and

$$\sum_{n=0}^{\infty}(an+1)\,u_n=r\sum_{n=0}^{\infty}u_n+1 \quad (170)$$

or

$$\frac{dS}{dr}+\frac{1-r}{ar}S=\frac{1}{ar};$$

whence

$$S=\frac{1}{r^{1/a}}e^{\frac{r}{a}}\int_0^r\frac{1}{ar}\,r^{1/a}e^{-r/a}\,dr. \quad (171)$$

Letting $r=ax^a$, then

$$S=\frac{1}{x}e^{x^a}\int_0^x e^{-x^a}\,dx, \quad x=\left(\frac{r}{a}\right)^{1/a}. \quad (172)$$

If $a>1$, the integral in (172) cannot be expressed in terms of elementary functions.

We also find $$\sum_{n=0}^{\infty}\frac{(-1)^n r^n}{\prod_{k=1}^{n}(ka+1)}=\frac{1}{x}e^{-x^a}\int_0^x e^{x^a}\,dx, \quad x=\left(\frac{r}{a}\right)^{1/a}. \quad (173)$$

CHAPTER XI.

THE SEPARATION OF TRIGONOMETRIC EXPRESSIONS INTO PARTIAL FRACTIONS.

WE shall here consider the separation into partial fractions of some trigonometrical expressions and then the separation of powers of the trigonometrical functions.

1. To separate into partial fractions of

$$\frac{\cos^p x}{\cos nx}, \quad p < n. \tag{1}$$

We must first find the factors of $\cos nx$.

Now $\cos nx = 0$ is satisfied by

$$x = \frac{2k+1}{2n}\pi, \quad k = 0, 1, 2, \ldots, n-1;$$

therefore

$$\cos nx = A \prod_{k=0}^{n-1}\left(\cos x - \cos\frac{2k+1}{2n}\pi\right). \tag{2}$$

We then have

$$\text{for } x = 0, \quad A \prod_{k=0}^{n-1}\left(1 - \cos\frac{2k+1}{2n}\pi\right) = 1, \tag{3}$$

and

$$\text{for } x = \pi, \quad A \prod_{k=0}^{n-1}\left(-1 - \cos\frac{2k+1}{2n}\pi\right) = (-1)^n$$

or

$$A \prod_{k=0}^{n-1}\left(1 + \cos\frac{2k+1}{2n}\pi\right) = 1. \tag{4}$$

Hence

$$A = \frac{1}{\prod\limits_{k=0}^{n-1} \sin\dfrac{2k+1}{2n}\pi}; \tag{5}$$

and since

$$\sin\frac{2k+1}{2n}\pi = \frac{i}{2}e^{-\frac{2k+1}{2n}\pi i}\left(1 - e^{\frac{2k+1}{n}\pi i}\right),$$

$$A = \frac{2^n e^{\frac{\pi i}{2n}\sum\limits_{k=0}^{n-1}(2k+1)}}{i^n \prod\limits_{k=0}^{n-1}\left(1 - e^{\frac{2k+1}{n}\pi}\right)}. \tag{6}$$

But $e^{\frac{2k+1}{n}\pi i}$ is a root of $1+x^n=0$, and

$$\prod_{k=0}^{n-1}\left(1-e^{\frac{2k+1}{n}\pi i}\right)=1+x^n\Big]_{x=1}=2\,;$$

therefore $$A=2^{n-1}$$

and $$\cos nx=2^{n-1}\sum_{k=0}^{n-1}\left(\cos x-\cos\frac{2k+1}{2n}\pi\right). \tag{7}$$

We then have $$\frac{\cos^p x}{\cos nx}=\sum_{k=0}^{n-1}\frac{A_k}{\cos x-\cos\dfrac{2k+1}{2n}\pi}, \tag{8}$$

from which $$A_k=\cos^p\frac{2k+1}{2n}\pi\;\frac{\cos x-\cos\dfrac{2k+1}{2n}\pi}{\cos nx}\Bigg]_{x=\frac{2k+1}{2n}\pi}$$

$$=(-1)^k\frac{1}{n}\cos^p\frac{2k+1}{2n}\pi\sin\frac{2k+1}{2n}\pi \tag{9}$$

and $$\frac{\cos^p x}{\cos nx}=\frac{1}{n}\sum_{k=0}^{n-1}(-1)^k\frac{\cos^p\dfrac{2k+1}{2n}\pi\sin\dfrac{2k+1}{2n}\pi}{\cos x-\cos\dfrac{2k+1}{2n}\pi}. \tag{10}$$

In a similar way we obtain

$$\frac{\sin^{2p} x}{\cos nx}=\frac{1}{n}\sum_{k=0}^{n-1}(-1)^k\frac{\sin^{2p+1}\dfrac{2k+1}{2n}\pi}{\cos x-\cos\dfrac{2k+1}{2n}\pi}. \tag{11}$$

For example:

$$\frac{\cos^2 x}{\cos 3x}=\frac{1}{4}\left(\frac{1}{2\cos x+\sqrt{3}}+\frac{1}{2\cos x-\sqrt{3}}\right), \tag{12}$$

$$\frac{\sin^2 x}{\cos 3x}=\frac{1}{12}\left(\frac{1}{2\cos x+\sqrt{3}}+\frac{1}{2\cos x-\sqrt{3}}\right)-\frac{1}{3\cos x}, \tag{13}$$

$$\frac{\cos^3 x}{\cos 4x}=\frac{\sqrt{2}}{32}\left(\frac{2+\sqrt{2}}{2\cos x+\sqrt{2+\sqrt{2}}}+\frac{2+\sqrt{2}}{2\cos x-\sqrt{2+\sqrt{2}}}\right.$$
$$\left.-\frac{2-\sqrt{2}}{2\cos x+\sqrt{2-\sqrt{2}}}-\frac{2-\sqrt{2}}{2\cos x-\sqrt{2-\sqrt{2}}}\right), \tag{14}$$

from which

$$\int_0^x\frac{\cos^3 x\,dx}{\cos 4x}=(\sqrt{2}+1)\sqrt{2+\sqrt{2}}\log\frac{\sqrt{2-\sqrt{2}}\sec^2\frac{1}{2}x+4\tan\frac{1}{2}x}{\sqrt{2-\sqrt{2}}\sec^2\frac{1}{2}x+4\tan\frac{1}{2}x}$$
$$-(\sqrt{2}-1)\sqrt{2-\sqrt{2}}\log\frac{\sqrt{2+\sqrt{2}}\sec^2\frac{1}{2}x+4\tan\frac{1}{2}x}{\sqrt{2+\sqrt{2}}\sec^2\frac{1}{2}x-4\tan\frac{1}{2}x}. \tag{15}$$

2. To separate into partial fractions

$$\frac{\sin^p x}{\sin(2n+1)x}, \quad p<2n+1. \tag{16}$$

Since $\sin(2n+1)x=0$, for values of

$$x=\pm\frac{k\pi}{2n+1}, \quad k=0, 1, 2, \ldots, n,$$

therefore
$$\sin(2n+1)x=A\sin x\prod_{k=1}^{n}\left(\sin^2 x-\sin^2\frac{k\pi}{2n+1}\right), \tag{17}$$

where
$$A=(-1)^n 2^{2n}.$$

Now
$$\frac{\sin^p x}{\sin(2n+1)x}=\frac{\sin^{p-1}x}{\sin(2n+1)x\div\sin x}$$

$$=\sum_{k=1}^{n}\left[\frac{A_k}{\sin x-\sin\dfrac{k\pi}{2n+1}}+\frac{B_k}{\sin x+\sin\dfrac{k\pi}{2n+1}}\right], \tag{18}$$

and we obtain

$$A_k=\sin^{p-1}\frac{k\pi}{2n+1}\left.\frac{\sin x\left(\sin x-\sin\dfrac{k\pi}{2n+1}\right)}{\sin(2n+1)x}\right]_{x=\frac{k\pi}{2n+1}} \tag{19}$$

$$=\frac{(-1)^k}{2n+1}\sin^p\frac{k\pi}{2n+1}\cos\frac{k\pi}{2n+1} \tag{20}$$

and
$$B_k=\frac{(-1)^{p+k}}{2n+1}\sin^p\frac{k\pi}{2n+1}\cos\frac{k\pi}{2n+1}. \tag{21}$$

Therefore

$$\frac{\sin^p x}{\sin(2n+1)x}=\frac{1}{2n+1}\left[\sum_{k=1}^{n}(-1)^k\frac{\sin^p\dfrac{k\pi}{2n+1}\cos\dfrac{k\pi}{2n+1}}{\sin x-\sin\dfrac{k\pi}{2n+1}}\right.$$

$$\left.+(-1)^p\sum_{k=1}^{n}(-1)^k\frac{\sin^p\dfrac{k\pi}{2n+1}\cos\dfrac{k\pi}{2n+1}}{\sin x+\sin\dfrac{k\pi}{2n+1}}\right]. \tag{22}$$

We also find

$$\frac{\sin^{2p}x}{\sin(2n+1)x}=\frac{2}{2n+1}\sum_{k=1}^{n}(-1)^k\frac{\sin^{2p}\dfrac{k\pi}{2n+1}\cos\dfrac{k\pi}{2n+1}\sin x}{\sin^2 x-\sin^2\dfrac{k\pi}{2n+1}} \tag{23}$$

and
$$\frac{\sin^{2p+1}x}{\sin(2n+1)x}=\frac{2}{2n+1}\sum_{k=1}^{n}(-1)^k\frac{\sin^{2p+2}\dfrac{k\pi}{2n+1}\cos\dfrac{k\pi}{2n+1}}{\sin^2 x-\sin^2\dfrac{k\pi}{2n+1}}. \tag{24}$$

For example:

$$\frac{\sin^3 x}{\sin 5x} = -\frac{1}{8\sqrt{5}}\left(\frac{\sqrt{10-2\sqrt{5}}}{4\sin x-\sqrt{10-2\sqrt{5}}} - \frac{\sqrt{10+2\sqrt{5}}}{4\sin x-\sqrt{10+2\sqrt{5}}} - \frac{\sqrt{10-2\sqrt{5}}}{4\sin x+\sqrt{10-2\sqrt{5}}} + \frac{\sqrt{10+2\sqrt{5}}}{4\sin x+\sqrt{10+2\sqrt{5}}}\right) \tag{25}$$

$$= \frac{1}{4}\left(\frac{\sqrt{5}-1}{8\sin^2 x-(5-\sqrt{5})} - \frac{\sqrt{5}+1}{8\sin^2 x-(5+\sqrt{5})}\right). \tag{26}$$

3. To separate into partial fractions

$$\frac{\cos^{2p+1} x}{\sin 2nx}, \quad 2p+1 < 2n. \tag{27}$$

Now
$$\sin 2nx = A \sin x \cos x \prod_{k=1}^{n-1}\left(\sin^2 x - \sin^2\frac{k\pi}{2n}\right), \tag{28}$$

where
$$A = (-1)^{n-1}\,2^{2n-1};$$

then
$$\frac{\cos^{2p+1} x}{\sin 2nx} = \frac{A}{\sin x} + \sum_{k=1}^{n-1}\left[\frac{A_k}{\sin x - \sin\frac{k\pi}{2n}} + \frac{B_k}{\sin x + \sin\frac{k\pi}{2n}}\right], \tag{29}$$

and we find
$$A = \frac{1}{2n}, \quad A_k = \frac{(-1)^k}{2n}\cos^{2p+2}\frac{k\pi}{2n},$$

and
$$B_k = \frac{(-1)^k}{2n}\cos^{2p+2}\frac{k\pi}{2n}. \tag{30}$$

Therefore

$$\frac{\cos^{2p+1} x}{\sin 2nx} = \frac{1}{2n\sin x} + \frac{1}{n}\sum_{k=1}^{n-1}(-1)^k\cos^{2p+2}\frac{k\pi}{2n}\,\frac{\sin x}{\sin^2 x - \sin^2\frac{k\pi}{2n}}. \tag{31}$$

We also find

$$\frac{\cos^{2p} x}{\sin(2n+1)x} = \frac{1}{(2n+1)\sin x} + \frac{2}{2n+1}\sum_{k=1}^{n}(-1)^k\frac{\cos^{2p+1}\frac{k\pi}{2n+1}\sin x}{\sin^2 x - \sin^2\frac{k\pi}{2n+1}}, \tag{32}$$

$$2p < 2n+1,$$

and
$$\frac{\cos mx}{\cos nx} = \frac{1}{n}\sum_{k=0}^{n-1}(-1)^k\frac{\cos m\frac{2k+1}{2n}\sin\frac{2k+1}{2n}\pi}{\cos x - \cos\frac{2k+1}{2n}\pi}, \quad m < n. \tag{33}$$

4. We shall next separate into partial fractions powers of the trigonometrical functions.

(i) To separate $\tan^p x$ into partial fractions.

Since
$$\cos x = \prod_{n=0}^{\infty}\left(1-\frac{2x}{(2n+1)\pi}\right)\left(1+\frac{2x}{(2n+1)\pi}\right), \tag{34}$$

we have
$$\tan^p x = \sum_{n=0}^{\infty}\sum_{v=0}^{p-1}\left[\frac{A_{n,v}}{\left(1-\frac{2x}{(2n+1)\pi}\right)^{p-v}}+\frac{B_{n,v}}{\left(1+\frac{2x}{(2n+1)\pi}\right)^{p-v}}\right]. \tag{35}$$

Multiplying both sides of (35) by

$$\left(1-\frac{2x}{(2n+1)\pi}\right)^p,$$

taking of the resulting equation the vth derivative with regard to x, and then letting $x=\frac{2n+1}{2}\pi$, we obtain

$$A_{n,v}=(-1)^v\frac{(\overline{2n+1}\,\pi)^v}{2^v v!}\frac{d^v}{dx^v}\frac{\left(1-\frac{2x}{(2n+1)\pi}\right)^p}{\cot^p x}\Bigg]_{x=\frac{2n+1}{2}\pi}. \tag{36}$$

To find
$$\frac{d^v}{dx^v}\frac{\cot^{-p}x}{\left(1-\frac{2x}{(2n+1)\pi}\right)^{-p}}\Bigg]_{x=\frac{2n+1}{2}\pi}=\frac{d^v}{dx^v}u^{-p}\Bigg]_{x=\frac{2n+1}{2}\pi} \tag{37}$$

we make use of

$$\frac{d^v u^{-p}}{dx^v}\Bigg]_{x=\frac{2n+1}{2}\pi}=p\binom{v+p}{p}\sum_{k=1}^{v}\frac{(-1)^k}{p+k}\binom{v}{k}u^{-p-k}\frac{d^v}{dx^v}u^k\Bigg]_{x=\frac{2n+1}{2}\pi}, \tag{38}$$

by Ch. I. (169);

and since
$$u^{-p-k}\Bigg]_{x=\frac{2n+1}{2}\pi}=\frac{2^{p+k}}{(2n+1)^{p+k}\pi^{p+k}},$$

therefore

$$\frac{d^v}{dx^v}u^{-p}\Bigg]_{x=\frac{2n+1}{2}\pi}=p\,2^p\binom{v+p}{p}\frac{1}{(\overline{2n+1}\,\pi)^p}\sum_{k=1}^{v}(-1)^k\frac{2^k}{(\overline{2n+1}\,\pi)^k}\frac{1}{p+k}\binom{v}{k}\frac{d^v}{dx^v}u^k\Bigg]_{x=\frac{2n+1}{2}\pi}. \tag{39}$$

We shall now obtain
$$\frac{d^v}{dx^v}u^k\Bigg]_{x=\frac{2n+1}{2}\pi}.$$

By Leibnitz's theorem the $(v+k)$th derivative of the identity

$$\left(1-\frac{2x}{(2n+1)\pi}\right)^k u^k\Bigg]_{x=\frac{2n+1}{2}\pi}=\cot^k x\Bigg]_{x=\frac{2n+1}{2}\pi} \tag{40}$$

is
$$\sum_{a=0}^{v+k}\binom{v+k}{a}\frac{d^{v+k-a}}{dx^{v+k-a}}\left(1-\frac{2x}{(2n+1)\pi}\right)^k\frac{d^a}{dx^a}u^k\Bigg]_{x=\frac{2n+1}{2}\pi}. \tag{41}$$

Now the first member vanishes, except when $\alpha = v$, in which case

$$\binom{v+k}{k} \frac{d^k}{dx^k}\left(1 - \frac{2x}{(2n+1)\pi}\right)^k \frac{d^v}{dx^v} u^k \Big]_{x=\frac{2n+1}{2}\pi} = \frac{d^{v+k}}{dx^{v+k}} \cot^k x \Big]_{x=\frac{2n+1}{2}\pi}. \tag{42}$$

Therefore

$$\frac{d^v}{dx^v} u^k \Big]_{x=\frac{2n+1}{2}\pi} = (-1)^k \frac{(\overline{2n+1}\,\pi)^k v!}{2^k (v+k)!} \frac{d^{v+k}}{dx^{v+k}} \cot^k x \Big]_{x=\frac{2n+1}{2}\pi}. \tag{43}$$

If we now let $x = \dfrac{2n+1}{2}\pi$ in Ch. IV. (111), we have

$$\frac{d^r}{dx^r} \cot^k x \Big]_{x=\frac{2n+1}{2}\pi} = i^{r+k} 2^r \sum_{\alpha=1}^{k} (-1)^\alpha \binom{k}{\alpha} \sum_{\beta=1}^{r} \binom{\alpha+\beta-1}{\beta} \frac{1}{2^\beta} \sum_{\gamma=1}^{\beta} (-1)^\gamma \binom{\beta}{\gamma} \gamma^r. \tag{44}$$

But $\displaystyle\sum_{\alpha=1}^{k} (-1)^\alpha \binom{k}{\alpha} \binom{\alpha+\beta-1}{\beta} = (-1)^k \binom{\beta-1}{k-1}$, $\beta \geqq k$, by Ch. IV. (73). (45)

Applying (45) to (44), and then replacing r by $r+k$, gives

$$\frac{d^{r+k}}{dx^{r+k}} \cot^k x \Big]_{x=\frac{2n+1}{2}\pi} = (-1)^k i^{r+2k} 2^{r+k} \sum_{\beta=k}^{r+k} \binom{\beta-1}{k-1} \frac{1}{2^\beta} \sum_{\gamma=1}^{\beta} (-1)^\gamma \binom{\beta}{\gamma} \gamma^{r+k}; \tag{46}$$

and since $\displaystyle\frac{d^{r+k}}{dx^{r+k}} \cot^k x \Big]_{x=\frac{2n+1}{2}\pi}$ is real,

therefore r must be even and

$$\frac{d^{2r+k}}{dx^{2r+k}} \cot^k x \Big]_{x=\frac{2n+1}{2}\pi} = (-1)^r 2^{2r+k} \sum_{\beta=k}^{2r+k} \binom{\beta-1}{k-1} \frac{1}{2^\beta} \sum_{\gamma=1}^{\beta} (-1)^\gamma \binom{\beta}{\gamma} \gamma^{2r+k}. \tag{47}$$

Then, by means of (47) and (43), we have from (39)

$$\frac{d^{2v}}{dx^{2v}} u^{-p} \Big]_{x=\frac{2n+1}{2}\pi} = (-1)^v \frac{p\,2^{p+2v}}{(\overline{2n+1}\,\pi)^p} (2v)! \binom{2v+p}{p} \sum_{k=1}^{2v} \frac{2^k}{(2v+k)!\,(p+k)} \binom{2v}{k} \sum_{\beta=k}^{2v+k} \binom{\beta-1}{k-1} \frac{1}{2^\beta} \sum_{\gamma=1}^{\beta} (-1)^\gamma \binom{\beta}{\gamma} \gamma^{2v+k}, \tag{48}$$

and from (36) we finally obtain

$$A_{n,2v} = (-1)^v \frac{p\,2^p}{(\overline{2n+1}\,\pi)^{p-2v}} \binom{2v+p}{2v} \sum_{k=1}^{2v} \frac{2^k}{(2v+k)!} \binom{2v}{k} \frac{1}{p+k} \sum_{\beta=k}^{2v+k} \binom{\beta-1}{k-1} \frac{1}{2^\beta} \sum_{\gamma=1}^{\beta} (-1)^\gamma \binom{\beta}{\gamma} \gamma^{2v+k}. \tag{49}$$

We also find

$$B_{n,2v} = (-1)^{p+k} A_{n,2v}. \tag{50}$$

If $p=1$, then $v=0$ and

$$\tan x=\sum_{n=0}^{\infty}\left[\frac{A_{n,0}}{1-\dfrac{2x}{(2n+1)\pi}}+\frac{B_{n,0}}{1+\dfrac{2x}{(2n+1)\pi}}\right], \tag{51}$$

and from (49) and (50),

$$A_{n,0}=\frac{2}{(2n+1)\pi} \quad\text{and}\quad B_{n,0}=-\frac{2}{(2n+1)\pi}. \tag{52}$$

(ii) To separate $\cot^p x$ into partial fractions.

Since
$$\sin x=x\prod_{n=1}^{\infty}\left(1-\frac{x}{n\pi}\right)\left(1+\frac{x}{n\pi}\right), \tag{53}$$

we may write

$$\cot^p x=\sum_{v=0}^{p-1}\frac{A_v}{x^{p-v}}+\sum_{n=1}^{\infty}\sum_{v=0}^{p-1}\left[\frac{B_{n,v}}{\left(1-\dfrac{x}{n\pi}\right)^{p-v}}+\frac{C_{n,v}}{\left(1+\dfrac{x}{n\pi}\right)^{p-v}}\right]. \tag{54}$$

Multiplying both sides of (54) by x^p, taking the vth derivative with respect to x and letting $x=0$, we obtain

$$A_v=\frac{1}{v!}\frac{d^v}{dx^v}(x^p\cot^p x)\Big]_{x\doteq 0}=\frac{1}{v!}\frac{d^v}{dx^v}\left(\frac{\tan x}{x}\right)^{-p}\Big]_{x\doteq 0}$$

$$=\frac{1}{v!}\frac{d^v}{dx^v}u^{-p}\Big]_{x\doteq 0}. \tag{55}$$

Following the method in (i), we find

$$\frac{d^v}{dx^v}u^{-p}\Big]_{x\doteq 0}=p\binom{v+p}{v}\sum_{k=0}^{v}\frac{(-1)^k}{p+k}\binom{v}{k}\frac{d^v}{dx^v}u^k\Big]_{x\doteq 0}, \tag{56}$$

$$\frac{d^v}{dx^v}u^k\Big]_{x\doteq 0}=\frac{v!}{(v+k)!}\frac{d^{v+k}}{dx^{v+k}}\tan^k x\Big]_{x\doteq 0}, \tag{57}$$

$$\frac{d^{2v+k}}{dx^{2v+k}}\tan^k x\Big]_{x\doteq 0}=(-1)^{v+k}2^{2v+k}\sum_{\beta=k}^{2v+k}\binom{\beta-1}{k-1}\frac{1}{2^\beta}\sum_{\gamma=1}^{\beta}(-1)^\gamma\binom{\beta}{\gamma}\gamma^{2v+k}, \tag{58}$$

and finally

$$A_{2v}=(-1)^v p\binom{2v+p}{2v}2^{2v}\sum_{k=1}^{2v}\frac{2^k}{(p+k)(2v+k)!}\binom{2v}{k}\sum_{\beta=k}^{2v+k}\binom{\beta-1}{k-1}\frac{1}{2^\beta}$$
$$\sum_{\gamma=1}^{\beta}(-1)^\gamma\binom{\beta}{\gamma}\gamma^{2v+k}. \tag{59}$$

In a similar way, we obtain

$$B_{n,2v}=(-1)^{v+p}\frac{p2^{2v}}{(\pi n)^{p-2v}}\binom{2v+p}{2v}\sum_{k=1}^{2v}\frac{(-1)^k 2^k}{(p+k)(2v+k)!}\binom{2v}{k}$$
$$\sum_{\beta=k}^{2v+k}\binom{\beta-1}{k-1}\frac{1}{2^\beta}\sum_{\gamma=1}^{\beta}(-1)^\gamma\binom{\beta}{\gamma}\gamma^{2v+k} \tag{60}$$

and
$$C_{n,2v}=(-1)^p B_{n,2v}. \tag{61}$$

If $p=1$, then $v=0$, and

$$\cot x=\frac{A_0}{x}+\sum_{n=1}^{\infty}\left[\frac{B_{n,0}}{1-\dfrac{x}{n\pi}}+\frac{C_{n,0}}{1+\dfrac{x}{n\pi}}\right]. \tag{62}$$

From (59), (60) and (61), we have

$$A_0=1, \qquad B_{n,0}=-\frac{1}{n\pi}, \qquad C_{n,0}=\frac{1}{n\pi}. \tag{63}$$

(iii) To separate $\sec^p x$ into partial fractions.

We may write

$$\sec^p x=\sum_{n=0}^{\infty}\sum_{v=0}^{p-1}\left[\frac{A_{n,v}}{\left(1-\dfrac{2x}{(2n+1)\pi}\right)^{p-v}}+\frac{B_{n,v}}{\left(1+\dfrac{2x}{(2n+1)\pi}\right)^{p-v}}\right]; \tag{64}$$

then $$A_{n,v}=(-1)^v\frac{(\overline{2n+1}\,\pi)^v}{2^v v!}\frac{d^v}{dx^v}\left.\frac{\left(1-\dfrac{2x}{(2n+1)\pi}\right)^p}{\cos^p x}\right]_{x=\frac{2n+1}{2}\pi}. \tag{65}$$

Now $$\frac{d^v}{dx^v}\left.\frac{\cos^{-p}x}{\left(1-\dfrac{2x}{(2n+1)\pi}\right)^{-p}}\right]_{x=\frac{2n+1}{2}\pi}=\frac{d^v}{dx^v}u^{-p}\Big]_{x=\frac{2n+1}{2}\pi} \tag{66}$$

$$=(-1)^{np}\frac{p2^p}{(\overline{2n+1}\,\pi)^p}\binom{v+p}{v}\sum_{k=1}^{v}\frac{(-1)^{(n+1)k}2^k}{(\overline{2n+1}\,\pi)^k}\binom{v}{k}\frac{1}{p+k}\frac{d^v}{dx^v}u^k\Big]_{x=\frac{2n+1}{2}\pi}; \tag{67}$$

and from $$\left(1-\frac{2x}{(2n+1)\pi}\right)^k u^k=\cos^k x$$

we obtain $$\frac{d^v}{dx^v}u^k\Big]_{x=\frac{2n+1}{2}\pi}=(-1)^k\frac{(\overline{2n+1}\,\pi)^k v!}{(v+k)!\,2^k}\frac{d^{v+k}}{dx^{v+k}}\cos^k x\Big]_{x=\frac{2n+1}{2}\pi}. \tag{68}$$

But $$\cos^k x=\frac{1}{2^k}\sum_{a=0}^{k}\binom{k}{a}e^{(k-2a)ix}$$

and $$\frac{d^{v+k}}{dx^{v+k}}\cos^k x\Big]_{x=\frac{2n+1}{2}\pi}=\frac{i^{v+k}}{2^k}\sum_{a=0}^{k}\binom{k}{a}(k-2a)^{v+k}e^{(k-2a)ix}\Big]_{x=\frac{2n+1}{2}\pi}. \tag{69}$$

To evaluate

$$R=e^{(k-2a)ix}\Big]_{x=\frac{2n+1}{2}\pi}=(-1)^a\left(\cos\frac{2n+1}{2}\pi+i\sin\frac{2n+1}{2}\pi\right), \tag{70}$$

we must distinguish between the cases when k is even and when k is odd.

(*a*) If k is even, then $\qquad R=(-1)^{k+a}$,

and (69) becomes

$$\frac{d^{v+2k}}{dx^{v+2k}}\cos^{2k}x\Big]_{x=\frac{2n+1}{2}\pi}=(-1)^k\frac{i^{v+2k}}{2^{2k}}\sum_{a=0}^{2k}(-1)^a\binom{2k}{a}(2k-2a)^{v+2k}; \tag{71}$$

hence v must be even, and

$$\frac{d^{2v+2k}}{dx^{2v+2k}}\cos^{2k}x\Big]_{x=\frac{2n+1}{2}\pi}=\frac{(-1)^v}{2^{2k}}\sum_{a=0}^{2k}(-1)^a\binom{2k}{a}(2k-2a)^{2v+2k}. \tag{72}$$

We then have

$$\frac{d^{2v}}{dx^{2v}}u^{-p}\Big]_{x=\frac{2n+1}{2}\pi}=(-1)^{np+v}\frac{p2^p(2v)!}{(\overline{2n+1}\,\pi)^p}\binom{2v+p}{2v}\sum_{k=1}^{2v}\frac{1}{(2v+2k)!\,2^{2k}}$$

$$\binom{2v}{2k}\frac{1}{p+2k}\sum_{a=0}^{2k}(-1)^a\binom{2k}{a}(2k-2a)^{2v+2k}. \tag{73}$$

(*b*) If k is odd, $$R=i(-1)^{n+k+a-1}, \tag{74}$$
and v must again be even.

Writing now in (69), $2v$ for v and $2k-1$ for k and for R its value from (64), we obtain from (67) the same form as (73), except that $2k-1$ is in place of $2k$.

Therefore, whether k be even or odd,

$$\frac{d^{2v}}{dx^{2v}}u^{-p}\Big]_{x=\frac{2n+1}{2}\pi}=(-1)^{np+v}\frac{p2^p(2v)!}{(\overline{2n+1}\,\pi)^p}\sum_{k=1}^{2v}\frac{1}{(2v+k)!\,2^k}$$

$$\binom{2v}{k}\frac{1}{p+k}\sum_{a=0}^{k}(-1)^a\binom{k}{a}(k-2a)^{v+k}, \tag{75}$$

and $$A_{n,2v}=(-1)^{np+v}\frac{p2^{p-2v}}{(\overline{2n+1}\,\pi)^{p-2v}}\binom{2v+p}{2v}\sum_{k=1}^{2v}\frac{1}{2^{k-1}(2v+k)!}$$

$$\binom{2v}{k}\frac{1}{p+k}\sum_{a=0}^{\left[\frac{k-1}{2}\right]}(-1)^a\binom{k}{a}(k-2a)^{2v+k}. \tag{76}$$

We also find $$B_{n,2v}=(-1)^pA_{n,2v}. \tag{77}$$
If $p=1$, then $v=0$, and

$$\sec x=\sum_{n=0}^{\infty}\left[\frac{A_{n,0}}{1-\dfrac{2x}{(2n+1)\pi}}+\frac{B_{n,0}}{1+\dfrac{2x}{(2n+1)\pi}}\right]; \tag{78}$$

and from (76) and (77), we have

$$A_{n,0}=(-1)^n\frac{2}{(2n+1)\pi},\qquad B_{n,0}=(-1)^{n-1}\frac{2}{(2n+1)\pi}. \tag{79}$$

(iv) To separate $\operatorname{cosec}^p x$ into partial fractions, we write

$$\operatorname{cosec}^p x=\sum_{v=0}^{p-1}\frac{A_v}{x^{p-v}}+\sum_{n=1}^{\infty}\sum_{v=0}^{p-1}\left[\frac{B_{n,v}}{\left(1-\dfrac{x}{n\pi}\right)^{p-v}}+\frac{C_{n,v}}{\left(1+\dfrac{x}{n\pi}\right)^{p-v}}\right]. \tag{80}$$

Following the preceding methods, we obtain

$$A_{2v}=(-1)p^v\binom{2v+p}{2v}\sum_{k=1}^{2v}\frac{(-1)^k}{2^{k-1}(2v+k)!}\binom{2v}{k}\frac{1}{p+k}\sum_{a=0}^{\left[\frac{k-1}{2}\right]}(-1)^a\binom{k}{a}(k-2a)^{2v+k}, \tag{81}$$

$$B_{n,2v} = (-1)^{(n-1)p+v} \frac{p}{(n\pi)^{p-2v}} \binom{2v+p}{2v} \sum_{k=1}^{2v} \frac{(-1)^k}{2^{k-1}(2v+k)!} \binom{2v}{k} \frac{1}{p+k} \sum_{a=0}^{\left[\frac{k-1}{2}\right]} (-1)^a \binom{k}{a} (k-2a)^{2v+k}, \quad (82)$$

and

$$C_{n,2v} = (-1)^p B_{n,2v}. \quad (83)$$

If $p=1$, then $v=0$, and

$$\operatorname{cosec} x = \frac{A_0}{x} + \sum_{n=1}^{\infty} \left[\frac{B_{n,0}}{1 - \frac{x}{n\pi}} + \frac{C_{n,0}}{1 + \frac{x}{n\pi}} \right]; \quad (84)$$

and from (81), (82) and (83), we have

$$A_0 = 1, \quad B_{n,0} = \frac{(-1)^{n-1}}{n\pi}, \quad C_{n,0} = \frac{(-1)^n}{n\pi}. \quad (85)$$

CHAPTER XII.

TRIGONOMETRIC SERIES.

IN the preceding chapters the sum of several series involving trigonometrical functions were found. Additional methods for obtaining the value of trigonometric series are given here.

1. We shall first consider a family of series which is related to Fourier's series.

(i) To find the value of

$$S=\sum_{n=1}^{\infty}\frac{\sin nx}{n}r^n, \quad |r| \lesseqgtr 1. \tag{1}$$

Now

$$S=\frac{1}{2i}\left[\sum_{n=1}^{\infty}\frac{(re^{ix})^n}{n}-\sum_{n=1}^{\infty}\frac{(re^{-ix})^n}{n}\right] \tag{2}$$

$$=\frac{1}{2i}\log\frac{1-re^{-ix}}{1-re^{ix}}$$

$$=\frac{1}{2i}\log\frac{1-r\cos x+ir\sin x}{1-r\cos x-ir\sin x}$$

$$=\frac{1}{2i}\log\frac{1+iu}{1-iu}, \quad \text{where } u=\frac{r\sin x}{1-r\cos x}; \tag{3}$$

and since

$$\log\frac{1+iu}{1-iu}=2i\tan^{-1}u, \tag{4}$$

therefore

$$S=\tan^{-1}\frac{r\sin x}{1-r\cos x}. \tag{5}$$

If $r=1$,

$$S=\sum_{n=1}^{\infty}\frac{\sin nx}{n}=\tfrac{1}{2}(\pi-x), \quad 0<x<2\pi. \tag{6}$$

In a similar way, we obtain

$$\sum_{n=1}^{\infty}\frac{\cos nx}{n}r^n=-\tfrac{1}{2}\log(1-2r\cos x+r^2), \tag{7}$$

$$\sum_{n=1}^{\infty}\frac{\cos nx}{n}=-\log(2\sin\tfrac{1}{2}x), \tag{8}$$

$$\sum_{n=1}^{\infty}(-1)^{n-1}\frac{\sin nx}{n}r^n=\tan^{-1}\frac{r\sin x}{1+r\cos x}, \tag{9}$$

$$\sum_{n=1}^{\infty}(-1)^{n-1}\frac{\sin nx}{n}=\frac{x}{2}, \quad -\pi<x<\pi. \tag{10}$$

$$\sum_{n=1}^{\infty}(-1)^{n-1}\frac{\cos nx}{n}r^n=\tfrac{1}{2}\log(1+2r\cos x+r^2), \tag{11}$$

$$\sum_{n=1}^{\infty}(-1)^{n-1}\frac{\cos nx}{n}=\log(2\cos\tfrac{1}{2}x). \tag{12}$$

(ii) To find
$$S=\sum_{n=1}^{\infty}\frac{\sin nx}{a+n}r^n, \quad |r|\leqq 1, \tag{13}$$

a a positive integer.

Now
$$S=\frac{1}{r^a}\sum_{n=1}^{\infty}\frac{\sin nx}{a+n}r^{a+n}=\frac{1}{r^a}S_1; \tag{14}$$

then
$$\frac{dS_1}{dr}=r^a\sum_{n=1}^{\infty}\sin nx r^{n-1} \tag{15}$$

$$=-\frac{1}{2i}\left(\frac{r^a e^{ix}}{re^{ix}-1}-\frac{r^a e^{-ix}}{re^{-ix}-1}\right)$$

$$=-\frac{1}{2i}\left(\sum_{n=1}^{a}e^{-i(n-1)x}r^{a-n}-\sum_{n=1}^{a}e^{i(n-1)x}r^{a-n}-\frac{e^{-(a-1)ix}}{1-re^{ix}}+\frac{e^{(a-1)ix}}{1-re^{-ix}}\right) \tag{16}$$

and
$$S_1=\sum_{n=2}^{a}\frac{\sin(n-1)x}{a-n+1}r^{a-n+1}-\frac{1}{2i}e^{-aix}\log(1-re^{ix})+\frac{1}{2i}e^{aix}\log(1-re^{-ix})$$

$$=\left[\sum_{n=2}^{a}\frac{\sin(n-1)x}{a-n+1}r^{a-n+1}+\frac{1}{2i}\cos ax\log\frac{1-re^{-ix}}{1-re^{ix}}\right.$$
$$\left.+\tfrac{1}{2}\sin ax\log(1-2r\cos x+r^2)\right]. \tag{17}$$

Therefore

$$S=\frac{1}{r^a}\left[\sum_{n=2}^{a}\frac{\sin(n-1)x}{a-n+1}r^{a-n+1}+\cos ax\tan^{-1}\frac{r\sin x}{1-r\cos x}\right.$$
$$\left.+\tfrac{1}{2}\sin ax\log(1-2r\cos x+r^2)\right]. \tag{18}$$

If $a=0$, then $\sum_{n=2}^{0}\frac{\sin(n-1)x}{1-n}$ is defined as zero, and we have

$$S=\sum_{n=1}^{\infty}\frac{\sin nx}{n}r^n=\tan^{-1}\frac{r\sin x}{1-r\cos x},$$

the same as (5).

If $r=1$,
$$S=\sum_{n=1}^{\infty}\frac{\sin nx}{a+n}=\sum_{n=2}^{a}\frac{\sin(n-1)x}{a-n+1}+\tfrac{1}{2}(\pi-x)\cos ax$$
$$+\sin ax\log(2\sin\tfrac{1}{2}x), \quad 0<x<2\pi. \tag{19}$$

Show that

$$\sum_{n=1}^{\infty}(-1)^{n-1}\frac{\sin nx}{a+n}r^n=\frac{(-1)^a}{r^a}\left[\sum_{n=2}^{a}(-1)^{a-n}\frac{\sin(n-1)x}{a-n+1}r^{a-n+1}\right.$$

$$\left.+\cos ax\tan^{-1}\frac{r\sin x}{1+r\cos x}-\tfrac{1}{2}\sin ax\log(1+2r\cos x+r^2)\right], \quad (20)$$

$$\sum_{n=1}^{\infty}\frac{\cos nx}{a+n}r^n=\frac{1}{r^a}\left[-\sum_{n=1}^{a}\frac{\cos(n-1)x}{a-n+1}r^{a-n+1}\right.$$

$$\left.+\sin ax\tan^{-1}\frac{r\sin x}{1-r\cos x}-\tfrac{1}{2}\cos ax\log(1-2r\cos x+r^2)\right], \quad (21)$$

$$\sum_{n=1}^{\infty}(-1)^{n-1}\frac{\cos nx}{a+n}r^n=\frac{(-1)^a}{r^a}\left[\sum_{n=1}^{a}(-1)^{a-n-1}\frac{\cos(n-1)x}{a-n+1}r^{a-n+1}\right.$$

$$\left.+\sin ax\tan^{-1}\frac{r\sin x}{1+r\cos x}+\tfrac{1}{2}\cos ax\log(1+2r\cos x+r^2)\right]. \quad (22)$$

(iii) To find the value of $S=\sum_{n=1}^{\infty}\frac{\sin^p nx}{n}r^n, \quad -1\leqq r<1.$ (23)

Now, if p be even, then, by Ch. IV. (29),

$$S=\frac{1}{2^{p-1}}\sum_{k=1}^{\frac{p}{2}}(-1)^k\binom{p}{\frac{p}{2}-k}\sum_{n=1}^{\infty}\frac{\cos 2nkx}{n}r^n+\frac{1}{2^p}\binom{p}{\frac{p}{2}}\sum_{n=1}^{\infty}\frac{r^n}{n}. \quad (24)$$

But $\sum_{n=1}^{\infty}\frac{\cos 2nkx}{n}r^n=-\tfrac{1}{2}\log(1-2r\cos 2kx+r^2)$, by (7),

and $\sum_{n=1}^{\infty}\frac{r^n}{n}=-\log(1-r)$;

therefore

$$S=\frac{1}{2^p}\sum_{k=1}^{\frac{p}{2}}(-1)^{k-1}\binom{p}{\frac{p}{2}-k}\log(1-2r\cos 2kx+r^2)-\frac{1}{2^p}\binom{p}{\frac{p}{2}}\log(1-r). \quad (25)$$

If p is odd,

then $S=\frac{1}{2^{p-1}}\sum_{k=0}^{\frac{p-1}{2}}(-1)^k\binom{p}{\frac{p-1}{2}-k}\sum_{n=1}^{\infty}\frac{\sin n(2k+1)x}{n}r^n$; (26)

and by means of (5), we obtain

$$S=\frac{1}{2^{p-1}}\sum_{k=0}^{\frac{p-1}{2}}(-1)^k\binom{p}{\frac{p-1}{2}-k}\tan^{-1}\frac{r\sin(2k+1)x}{1-r\cos(2k+1)x}. \quad (27)$$

If $p=1$, $S=\sum_{n=1}^{\infty}\frac{\sin nx}{n}r^n=\tan^{-1}\frac{r\sin x}{1-r\cos x}$,

which is the same as (5).

If $p=1$ and $r=1$, $S=\sum_{n=1}^{\infty}\frac{\sin nx}{n}=\frac{1}{2}(\pi-x),\quad 0<x<2\pi,$
the same as (6).

Show that

$$\sum_{n=1}^{\infty}(-1)^{n-1}\frac{\sin^p nx}{n}r^n=\frac{1}{2^p}\sum_{k=1}^{\frac{p}{2}}(-1)^k\binom{p}{\frac{p}{2}-k}\log(1+2r\cos 2kx+r^2)$$

$$+\frac{1}{2^p}\binom{p}{\frac{p}{2}}\log(1+r),\quad -1<r\leqq 1,\quad \text{when } p \text{ is even,} \tag{28}$$

$$=\frac{1}{2^{p-1}}\sum_{k=0}^{\frac{p-1}{2}}(-1)^k\binom{p}{\frac{p-1}{2}-k}\tan^{-1}\frac{r\sin(2k+1)x}{1+r\cos(2k+1)x},\quad -1\leqq r\leqq 1,$$
$$\text{when } p \text{ is odd.} \tag{29}$$

$$\sum_{n=1}^{\infty}\frac{\cos^p nx}{n}r^n=-\frac{1}{2^p}\sum_{k=1}^{\frac{p}{2}}\binom{p}{\frac{p}{2}-k}\log(1-2r\cos 2kx+r^2)$$

$$-\frac{1}{2^p}\binom{p}{\frac{p}{2}}\log(1-r),\quad -1\leqq r<1,\quad \text{when } p \text{ is even,} \tag{30}$$

$$=-\frac{1}{2^p}\sum_{k=0}^{\frac{p-1}{2}}\binom{p}{\frac{p-1}{2}-k}\log(1-2r\cos\overline{2k+1}x+r^2),\quad -1\leqq r\leqq 1,$$
$$\text{when } p \text{ is odd.} \tag{31}$$

Also

$$\sum_{n=1}^{\infty}(-1)^{n-1}\frac{\cos^p nx}{n}r^n=\frac{1}{2^p}\sum_{k=1}^{\frac{p}{2}}\binom{p}{\frac{p}{2}-k}\log(1+2r\cos 2kx+r^2)$$

$$+\frac{1}{2^p}\binom{p}{\frac{p}{2}}\log(1+r),\quad -1<r\leqq 1,\quad \text{when } p \text{ is even,} \tag{32}$$

$$=\frac{1}{2^p}\sum_{k=0}^{\frac{p-1}{2}}\binom{p}{\frac{p-1}{2}-k}\log(1+2r\cos\overline{2k+1}x+r^2),\quad -1\leqq r\leqq 1,$$
$$\text{when } p \text{ is odd.} \tag{33}$$

2. We shall give here a method for finding the value of another type of trigonometric series.

(i) To find
$$S=\sum_{k=1}^{n}(-1)^{k-1}\binom{n}{k}\sin kx. \tag{34}$$

Now
$$S=\frac{1}{2i}\sum_{k=1}^{n}(-1)^{k-1}\binom{n}{k}e^{ikx}-\frac{1}{2i}\sum_{k=1}^{n}(-1)^{k-1}\binom{n}{k}e^{-ikx} \tag{35}$$

$$=-\frac{1}{2i}(1-e^{ix})^n+\frac{1}{2i}+\frac{1}{2i}(1-e^{-ix})^n-\frac{1}{2i}$$

$$=-\frac{1}{2i}e^{\frac{nix}{2}}\left(e^{-\frac{ix}{2}}-e^{\frac{ix}{2}}\right)^n+\frac{1}{2i}e^{-\frac{nix}{2}}\left(e^{\frac{ix}{2}}-e^{-\frac{ix}{2}}\right)^n \tag{36}$$

$$= -\frac{(2i)^n}{2i}\sin^n\frac{x}{2}\left[(-1)^n e^{\frac{nix}{2}} - e^{-\frac{nix}{2}}\right] \tag{37}$$

$$= (-1)^{\frac{n+2}{2}}\, 2^n \sin^n\frac{x}{2}\sin\frac{nx}{2}, \quad \text{when } n \text{ is even,} \tag{38}$$

$$= (-1)^{\frac{n-1}{2}}\, 2^n \sin^n\frac{x}{2}\cos\frac{nx}{2}, \quad \text{when } n \text{ is odd.} \tag{39}$$

$$= (-1)^{n-1} 2^n \sin^n\frac{x}{2}\sin\frac{n(\pi+x)}{2}, \text{ whether } n \text{ be even or odd.} \tag{40}$$

Show that

$$\sum_{k=1}^{n}(-1)^{k-1}\binom{n}{k}\cos kx = (-1)^{\frac{n+2}{2}}\, 2^n \sin^n\frac{x}{2}\cos\frac{nx}{2} + 1, \quad \text{when } n \text{ is even,} \tag{41}$$

$$= (-1)^{\frac{n+1}{2}}\, 2^n \sin^n\frac{x}{2}\sin\frac{nx}{2} + 1, \quad \text{when } n \text{ is odd.} \tag{42}$$

$$= (-1)^{n-1} 2^n \sin^n\frac{x}{2}\cos\frac{n(\pi+x)}{2} + 1, \tag{43}$$

whether n be even or odd.

(ii) To find the value of $S_1 = \sum_{n=1}^{p}\sum_{k=1}^{n}\binom{n}{k}\cos kx$ (44)

and

$$S_2 = \sum_{n=1}^{p}\sum_{k=1}^{n}\binom{n}{k}\sin kx. \tag{45}$$

Following the method in (i), we obtain

$$\sum_{k=1}^{n}\binom{n}{k}\cos kx = 2^n\cos^n\frac{x}{2}\cos\frac{nx}{2} - 1 \tag{46}$$

and

$$\sum_{k=1}^{n}\binom{n}{k}\sin kx = 2^n\cos^n\frac{x}{2}\sin\frac{nx}{2}. \tag{47}$$

Applying (46) to (44) and (47) to (45), we have

$$S_1 + iS_2 = \sum_{n=1}^{p} 2^n\cos^n\frac{x}{2}\, e^{\frac{inx}{2}} - p$$

$$= \sum_{n=1}^{p} 2^n\left(\frac{e^{\frac{ix}{2}} + e^{-\frac{ix}{2}}}{2}\right)^n e^{\frac{inx}{2}} - p = \sum_{n=1}^{p}(e^{ix}+1)^n - p$$

$$= \frac{2^{p+1}\cos^{p+1}\frac{x}{2}}{e^{-\frac{ix}{2}(p-1)}} - \frac{2\cos x}{e^{\frac{ix}{2}}} - p$$

$$=2\cos\frac{x}{2}\left(2^p\cos^p\frac{x}{2}\cos\overline{p-1}\,\frac{x}{2}-\cos\frac{x}{2}\right)$$

$$+2i\cos\frac{x}{2}\left(2^p\cos^p\frac{x}{2}\sin\overline{p-1}\,\frac{x}{2}+\sin\frac{x}{2}\right)-p. \qquad (48)$$

From (48), we obtain

$$S_1=2\cos\frac{x}{2}\left(2^p\cos^p\frac{x}{2}\cos\overline{p-1}\,\frac{x}{2}-\cos\frac{x}{2}\right)-p \qquad (49)$$

and

$$S_2=2\cos\frac{x}{2}\left(2^p\cos^p\frac{x}{2}\sin\overline{p-1}\,\frac{x}{2}+\sin\frac{x}{2}\right). \qquad (50)$$

If

$$S_1=\sum_{n=1}^{p}(-1)^{n-1}\sum_{k=1}^{n}\binom{n}{k}\cos kx$$

and

$$S_2=\sum_{n=1}^{p}(-1)^{n-1}\sum_{k=1}^{n}\binom{n}{k}\sin kx,$$

show that

$$S_1=\left[(-1)^{p-1}2^p\cos^p\frac{x}{2}\left(\cos\frac{p-1}{2}x+2\cos\frac{p+1}{2}x\right)+3\cos\frac{x}{2}\right]\frac{2\cos\frac{x}{2}}{5+4\cos x}-\frac{1-(-1)^p}{2}$$

and

$$S_2=\left[(-1)^{p-1}2^p\cos^p\frac{x}{2}\left(\sin\frac{p-1}{2}x+2\sin\frac{p+1}{2}x\right)+\sin\frac{x}{2}\right]\frac{2\cos\frac{x}{2}}{5+4\cos x}.$$

If

$$S_1=\sum_{n=1}^{p}\sum_{k=1}^{n}(-1)^{k-1}\binom{n}{k}\cos kx$$

and

$$S_2=\sum_{n=1}^{p}\sum_{k=1}^{n}(-1)^{k-1}\binom{n}{k}\sin kx;$$

then, if p is even,

$$S_1=\left[(-1)^p2^{2p}\sin^{2p}\frac{x}{2}(\cos\overline{p-1}\,x-2\cos px)-\cos x+2\right]\frac{4\sin^2\frac{x}{2}}{5-4\cos x}+p$$

and

$$S_2=\left[(-1)^p2^{2p}\sin^{2p}\frac{x}{2}(\sin\overline{p-1}\,x-2\sin px)+\sin x\right]\frac{4\sin^2\frac{x}{2}}{5-4\cos x};$$

and if p is odd,

$$S_1=\left[(-1)^{p-1}2^{2p}\sin^{2p-1}\frac{x}{2}\left(\sin\frac{2p-3}{2}x-2\sin\frac{2p-1}{2}x\right)+1-2\cos x\right]\frac{2\sin^2\frac{1}{2}x}{5-4\cos x}$$

and

$$S_2=\left[(-1)^p2^{2p}\sin^{2p}\frac{x}{2}\left(\cos\frac{2p-3}{2}x-2\cos\frac{2p-1}{2}x\right)\right.$$

$$\left.-(2\cos x-3)\cos\tfrac{1}{2}x\right]\frac{2\sin\frac{1}{2}x}{5-4\cos x}.$$

3. The Summation of Trigonometric Series by Means of the Operator $\left(r\dfrac{d}{dr}\right)^p$.

(i) To find the value of $$S=\sum_{k=1}^{n} k^p \sin kx. \tag{51}$$

Let $$S_1=\sum_{k=1}^{n} \sin kx r^k; \tag{52}$$

then $$S=\left(r\frac{d}{dr}\right)^p S_1\Big]_{r=1} \tag{53}$$

$$=\sum_{\alpha=1}^{p}\frac{(-1)^\alpha}{\alpha!}\sum_{\beta=1}^{\alpha}(-1)^\beta\binom{\alpha}{\beta}\beta^p r^\alpha\frac{d^\alpha}{dr^\alpha}S_1\Big]_{r=1}. \tag{54}$$

Carrying out the summation in (52) gives

$$S_1=\frac{r\sin x-r^{n+1}\sin(n+1)x+r^{n+2}\sin nx}{1-2r\cos x+r^2}. \tag{55}$$

Designating the numerator in (55) by N_1 and the denominator by N_2, we have

$$\frac{d^\alpha}{dr^\alpha}S_1=\sum_{\gamma=0}^{\alpha}\binom{\alpha}{\gamma}\frac{d^{\alpha-\gamma}}{dr^{\alpha-\gamma}}N_1\frac{d^\gamma}{dr^\gamma}N_2^{-1}. \tag{56}$$

But

$$\frac{d^{\alpha-\gamma}}{dr^{\alpha-\gamma}}N_1\Big]_{r=1}=(\alpha-\gamma)!\left[\binom{1}{\alpha-\gamma}\sin x-\binom{n+1}{\alpha-\gamma}\sin(n+1)x+\binom{n+2}{\alpha-\gamma}\sin nx\right] \tag{57}$$

and

$$\frac{d^\gamma}{dr^\gamma}N_2^{-1}\Big]_{r=1}=(-1)^\gamma\frac{\gamma!}{4}\operatorname{cosec}^2\frac{x}{2}\sum_{\gamma_1=0}^{\left[\frac{\gamma}{2}\right]}(-1)^{\gamma_1}\binom{\gamma-\gamma_1}{\gamma_1}\frac{1}{2^{2\gamma_1}}\operatorname{cosec}^{2\gamma_1}\frac{x}{2}. \tag{58}$$

Applying (57) and (58) to (56) and the changed form of (56) to (54), we obtain the desired result.

An expression for (51) may also be found as follows. We have

$$\sum_{k=1}^{n}k^{2p}\sin kx=(-1)^p\frac{d^{2p}}{dx^{2p}}\sum_{k=1}^{n}\sin kx \tag{59}$$

and $$\sum_{k=1}^{n}k^{2p-1}\sin kx=(-1)^p\frac{d^{2p-1}}{dx^{2p-1}}\sum_{k=1}^{n}\cos kx. \tag{60}$$

Combining (59) and (60) gives

$$\sum_{k=1}^{p}k^p\sin kx=(-1)^{\left[\frac{p+1}{2}\right]}(-1)^{\left[\frac{p}{2}\right]}\frac{d^p}{dx^p}S_2$$

$$=(-1)^p\frac{d^p}{dx^p}S_2, \tag{61}$$

where $$S_2=\sum_{k=1}^{n}\sin\left(\frac{p\pi}{2}+kx\right). \tag{62}$$

Carrying out the summation in (62), we have

$$S_2 = \sin\left(\frac{p\pi}{2} + \frac{n+1}{2}x\right)\sin\frac{nx}{2}\operatorname{cosec}\frac{x}{2}$$

$$= \frac{1}{2}\left[\cos\left(\frac{p\pi}{2} + \frac{x}{2}\right) - \cos\left(\frac{p\pi}{2} + \overline{n + \frac{1}{2}}\,x\right)\right]\operatorname{cosec}\tfrac{1}{2}x; \tag{63}$$

$$\frac{d^p}{dx^p}S_2 = \frac{1}{2}\sum_{a=0}^{p}\binom{p}{a}\frac{d^{p-a}}{dx^{p-a}}\left[\cos\left(\frac{p\pi}{2} + \frac{1}{2}x\right) - \cos\left(\frac{p\pi}{2} + \overline{n + \frac{1}{2}}\,x\right)\right]\frac{d^a}{dx^a}\operatorname{cosec}\frac{x}{2}$$

$$= (-1)^{p-1}\sum_{a=0}^{p}\binom{p}{a}\sin\left(\frac{a\pi}{2} - \frac{n+1}{2}x\right)\sin\frac{nx}{2}\frac{d^a}{dx^a}\operatorname{cosec}\frac{x}{2}, \tag{64}$$

and by Ch. II. (120)

$$\frac{d^a}{dx^a}\operatorname{cosec}\frac{x}{2} = \frac{(-1)^{\left[\frac{a}{2}\right]}}{2^a}\operatorname{cosec}\frac{x}{2}\sum_{\beta=0}^{a}\frac{1}{2^\beta}\sum_{\gamma=0}^{\beta}(-1)^\gamma\binom{\beta}{\gamma}(1+2\gamma)^a M_{2\gamma_1+\delta}, \tag{65}$$

where $\displaystyle M_{2\gamma_1+\delta} = \sum_{\gamma_1=0}^{\left[\frac{\beta-\delta}{2}\right]}(-1)^{\gamma_1}\binom{\beta}{2\gamma_1+\delta}\cot^{2\gamma_1+\delta}\frac{x}{2}, \quad \delta = \frac{1-(-1)^a}{2}.$

Substituting (65) in (64), and the resulting expression in (61), gives S.

(ii) To find
$$S = \sum_{k=1}^{n} k^p \cos kx, \tag{66}$$

we either operate with $\left(r\dfrac{d}{dr}\right)^p$ on S_1,

where $\displaystyle S_1 = \sum_{k=1}^{n}\cos kxr^k = \frac{r\cos x - r^{n+1}\cos(n+1)x + r^{n+2}\cos nx - r^2}{1 - 2r\cos x + r^2},$ (67)

and let then $r=1$; or, by means of

$$\sum_{k=1}^{n} k^{2p}\cos kx = (-1)^p\frac{d^{2p}}{dx^{2p}}\sum_{k=1}^{n}\cos kx \tag{68}$$

and
$$\sum_{k=1}^{n} k^{2p-1}\cos kx = (-1)^p\frac{d^{2p-1}}{dx^{2p-1}}\sum_{k=1}^{n}\sin kx, \tag{69}$$

from which
$$\sum_{k=1}^{p} k^p\cos kx = \frac{d^p}{dx^p}\sum_{k=1}^{n}\cos\left(\frac{p\pi}{2} + kx\right) \tag{70}$$

$$= \frac{d^p}{dx^p}\left[\cos\left(\frac{p\pi}{2} + \frac{n+1}{2}x\right)\sin\frac{nx}{2}\operatorname{cosec}\frac{x}{2}\right]. \tag{71}$$

(iii) To find
$$S = \sum_{k=1}^{n}(-1)^{k-1}k^p\sin kx. \tag{72}$$

Then

$$S = \left(r\frac{d}{dr}\right)^p\sum_{k=1}^{n}(-1)^{k-1}\sin kxr^k\Bigg]_{r=1}$$

$$= \left(r\frac{d}{dr}\right)^p\frac{r\sin x + (-1)^{n-1}r^{n+1}\sin(n+1)x + (-1)^{n-1}r^{n+2}\sin nx}{1 + 2r\cos x + r^2}\Bigg]_{r=1}. \tag{73}$$

Following the method in (i) leads to the result.

The sum might also be obtained thus:

We have $$\sum_{k=1}^{n}(-1)^{k-1}k^{2p}\sin kx=(-1)^p\frac{d^{2p}}{dx^{2p}}\sum_{k=1}^{n}(-1)k^{-1}\sin kx \tag{74}$$

and $$\sum_{k=1}^{n}(-1)^{k-1}k^{2p-1}\sin kx=(-1)^{p-1}\frac{d^{2p-1}}{dx^{2p-1}}\sum_{k=1}^{n}(-1)^{k-1}\cos kx. \tag{75}$$

Combining (74) and (75) gives

$$\sum_{k=1}^{n}(-1)^{k-1}k^p\sin kx=\frac{d^p}{dx^p}\sum_{k=1}^{n}(-1)^{k-1}\sin\left(\frac{p\pi}{2}+kx\right) \tag{76}$$

$$=\tfrac{1}{2}\frac{d^p}{dx^p}\left[\sin\left(\frac{p\pi}{2}+\tfrac{1}{2}x\right)+(-1)^{n-1}\sin\left(\frac{p\pi}{2}+\overline{n+\tfrac{1}{2}}x\right)\right]\sec\tfrac{1}{2}x. \tag{77}$$

(iv) In a way similar to the above,

$$\sum_{k=1}^{n}(-1)^{k-1}k^p\cos kx=\left(r\frac{d}{dr}\right)^p\sum_{k=1}^{n}(-1)^{k-1}\cos kxr^k\Big]_{r=1} \tag{78}$$

$$=\left(r\frac{d}{dr}\right)^p\frac{r\cos x+(-1)^{n-1}r^{n+1}\cos(n+1)x+(-1)^{n-1}r^{n+2}\cos nx+r^2}{1+2r\cos x+r^2}\Bigg]_{r=1}; \tag{79}$$

or, by means of

$$\sum_{k=1}^{n}(-1)^{k-1}k^{2p}\cos kx=(-1)^p\frac{d^{2p}}{dx^{2p}}\sum_{k=1}^{n}(-1)^{k-1}\cos kx \tag{80}$$

and $$\sum_{k=1}^{n}(-1)^{k-1}k^{2p-1}\cos kx=(-1)^{p-1}\frac{d^{2p-1}}{dx^{2p-1}}\sum_{k=1}^{n}(-1)^{k-1}\sin kx. \tag{81}$$

Then, from (80) and (81), we have

$$\sum_{k=1}^{n}(-1)^{k-1}k^p\cos kx=(-1)^p\frac{d^p}{dx^p}\sum_{k=1}^{n}(-1)^{k-1}\cos\left(\frac{p\pi}{2}+kx\right) \tag{82}$$

$$=\frac{(-1)^p}{2}\frac{d^p}{dx^p}\left[\cos\left(\frac{p\pi}{2}+\frac{x}{2}\right)+(-1)^{n-1}\cos\left(\frac{p\pi}{2}+\overline{n+\tfrac{1}{2}}x\right)\right]\sec\frac{x}{2}. \tag{83}$$

4. (i) To find the value of

$$S=\sum_{n=1}^{\infty}n^p\sin nxr^n,\quad |r|<1. \tag{84}$$

Let $$S_1=\sum_{n=1}^{\infty}\sin nxr^n; \tag{85}$$

then $$S=\left(r\frac{d}{dr}\right)^p S_1. \tag{86}$$

Now $$S_1=\frac{1}{2i}\left(\frac{1}{1-r_1}-\frac{1}{1-r_2}\right). \tag{87}$$

where $r_1=re^{ix}$ and $r_2=re^{-ix}$.

Therefore, from (86),

$$S=\frac{1}{2i}\sum_{k=0}^{p}\frac{(-1)^k}{k!}\sum_{a=0}^{k}(-2)^a\binom{k}{a}a^pD_k, \tag{88}$$

where
$$D_k = r_1{}^k \frac{d^k}{dr_1{}^k}\frac{1}{1-r_1} - r_2{}^k \frac{d^k}{dr_2{}^k}\frac{1}{1-r_2}$$
$$= k!\sum_{\beta=0}^{k+1}(-1)^\beta\binom{k+1}{\beta}r^{k+\beta}\frac{\sin(k-\beta)x}{(1-2r\cos x+r^2)^{k+1}}. \tag{89}$$

If $p=0$, then from (88)
$$\sum_{n=1}^{\infty}\sin nxr^n = \frac{r\sin x}{1-2r\cos x+r^2}, \tag{90}$$
and if $p=1$,
$$\sum_{n=1}^{\infty} n\sin nxr^n = \frac{r(1-r^2)\sin x}{(1-2r\cos x+r^2)^2}. \tag{91}$$

Show that

(ii)
$$\sum_{n=1}^{\infty} n^p\cos nxr^n = \sum_{k=0}^{p}(-1)^k\sum_{\alpha=0}^{k}(-1)^\alpha\binom{k}{\alpha}\alpha^p\sum_{\beta=0}^{k+1}(-1)^\beta\binom{k+1}{\beta}r^{k+\beta}\frac{\cos(k-\beta)n}{(1-2r\cos x+r^2)^{k+1}}, \tag{92}$$
from which
$$\sum_{n=1}^{\infty}\cos nxr^n = -1+\frac{1-r\cos x}{1-2r\cos x+r^2} = \frac{r(\cos x-r)}{1-2r\cos x+r^2} \tag{93}$$
and
$$\sum_{n=1}^{\infty} n\cos nxr^n = \frac{r(1+r^2)\cos x-2r^2}{(1-2r\cos x+r^2)^2}. \tag{94}$$

(iii)
$$\sum_{n=1}^{\infty}(-1)^{n-1}n^p\sin nxr^n = \sum_{k=0}^{p}\sum_{\alpha=0}^{k}(-1)^{\alpha-1}\binom{k}{\alpha}\alpha^p\sum_{\beta=0}^{k+1}\binom{k+1}{\beta}r^{k+\beta}\frac{\sin(k-\beta)x}{(1+2r\cos x+r^2)^{k+1}} \tag{95}$$

From (95)
$$\sum_{n=1}^{\infty}(-1)^{n-1}\sin nxr^n = \frac{r\sin x}{1+2r\cos x+r^2} \tag{96}$$
and
$$\sum_{n=1}^{\infty}(-1)^{n-1}n\sin nxr^n = \frac{r(1-r^2)\sin x}{(1+2r\cos x+r^2)^2}. \tag{97}$$

(iv)
$$\sum_{n=1}^{\infty}(-1)^{n-1}n^p\cos nxr^n = \sum_{k=0}^{p}\sum_{\alpha=0}^{k}(-1)^{\alpha-1}\binom{k}{\alpha}\alpha^p\sum_{\beta=0}^{k+1}\binom{k+1}{\beta}r^{k+\beta}\frac{\cos(k-\beta)x}{(1+2r\cos x+r^2)^{k+1}}. \tag{98}$$

This result gives
$$\sum_{n=1}^{\infty}(-1)^{n-1}\cos nxr^n = 1-\frac{1+r\cos x}{1+2r\cos x+r^2} = \frac{r(\cos x+r)}{1+2r\cos x+r^2} \tag{99}$$
and
$$\sum_{n=1}^{\infty}(-1)^{n-1}n\cos nxr^n = \frac{r(1+r^2)\cos x+2r^2}{(1+2r\cos x+r^2)^2}. \tag{100}$$

5. (i) To find the sum of
$$S = \sum_{k=1}^{n} k^q\sin^p kx. \tag{101}$$

Then
$$S = \left(r\frac{d}{dr}\right)^q\sum_{k=1}^{n}\sin^p kxr^k\Big]_{r=1}. \tag{102}$$

Now, by Ch. II. (29), if p is even,

$$\sum_{k=1}^{n} \sin^p kxr^k = \frac{1}{2^{p-1}} \sum_{a=1}^{\frac{p}{2}} (-1)^a \binom{p}{\frac{p}{2}-a} \sum_{k=1}^{n} \cos 2akxr^k + \frac{1}{2^p}\binom{p}{\frac{p}{2}} \frac{r(1-r^n)}{1-r}. \quad (103)$$

Applying (67) to (103) and operating on the resulting expression by $\left(r\frac{d}{dr}\right)^q$ we obtain the value of S.

If $q=0$, we have from (103), when p is even,

$$\sum_{k=1}^{n} \sin^p kx = \frac{1}{2^{p-1}} \sum_{a=1}^{\frac{p}{2}} (-1)^a \binom{p}{\frac{p}{2}-a} \frac{\cos(n+1)ax \sin nax}{\sin ax} + \frac{n}{2^p}\binom{p}{\frac{p}{2}}, \quad (104)$$

and when p is odd,

$$\sum_{k=1}^{n} \sin^p kx = \frac{1}{2^{p-1}} \sum_{a=0}^{\frac{p-1}{2}} (-1)^a \binom{p}{\frac{p-1}{2}-a} \frac{\sin(2a+1)\frac{n+1}{2}x \sin(2a+1)\frac{nx}{2}}{\sin(2a+1)\frac{x}{2}}. \quad (105)$$

(ii) $$\sum_{k=1}^{n} k^q \cos^p kx = \left(r\frac{d}{dr}\right)^q \sum_{k=1}^{n} \cos^p kxr^k \Big]_{r=1}. \quad (106)$$

Then, if $q=0$ and p is even,

$$\sum_{k=1}^{n} \cos^p kx = \frac{1}{2^{p-1}} \sum_{a=1}^{\frac{p}{2}} \binom{p}{\frac{p}{2}-a} \frac{\cos(n+1)ax \sin nax}{\sin ax} + \frac{n}{2^p}\binom{p}{\frac{p}{2}}; \quad (107)$$

and if p is odd,

$$\sum_{k=1}^{n} \cos^p kx = \frac{1}{2^{p-1}} \sum_{a=0}^{\frac{p-1}{2}} \binom{p}{\frac{p-1}{2}-a} \frac{\cos(2a+1)\frac{n+1}{2}x \sin(2a+1)\frac{nx}{2}}{\sin(2a+1)\frac{x}{2}}. \quad (108)$$

(iii) $$\sum_{k=1}^{n} (-1)^{k-1} k^q \sin^p kx = \left(r\frac{d}{dr}\right)^q \sum_{k=1}^{n} (-1)^{k-1} \sin^p kxr^k \Big]_{r=1}. \quad (109)$$

If $q=0$ and p is even,

$$\sum_{k=1}^{n} (-1)^{k-1} \sin^p kx = \frac{1}{2^p} \sum_{a=1}^{\frac{p}{2}} (-1)^a \binom{p}{\frac{p}{2}-a} \frac{\cos ax + (-1)^{n-1}\cos(2n+1)ax}{\cos ax}$$
$$+ \frac{1-(-1)^n}{2^{p+1}}\binom{p}{\frac{p}{2}}; \quad (110)$$

and if p is odd,

$$\sum_{k=1}^{n} (-1)^{k-1} \sin^p kx$$
$$= \frac{1}{2^p} \sum_{a=0}^{\frac{p-1}{2}} (-1)^a \binom{p}{\frac{p-1}{2}-a} \frac{\sin\frac{2a+1}{2}x + (-1)^{n-1}\sin(2a+1)\frac{2n+1}{2}x}{\cos(2a+1)\frac{x}{2}}. \quad (111)$$

(iv) $$\sum_{k=1}^{n}(-1)^{k-1}k^q\cos^p kx=\left(r\frac{d}{dr}\right)^q\sum_{k=1}^{n}(-1)^{k-1}\cos^p kx r^k\Big]_{r=1}. \quad (112)$$

If $q=0$ and p is even,

$$\sum_{k=1}^{n}(-1)^{k-1}\cos^p kx=\frac{1}{2^p}\sum_{a=1}^{\frac{p}{2}}\binom{p}{\frac{p}{2}-a}\frac{\cos ax+(-1)^{n-1}\cos(2n+1)ax}{\cos ax}+\frac{1-(-1)^n}{2^{p+1}}\binom{p}{\frac{p}{2}}; \quad (113)$$

and if p is odd,

$$\sum_{k=1}^{n}(-1)^{k-1}\cos^p kx$$

$$=\frac{1}{2^p}\sum_{a=0}^{\frac{p-1}{2}}\binom{p}{\frac{p-1}{2}-a}\frac{\cos(2a+1)\frac{x}{2}-(-1)^{n-1}\cos(2a+1)\frac{2n+1}{2}x}{\cos(2a+1)\frac{x}{2}}. \quad (114)$$

6. To find $$S=\sum_{n=1}^{\infty}n^q\sin^p nxr^n, \quad |r|<1. \quad (115)$$

Then $$S=\left(r\frac{d}{dr}\right)^q\sum_{n=1}^{\infty}\sin^p nxr^n. \quad (116)$$

If p is even, we have

$$\sum_{n=1}^{\infty}\sin^p nxr^n=\frac{1}{2^{p-1}}\sum_{a=1}^{\frac{p}{2}}(-1)^a\binom{p}{\frac{p}{2}-a}\sum_{n=1}^{\infty}\cos 2anxr^n+\frac{1}{2^p}\binom{p}{\frac{p}{2}}\sum_{n=1}^{\infty}r^n. \quad (117)$$

But $$\sum_{n=1}^{\infty}\cos 2anxr^n=\frac{r\cos 2ax-r^2}{1-2r\cos 2ax+r^2}=\frac{N_1}{N_2},\text{ by (93)}; \quad (118)$$

then $$S=\frac{1}{2^{p-1}}\sum_{a=1}^{\frac{p}{2}}(-1)^a\binom{p}{\frac{p}{2}-a}\left(r\frac{d}{dr}\right)^q\frac{N_1}{N_2}+\frac{1}{2^p}\binom{p}{\frac{p}{2}}\left(r\frac{d}{dr}\right)^q\frac{r}{1-r}. \quad (119)$$

But $$\left(r\frac{d}{dr}\right)^q\frac{N_1}{N_2}=\sum_{k=0}^{q}\frac{(-1)^k}{k!}\sum_{\beta=0}^{k}(-1)^\beta\binom{k}{\beta}\beta^q r^k\frac{d^k}{dr^k}\frac{N_1}{N_2} \quad (120)$$

and $$\frac{d^k}{dr^k}\frac{N_2}{N_1}=\sum_{\gamma=0}^{k}\binom{k}{\gamma}\frac{d^{k-\gamma}}{dr^{k-\gamma}}N_1\frac{d^\gamma}{dr^\gamma}N_2^{-1} \quad (121)$$

$$=N_1\frac{d^k}{dr^k}N_2^{-1}+k(\cos 2ax-2r)\frac{d^{k-1}}{dr^{k-1}}N_2^{-1}-k(k-1)\frac{d^{k-2}}{dr^{k-2}}N_2^{-1}. \quad (122)$$

Now, by Ch. I. (6),

$$\frac{d^k}{dr^k}N_2^{-1}=\frac{(-1)^k2^kk!}{N_2^{k+1}}(r-\cos 2ax)^k\sum_{\gamma_1=0}^{\left[\frac{k}{2}\right]}(-1)^{\gamma_1}\binom{k-\gamma_1}{\gamma_1}\frac{1}{2^{2\gamma_1}}\frac{N_2^{\gamma_1}}{(r-\cos 2ax)^{2\gamma_1}}. \quad (123)$$

Writing $k-1$ and then $k-2$ for k in (123) gives

$$\frac{d^{k-1}}{dr^{k-1}} N_2^{-1} \quad \text{and} \quad \frac{d^{k-2}}{dr^{k-2}} N_2^{-1}.$$

In this way the result is obtained.
Similar considerations lead to the value of S when p is odd.

Find the value of $$S=\sum_{n=1}^{\infty} n^q \cos^p nx r^n.$$

7. (i) To find the value of $S=\sum_{n=0}^{\infty} \frac{\sin^p(a+nx)}{n!} r^n.$ (124)

Now $$\sin^p(a+nx)=\frac{(-1)^p i^p}{2^p} \sum_{k=0}^{p} (-1)^k \binom{p}{k} e^{i(p-2k)(a+nx)}; \qquad (125)$$

then $$S=\frac{(-1)^p i^p}{2^p} \sum_{k=0}^{p} (-1)^k \binom{p}{k} e^{i(p-2k)a} \sum_{n=0}^{\infty} \frac{(re^{i(p-2k)x})^n}{n!}$$

$$=(-1)^p \frac{i^p}{2^p} \sum_{k=0}^{p} (-1)^k \binom{p}{k} e^{r\cos(p-2k)x}[\cos\{(p-2k)a+r\sin(p-2k)x\}$$
$$+i\sin\{(p-2k)a+r\sin(p-2k)x\}]. \qquad (126)$$

And since S is real, therefore

$$S=\frac{(-1)^{\frac{p}{2}}}{2^{p-1}} \sum_{k=0}^{\frac{p}{2}} (-1)^k \binom{p}{k} e^{r\cos(p-2k)x} \cos\{(p-2k)a+r\sin(p-2k)x\},$$
when p is even, (127)

$$=\frac{(-1)^{\frac{p-1}{2}}}{2^{p-1}} \sum_{k=0}^{\frac{p-1}{2}} (-1)^k \binom{p}{k} e^{r\cos(p-2k)x} \sin\{(p-2k)a+r\sin(p-2k)x\},$$
when p is odd. (128)

Combining (127) and (128) gives

$$S=\frac{(-1)^{\left[\frac{p}{2}\right]}}{2^{p-1}} \sum_{k=0}^{\left[\frac{p}{2}\right]} (-1)^k \binom{p}{k} e^{r\cos(p-2k)x} \cos\left[\frac{\pi}{2}\beta-\{(p-2k)a\right.$$
$$\left.+r\sin(p-2k)x\}\right], \qquad (129)$$

where $$\beta=\frac{1-(-1)^p}{2}.$$

Show that

(ii) $$\sum_{n=0}^{\infty} \frac{\cos^p(a+nx)}{n!} r^n=\frac{1}{2^{p-1}} \sum_{k=0}^{\left[\frac{p}{2}\right]} \binom{p}{k} e^{r\cos(p-2k)x} \cos\{(p-2k)a$$
$$+r\sin(p-2k)x\}. \qquad (130)$$

(iii) $$\sum_{n=0}^{\infty} (-1)^n \frac{\sin^p(a+nx)}{n!} r^n=\frac{(-1)^{\left[\frac{p}{2}\right]}}{2^{p-1}} \sum_{k=0}^{\left[\frac{p}{2}\right]} (-1)^k \binom{p}{k} e^{-r\cos(p-2k)x}$$
$$\cos\left[\frac{\pi}{2}\beta-\{(p-2k)a-r\sin(p-2k)x\}\right], \qquad (131)$$

where $$\beta=\frac{1-(-1)^p}{2}.$$

(iv) $$\sum_{n=0}^{\infty}(-1)^n \frac{\cos^p(a+nx)}{n!} r^n = \frac{1}{2^{p-1}} \sum_{k=0}^{\left[\frac{p}{2}\right]} \binom{p}{k} e^{-r\cos(p-2k)x} \cos\{(p-2k)a - r\sin(p-2k)x\}. \quad (132)$$

Letting in (129)-(132) $p=1$ and $a=0$, we obtain

(v) $$\sum_{n=0}^{\infty} \frac{\sin nx}{n!} = e^{\cos x} \sin(\sin x). \quad (133)$$

(vi) $$\sum_{n=0}^{\infty} \frac{\cos nx}{n!} = e^{\cos x} \cos(\sin x). \quad (134)$$

(vii) $$\sum_{n=0}^{\infty}(-1)^n \frac{\sin nx}{n!} = e^{-\cos x} \sin(\sin x). \quad (135)$$

(viii) $$\sum_{n=0}^{\infty}(-1)^n \frac{\cos nx}{n!} = e^{-\cos x} \cos(\sin x). \quad (136)$$

8. (i) To find the value of $$S = \sum_{n=0}^{\infty} \frac{\sin nx}{(nh)!} r^n. \quad (137)$$

Now $$S = \frac{1}{2i} \sum_{n=0}^{\infty} \frac{(e^{ix}r)^n}{(nh)!} - \frac{1}{2i} \sum_{n=0}^{\infty} \frac{(e^{-ix}r)^n}{(nh)!}. \quad (138)$$

We shall first derive the value of

$$S_1 = \sum_{n=0}^{\infty} \frac{r^n}{(nh)!}. \quad (139)$$

Let $r = x^h$; then $$S_1 = \sum_{n=0}^{\infty} \frac{x^{nh}}{(nh)!}. \quad (140)$$

Let now θ_a stand for one of the h roots of unity; then

$$e^{\theta_a x} = \sum_{n=0}^{\infty} \frac{x^n}{n!} \theta_a{}^n \quad (141)$$

and $$\sum_{a=1}^{h} e^{\theta_a x} = \sum_{n=0}^{\infty} \frac{x^n}{n!} \sum_{a=1}^{h} \theta_a{}^n. \quad (142)$$

But $$\sum_{a=1}^{h} \theta_a{}^n = \sum_{a=1}^{h} e^{\frac{2an\pi i}{h}} = \frac{e^{2n\pi i} - 1}{e^{\frac{2n\pi i}{h}} - 1}$$

$$= 0, \text{ if } n \text{ is not a multiple of } h, \quad (143)$$

$$= h, \text{ if } n \text{ is a multiple of } h. \quad (144)$$

Therefore $$\sum_{a=1}^{h} e^{\theta_a x} = h \sum_{n=0}^{\infty} \frac{x^{nh}}{(nh)!} = hS_1 \quad (145)$$

and $$S_1 = \frac{1}{h} \sum_{a=1}^{h} e^{\theta_a x} = \frac{1}{h} \sum_{a=1}^{h} e^{\theta_a r^{1/h}}. \quad (146)$$

To reduce S_1 we have, since $\theta_a = e^{\frac{2a\pi i}{h}}$,

$$e^{\theta_a r^{1/h}} = e^{r^{1/h}\cos\frac{2a\pi}{h}}\left[\cos\left(r^{1/h}\sin\frac{2a\pi}{h}\right) + i\sin\left(r^{1/h}\sin\frac{2a\pi}{h}\right)\right]; \tag{147}$$

and since S_1 is real, $$S_1 = \frac{1}{h}\sum_{a=1}^{h} e^{r^{1/h}\cos\frac{2a\pi}{h}}\cos\left(r^{1/h}\sin\frac{2a\pi}{h}\right). \tag{148}$$

If h is even,

$$S_1 = \frac{1}{h}\left[e^{r^{1/h}} + e^{-r^{1/h}} + \sum_{a=1}^{\frac{h}{2}-1} e^{r^{1/h}\cos\frac{2a\pi}{h}}\cos\left(r^{1/h}\sin\frac{2a\pi}{h}\right)\right.$$
$$\left. + \sum_{a=\frac{h}{2}+1}^{h-1} e^{r^{1/h}\cos\frac{2a\pi}{h}}\cos\left(r^{1/h}\sin\frac{2a\pi}{h}\right)\right]. \tag{149}$$

Letting $h - a = a'$ in the second summation, we obtain

$$S_1 = \frac{1}{h}\left[e^{r^{1/h}} + e^{-r^{1/h}} + 2\sum_{a=1}^{\frac{h}{2}-1} e^{r^{1/h}\cos\frac{2a\pi}{h}}\cos\left(r^{1/h}\sin\frac{2a\pi}{h}\right)\right]. \tag{150}$$

If h is odd,

$$S_1 = \frac{1}{h}\left[e^{r^{1/h}} + 2\sum_{a=1}^{\frac{h-1}{2}} e^{r^{1/h}\cos\frac{2a\pi}{h}}\cos\left(r^{1/h}\sin\frac{2a\pi}{h}\right)\right]. \tag{151}$$

Combining (150) and (151) gives

$$S_1 = \frac{1}{h}\left[e^{r^{1/h}} + \frac{1+(-1)^h}{2}e^{-r^{1/h}} + 2\sum_{a=1}^{\left[\frac{h-1}{2}\right]} e^{r^{1/h}\cos\frac{2a\pi}{h}}\cos\left(r^{1/h}\sin\frac{2a\pi}{h}\right)\right], \tag{152}$$

the summation in the second member of (152) being zero if $h < 3$.

If $h = 1$, $$\sum_{n=0}^{\infty}\frac{r^n}{n!} = e^r. \tag{153}$$

If $h = 2$, $$\sum_{n=0}^{\infty}\frac{r^n}{(2n)!} = \tfrac{1}{2}(e^{r^{1/2}} + e^{-r^{1/2}}). \tag{154}$$

Applying (152) to (138), we obtain S in the following way:

Letting $$e^{ix}r = r_1, \tag{155}$$

then $$e^{r_1^{1/h}} = e^{r^{1/h}e^{\frac{ix}{h}}}$$

$$= e^{r^{1/h}\cos\frac{x}{h}}\left[\cos\left(r^{1/h}\sin\frac{x}{h}\right) + i\sin\left(r^{1/h}\sin\frac{x}{h}\right)\right], \tag{156}$$

$$e^{-r_1^{1/h}} = e^{-r^{1/h}\cos\frac{x}{h}}\left[\cos\left(r^{1/h}\sin\frac{x}{h}\right) - i\sin\left(r^{1/h}\sin\frac{x}{h}\right)\right], \tag{157}$$

$$e^{r_1^{1/h}\cos\frac{2a\pi}{h}}=e^{r^{1/h}\cos\frac{2a\pi}{h}\cos\frac{x}{h}}\left[\cos\left(r^{1/h}\cos\frac{2a\pi}{h}\sin\frac{x}{h}\right)\right.$$

$$\left.+i\sin\left(r^{1/h}\cos\frac{2a\pi}{h}\sin\frac{x}{h}\right)\right], \quad (158)$$

$$\cos\left(r_1^{1/h}\sin\frac{2a\pi}{h}\right)=\tfrac{1}{2}(e^s+e^{-s})\cos\left(r^{1/h}\sin\frac{2a\pi}{h}\cos\frac{x}{h}\right)$$

$$-\tfrac{1}{2}i(e^s-e^{-s})\sin\left(r^{1/h}\sin\frac{2a\pi}{h}\cos\frac{x}{h}\right), \quad (159)$$

where
$$s=r^{1/h}\sin\frac{2a\pi}{h}\sin\frac{x}{h}. \quad (160)$$

From (158) and (159) we have

$$e^{r_1^{1/h}\cos\frac{2a\pi}{h}}\cos\left(r_1^{1/h}\sin\frac{2a\pi}{h}\right)=\tfrac{1}{2}e^{r^{1/h}\cos\frac{2a\pi+x}{h}}\cos\left(r^{1/h}\sin\frac{2a\pi+x}{h}\right)$$

$$+\tfrac{1}{2}e^{r^{1/h}\cos\frac{2a\pi-x}{h}}\cos\left(r^{1/h}\sin\frac{2a\pi-x}{h}\right)+i\left[\tfrac{1}{2}e^{r^{1/h}\cos\frac{2a\pi+x}{h}}\sin\left(r^{1/h}\sin\frac{2a\pi+x}{h}\right)\right.$$

$$\left.-\tfrac{1}{2}e^{r^{1/h}\cos\frac{2a\pi-x}{h}}\sin\left(r^{1/h}\sin\frac{2a\pi-x}{h}\right)\right]. \quad (161)$$

Applying (156), (157) and (159) to (161), we obtain the value of the first summation in (138). The value of the second summation in (138) is the same as the first, except that i is negative.

Therefore

$$\sum_{n=0}^{\infty}\frac{\sin nx}{(nh)!}r^n=\frac{1}{h}\left[e^{r^{1/h}\cos\frac{x}{h}}\sin\left(r^{1/h}\sin\frac{x}{h}\right)-\frac{1+(-1)^h}{2}e^{-r^{1/h}\cos\frac{x}{h}}\sin\left(r^{1/h}\sin\frac{x}{h}\right)\right.$$

$$+\sum_{a=1}^{\left[\frac{h-1}{2}\right]}\left\{e^{r^{1/h}\cos\frac{2a\pi-x}{h}}\sin\left(r^{1/h}\sin\frac{2a\pi+x}{h}\right)\right.$$

$$\left.\left.-e^{r^{1/h}\cos\frac{2a\pi-x}{h}}\sin\left(r^{1/h}\sin\frac{2a\pi-x}{h}\right)\right\}\right]. \quad (162)$$

If $h=1$ and $r=1$, then from (162)

$$\sum_{n=0}^{\infty}\frac{\sin nx}{n!}=e^{\cos x}\sin(\sin x),$$

the same as (133).

If $h=2$ and $r=1$, then

$$\sum_{n=0}^{\infty}\frac{\sin nx}{(2n)!}=\frac{1}{2}\left(e^{\cos\frac{x}{2}}-e^{-\cos\frac{x}{2}}\right)\sin\left(\sin\frac{x}{2}\right). \quad (163)$$

(ii) Show that

$$\sum_{n=0}^{\infty} \frac{\cos nx}{(nh)!} r^n = \frac{1}{h}\Bigg[e^{r^{1/h}\cos\frac{x}{h}} \cos\left(r^{1/h}\sin\frac{x}{h}\right) + \frac{1+(-1)^h}{2} e^{-r^{1/h}\cos\frac{x}{h}} \cos\left(r^{1/h}\sin\frac{x}{h}\right)$$

$$+ \sum_{a=1}^{\left[\frac{h-1}{2}\right]} \Bigg\{ e^{r^{1/h}\cos\frac{2a\pi+x}{h}} \cos\left(r^{1/h}\sin\frac{2a\pi+x}{h}\right)$$

$$+ e^{r^{1/h}\cos\frac{2a\pi-x}{h}} \cos\left(r^{1/h}\sin\frac{2a\pi-x}{h}\right)\Bigg\}\Bigg]. \quad (164)$$

9. To obtain the value of

$$S = \sum_{n=0}^{\infty} (-1)^n \frac{\sin nx}{(nh)!} r^n, \quad (165)$$

we shall first find

$$S_1 = \sum_{n=0}^{\infty} (-1)^n \frac{r^n}{(nh)!}. \quad (166)$$

If h is odd, S_1 is obtained by writing in (151) $-r$ for r; we then have

$$S_1 = \frac{1}{h}\left[e^{-r^{1/h}} + 2\sum_{a=1}^{\frac{h-1}{2}} e^{-r^{1/h}\cos\frac{2a\pi}{h}} \cos\left(r^{1/h}\sin\frac{2a\pi}{h}\right)\right]. \quad (167)$$

If h is even, then

$$(-1)^{1/h} r^{1/h} = e^{\frac{\pi i}{h}} r^{1/h}$$

and

$$e^{\theta_a (-1)^{1/h} r^{1/h}} = e^{r^{1/h}\cos\frac{2a+1}{h}\pi}\left[\cos\left(r^{1/h}\sin\frac{2x+1}{h}\pi\right) + i\sin\left(r^{1/h}\sin\frac{2k+1}{h}\pi\right)\right], \quad (168)$$

and (148) becomes

$$S_1 = \frac{1}{h}\sum_{a=1}^{h} e^{r^{1/h}\cos\frac{2a+1}{h}\pi} \cos\left(r^{1/h}\sin\frac{2a+1}{h}\pi\right). \quad (169)$$

Now the terms corresponding to $a=0$ and $a=h$ in the second member of (169) are equal; we may therefore write

$$S_1 = \frac{1}{h}\Bigg[\sum_{a=0}^{\frac{h-2}{2}} e^{r^{1/h}\cos\frac{2a+1}{h}\pi} \cos\left(r^{1/h}\sin\frac{2a+1}{h}\pi\right)$$

$$+ \sum_{a=\frac{h}{2}}^{h-1} e^{r^{1/h}\cos\frac{2a+1}{h}\pi} \cos\left(r^{1/h}\sin\frac{2a+1}{h}\pi\right)\Bigg]. \quad (170)$$

Letting in the second summation $h-1-a=a'$, we obtain

$$S_1 = \frac{2}{h}\sum_{a=0}^{\frac{h-2}{k}} e^{r^{1/h}\cos\frac{2a+1}{h}\pi} \cos\left(r^{1/h}\sin\frac{2a+1}{h}\pi\right). \quad (171)$$

Then, by the method which led to (162), we find by means of (167) and (171) the value of (165), and also of

$$\sum_{n=0}^{\infty} (-1)^n \frac{\cos nx}{(nh)!} r^n.$$

10. To find the sum of $$S=\sum_{n=0}^{\infty}\frac{\sin^p nx}{(nh)!}r^n. \tag{172}$$

Then, if p is even, we have from (24)

$$S=\frac{1}{2^{p-1}}\sum_{k=1}^{\frac{p}{2}}(-1)^k\binom{p}{\frac{p}{2}-k}\sum_{n=0}^{\infty}\frac{\cos 2knx}{(nh)!}r^n+\frac{1}{2^p}\binom{p}{\frac{p}{2}}\sum_{n=0}^{\infty}\frac{r^n}{n!}; \tag{173}$$

and if p is odd, from (26),

$$S=\frac{1}{2^{p-1}}\sum_{k=1}^{\frac{p-1}{2}}(-1)^k\binom{p}{\frac{p-1}{2}-k}\sum_{n=0}^{\infty}\frac{\sin(2k+1)nx}{(nh)!}r^n. \tag{174}$$

Then, by means of (162) and (164), the values (173) and (174) are obtained.

In a similar way $$\sum_{n=0}^{\infty}\frac{\cos^p nx}{(nh)!}r^n \tag{175}$$

and (172) and (175) with the terms alternating in sign are found.

11. To find the value of $$S=\sum_{n=0}^{\infty}\frac{r^n}{(b+nh)!}. \tag{176}$$

Letting $r_1=x^h$, then $$S=\frac{1}{x^b}\sum_{n=0}^{\infty}\frac{x^{b+nh}}{(b+nh)!}. \tag{177}$$

We now define $$f(n)=\frac{x^n}{(b+n)!}\sum_{a=1}^{h}\theta_a{}^n, \tag{178}$$

where as before θ_a is one of the hth roots of unity.

Then, since $$\sum_{a=1}^{h}\theta_a{}^n=0, \text{ if } n \text{ is not a multiple of } h,$$
$$=h, \text{ if } n \text{ is a multiple of } h,$$

therefore $$\sum_{n=0}^{\infty}f(n)=\sum_{n=0}^{\infty}\frac{x^n}{(b+n)!}\sum_{a=1}^{h}\theta_a{}^n \tag{179}$$

$$=h\sum_{n=0}^{\infty}\frac{x^{nh}}{(b+nh)!}=hS_1. \tag{180}$$

Adding the terms in the second member of (181) by columns, we obtain

$$hS=\sum_{a=1}^{h}\sum_{n=0}^{\infty}\frac{(\theta_a x)^n}{(b+n)!} \tag{181}$$

$$=\sum_{a=1}^{h}\frac{1}{(\theta_a x)^b}\sum_{n=0}^{\infty}\frac{(\theta_a x)^{b+n}}{(b+n)!} \tag{182}$$

$$=\sum_{a=1}^{h}\frac{1}{(\theta_a x)^b}\left[e^{\theta_a x}-\sum_{n=0}^{b-1}\frac{(\theta_a x)^n}{n!}\right]. \tag{183}$$

Therefore $$S=\frac{1}{hx^b}\left[\sum_{a=1}^{h}\left\{\frac{e^{\theta_a x}}{\theta_a{}^b}-\sum_{n=0}^{b-1}\frac{(\theta_a x)^n}{n!}\right\}\right]; \tag{184}$$

and since $$\sum_{a=1}^{h}\theta_a{}^{n-b}=0, \text{ if } n-b \text{ is not a multiple of } h,$$

$$=h, \text{ if } n-b \text{ is a multiple of } h,$$

we need consider only such values of n as will make $n-b=ah$, or $n=b-ah$.

Now when $n=0$, $a=\frac{b}{h}$, and when $n=b-1$, $a=\frac{1}{h}$; hence

$$\sum_{n=0}^{b-1}\frac{x^n}{n!}\sum_{a=1}^{h}\theta_a{}^{n-b}=h\sum_{a=1}^{\left[\frac{b}{h}\right]}\frac{x^{b-ah}}{(b-ah)!} \tag{185}$$

and $$S_1=\frac{1}{hx^b}\left[\sum_{a=1}^{h}\frac{e^{\theta_a x}}{\theta_a{}^b}-h\sum_{a=1}^{\left[\frac{b}{h}\right]}\frac{x^{b-ah}}{(b-ah)!}\right], \tag{186}$$

or $$\sum_{n=0}^{\infty}\frac{r^n}{(b+nh)!}=\frac{1}{hr_1^{b/h}}\left[\sum_{a=1}^{h}\frac{e^{\theta_a r^{1/h}}}{\theta_a{}^b}-h\sum_{a=1}^{\left[\frac{b}{h}\right]}\frac{r^{\frac{b-ah}{h}}}{(b-ah)!}\right]. \tag{187}$$

In the following we shall give another derivation of (187):

Let $$\sum_{n=0}^{\infty}\frac{x^{nh}}{(b-\beta+nh)!}=S_\beta, \quad S_0=S; \tag{188}$$

then $$\left(b-\beta+x\frac{d}{dx}\right)S_\beta=\sum_{n=0}^{\infty}\frac{x^{nh}}{(b-\beta-1+nh)!}. \tag{189}$$

If now to β are assigned the values 0, 1, 2, ... $b-1$, b relations are obtained, the one corresponding to $\beta=b-1$ being

$$\left(1+x\frac{d}{dx}\right)S_{b-1}=\sum_{n=0}^{\infty}\frac{x^{nh}}{(nh)!}$$

$$=\frac{1}{h}\sum_{a=1}^{h}e^{\theta_a x}, \text{ by (146)}, \tag{190}$$

or $$\frac{dS_{b-1}}{dx}+\frac{1}{x}S_{b-1}=\frac{1}{hx}\sum_{a=1}^{h}e^{\theta_a x}. \tag{191}$$

Solving (191) gives $$S_{b-1}=\frac{1}{hx}\sum_{a=1}^{h}\frac{e^{\theta_a x}}{\theta_a}+\frac{C_1}{x}. \tag{192}$$

To determine C_1 we write

$$C_1=xS_{b-1}-\frac{1}{h}\sum_{a=1}^{h}\frac{e^{\theta_a x}}{\theta_a}. \tag{193}$$

Now when $x=0$, S_{b-1} being finite,

$$C_1 = -\frac{1}{h}\sum_{a=1}^{h}\frac{1}{\theta_a};$$

and since $\theta_a^{\,h}=1$,

$$C_1 = -\frac{1}{h}\sum_{a=1}^{h}\theta_a^{\,h-1}$$

$$=0, \quad h-1 \text{ not being a multiple of } h. \tag{194}$$

Therefore
$$S_{b-1} = \frac{1}{hx}\sum_{a=1}^{h}\frac{e^{\theta_a x}}{\theta_a}. \tag{195}$$

Next, from
$$\left(2 + x\frac{d}{dx}\right)S_{b-2} = S_{b-1}, \tag{196}$$

we obtain
$$S_{b-2} = \frac{1}{hx^2}\sum_{a=1}^{h}\frac{e^{\theta_a x}}{\theta_a^{\,2}} + \frac{C_2}{x^2}; \tag{197}$$

and again, since
$$\sum_{a=1}^{h}\theta_a^{\,h-2}=0, \quad h \neq 2, \quad C_2 = 0, \tag{198}$$

hence
$$S_{b-2} = \frac{1}{hx^2}\sum_{a=1}^{h}\frac{e^{\theta_a x}}{\theta_a^{\,2}}. \tag{199}$$

We now assume
$$S_{b-\gamma} = \frac{1}{hx^\gamma}\sum_{a=1}^{h}\frac{e^{\theta_a x}}{\theta_a^{\,\gamma}}, \quad \gamma < h-1, \tag{200}$$

and shall show that this form holds also for $S_{b-(\gamma+1)}$.

For, from
$$\left(\gamma+1 + x\frac{d}{dx}\right)S_{b-\gamma-1} = S_{b-\gamma} \tag{201}$$

follows
$$S_{b-\gamma-1} = \frac{1}{hx^{\gamma+1}}\sum_{a=1}^{h}\frac{e^{\theta_a x}}{\theta_a^{\,\gamma+1}} + \frac{C_{\gamma+1}}{x^{\gamma+1}}; \tag{202}$$

and since $\gamma+1 < h$,
$$C_{\gamma+1} = 0$$

and
$$S_{b-\gamma-1} = \frac{1}{hx^{\gamma+1}}\sum_{a=1}^{h}\frac{e^{\theta_a x}}{\theta_a^{\,\gamma+1}}, \tag{203}$$

which is of the same form as (200). We therefore conclude that (200) holds for all values of γ up to and including $\gamma = h-1$.

For $\gamma = h$, we find
$$S_{b-h} = \frac{1}{hx^h}\sum_{a=1}^{h}\frac{e^{\theta_a x}}{\theta_a^{\,h}} + \frac{C_h}{x^h}, \tag{204}$$

from which
$$C_h = -\frac{1}{h}\sum_{a=1}^{h}\frac{1}{\theta_a^{\,h}} = -\frac{1}{h}h = -1. \tag{205}$$

Therefore
$$S_{b-h} = \frac{1}{hx^h}\sum_{a=1}^{h}\frac{e^{\theta_a x}}{\theta_a^{\,h}} - \frac{1}{x^h}. \tag{206}$$

In a similar way we find

$$S_{b-h-1}=\frac{1}{hx^{h+1}}\sum_{a=1}^{h}\frac{e^{\theta_a x}}{\theta_a{}^{h+1}}-\frac{1}{1!\,x^h},$$

$$S_{b-h-2}=\frac{1}{hx^{h+2}}\sum_{a=1}^{h}\frac{e^{\theta_a x}}{\theta_a{}^{h+2}}-\frac{1}{2!\,x^h},$$

$$\cdots\cdots\cdots\cdots\cdots\cdots,$$

$$S_{b-2h+1}=\frac{1}{hx^{2h-1}}\sum_{a=1}^{h}\frac{e^{\theta_a x}}{\theta_a{}^{2h-1}}-\frac{1}{(h-1)!\,x^h},$$

and

$$S_{b-2h}=\frac{1}{hx^{2h}}\sum_{a=1}^{h}\frac{e^{\theta_a x}}{\theta_a{}^{2h}}-\frac{1}{h!\,x^h}+\frac{C_{2h}}{x^{2h}}, \tag{207}$$

where

$$C_{2h}=-1.$$

We further obtain

$$S_{b-3h}=\frac{1}{hx^{3h}}\sum_{a=1}^{h}\frac{e^{\theta_a x}}{\theta_a{}^{3h}}-\frac{1}{(2h)!\,x^h}-\frac{1}{h!\,x^{2h}}-\frac{1}{x^{3h}}. \tag{208}$$

Let now $b=ch+m$, $m<h$; then

$$S_m=S_{b-ch}=\frac{1}{hx^{ch}}\sum_{a=1}^{h}\frac{e^{\theta_a x}}{\theta_a{}^{ch}}-\frac{1}{(\overline{c-1h})!\,x^h}-\frac{1}{(\overline{c-2h})!\,x^{2h}}$$

$$-\cdots-\frac{1}{h!\,x^{(c-1)h}}-\frac{1}{x^{ch}}$$

$$=\frac{1}{hx^{ch}}\sum_{a=1}^{h}\frac{e^{\theta_a x}}{\theta_a{}^{ch}}-\sum_{a=1}^{c}\frac{1}{(\overline{c-ah})!\,x^{ah}}. \tag{209}$$

Therefore

$$S_{b-b}=\frac{1}{hx^{b}}\sum_{a=1}^{h}\frac{e^{\theta_a x}}{\theta_a{}^{b}}-\sum_{a=1}^{\left[\frac{b}{h}\right]}\frac{1}{(\overline{c-ah})!\,x^{ah}}$$

$$=\frac{1}{hr^{b/h}}\left[\sum_{a=1}^{h}\frac{e^{\theta_a r^{1/h}}}{\theta_a{}^{b}}-h\sum_{a=1}^{\left[\frac{b}{h}\right]}\frac{r_1^{\frac{b-ah}{h}}}{(b-ah)!}\right], \tag{210}$$

which is the same as (187).

We shall now evaluate

$$N=\sum_{a=1}^{h}\frac{e^{\theta_a r^{1/h}}}{\theta_a{}^{b}}, \tag{211}$$

and show that N is real.

Denoting $r^{1/h}$ by u and writing

$$\frac{1}{\theta_a{}^{b}}=\frac{\theta_a{}^{h}}{\theta_a{}^{b}}=\theta_a{}^{h-b}=\theta_a{}^{d},$$

then

$$N=\sum_{a=1}^{h}\theta_a{}^{d}e^{\theta_a u}. \tag{212}$$

(i) If r is positive and h is even, the real roots of u are

$$\theta_h = \cos 2\pi + i \sin 2\pi = 1$$

and
$$\theta_{\frac{h}{2}} = \cos \pi + i \sin \pi = -1,$$

and the conjugate roots
$$\theta_a = \cos \frac{2a\pi}{h} + i \sin \frac{2a\pi}{h}$$

and
$$\theta_{h-a} = \cos \frac{2a\pi}{h} - i \sin \frac{2a\pi}{h},$$

corresponding to the sets of subscripts

$$1,\ h-1;\ 2,\ h-2;\ \ldots;\ \frac{h-2}{2},\ \frac{h+2}{2};\ \frac{h}{2}-1,\ \frac{h}{2}+1.$$

We then have

$$N = e^u + (-1)^d e^{-u} + \sum_{a=1}^{\frac{h}{2}-1} (\theta_a{}^d e^{\theta_a u} + \theta_{h-a}^d e^{\theta_{h-a} u}) \tag{213}$$

$$= e^u + (-1)^d e^{-u} + N_1, \tag{214}$$

where N_1 is the summation in the second member of (213).

Now, since
$$\theta_a{}^d = \cos \frac{2a\pi d}{h} + i \sin \frac{2a\pi d}{h}$$

and
$$\theta_{h-a}^d = \cos \frac{2a\pi d}{h} - i \sin \frac{2a\pi d}{h},$$

therefore
$$N_1 = 2 \sum_{a=1}^{\frac{h}{2}-1} e^{r^{1/h} \cos \frac{2a\pi}{h}} \cos\left(r^{1/h} \sin \frac{2a\pi}{h} - \frac{2ab\pi}{h}\right) \tag{215}$$

and
$$N = e^{r^{1/h}} + (-1)^b e^{-r^{1/h}} + 2 \sum_{a=1}^{\frac{h}{2}-1} e^{r^{1/h} \cos \frac{2a\pi}{h}} \cos\left(r^{1/h} \sin \frac{2a\pi}{h} - \frac{2ab\pi}{h}\right). \tag{216}$$

(ii) If r is positive and h is odd, then $a = h$ gives the only real root, 1. The pairs of conjugate roots correspond to the set of subscripts

$$1,\ h-1;\ 2,\ h-2;\ \ldots;\ \frac{h-3}{2},\ \frac{h+3}{2};\ \frac{h-1}{2},\ \frac{h+1}{2}.$$

We then obtain

$$N = e^{r^{1/h}} + 2 \sum_{a=1}^{\frac{h-1}{2}} e^{r^{1/h} \cos \frac{2a\pi}{h}} \cos\left(r^{1/h} \sin \frac{2a\pi}{h} - \frac{2ab\pi}{h}\right). \tag{217}$$

(iii) If r is negative and h is even, we let

$$x = e^{\frac{\pi i}{h}} r^{1/h};$$

then $$\frac{1}{hx^b}\sum_{a=1}^{h}\frac{e^{\theta_a x}}{\theta_a{}^b}=\frac{1}{hr^{b/h}}\sum_{a=1}^{h}\frac{e^{t_a r^{1/h}}}{t_a{}^b}$$

$$=-\frac{1}{hr^{b/h}}\sum_{a=1}^{h}t_a{}^d e^{t_a u}, \tag{218}$$

where $t_a=\cos\frac{2a+1}{h}\pi+i\sin\frac{2a+1}{h}\pi$.

The roots t_a and t_{h-1-a} are conjugate and correspond to the sets of subscripts 0, $h-1$; 1, $h-2$; 2, $h-3$; ... ; $\frac{h}{2}-1$, $\frac{h}{2}$. It is to be noted that $t_h=t_0$.

Therefore

$$\sum_{a=1}^{h}t_a{}^d e^{t_a u}=\sum_{a=0}^{\frac{h}{2}-1}\left(t_a{}^d e^{t_a u}+t_{h-1-a}^d e^{t_{h-1-a}u}\right)$$

$$=-2\sum_{a=0}^{\frac{h}{2}-1}e^{r^{1/h}\cos\frac{2a+1}{h}\pi}\cos\left(r^{1/h}\sin\frac{2a+1}{h}\pi-\frac{(2a+1)\,b\pi}{h}\right) \tag{219}$$

and $$N=\frac{2}{hr^{b/h}}\sum_{a=0}^{\frac{h}{2}-1}e^{r^{1/h}\cos\frac{2a+1}{h}\pi}\cos\left(r^{1/h}\sin\frac{2a+1}{h}\pi-\frac{(2a+1)\,b\pi}{h}\right). \tag{220}$$

By means of the above results the values of

$$S=\sum_{n=0}^{\infty}\frac{\sin^p(a+ng)}{(b+nh)!}r^n=\frac{(-1)^p i^p}{2^p}\sum_{k=0}^{p}(-1)^k\binom{p}{k}e^{(p-2k)ai}\sum_{n=0}^{\infty}\frac{r_1{}^n}{(b+nh)!},$$

where $$r_1=re^{(p-2k)gi}$$

and $$S=\sum_{n=0}^{\infty}\frac{\cos^p(a+ng)}{(b+nh)!}r^n$$

are obtained.

(iv) If r is negative and h is odd, then $a=\frac{h-1}{2}$ gives the only real root, -1. The pairs of conjugate roots correspond to the subscripts

$$0,\ h-1;\ 1,\ h-2;\ 2,\ h-3;\ \dots;\ \frac{h-3}{2},\ \frac{h+1}{2}.$$

Hence

$$N=e^{-r^{1/h}}+2\sum_{a=}^{\frac{h-3}{2}}e^{r^{1/h}\cos\frac{2a+1}{h}\pi}\cos\left(r^{1/h}\sin\frac{2a+1}{h}\pi-\frac{(2a+1)\,b\pi}{h}\right). \tag{221}$$

12. To find the value of

$$S=\sum_{n=0}^{\infty}(-1)^n\frac{\sin(a+ng)}{b+nh}r^n,\quad |r|\leqq 1. \tag{222}$$

Now $$S=\frac{1}{2i}\left(\frac{e^{ai}}{x_1{}^b}\sum_{n=0}^{\infty}(-1)^n\frac{x_1{}^{b+nh}}{b+nh}-\frac{e^{-ai}}{x_2{}^b}\sum_{n=0}^{\infty}(-1)^n\frac{x_2{}^{b+nh}}{b+nh}\right), \tag{223}$$

where $$x_1=e^{\frac{g}{h}i}r^{1/h}\quad\text{and}\quad x_2=e^{-\frac{g}{h}i}r^{1/h}.$$

Letting $\frac{1}{h}(ah-bg)=f$, then, by Ch. IX. (47),

$$S=\frac{1}{2ir^{b/h}}\left[e^{fi}\sum_{k=1}^{\left[\frac{b-1}{h}\right]}(-1)^{k-1}\frac{x_1^{b-kh}}{b-kh}-e^{-fi}\sum_{k=1}^{\left[\frac{b-1}{h}\right]}(-1)^{k-1}\frac{x_2^{b-kh}}{b-kh}\right.$$

$$+\cos f\left\{\frac{2}{h}\sum_{k=0}^{\left[\frac{h-2}{2}\right]}\sin\frac{2k+1}{h}b\pi(\tan^{-1}m_1-\tan^{-1}m_2)\right.$$

$$\left.-\frac{1}{h}\sum_{k=0}^{\left[\frac{h-2}{2}\right]}\cos\frac{2k+1}{h}b\pi\log\frac{p_1}{p_2}+\frac{1}{2h}(-1)^{b-1}(1-(-1)^h)\log\frac{1+x_1}{1+x_2}\right\}$$

$$+\sin f\left\{\frac{2}{h}\sum_{k=0}^{\left[\frac{h-2}{2}\right]}\sin\frac{2k+1}{h}b\pi(\tan^{-1}m_1+\tan^{-1}m_2)\right.$$

$$\left.\left.-\frac{1}{h}\sum_{k=0}^{\left[\frac{h-2}{2}\right]}\cos\frac{2k+1}{h}b\pi\log(p_1p_2)+\frac{1}{2h}(-1)^{b-1}(1-(-1)^h)\log(1+x_1)(1+x_2)\right\}\right], \tag{224}$$

where
$$m_1=\frac{x_1\sin\frac{2k+1}{h}\pi}{1-x_1\cos\frac{2k+1}{h}\pi} \tag{225}$$

and
$$p_1=x_1^2-2x_1\cos\frac{2k+1}{h}\pi+1; \tag{226}$$

m_2 and p_2 are of the same form as m_1 and p_1 respectively, except that x_2 takes the place of x_1.

We shall reduce (224) and separate in it the real and imaginary parts.

Now
$$\tan^{-1}m_1-\tan^{-1}m_2=\tan^{-1}\frac{i2r^{1/h}\sin\frac{g}{h}\sin\frac{2k+1}{h}\pi}{1-2r^{1/h}\cos\frac{g}{h}\cos\frac{2k+1}{h}\pi+r^{2/h}}; \tag{227}$$

then, by Ch. IX. (86), we find

$$\tan^{-1}m_1-\tan^{-1}m_2=-\frac{i}{2}\log\frac{1-2r^{1/h}\cos\frac{1}{h}\Delta_1+r^{2/h}}{1-2r^{1/h}\cos\frac{1}{h}\Delta_2+r^{2/h}}, \tag{228}$$

where $\Delta_1=(2k+1)\pi-g$ and $\Delta_2=(2k+1)\pi+g$.

Similarly

$$\tan^{-1}m_1+\tan^{-1}m_2=\tan^{-1}\frac{2r^{1/h}\Delta_3\sin\frac{2k+1}{h}\pi}{1-r^{2/h}-2r^{1/h}\Delta_3\cos\frac{2k+1}{h}\pi}, \tag{229}$$

where
$$\Delta_3=\cos\frac{g}{h}-r^{1/h}\cos\frac{2k+1}{h}\pi.$$

Next $$\log p_1 = \log\left(2r^{1/h}\Delta_4 \cos\frac{g}{h} + 1 - r^{2/h} + 2ir^{1/h}\Delta_4 \sin\frac{g}{h}\right), \tag{230}$$

where $$\Delta_4 = r^{1/h}\cos\frac{g}{h} - \cos\frac{2k+1}{h}\pi,$$

and the same form for $\log p_2$ except that i is negative.

Then, by means of Ch. IX. (33), we obtain

$$\log\frac{p_1}{p_2} = 2i\tan^{-1}\frac{2r^{1/h}\Delta_4 \sin\frac{g}{h}}{1 - r^{2/h} + 2r^{1/h}\Delta_4 \cos\frac{g}{h}} \tag{231}$$

and $$\log(p_1p_2) = \log\left[4\Delta_4^2 r^{2/h} + (1-r^{2/h})^2 + 4\Delta_4 r^{1/h}(1-r^{2/h})\cos\frac{g}{h}\right]; \tag{232}$$

also $$\log\frac{1+x_1}{1+x_2} = 2i\tan^{-1}\frac{r^{1/h}\sin\frac{g}{h}}{1 + r^{1/h}\cos\frac{g}{h}} \tag{233}$$

and $$\log(1+x_1)(1+x_2) = \log\left(1 + 2r^{1/h}\cos\frac{g}{h} + r^{2/h}\right). \tag{234}$$

Applying (228)–(234) to (224), we obtain the value of S.

If $r=1$, then, from (224) and by means of Ch. IX. (115), we find

$$\begin{aligned}\sum_{n=0}^{\infty}(-1)^n\frac{\sin(a+ng)}{b+nh} &= \sum_{k=1}^{\left[\frac{b-1}{h}\right]}\frac{(-1)^{k-1}}{b-kh}\sin\left(\overline{b-k}\,\frac{g}{h}+f\right)\\ &+\frac{1}{h}\sum_{k=0}^{\left[\frac{h-2}{2}\right]}\left[\sin\left(\frac{\overline{2k+1}\,b\pi}{h}-f\right)\log\sin\frac{(2k+1)\pi+g}{2h}\right.\\ &\qquad\left.-\sin\left(\frac{\overline{2k+1}\,b\pi}{h}+f\right)\log\sin\frac{(2k+1)\pi-g}{2h}\right]\\ &+\frac{(-1)^b}{2h}\sin f\left[\frac{\pi}{2}\left(\cot\frac{b\pi}{2h}+(-1)^h\tan\frac{b\pi}{2h}\right)-(1-(-1)^h)\log\cos\frac{g}{2h}\right].\end{aligned} \tag{235}$$

By Ch. IX. (136), we also obtain

$$\begin{aligned}\sum_{n=0}^{\infty}\frac{\sin(a+ng)}{b+nh} &= \sum_{k=1}^{\left[\frac{b-1}{h}\right]}\frac{1}{b-kh}\sin\left(\overline{b-k}\,\frac{g}{h}+f\right)\\ &+\frac{1}{h}\sum_{k=1}^{\left[\frac{h-1}{2}\right]}\left[\sin\left(\frac{2kb\pi}{h}-f\right)\log\sin\frac{2k\pi+g}{2h}\right.\\ &\qquad\left.-\sin\left(\frac{2kb\pi}{h}+f\right)\log\sin\frac{2k\pi-g}{2h}\right]\\ &+\frac{(-1)^b}{2h}\sin f\left[\frac{\pi}{2}\left(\cot\frac{b\pi}{2h}-(-1)^h\tan\frac{b\pi}{2h}\right)-(1+(-1)^h)\log\cos\frac{g}{2h}\right.\\ &\left.+2(-1)^{b-1}\log\sin\frac{g}{2h}\right]+\frac{\pi}{2h}\cos f.\end{aligned} \tag{236}$$

The above methods enable us to find the value of

$$\sum_{n=0}^{\infty} \frac{\sin^p(a+ng)}{b+nh} r^n, \qquad \sum_{n=0}^{\infty} \frac{\sin^p(a+ng)}{(b+nh)!} r^n,$$

$$\sum_{n=0}^{\infty} (a_1+ng_1)^{p_1} \frac{\sin^{p_2}(a_2+ng_2)}{(b+nh)!} r^n,$$

and similar forms.

13. We shall now consider a type of series the terms of which are products of trigonometric functions.

(i) To find the value of $S=\sum_{k=1}^{n} \prod_{a=1}^{2k} \sin\frac{a\pi}{2k+1}$. (237)

Let $$\prod_{a=1}^{2k} \sin\frac{a\pi}{2k+1}=P;$$

then $$P=\prod_{a=1}^{2k} \frac{1-e^{\frac{2a\pi i}{2k+1}}}{-2ie^{\frac{a\pi i}{2k+1}}}=\frac{P_1}{P_2}. \tag{238}$$

Now $$1-e^{\frac{2a\pi i}{2k+1}} \text{ is a factor of } 1-x^{2k+1}\Big]_{x=1};$$

therefore $$P_1=\prod_{a=1}^{2k}\left(1-e^{\frac{2a\pi i}{2k+1}}\right)=\frac{1-x^{2k+1}}{1-x}\Big]_{x=1}=2k+1. \tag{239}$$

We also find $$P_2=(-2)^{2k}i^{2k}e^{k\pi i}=2^{2k}. \tag{240}$$

Therefore $$P=\frac{2k+1}{2^{2k}} \quad\text{and}\quad S=\sum_{k=1}^{n}\frac{2k+1}{2^{2k}}. \tag{241}$$

Letting $\frac{1}{2}=r$, then

$$S=2\sum_{k=1}^{n}(2k+1)r^{2k+1}\Big]_{r=\frac{1}{2}}=\frac{d}{dr}\sum_{k=1}^{n} r^{2k+1}\Big]_{r=\frac{1}{2}} \tag{242}$$

$$=\frac{d}{dr}\frac{r^3-r^{2n+3}}{1-r^2}\Big]_{r=\frac{1}{2}}=\frac{1}{9}\left[11-\frac{1}{2^{2n}}(6n+11)\right]. \tag{243}$$

Show that

$$\sum_{k=1}^{n}(-1)^{k-1}\prod_{a=1}^{2k}\sin\frac{a\pi}{2k+1}=\frac{1}{25}\left[13+\frac{(-1)^{n-1}}{2^{2n}}(10n+13)\right]. \tag{244}$$

$$\sum_{k=1}^{n}\prod_{a=1}^{2k}\cos\frac{a\pi}{2k+1}=\frac{(-1)^n-4^n}{5 \,.\, 4^n}. \tag{245}$$

$$\sum_{k=1}^{n}(-1)^{k-1}\prod_{a=0}^{2k}\cos\frac{a\pi}{2k+1}=\frac{1-4^n}{3 \,.\, 4^n}. \tag{246}$$

$$\sum_{k=1}^{n}\prod_{a=0}^{k-1}\sin\frac{2a+1}{2k}\pi=2-\frac{1}{2^{n-1}}. \tag{247}$$

$$\sum_{k=1}^{n}(-1)^{k-1}\prod_{a=0}^{k-1}\sin\frac{2a+1}{2k}\pi=\frac{2}{3}+\frac{(-1)^{n-1}}{3\,.\,2^{n-1}}. \tag{248}$$

$$\sum_{k=1}^{n}\prod_{a=0}^{k-1}(-1)^{a}\sin\frac{2a+1}{2k}\pi=\sum_{k=1}^{n}(-1)^{\left[\frac{k}{2}\right]}\frac{1}{2^{k-1}}$$

$$=\frac{2}{5}+\frac{(-1)^{\left[\frac{n}{2}\right]}}{5\times 2^{n-1}}[1-2(-1)^{n}]. \tag{249}$$

(ii) To find the value of

$$S=\sum_{k=2}^{n}\prod_{a=0}^{k=1}\cos\frac{2a+1}{2k}\pi. \tag{250}$$

Let $$S=\sum_{k=2}^{n}P,\quad\text{then } P=\frac{1}{2^{k-1}i^{k}};$$

and since P is real, k must be even.

And indeed, if k is odd, then for $a=\frac{k-1}{2}$, $P=0$.

Therefore $$S=\sum_{k=1}^{\left[\frac{n}{2}\right]}\prod_{a=0}^{2k-1}\cos\frac{2a+1}{4k}\pi=\sum_{k=1}^{\left[\frac{n}{2}\right]}\frac{(-1)^{k}}{2^{2k-1}} \tag{251}$$

$$=\frac{(-1)^{\frac{n}{2}}-2^{n}}{5\times 2^{n-1}},\quad\text{when } n \text{ is even,}$$

$$=\frac{(-1)^{\frac{n-1}{2}}-2^{n-1}}{5\times 2^{n-2}},\quad\text{when } n \text{ is odd,}$$

and $$S=\frac{1+(-1)^{n}}{2}\,\frac{(-1)^{\frac{n}{2}}-2^{n}}{5\times 2^{n-1}}+\frac{1-(-1)^{n}}{2}\,\frac{(-1)^{\left[\frac{n}{2}\right]}-2^{n-1}}{5\times 2^{n-2}}, \tag{252}$$

whether n be even or odd.

And since $$(-1)^{\left[\frac{n}{2}\right]}(-1)^{n}=-(-1)^{\left[\frac{n-1}{2}\right]},$$
we obtain, after reducing (252),

$$S=\frac{1}{5\times 2^{n}}\left[(-1)^{\left[\frac{n-1}{2}\right]}+3(-1)^{\left[\frac{n}{2}\right]}-2^{n+1}\right]. \tag{253}$$

(iii) To find the value of $$S=\sum_{k=2}^{n}\prod_{a=1}^{k-1}\cos\frac{a\pi}{k}. \tag{254}$$

Let $$S=\sum_{k=2}^{n}P;\quad\text{then, if } k \text{ is odd, } P=(-1)^{k-1}\frac{(-1)^{\frac{k-1}{2}}}{2^{k-1}}, \tag{255}$$

and $$\sum_{k=1}^{\left[\frac{n-1}{2}\right]}\prod_{a=1}^{2k-1}\cos\frac{a\pi}{2k+1}=\sum_{k=1}^{\left[\frac{n-1}{2}\right]}\frac{(-1)^{k}}{2^{2k}}. \tag{256}$$

We then obtain

$$S=-\frac{1}{5}\left[1+\frac{(-1)^{\frac{n}{2}}}{2^{n-2}}\right],\quad \text{when } n \text{ is even,}$$

$$=-\frac{1}{5}\left[1+\frac{(-1)^{\frac{n+1}{2}}}{2^{n-1}}\right],\quad \text{when } n \text{ is odd;}$$

and since $$(-1)^{\left[\frac{n}{2}\right]}(-1)^n=(-1)^{\left[\frac{n+1}{2}\right]}$$

and $$(-1)^n(-1)^{\left[\frac{n+1}{2}\right]}=(-1)^{\left[\frac{n}{2}\right]},$$

therefore $$S=-\frac{1}{5\times 2^n}\left[2^n+(-1)^{\left[\frac{n}{2}\right]}+3(-1)^{\left[\frac{n+1}{2}\right]}\right], \tag{257}$$

whether n be even or odd.

Show that $$\sum_{k=2}^{n}\prod_{a=1}^{k-1}\sin\frac{a\pi}{k}=3-\frac{n+2}{2^{n-1}}, \tag{258}$$

$$\sum_{k=2}^{n}(-1)^k\prod_{a=1}^{k-1}\sin\frac{a\pi}{k}=\frac{5}{9}+(-1)^n\frac{3n+2}{9\times 2^{n-1}}. \tag{259}$$

We find $$\prod_{a=1}^{2^k-1}\sin\frac{a\pi}{2^k}=2\frac{2^k}{2^{2^k}},\qquad \prod_{a=1}^{2^k-1}\cos\frac{a\pi}{2^k}=0,$$

$$\prod_{a=1}^{2^{k-1}-1}\sin\frac{a\pi}{2^k}=\prod_{a=1}^{2^{k-1}-1}\cos\frac{a\pi}{2^k}=2^{1/2}\cdot\frac{2^{\frac{1}{2}k}}{2^{\frac{1}{2}2^k}},$$

$$\prod_{a=1}^{(2m+1)2^k-1}\sin\frac{a\pi}{(2m+1)2^k}=2\frac{(2m+1)2^k}{2^{(2m+1)2^k}},$$

$$\prod_{a=1}^{(2m+1)2^{k-1}-1}\sin\frac{a\pi}{(2m+1)2^k}=\prod_{a=1}^{(2m+1)2^{k-1}-1}\cos\frac{a\pi}{(2m+1)2^k}=2^{1/2}\frac{(2m+1)^{1/2}2^{1/2k}}{2^{1/2(2m+1)2^k}},$$

$$\prod_{a=0}^{2^{k-1}-1}\sin\frac{2a+1}{2^k}\pi=(-1)^{2^{k-2}}\prod_{a=0}^{2^{k-1}-1}\cos\frac{2a+1}{2^k}\pi=\frac{2}{2^{2^{k-1}}},$$

$$\prod_{a=0}^{(2m+1)2^{k-1}-1}\sin\frac{2a+1}{(2m+1)2^k}\pi=(-1)^{(2m+1)2^{x-2}}\prod_{a=0}^{(2m+1)2^{k-1}-1}\cos\frac{2a+1}{(2m+1)2^k}\pi$$

$$=\frac{2}{2^{(2m+1)2^{k-1}}}.$$

It follows that whether n be even or odd,

$$\prod_{a=1}^{n-1}\sin\frac{a\pi}{n}=\frac{n}{2^{n-1}}\quad\text{and}\quad\prod_{a=1}^{n-1}\sin\frac{a\pi}{2n}=\prod_{a=1}^{n-1}\cos\frac{a\pi}{2n}=\frac{n^{1/2}}{2^{n-1}},$$

and when n is even whether it be of the form 2^k or $(2m+1)2^k$,

$$\prod_{a=0}^{\frac{n-2}{2}}\sin\frac{2a+1}{n}\pi=(-1)^{\frac{n}{4}}\prod_{a=0}^{\frac{n-2}{2}}\cos\frac{2a+1}{n}\pi=\frac{2}{2^{\frac{1}{2}n}}.$$

(iv) To find the value of

$$S=\sum_{k=1}^{\infty} r^k \prod_{a=1}^{2k} \sin\frac{a\pi}{2k+1}, \quad |r|<4. \tag{260}$$

Then

$$S=\sum_{k=1}^{\infty} \frac{2k+1}{2^{2k}} r^k \tag{261}$$

$$=\frac{2}{r^{1/2}}\sum_{k=1}^{\infty} (2k+1)\left(\frac{r^{1/2}}{2}\right)^{2k+1}. \tag{262}$$

Letting $\frac{r^{1/2}}{2}=r_1$, we have

$$S_1=\sum_{k=1}^{\infty} (2k+1) r_1^{2k+1}=\left(r_1\frac{d}{dr_1}\right)\sum_{k=1}^{\infty} r_1^{k+1}$$

$$=\frac{r_1^3(3-r_1^2)}{(1-r_1^2)^2}, \tag{263}$$

and

$$S=\frac{r(12-r)}{(4-r)^2}. \tag{264}$$

Show that

$$\sum_{k=1}^{\infty} (-1)^{k-1} r^k \prod_{a=1}^{2k} \sin\frac{a\pi}{2k+1}=\frac{r(12+r)}{(4+r)^2}, \tag{265}$$

$$\sum_{k=1}^{\infty} r^k \prod_{a=1}^{2k} \cos\frac{a\pi}{2k+1}=-\frac{r}{4+r}, \tag{266}$$

$$\sum_{k=1}^{\infty} (-1)^{k-1} r^k \prod_{a=1}^{2k} \cos\frac{a\pi}{2k+1}=-\frac{r}{4-r}. \tag{267}$$

14. By combining the results obtained above we can find the value of series, the terms of which are products of tangents and cotangents of certain angles.

We find, for example,

(i)
$$\sum_{k=1}^{n} \prod_{a=1}^{2k} \tan\frac{a\pi}{2k+1}=\sum_{k=1}^{n} (-1)^k (2k+1) \tag{268}$$

$$=n, \quad \text{when } n \text{ is even,}$$

$$=-(n+2), \quad \text{when } n \text{ is odd,}$$

$$=(-1)^n(n+1)-1, \tag{269}$$

whether n be even or odd.

(ii)
$$\sum_{k=1}^{n} \prod_{a=0}^{2k-1} \tan\frac{2a+1}{4k}\pi=\sum_{k=1}^{n} \prod_{a=0}^{2k-1} \cot\frac{2a+1}{4k}\pi=\sum_{k=1}^{n} (-1)^k \tag{270}$$

$$=0, \quad \text{when } n \text{ is even,}$$

$$=-1, \quad \text{when is odd,}$$

$$=-\frac{1-(-1)^n}{2}, \tag{271}$$

whether n be even or odd.

(iii) $$\sum_{k=1}^{\infty}\prod_{a=1}^{2k}\cot\frac{a\pi}{2k+1}=\sum_{k=1}^{\infty}\frac{(-1)^k}{2k+1}=\sum_{k=0}^{\infty}\frac{(-1)^k}{2k+1}-1=\frac{\pi}{4}-1. \tag{272}$$

Show that $$\sum_{k=1}^{\infty}r^k\prod_{a=1}^{2k}\tan\frac{a\pi}{2k+1}=-\frac{r(3+r)}{(1+r)^2},\quad |r|<1, \tag{273}$$

$$\sum_{k=1}^{\infty}(-1)^{k-1}r^k\prod_{a=1}^{2k}\tan\frac{a\pi}{2k+1}=-\frac{r(3-r)}{(1-r)^2},\quad |r|<1. \tag{274}$$

15. We shall here find the value of series, the terms of which are products of powers of trigonometric functions.

(i) To find the value of
$$S=\sum_{k=1}^{n}\prod_{a=1}^{2k}\sin^p\frac{a\pi}{2k+1}. \tag{275}$$

Now $$S=\sum_{k=1}^{n}\sum_{a=1}^{2k}\frac{(2k+1)^p}{2^{2kp}},\quad \text{by (241).} \tag{276}$$

Letting $\frac{1}{2^p}=r$, then $$S=2^p\sum_{k=1}^{n}(2k+1)^p r^{2k+1}\Big]_{r=1} \tag{277}$$

$$=2^p\left(r\frac{d}{dr}\right)^p\sum_{k=1}^{n}r^{2k+1}$$

$$=2^p\sum_{\beta=1}^{p}\frac{(-1)^\beta}{\beta!}\sum_{\gamma=1}^{\beta}(-1)^\gamma\binom{\beta}{\gamma}\gamma^p r^\beta\frac{d^\beta}{dr^\beta}\sum_{k=1}^{n}r^{2k+1}\Big]_{r=\frac{1}{2^p}}. \tag{278}$$

But $$r^\beta\frac{d^\beta}{dr^\beta}\sum_{k=1}^{n}r^{2k+1}\Big]_{r=\frac{1}{2^p}}=\frac{d^\beta}{dr^\beta}\frac{r^3-r^{2n+3}}{1-r^2}\Big]_{r=\frac{1}{2^p}}$$

$$=\frac{\beta!\,r^\beta}{2}\sum_{\gamma_1=0}^{\beta}\left\{\binom{3}{3-\gamma_1}-\binom{2n+3}{\beta-\gamma_1}r^{2n}\right\}r^{3-\beta+\gamma_1}\left\{\frac{(-1)^{\gamma_1}}{(1+r)^{\gamma_1+1}}+\frac{1}{(1-r)^{\gamma_1+1}}\right\}\Big]_{r=\frac{1}{2^p}}$$

$$=\frac{\beta!}{2^{2p+1}}\sum_{\gamma_1=0}^{\beta}\left\{\binom{3}{\beta-\gamma_1}-\binom{2n+3}{\beta-\gamma_1}\frac{1}{2^{2np}}\right\}\left\{\frac{(-1)^{\gamma_1}}{(2^p+1)^{\gamma_1+1}}+\frac{1}{(2^p-1)^{\gamma_1+1}}\right\}. \tag{279}$$

Denoting the summation in (279) by P_{γ_1},

we obtain $$S=\frac{1}{2^{p+1}}\sum_{\beta=1}^{p}(-1)^\beta\sum_{\gamma=1}^{\beta}(-1)^\gamma\binom{\beta}{\gamma}\gamma^p P_{\gamma_1}. \tag{280}$$

Letting in (275) $p=1$, then from (280)

$$\sum_{k=1}^{n}\prod_{a=1}^{2k}\sin\frac{a\pi}{2k+1}=\frac{1}{4}\left[\left\{3-(2n+3)\frac{1}{2^{2n}}\right\}\frac{4}{3}+\left(1-\frac{1}{2^{2n}}\right)\frac{8}{9}\right]$$

$$=\frac{1}{9}\left[11-\frac{1}{2^{2n}}(6n+11)\right],$$ which is the same as (243).

(ii) If in (275) we let $n=\infty$, then

$$S=\sum_{k=1}^{\infty}\prod_{a=1}^{2k}\sin^p\frac{a\pi}{2k+1}, \tag{281}$$

and similar to (277) $$S=2^p \sum_{k=1}^{\infty}(2k+1)^p r^{2k+1}\Big]_{r=\frac{1}{2^p}}$$

$$=\frac{1}{2^{p+1}}\sum_{\beta=1}^{p}(-1)^{\beta}\sum_{\gamma=1}^{\beta}(-1)^{\gamma}\binom{\beta}{\gamma}\gamma^p P'_{\gamma_1}, \tag{282}$$

where $$P'_{\gamma_1}=\sum_{\gamma_1=0}^{\beta}\binom{3}{\beta-\gamma_1}\left\{\frac{(-1)^{\gamma_1}}{(2^p+1)^{\gamma_1+1}}+\frac{1}{(2^p-1)^{\gamma_1-1}}\right\}.$$

If $p=1$, $S=\frac{11}{9}$, the result also obtained by letting $r=1$ in (264).

(iii) To find the value of

$$S=\sum_{k=1}^{n}\prod_{a=1}^{2k}\cos^p\frac{a\pi}{2k+1}. \tag{283}$$

Now $$S=\sum_{k=1}^{n}\frac{(-1)^{kp}}{2^{2kp}}=\frac{2^{2np}-1}{2^{2np}(2^{2p}-1)}, \quad \text{when } p \text{ is even,}$$

$$=-\frac{2^{2np}-(-1)^n}{2^{2np}(2^{2p}+1)}, \quad \text{when } p \text{ is odd,}$$

$$=(-1)^p\frac{2^{2np}-(-1)^{np}}{2^{2np}[2^{2p}-(-1)^p]}, \tag{284}$$

whether p be even or odd.

(iv) If in (283) we let $n=\infty$, then

$$S=\sum_{k=1}^{\infty}\prod_{a=1}^{2k}\cos^p\frac{a\pi}{2k+1}=\frac{1}{2^{2p}-1}, \quad \text{when } p \text{ is even,}$$

$$=-\frac{1}{2^{2p}+1}, \quad \text{when } p \text{ is odd,}$$

$$=\frac{1}{2^{4p}-1}[1+(-1)^p 2^{2p}], \tag{285}$$

whether p be even or odd.

If in (285) $p=1$, then $S=-\frac{1}{5}$, the value also obtained by letting $r=1$ in (266).

Show that $$\sum_{k=1}^{n}\prod_{a=0}^{k-1}\sin^p\frac{2a+1}{2k}\pi=\frac{2^{np}-1}{2^{(n-1)p}(2^p-1)}, \tag{286}$$

and that the value of $$\sum_{k=1}^{n}\prod_{a=0}^{2k-1}\cos^p\frac{2a+1}{4k}\pi \tag{287}$$

is 2^p multiplied by (284).

16. To find the value of $$S=\sum_{k=1}^{n}\prod_{a=1}^{2k}\tan^p\frac{a\pi}{2k+1}. \tag{288}$$

(i) If p is even, $$S=\sum_{k=1}^{n}(2k+1)^p. \tag{289}$$

Then
$$S=\sum_{k=1}^{n}(2k+1)^p r^{2k+1}\Big]_{r=1} \tag{290}$$

$$=\left(r\frac{d}{dr}\right)^p\sum_{k=1}^{n}r^{2k+1}\Big]_{r=1}=\sum_{\beta=1}^{p}\frac{(-1)^\beta}{\beta!}\sum_{\gamma=1}^{\beta}(-1)^\beta\binom{\beta}{\gamma}\gamma^p r^\beta\frac{d^\beta}{dr^\beta}\sum_{k=1}^{n}r^{2k+1}\Big]_{r=1}. \tag{291}$$

Now
$$r^\beta\frac{d^\beta}{dr^\beta}\sum_{k=1}^{n}r^{2k+1}\Big]_{r=1}=\beta!\sum_{k=\left[\frac{\beta}{2}\right]}^{n}\binom{2k+1}{\beta};$$

and since the value of S in (288) is one less than the value of (157) in Ch. V., we have from Ch. III. (85)
$$S=-1+\tfrac{1}{4}\sum_{\beta=1}^{p}\frac{1}{2^\beta}\sum_{\gamma=1}^{\beta}(-1)^{\gamma-1}\binom{\beta}{\gamma}\gamma^p S_{\gamma_1}, \tag{292}$$

where
$$S_{\gamma_1}=\sum_{\gamma_1=0}^{\beta+1}(-1)^{\gamma_1}\binom{2n+3}{\gamma_1}2^{\gamma_1}+1. \tag{293}$$

(ii) If p is odd,
$$S=\sum_{k=1}^{n}(-1)^k(2k+1)^p.$$

The value of S being one less than the value of (162) in Ch. V., we obtain from Ch. III. (99)
$$S=-1+\tfrac{1}{2}\sum_{\beta=1}^{p}\sum_{\gamma=1}^{\beta}(-1)^\gamma\binom{\beta}{\gamma}\gamma^p S_\gamma, \tag{294}$$

where
$$S_{\gamma_1}=\sum_{\gamma_1=0}^{\beta}(-1)^{\gamma_1}\left[(-1)^{\frac{\beta-\delta}{2}}\binom{\beta+1-\delta}{\gamma_1}+(-1)^n\binom{2n+3}{\gamma_1}\right]$$
$$\sum_{\gamma_2=0}^{\left[\frac{\beta-\gamma_1}{2}\right]}(-1)^{\gamma_2}\binom{\beta-\gamma_1-\gamma_2}{\gamma_2}\frac{1}{2^{\gamma_2}},$$
$$\delta=\frac{1-(-1)^\beta}{2}.$$

If $p=1$, then from (294)
$$\sum_{k=1}^{n}\prod_{a=1}^{2k}\tan\frac{a\pi}{2k+1}=-1-\tfrac{1}{2}\sum_{\gamma_1=1}^{1}(-1)^{\gamma_1}\left[\binom{1}{\gamma_1}+(-1)^n\binom{2n+3}{\gamma_1}\right]$$
$$\sum_{\gamma_2=0}^{\left[\frac{1-\gamma_1}{2}\right]}(-1)^{\gamma_2}\binom{1-\gamma_1-\gamma_2}{\gamma_2}\frac{1}{2^{\gamma_2}}$$
$$=-1-\tfrac{1}{2}\{1+(-1)^n\}+\tfrac{1}{2}\{1+(-1)^n(2n+3)\}$$
$$=-1+(-1)^n(n+1),\text{ the same as (269).}$$

17. To find the value of $P=\prod_{k=0}^{2n}\left(e^{\frac{p}{q}\pi i}+e^{\pm\frac{2k\pi i}{2n+1}}\right)$.

Since $e^{\frac{p}{q}\pi i}+e^{\pm\frac{2k\pi i}{2n+1}}$ is a factor of $x^{2n+1}+1$, $x=e^{\frac{p}{q}\pi i}$, therefore
$$P=\cos(2n+1)\frac{p\pi}{q}+i\sin(2n+1)\frac{p\pi}{q}+1, \tag{295}$$
where p and q may have any real value.

Similarly

$$\prod_{k=0}^{2n}\left(e^{\frac{p}{q}\pi i}-e^{\pm\frac{2k\pi i}{2n+1}}\right)=\cos(2n+1)\frac{p\pi}{q}+i\sin(2n+1)\frac{p\pi}{q}-1; \tag{296}$$

$$\prod_{k=0}^{2n-1}\left(e^{\frac{p}{q}\pi i}\pm e^{\pm\frac{2k+1}{2n}\pi i}\right)=\cos\frac{2np\pi}{q}+i\sin\frac{2np\pi}{q}+1; \tag{297}$$

$$\prod_{k=0}^{2n}\left(e^{\frac{p}{q}\pi i}+e^{\pm\frac{2k+1}{2n+1}\pi i}\right)=\cos(2n+1)\frac{p\pi}{q}+i\sin(2n+1)\frac{p\pi}{q}-1; \tag{298}$$

$$\prod_{k=0}^{2n}\left(e^{\frac{p}{q}\pi i}-e^{\pm\frac{2k+1}{2n+1}\pi i}\right)=\cos(2n+1)\frac{p\pi}{q}+i\sin(2n+1)\frac{p\pi}{q}+1. \tag{299}$$

18. Show that

(i) $$\sum_{k=1}^{n}(-1)^{\left[\frac{k}{2}\right]}\sin kx=\frac{\sin\left(\frac{n\pi}{2}-\frac{x}{2}\right)}{\cos x}\left\{\cos\left(\frac{n\pi}{2}+\frac{x}{2}\right)-(-1)^{\left[\frac{n}{2}\right]}\cos\left(\frac{n\pi}{2}+\overline{n+\tfrac{1}{2}}x\right)\right\}.$$

(ii) $$\sum_{k=1}^{n}(-1)^{\left[\frac{k}{2}\right]}\cos kx=\frac{1-(-1)^n}{2\cos x}+(-1)^n\frac{\sin\left(\frac{n\pi}{2}-\frac{x}{2}\right)}{\cos x}\left\{\sin\left(\frac{n\pi}{2}-\frac{x}{2}\right)-(-1)^{\left[\frac{n}{2}\right]}\sin\left(\frac{n\pi}{2}-\overline{n+\tfrac{1}{2}}x\right)\right\}.$$

(iii) $$\sum_{k=1}^{\left[\frac{n}{2}\right]}(-1)^{\left[\frac{k}{2}\right]}\sin kx=\frac{\sin\frac{1}{2}x}{\cos x}\left\{(-1)^{\left[\frac{n}{4}\right]}\cos\left(2\left[\frac{n}{4}\right]+\frac{1}{2}\right)x-\cos\tfrac{1}{2}x\right\}+\frac{1-(-1)^{\left[\frac{n}{2}\right]}}{2}(-1)^{\left[\frac{n}{4}\right]}\sin\left[\frac{n}{2}\right]x.$$

(iv) $$\sum_{k=1}^{\left[\frac{n}{2}\right]}(-1)^{\left[\frac{k}{2}\right]}\cos kx=-\frac{\sin\frac{1}{2}x}{\cos x}\left\{(-1)^{\left[\frac{n}{4}\right]}\sin\left(2\left[\frac{n}{4}\right]+\frac{1}{2}\right)x-\sin\tfrac{1}{2}x\right\}+\frac{1-(-1)^{\left[\frac{n}{2}\right]}}{2}(-1)^{\left[\frac{n}{4}\right]}\cos\left[\frac{n}{2}\right]x.$$

(v) $$\sum_{k=1}^{\left[\frac{n}{2}\right]}(-1)^{\left[\frac{k}{2}\right]}k\sin kx=\frac{\sin\frac{1}{2}x}{\cos x}\left\{(-1)^{\left[\frac{n}{4}\right]}\cos\left(2\left[\frac{n}{4}\right]-\frac{1}{2}\right)x-\cos\tfrac{1}{2}x\right\}$$
$$+(-1)^{\left[\frac{n}{4}\right]}2\left[\frac{n}{4}\right]\frac{\sin\frac{1}{2}x}{\cos x}\cos\left(2\left[\frac{n}{4}\right]+\frac{1}{2}\right)x$$
$$+(-1)^{\left[\frac{n}{4}\right]}\frac{\sin 2\left[\frac{n}{4}\right]x}{2\cos x}+\frac{1-(-1)^{\left[\frac{n}{2}\right]}}{2}(-1)^{\left[\frac{n}{4}\right]}\left(2\left[\frac{n}{4}\right]+1\right)\sin\left[\frac{n}{2}\right]x,$$

and a similar form for $$\sum_{k=1}^{\left[\frac{n}{2}\right]}(-1)^{\left[\frac{k}{2}\right]}k\cos kx.$$

Additional examples will be found in the Appendix.

CHAPTER XIII.

EVALUATION OF DEFINITE INTEGRALS.

THE evaluation of a definite integral from its definition as a summation presents in general considerable difficulty. Moreover, in many cases the value of the sum of the series resulting from the definition cannot be expressed in terms of known functions.

For example, from the definition we have

$$\int_a^b \frac{\sin x}{x}\,dx = h\sum_{k=0}^{n-1} \frac{\sin(a+kh)}{a+kh}\Bigg]_{h\doteq 0}, \quad nh=b-a,$$

$$= \sum_{k=0}^{\infty}(-1)^k \frac{b^{2k+1}}{(2k+1)(2k+1)!} - \sum_{k=0}^{\infty}(-1)^k \frac{a^{2k+1}}{(2k+1)(2k+1)!}; \tag{1}$$

$$\int_a^b \frac{e^x}{x}\,dx = h\sum_{k=0}^{n-1} \frac{e^{a+kh}}{a+kh}\Bigg]_{h\doteq 0}, \quad nh=b-a,$$

$$= \log b - \log a + \sum_{k=0}^{\infty} \frac{b^{k+1}}{(k+1)(k+1)!} - \sum_{k=0}^{\infty} \frac{a^{k+1}}{(k+1)(k+1)!}; \tag{2}$$

$$\int_a^b (\tan^{-1}x)^2 dx = h\sum_{k=0}^{n-1} \left\{\tan^{-1}(a+kh)\right\}^2\Bigg]_{h\doteq 0}, \quad nh=b-a,$$

$$= b(\tan^{-1}b)^2 - a(\tan^{-1}a)^2 - \tan^{-1}b\log(1+b^2)$$

$$+ \tan^{-1}a\log(1+a^2) + \sum_{k=1}^{\infty}(-1)^k \frac{b^{2k+1}-a^{2k+1}}{2k+1}\sum_{k_1=1}^{k}\frac{1}{k_1}, \quad |b| \leqq 1, \ |a| \leqq 1. \tag{3}$$

No methods for obtaining the sums in (1), (2) have been devised.

If a personal reference be permitted, the author has spent considerable effort in trying to express in terms of elementary functions

$$S = \sum_{n=1}^{\infty} \frac{x^n}{n!\,n} \tag{4}$$

and the solution of the differential equation

$$\frac{d^2S}{dx^2} + \frac{1-x}{x}\frac{dS}{dx} = \frac{1}{x},$$

which is satisfied by S in (4).

It is hoped that mathematicians will feel induced to take up this and similar problems in the operation with series which are waiting solution and which have such an important bearing on mathematical analysis.

We shall now evaluate the following integrals:

1. (i) $$I=\int_a^b (\sin^{-1}x)^2\,dx. \tag{5}$$

Then, by the definition,

$$I=h\sum_{k=0}^{n-1}\left\{\sin^{-1}(a+kh)\right\}^2\Big]_{h=0},\quad nh=b-a. \tag{6}$$

Now $$(\sin^{-1}x)^2=\sum_{\beta=0}^{\infty}\frac{2^\beta\beta!}{\prod\limits_{\gamma=0}^{\beta}(2\gamma+1)}\frac{x^{2\beta+2}}{\beta+1},\text{ by Ch. VII. (52);} \tag{7}$$

then

$$I=\sum_{\beta=0}^{\infty}\frac{2^\beta\beta!}{(\beta+1)\prod\limits_{\gamma=0}^{\beta}(2\gamma+1)}h\sum_{k=0}^{n-1}(a+kh)^{2\beta+2}\Big]_{h=0},\quad nh=b-a,\ |b|\leqq 1,\ |a|\leqq 1. \tag{8}$$

We shall first find the value of

$$S=h\sum_{k=0}^{n-1}(a+kh)^{2\beta+2}\Big]_{h=0},\quad nh=b-a. \tag{9}$$

Writing p for $2\beta+2$, then

$$S=\sum_{m=0}^{p}\binom{p}{m}h^{m+1}a^{p-m}\sum_{k=1}^{n-1}k^m. \tag{10}$$

Now, by Ch. V. (95), $$\sum_{k=1}^{n-1}k^m=\frac{n^{m+1}+F_m(n)}{m+1},$$

where $F_m(n)$ is a rational, integral function in n of not higher degree than m; therefore

$$h^{m+1}F_m(n)]_{h=0}=0$$

and $$S=\sum_{m=0}^{p}\binom{p}{m}a^{p-m}(b-a)^{m+1}$$

$$=\frac{1}{p+1}\left[\sum_{m=0}^{p+1}\binom{p+1}{m}a^{p+1-m}(b-a)^m-a^{p+1}\right]$$

$$=\frac{1}{p+1}(b^{p+1}-a^{p+1})=\frac{1}{2\beta+3}(b^{2\beta+3}-a^{2\beta+3}). \tag{11}$$

Therefore $$I=b^3\sum_{\beta=0}^{\infty}\frac{2^\beta\beta!}{(\beta+1)\prod\limits_{\gamma=0}^{a}(2\gamma+1)}\frac{1}{2\beta+3}(b^2)^\beta, \tag{12}$$

minus the expression of the same form, and in which b is replaced by a.

Letting in Ch. X. (156) $x=b^2$ and then $x=a^2$, we obtain

$$I=2(1-b^2)^{1/2}\sin^{-1}b+b(\sin^{-1}b)^2-2b$$
$$-2(1-a^2)^{1/2}\sin^{-1}a-a(\sin^{-1}a)^2+2a. \tag{13}$$

(ii) By means of Ch. VII. (53), we find

$$\int_a^b (\sin^{-1} x)^3 dx = h \sum_{k=0}^{n-1} \{\sin^{-1}(a+kh)\}^3]_{h \doteq 0}, \quad nh = b-a,$$

$$= b(\sin^{-1} b)^3 + 3(1-b^2)^{1/2}(\sin^{-1} b)^2 - 6b \sin^{-1} b - 6b(1-b^2)^{1/2}, \tag{14}$$

minus the expression of the same form as (14), except that b is replaced by a.

And by means of Ch. VII. (54), we obtain

$$\int_a^b (\sin^{-1} x)^4 dx = h \sum_{k=0}^{n-1} \{\sin^{-1}(a+kh)\}^4]_{h \doteq 0}, \quad nh = b-a,$$

$$= b(\sin^{-1} b)^4 + 4(1-b^2)^{1/2}(\sin^{-1} b)^3 - 12b(\sin^{-1} b)^2$$
$$- 24(1-b^2)^{1/2} \sin^{-1} b + 24b, \tag{15}$$

minus the same expression as (15), only a appearing in place of b.

2. To find the value of $\quad I = \int_a^b x^2 (\log x)^2 \, dx. \quad (16)$

Now $$I = h \sum_{k=0}^{n-1} (a+kh)^2 \log^2 (a+kh)]_{h \doteq 0}, \quad nh = b-a. \tag{17}$$

I can be obtained by evaluating

$$I_1 = h \sum_{k=0}^{n-1} (1+kh)^2 \log^2 (1+kh)]_{h=0}, \tag{18}$$

first for $nh = b-1$ and then for $nh = a-1$, and by subtracting the last result from the first.

Now $$\log (1+kh) = \sum_{\beta=1}^{\infty} (-1)^{\beta-1} \frac{(kh)^\beta}{\beta}, \quad |kh| \leqq 1,$$

and $$S = \log^2 (1+kh) = \sum_{\beta=1}^{\infty} (-1)^{\beta-1} \frac{(kh)^\beta}{\beta} \sum_{\gamma=1}^{\infty} (-1)^{\gamma-1} \frac{(kh)^\gamma}{\gamma}. \tag{19}$$

Letting $\beta + \gamma = \gamma'$, then

$$S = \sum_{\beta=1}^{\infty} \frac{1}{\beta} \sum_{\gamma=\beta+1}^{\infty} (-1)^\gamma \frac{(kh)^\gamma}{\gamma - \beta}; \tag{20}$$

and since $$\sum_{\beta=k}^{\infty} \sum_{\gamma=\beta+1}^{\infty} A_{\beta,\gamma} = \sum_{\gamma=k+1}^{\infty} \sum_{\beta=k}^{\gamma-1} A_{\beta,\gamma}, \tag{21}$$

$$S = \sum_{\beta=2}^{\infty} (-1)^\beta \frac{(kh)^\beta}{\beta} \sum_{\gamma=1}^{\beta-1} \frac{\beta}{\gamma(\beta-\gamma)}. \tag{22}$$

But $$\sum_{\gamma=1}^{\beta-1} \frac{\beta}{\gamma(\beta-\gamma)} = \sum_{\gamma=1}^{\beta-1} \frac{1}{\gamma} + \sum_{\gamma=1}^{\beta-1} \frac{1}{\beta-\gamma}.$$

Letting in the second summation $\beta - \gamma = \gamma'$, we have

$$\sum_{\gamma=1}^{\beta-1} \frac{\beta}{\gamma(\beta-\gamma)} = 2 \sum_{\gamma=1}^{\beta-1} \frac{1}{\gamma},$$

and (22) becomes $$S = 2 \sum_{\beta=2}^{\infty} (-1)^\beta \frac{(kh)^\beta}{\beta} \sum_{\gamma=1}^{\beta-1} \frac{1}{\gamma}. \tag{23}$$

Applying (23) to (18) gives

$$I_1 = 2h\sum_{k=0}^{n-1}(1+kh)^2\sum_{\beta=2}^{\infty}(-1)^\beta\frac{(kh)^\beta}{\beta}\sum_{\gamma=1}^{\beta-1}\frac{1}{\gamma}. \tag{24}$$

We may write

$$I_1 = 2h\sum_{\beta=2}^{\infty}\frac{(-1)^\beta}{\beta}\sum_{\gamma=1}^{\beta-1}\frac{1}{\gamma}\sum_{k=0}^{n-1}k^\beta h^\beta(1+kh)^2\Big]_{h\doteq 0}$$

$$=2\sum_{\beta=2}^{\infty}\frac{(-1)^\beta}{\beta}\left[\frac{(b-1)^{\beta+1}}{\beta+1}+\frac{2(b-1)^{\beta+2}}{\beta+2}+\frac{(b-1)^{\beta+3}}{\beta+3}\right]\sum_{\gamma=1}^{\beta-1}\frac{1}{\gamma} \tag{25}$$

$$=2\sum_{\beta=2}^{\infty}(-1)^\beta\left[\left(\frac{1}{\beta}-\frac{1}{\beta+1}\right)(b-1)^{\beta+1}+\left(\frac{1}{\beta}-\frac{1}{\beta+2}\right)(b-1)^{\beta+2}\right.$$

$$\left.+\tfrac{1}{3}\left(\frac{1}{\beta}-\frac{1}{\beta+3}\right)(b-1)^{\beta+3}\right]\sum_{\gamma=1}^{\beta-1}\frac{1}{\gamma} \tag{26}$$

$$=\tfrac{2}{3}(b^3-1)\sum_{\beta=2}^{\infty}\frac{(-1)^\beta}{\beta}(b-1)^\beta\sum_{\gamma=1}^{\beta-1}\frac{1}{\gamma}-2\sum_{\beta=2}^{\infty}\frac{(-1)^\beta}{\beta+1}(b-1)^{\beta+1}\sum_{\gamma=1}^{\beta-1}\frac{1}{\gamma}$$

$$-2\sum_{\beta=2}^{\infty}\frac{(-1)^\beta}{\beta+2}(b-1)^{\beta+2}\sum_{\gamma=1}^{\beta-1}\frac{1}{\gamma}-\tfrac{2}{3}\sum_{\beta=2}^{\infty}\frac{(-1)^\beta}{\beta+3}(b-1)^{\beta+3}\sum_{\gamma=1}^{\beta-1}\frac{1}{\gamma} \tag{27}$$

$$=\tfrac{1}{3}(b^3-1)\log^2 b+2\sum_{\beta=3}^{\infty}\frac{(-1)^\beta}{\beta}(b-1)^\beta\sum_{\gamma=1}^{\beta-2}\frac{1}{\gamma}$$

$$-2\sum_{\beta=4}^{\infty}\frac{(b-1)^\beta}{\beta}(b-1)^\beta\sum_{\gamma=1}^{\beta-3}\frac{1}{\gamma}+\tfrac{2}{3}\sum_{\beta=5}^{\infty}\frac{(-1)^\beta}{\beta}(b-1)^\beta\sum_{\gamma=1}^{\beta-4}\frac{1}{\gamma} \tag{28}$$

$$=\tfrac{1}{3}(b^3-1)\log^2 b+2\sum_{\beta=3}^{\infty}\frac{(-1)^\beta}{\beta}(b-1)^\beta\sum_{\gamma=1}^{\beta-1}\frac{1}{\beta}$$

$$-2\sum_{\beta=3}^{\infty}(-1)^\beta(b-1)^\beta\frac{1}{\beta(\beta-1)}-2\sum_{\beta=4}^{\infty}\frac{(-1)^\beta}{\beta}(b-1)^\beta\sum_{\gamma=1}^{\beta-1}\frac{1}{\beta}$$

$$+2\sum_{\beta=4}^{\infty}\frac{(-1)^\beta}{\beta}(b-1)^\beta\left(\frac{1}{\beta-1}+\frac{1}{\beta-2}\right)+\tfrac{2}{3}\sum_{\beta=5}^{\infty}\frac{(-1)^\beta}{\beta}(b-1)^\beta\sum_{\gamma=1}^{\beta-1}\frac{1}{\gamma}$$

$$-\tfrac{2}{3}\sum_{\beta=5}^{\infty}\frac{(-1)^\beta}{\beta}(b-1)^\beta\left(\frac{1}{\beta-1}+\frac{1}{\beta-2}+\frac{1}{\beta-3}\right) \tag{29}$$

$$=\tfrac{1}{3}b^3\log^2 b-\tfrac{1}{3}(b-1)^2+\tfrac{1}{3}(b-1)^3-\tfrac{1}{18}(b-1)^4$$

$$-\tfrac{2}{3}\sum_{\beta=5}^{\infty}\frac{(-1)^\beta}{\beta}(b-1)^\beta\left(\frac{1}{\beta-1}-\frac{2}{\beta-2}+\frac{1}{\beta-3}\right) \tag{30}$$

$$=\tfrac{1}{3}b^3\log^2 b-\tfrac{1}{3}(b-1)^2+\tfrac{1}{3}(b-1)^3-\tfrac{2}{3}\sum_{\beta=4}^{\infty}\frac{(-1)^\beta}{\beta}(b-1)^\beta$$

$$\left(\frac{1}{\beta-1}-\frac{2}{\beta-2}+\frac{1}{\beta-3}\right). \tag{31}$$

Now $$\sum_{\beta=4}^{\infty}\frac{(-1)^\beta}{\beta}(b-1)^\beta\left(\frac{1}{\beta-1}-\frac{2}{\beta-2}+\frac{1}{\beta-3}\right)=\tfrac{1}{3}\sum_{\beta=4}^{\infty}\frac{(-1)^{\beta-1}}{\beta}(b-1)^\beta$$

$$-(b-1)\sum_{\beta=4}^{\infty}\frac{(-1)^{\beta-1}}{\beta-1}(b-1)^{\beta-1}+(b-1)^2\sum_{\beta=4}^{\infty}\frac{(-1)^{\beta-1}}{\beta-2}(b-1)^{\beta-2}$$

$$-\tfrac{1}{3}(b-1)^3\sum_{\beta=4}^{\infty}\frac{(-1)^{\beta-1}}{\beta-3}(b-1)^{\beta-3}$$

$$=\tfrac{1}{3}b^3\log b-\tfrac{1}{3}(b-1)-\tfrac{5}{6}(b-1)^2+\tfrac{7}{18}(b-1)^3. \tag{32}$$

Applying (32) to (31), we obtain

$$I_1=\tfrac{1}{3}b^3\log^2 b-\tfrac{2}{9}b^3\log b+\tfrac{2}{9}(b-1)+\tfrac{5}{9}(b-1)^2$$
$$-\tfrac{7}{27}(b-1)^3-\tfrac{1}{3}(b-1)^2+\tfrac{1}{3}(b-1)^3$$
$$=\tfrac{1}{3}b^3\log^2 b-\tfrac{2}{9}b^3\log b+\tfrac{2}{27}b^3-\tfrac{2}{27}, \tag{33}$$

and finally

$$I=\tfrac{1}{3}b^3\log^2 b-\tfrac{2}{9}b^3\log b+\tfrac{2}{27}b^3-\tfrac{1}{3}a^3\log^2 a+\tfrac{2}{9}a^3\log a-\tfrac{2}{27}a^3. \tag{34}$$

3. To find the value of

$$I=\int_a^b x^p e^{mx}\,dx$$

$$=h\sum_{k\neq 0}^{n-1}(a+kh)^p e^{m(a+kh)}\Big]_{h\doteq 0},\quad nh=b-a,\ 0<b\leqq 2,\ 0<a\leqq 2. \tag{35}$$

In evaluating (52), we shall make use of the method of Finite Differences.

Letting $$S=\sum_{k=0}^{n-1}(a+kh)^p e^{m(a+kh)} \tag{36}$$

and $$S_1=e^{-ma}S, \tag{37}$$

then $$S_1=\sum_{k=0}^{n-1}u_k t^k, \tag{38}$$

where $$u_k=(a+kh)^p\quad\text{and}\quad t=e^{mh}.$$

Subtracting tS_1 from S_1 and designating

$$u_{k+1}-u_k\ \text{ by }\ \Delta' u_k,$$

and in general $$\Delta^{(r-1)}u_{k+1}-\Delta^{(r-1)}u_k\ \text{ by }\ \Delta^{(r)}u_k,$$

we have $$(1-t)S_1-u_0=\sum_{k=0}^{n-2}\Delta' u_k t^{k+1}-u_{n-1}t^n. \tag{39}$$

Subtracting the product of (39) by t from (39) gives

$$(1-t)^2S_1-(1-t)u_0-t\Delta' u_0=\sum_{k=0}^{n-3}t^{k+2}\Delta'' u_k-t^n(\overline{1-t}\,u_{n-1}+\Delta' u_{n-2}). \tag{40}$$

Subtracting next from (40) its product by t, we have

$$(1-t)^3S_1-(1-t)^2u_0-t(1-t)\Delta'u_0-t^2\Delta''u_0$$
$$=\sum_{k=0}^{n-4}t^{k+3}\Delta''u_k-t^n\left[(1-t)^2u_{n-1}+(1-t)\Delta'u_{n-2}+\Delta''u_{n-3}\right]. \quad (41)$$

Continuing this process, we obtain

$$(1-t)^{p+1}S_1-\sum_{k=0}^{p}t^k(1-t)^{p-k}\Delta^{(k)}u_0$$
$$=\sum_{k=0}^{n-p-2}t^{p+k-1}\Delta^{(p+1)}u_k-t^n\sum_{k=0}^{p}(1-t)^{p-k}\Delta^{(k)}u_{n-1-k}, \quad (42)$$

where $\Delta^0u_k=u_k$;

and since $\Delta^{(p+1)}u_k=0$,

therefore
$$S_1=\sum_{k=0}^{p}\frac{t^k}{(1-t)^{k+1}}\Delta^{(k)}u_0-t^n\sum_{k=0}^{p}\frac{1}{(1-t)^{k+1}}\Delta^{(k)}u_{n-1-k} \quad (43)$$

and

$$I=hS]_{h\doteq 0}=he^{ma}S_1]_{h\doteq 0},\ \text{by (37)},$$
$$=he^{ma}\sum_{k=0}^{p}\frac{t^k}{(1-t)^{k+1}}\Delta^{(k)}u_0-he^{ma}t^n\sum_{k=0}^{p}\frac{1}{(1-t)^{k+1}}\Delta^{(k)}u_{n-1-k}\Big]_{h\doteq 0}, \quad (44)$$

Now $u_0=a^p,\quad \Delta'u_0=\binom{p}{1}ha^{p-1},\ \ldots,\ \Delta^{(k)}u_0=k!\binom{p}{k}h^ka^{p-k}$

and $u_{n-1}=b^p,\quad \Delta'u_{n-2}=\binom{p}{1}hb^{p-1},\ \ldots,\ \Delta^{(k)}u_{n-1-k}=k!\binom{p}{k}h^kb^{p-k}.$

We then have

$$h\frac{t^k}{(1-t)^{k+1}}\Delta^{(k)}u_0\Big]_{h\doteq 0}=(-1)^{k-1}k!\binom{p}{k}\frac{h^{k+1}e^{mkh}a^{p-k}}{h^{k+1}m^{k+1}P_r}\Big]_{h\doteq 0}$$
$$=(-1)^{k-1}k!\binom{p}{k}\frac{1}{m^{k+1}}a^{p-k}$$

and
$$h\frac{1}{(1-t)^{k+1}}\Delta^{(k)}u_{n-1-k}\Big]_{h\doteq 0}=(-1)^{k-1}k!\binom{p}{k}\frac{h^{k+1}b^{p-k}}{h^{k+1}m^{k+1}P_r}\Big]_{h\doteq 0}$$
$$=(-1)^{k-1}k!\binom{p}{k}\frac{b^{p-k}}{m^{k+1}},$$

since
$$P_r=\left\{\sum_{r=0}^{\infty}\frac{(mh)^r}{(r+1)!}\right\}^{k+1}\Big]_{h\doteq 0}=1.$$

Therefore
$$I=\sum_{k=0}^{p}(-1)^kk!\binom{p}{k}\frac{1}{m^{k+1}}\left[e^{mb}b^{p-k}-e^{ma}a^{p-k}\right]. \quad (45)$$

We might have developed (35) first for $nh=b-1$ and then for $nh=a-1$. But the work would not have been much simplified thereby.

CHAPTER XIV.

DERANGED SERIES.

It has been shown * that if the terms of a conditionally convergent series are deranged, the sum of the resulting series is, in general, different from the sum of the given series, but no method for finding the sum of a deranged series seems to have been given.

1. We shall consider the sum of the series obtained by deranging

$$\sum_{k=0}^{\infty}(-1)^k\frac{1}{b+kh}, \tag{1}$$

so that m positive terms are followed by n negative terms, that is, we shall find

$$S=\sum_{k=0}^{\infty}\left[\sum_{a=0}^{m-1}\frac{1}{b+2kmh+2ah}-\sum_{a=0}^{n-1}\frac{1}{b+2knh+(2a+1)h}\right], \tag{2}$$

where b and h are positive integers, and without loss of generality it may be assumed that $b<h$.

Let now

$$R=\sum_{k=0}^{\infty}S_k r^{2mnkh}, \tag{3}$$

where S_k is the expression within the brackets in (2); then

$$S=R]_{r=1}.$$

If R is uniformly convergent, we may write

$$R=\sum_{a=0}^{m-1}\frac{1}{r^{n(b+2ah)}}\sum_{k=0}^{\infty}\frac{r^{n(b+2kmh+2ah)}}{b+2kmh+2ah}$$

$$-\sum_{a=0}^{n-1}\frac{1}{r^{m(b+\overline{2a+1}\,h}}\sum_{k=0}^{\infty}\frac{r^{m(b+2knh+\overline{2a+1}\,h)}}{b+2knh+(2a+1)h}. \tag{4}$$

Let now

$$\sum_{k=0}^{\infty}\frac{r^{n(b+2kmh+2ah)}}{b+2kmh+2ah}=P_{k,a} \tag{5}$$

and

$$\sum_{k=0}^{\infty}\frac{r^{m(b+2knh+\overline{2a+1}\,h)}}{b+2knh+(2a+1)h}=Q_{k,a}. \tag{6}$$

* Dirichlet, *Werke*, vol. i. p. 318.—Riemann, *Werke*, p. 235.—Scheibner, *Ueber Unendliche Reihen und deren Konvergenz.*—Pringsheim, *Mathematische Annalen*, vol. 22, p. 455.—Pascal, *Repertorium der höheren Mathematik*, vol. i. p. 425.

Then $$\frac{dP_{k,a}}{dr}=\frac{nr^{(b+2ah)n-1}}{1-r^{2mnh}}$$

and $$P_{k,a}=n\int_0^r \frac{r^{(b+2ah)n-1}}{1-r^{2mnh}}\,dr. \tag{7}$$

Letting $(b+2ah)n-1=2mnhp_a+q_a$, $q_a<2mnh$, we have

$$\frac{r^{(b+2ah)n-1}}{1-r^{2mnh}}=\frac{r^{q_a}}{1-r^{2mnh}}-\sum_{\beta=0}^{p_a-1} r^{2mnh(p_a-\beta-1)+q_a}; \tag{8}$$

and if we write $$\frac{r^{q_a}}{1-r^{2mnh}}=\sum_{k=1}^{2mnh}\frac{A_k}{\rho_k-r},\quad \text{where } \rho_k=e^{\frac{k\pi i}{mnh}}, \tag{9}$$

then $$A_k=\rho_k{}^{q_a}\left.\frac{\rho_k-r}{1-r^{2mnh}}\right]_{r=\rho_k}=\frac{\rho_k{}^{q_a+1}}{2mnh\rho_k{}^{2mnh}};$$

and since $$\rho_k{}^{2mnh}=1,$$

$$A_k=\frac{1}{2mnh}\rho_k{}^{(b+2ah)n}; \tag{10}$$

therefore $$P_{k,a}=-\frac{1}{2mh}\sum_{k=1}^{2mnh}\rho_k{}^{(b+2ah)n}\log\frac{\rho_k-r}{\rho_k}$$

$$-n\sum_{\beta=0}^{\left[\frac{(b+2ah)n-1}{2mnh}\right]}\frac{r^{(b+2ah-\overline{\beta+1}\,2mh)n}}{b+2ah-(\beta+1)2mh}. \tag{11}$$

Now $Q_{k,a}$ is of the same form as $P_{k,a}$, except that m and n are interchanged and that $2a+1$ is written in place of $2a$.

Then (4) becomes

$$R=\frac{1}{2nh}\sum_{k=1}^{2mnh}\log\frac{\rho_k-r}{\rho_k}\sum_{a=0}^{n-1}\left(\frac{\rho_k}{r}\right)^{(b+\overline{2a+1}\,h)m} \tag{12}$$

$$-\frac{1}{2mh}\sum_{k=1}^{2mnh}\log\frac{\rho_k-r}{\rho_k}\sum_{a=0}^{m-1}\left(\frac{\rho_k}{r}\right)^{(b+2ah)n} \tag{13}$$

$$+m\sum_{a=0}^{n-1}\sum_{\beta=0}^{\left[\frac{(b+\overline{2a+1}\,h)m-1}{2mnh}\right]-1}\frac{1}{(b+\overline{2a+1}\,h-\overline{\beta+1}\,2nh)m}\,\frac{1}{r^{(\beta+1)2mnh}} \tag{14}$$

$$-n\sum_{a=0}^{m-1}\sum_{\beta=0}^{\left[\frac{(b+2ah)n-1}{2mnh}\right]-1}\frac{1}{(b+2ah-\overline{\beta+1}\,2mh)n}\,\frac{1}{r^{(\beta+1)2mnh}}. \tag{15}$$

Now when $r=1$, the terms in (12) and (13) corresponding to $k=2mnh$ cancel each other, and there remains

$$S_1=\frac{1}{2nh}\sum_{k=1}^{2mnh-1}\log\frac{\rho_k-r}{\rho_k}(\rho_k r^{-1})^{(b+h)m}\left.\frac{1-(\rho_k r^{-1})^{2mnh}}{1-(\rho_k r^{-1})^{2mh}}\right]_{r=1}$$

$$-\frac{1}{2mh}\sum_{k=1}^{2mnh-1}\log\frac{\rho_k-r}{\rho_k}(\rho_k r^{-1})^{bn}\left.\frac{1-(\rho_k r^{-1})^{2mnh}}{1-(\rho_k r^{-1})^{2nh}}\right]_{r=1}. \tag{16}$$

But for $r=1$, $1-\rho_k{}^{2mnh}=0$ and $1-\rho_k{}^{2mh}=0$,

unless k is a multiple of n, in which case

$$\left.\frac{1-(\rho_k r^{-1})^{2mnh}}{1-(\rho_k r^{-1})^{2mh}}\right]_{r=1}=\frac{2mnh}{2mh}=n. \tag{17}$$

Then (16) becomes

$$S_1=\frac{1}{2h}\left[\sum_{k=1}^{2mh-1}\rho_{kn}^{(b+h)m}\log\frac{\rho_{kn}-1}{\rho_{kn}}-\sum_{k=1}^{2nh-1}\rho_{km}^{bn}\log\frac{\rho_{km}-1}{\rho_{km}}\right] \tag{18}$$

or

$$\begin{aligned}S_1=\frac{1}{2h}\Bigg[&\sum_{k=1}^{2mh-1}(-1)^k\cos\frac{kb\pi}{h}\log\sin\frac{k\pi}{2mh}\\&-\sum_{k=1}^{2nh-1}\cos\frac{kb\pi}{h}\log\sin\frac{k\pi}{2nh}+\left\{\sum_{k=1}^{2mh-1}(-1)^k\cos\frac{kb\pi}{h}\right.\\&\left.-\sum_{k=1}^{2nh-1}\cos\frac{kb\pi}{h}\right\}\log 2-\frac{\pi}{2}\left\{\sum_{k=1}^{2mh-}(-1)^k\left(1-\frac{k}{mh}\right)\sin\frac{kb\pi}{h}\right.\\&\left.-\sum_{k=1}^{2nh-1}\left(1-\frac{k}{nh}\right)\sin\frac{kb\pi}{h}\right\}\Bigg].\end{aligned} \tag{19}$$

2. To reduce the summations in (19), we proceed as follows: Letting $p=2mh-1$ and $x=\dfrac{b\pi}{h}$ in

$$\sum_{k=1}^{p}(-1)^k\cos kx=\tfrac{1}{2}(-1)^p\cos\frac{2p+1}{2}x\sec\tfrac{1}{2}x-\tfrac{1}{2},$$

and $p=2nh-1$ and $x=\dfrac{b\pi}{h}$ in

$$\sum_{k=1}^{p}\cos kx=\cos\frac{p+1}{2}x\sin\frac{p}{2}x\operatorname{cosec}\tfrac{1}{2}x,$$

then

$$\sum_{k=1}^{2mh-1}(-1)^k\cos\frac{kb\pi}{h}=-1 \tag{20}$$

and

$$\sum_{k=1}^{2nh-1}\cos\frac{kb\pi}{h}=-1. \tag{21}$$

Again, letting $p=2mh-1$ and $x=\dfrac{b\pi}{h}$ in

$$\sum_{k=1}^{p}(-1)^k\sin kx=\tfrac{1}{2}(-1)^p\sin\frac{2p+1}{2}x\sec\tfrac{1}{2}x-\tfrac{1}{2}\tan\tfrac{1}{2}x,$$

and $p=2nh-1$ and $x=\dfrac{b\pi}{h}$ in

$$\sum_{k=1}^{p}\sin kx=\sin\frac{p+1}{2}x\sin\frac{p}{2}x\operatorname{cosec}\tfrac{1}{2}x,$$

we have
$$\sum_{k=1}^{2mh-1} (-1)^k \sin\frac{kb\pi}{h} = 0 \tag{22}$$

and
$$\sum_{k=1}^{2nh-1} \sin\frac{kb\pi}{h} = 0. \tag{23}$$

The results (20) and (22) can also be obtained in the following way:

Let $S_2 = \sum_{k=0}^{2mh-1} (-1)^k \sin\frac{kb\pi}{h}$ and $S_3 = \sum_{k=0}^{2mh-1} (-1)^k \cos\frac{kb\pi}{h}$;

then
$$S_3 + iS_2 = \sum_{k=0}^{2mh-1} (-1)^k \left(\cos\frac{kb\pi}{h} + i\sin\frac{kb\pi}{h}\right)$$
$$= \sum_{k=0}^{2mh-1} (-1)^k \left(e^{\frac{b\pi i}{h}}\right)^k,$$

and
$$S_3 - iS_2 = \sum_{k=0}^{2mh-1} (-1)^k \left(e^{-\frac{b\pi i}{h}}\right)^k.$$

Letting now $e^{\frac{b\pi i}{h}} = r$, then
$$\sum_{k=0}^{2mh-1} (-1)^k r^k = \frac{1 - r^{2mh}}{1+r};$$

and since
$$r^{2mh} = r^{-2mh} = 1,$$
$$S_3 + iS_2 = 0 \quad \text{and} \quad S_3 - iS_2 = 0, \quad \text{unless } b = (2g+1)h.$$

Hence
$$S_3 = S_2 = 0 \quad \text{and} \quad \sum_{k=1}^{2mh-1} (-1)^k \cos\frac{kb\pi}{h} = -1.$$

If $b = (2g+1)h$, then, since
$$\sin(2g+1)k\pi = 0, \quad S_2 = 0,$$

and since
$$\cos(2g+1)k\pi = (-1)^k, \quad S_3 = \sum_{k=0}^{2mh-1} (-1)^{2k} = 2mh.$$

In a similar way (21) and (23) are derived. These results may also be obtained by replacing b by $b+h$ in (20) and (22).

We shall next evaluate
$$S_4 = \sum_{k=1}^{2mh-1} (-1)^k k \sin\frac{kb\pi}{h}. \tag{24}$$

Now
$$S_4 = \frac{d}{dx} \sum_{k=1}^{2mh-1} (-1)^{k-1} \cos kx$$
$$= \frac{d}{dx}\left(\tfrac{1}{2} + \tfrac{1}{2}\cos\frac{4mh-1}{2} x \sec x\, \tfrac{1}{2}x\right), \quad x = \frac{b\pi}{h},$$
$$= mh \tan\frac{b\pi}{2h}$$
$$= 0, \text{ if } b = 2gh. \tag{25}$$

Similarly
$$\sum_{k=1}^{2nh-1} k\sin\frac{kb\pi}{h} = -nh\cot\frac{b\pi}{2h}$$
$$=0, \text{ if } b=(2g+1)h, \tag{26}$$

and
$$\sum_{k=1}^{2mh-1} (-1)^k k\cos\frac{kb\pi}{h} = -mh. \tag{27}$$

Applying (20)–(23) and (25)–(27) to (19), we obtain

$$S_1 = \frac{1}{2h}\left[\sum_{k=1}^{2mh-1}(-1)^k\cos\frac{kb\pi}{h}\log\sin\frac{k\pi}{2mh} - \sum_{k=1}^{2nh-1}\cos\frac{kb\pi}{h}\log\sin\frac{k\pi}{2nh}\right]. \tag{28}$$

Therefore

$$S = m\sum_{\alpha=0}^{n-1}\sum_{\beta=0}^{\left[\frac{(b+\overline{2\alpha+1}\,h)m-1}{2mnh}\right]-1}\frac{1}{(b+\overline{2\alpha+1}\,h-\overline{\beta+1}\,2nh)m}$$
$$-n\sum_{\alpha=0}^{m-1}\sum_{\beta=0}^{\left[\frac{(b+2\alpha h)n-1}{2mnh}\right]-1}\frac{1}{(b+2\alpha h-\overline{\beta+1}\,2mh)n}+S_1, \tag{29}$$

where S_1 is the value in (28).

If $m=n=1$, then, from (29),

$$S = \frac{1}{2h}\left[\sum_{k=1}^{2h-1}(-1)^k\cos\frac{kb\pi}{h}\log\sin\frac{k\pi}{2h} - \sum_{k=1}^{2h-1}\cos\frac{kb\pi}{h}\log\sin\frac{k\pi}{2h}\right]+\frac{\pi}{2h}\operatorname{cosec}\frac{b\pi}{h}. \tag{30}$$

Now, within the brackets of (30), the terms of the two summations corresponding to the same even values of k cancel each other, and the sum of the remaining terms is equal to

$$-2\sum_{k=0}^{h-1}\cos\frac{2k+1}{h}b\pi\log\sin\frac{2k+1}{2h}\pi. \tag{31}$$

Denoting by P_k the expression under the summation sign in (31), then if h is even

$$\sum_{k=0}^{h-1}P_k = \sum_{k=0}^{\frac{h-2}{2}}P_k + \sum_{k=\frac{h}{2}}^{h-1}P_k$$
$$=2\sum_{k=0}^{\frac{h-2}{2}}P_k;$$

and when h is odd,
$$\sum_{k=0}^{h-1}P_k = \sum_{k=0}^{\frac{h-3}{2}}P_k + \sum_{k=\frac{h+1}{2}}^{h-1}P_k$$
$$=2\sum_{k=0}^{\frac{h-3}{2}}P_k.$$

We then obtain

$$S=\frac{\pi}{2h}\operatorname{cosec}\frac{b\pi}{h}-\frac{2}{h}\sum_{k=0}^{\left[\frac{h-2}{2}\right]}\cos\frac{2k+1}{h}b\pi\log\sin\frac{2k+1}{2h}\pi, \tag{32}$$

which is the value of (1) and the same as Ch. IX. (156).

From (29) the following is evident: If the terms of a series like (1) are arranged in groups so that a group of positive terms is followed by a group of negative terms, each group containing the same number of terms, then the sum of the series is the same whatever the number of terms in each group might be and is equal to the sum of the given series.

3. We shall now evaluate (29) for $b=1$, $h=3$, and then for $b=1$, $h=4$. That is, we shall find the sum of the series obtained by letting n negative terms follow m positive terms throughout

$$\sum_{h=0}^{\infty}(-1)^k\frac{1}{1+3k} \tag{33}$$

and

$$\sum_{k=0}^{\infty}(-1)^k\frac{1}{1+4k}. \tag{34}$$

(i) Applying (29) to (33), we have

$$S=\frac{\pi\sqrt{3}}{9}+\frac{1}{6}\left[\sum_{k=1}^{6m-1}(-1)^k\cos\frac{k\pi}{3}\log\sin\frac{k\pi}{6m}-\sum_{k=1}^{6n-1}\cos\frac{k\pi}{3}\log\sin\frac{k\pi}{6n}\right]. \tag{35}$$

Denoting in (35) the summations in order by S_1 and S_2 respectively, we have

$$S_1=\sum_{k=1}^{2m}(-1)^{3k-2}\cos\frac{3k-2}{3}\pi\log\sin\frac{3k-2}{6m}\pi$$

$$+\sum_{k=1}^{2m}(-1)^{3k-1}\cos\frac{3k-1}{3}\pi\log\sin\frac{3k-1}{6m}\pi$$

$$+\sum_{k=1}^{2m-1}(-1)^{3k}\cos\frac{3k}{3}\pi\log\sin\frac{3k}{6m}\pi$$

$$=\sum_{k=1}^{2m-1}\log\sin\frac{k\pi}{2m}-\frac{1}{2}\sum_{k=1}^{2m}\log\sin\frac{3k-2}{6m}\pi-\frac{1}{2}\sum_{k=1}^{2m}\log\sin\frac{3k-1}{6m}\pi. \tag{36}$$

But

$$\sum_{k=1}^{2m-1}\log\sin\frac{k\pi}{2m}=\frac{3}{2}\sum_{k=1}^{2m-1}\log\sin\frac{k\pi}{2m}-\frac{1}{2}\sum_{k=1}^{2m-1}\log\sin\frac{k\pi}{2m}. \tag{37}$$

Applying (37) to (36), we obtain

$$S_1=\frac{3}{2}\sum_{k=1}^{2m-1}\log\sin\frac{k\pi}{2m}-\frac{1}{2}\sum_{k=1}^{6m-1}\log\sin\frac{k\pi}{6m}. \tag{38}$$

We may write

$$S_2 = \sum_{k=1}^{2n} \cos\frac{3k-2}{3}\pi \log\sin\frac{3k-2}{6n}\pi + \sum_{k=1}^{2n}\cos\frac{3k-1}{3}\pi\log\sin\frac{3k-1}{6n}\pi$$

$$+\sum_{k=1}^{2n-1}\cos\frac{3k}{3}\pi\log\sin\frac{3k}{6n}\pi \tag{39}$$

$$=\frac{3}{2}\sum_{k=1}^{2n-1}(-1)^k\log\sin\frac{k\pi}{2n}-\frac{1}{2}\sum_{k=1}^{2n-1}(-1)^k\log\sin\frac{k\pi}{2n}$$

$$-\frac{1}{2}\sum_{k=1}^{2n}(-1)^k\log\sin\frac{3k-2}{6n}\pi+\frac{1}{2}\sum_{k=1}^{2n}(-1)^k\log\sin\frac{3k-1}{6n}\pi$$

$$=\frac{3}{2}\sum_{k=1}^{2n-1}(-1)^k\log\sin\frac{k\pi}{2n}-\frac{1}{2}\sum_{k=1}^{6n-1}(-1)^k\log\sin\frac{k\pi}{6n} \tag{40}$$

$$=3\sum_{k=1}^{n-1}\log\sin\frac{k\pi}{n}-\frac{3}{2}\sum_{k=1}^{2n-1}\log\sin\frac{k\pi}{n}-\sum_{k=1}^{3n-1}\log\sin\frac{k\pi}{3n}$$

$$+\frac{1}{2}\sum_{k=1}^{6n-1}\log\sin\frac{k\pi}{6n}. \tag{41}$$

To reduce (38) and (41) we first evaluate

$$S_3=\sum_{k=1}^{pn-1}\log\sin\frac{k\pi}{pn}. \tag{42}$$

Now $$\sin\frac{k\pi}{pn}=\frac{i}{2}e^{-\frac{k\pi i}{pn}}\left(1-e^{\frac{2k\pi i}{pn}}\right)$$

and $$\log\sin\frac{k\pi}{pn}=\log i-\log 2-\frac{k\pi i}{pn}+\log\left(1-e^{\frac{2k\pi i}{pn}}\right).$$

We then have

$$S_3=(pn-1)\frac{\pi i}{2}-(pn-1)\log 2-(pn-1)\frac{\pi i}{2}+\log\prod_{k=1}^{pn-1}\left(1-e^{\frac{2k\pi i}{pn}}\right); \tag{43}$$

and since $$x-e^{\frac{2k\pi i}{pn}} \text{ is a factor of } x^{pn}-1,$$

therefore $$\prod_{k=1}^{pn-1}\left(1-e^{\frac{2k\pi i}{pn}}\right)=\left.\frac{x^{pn}-1}{x-1}\right]_{x=1}=pn$$

and $$S_3=\log(pn)-(pn-1)\log 2. \tag{44}$$

Applying (44) to (41) gives

$$S_1=-\tfrac{1}{2}\log(6m)+\tfrac{1}{2}(6m-1)\log 2+\tfrac{3}{2}\log(2m)$$

$$-\tfrac{3}{2}(2m-1)\log 2=\log\frac{4m}{\sqrt{3}} \tag{45}$$

and $$S_2=\tfrac{1}{2}\log(6n)-\tfrac{1}{2}(6n-1)\log 2-\log(3n)+(3n-1)\log 2$$

$$-\tfrac{3}{2}\log(2n)+\tfrac{3}{2}(2n-1)\log 2+3\log n$$

$$-3(n-1)\log 2=\log\frac{n}{\sqrt{3}}. \tag{46}$$

We then obtain

$$\sum_{k=0}^{\infty}(-1)^k\frac{1}{1+3k}=\frac{\pi}{9}\sqrt{3}+\frac{1}{6}\left(\log\frac{4m}{\sqrt{3}}-\log\frac{n}{\sqrt{3}}\right)$$

$$=\frac{\pi}{9}\sqrt{3}+\frac{1}{6}\log\frac{4m}{n}. \tag{47}$$

(ii) We shall next find the value of the series obtained by deranging (34). Then, by (29),

$$S=\frac{\pi}{8}\sqrt{2}+\frac{1}{8}\left[\sum_{k=1}^{8m-1}(-1)^k\cos\frac{k\pi}{4}\log\sin\frac{k\pi}{8m}-\sum_{k=1}^{8n-1}\cos\frac{k\pi}{4}\log\sin\frac{k\pi}{8n}\right]. \tag{48}$$

To evaluate (48) we separate the first summation S_1 into groups of terms corresponding to $k=4k'$, $4k'+1$, $4k'+2$, and $4k'+3$. Now, for $k=4k'+2$, the group is zero, and the sum of the remaining three groups is

$$S_1=\sum_{k=1}^{2m-1}(-1)^k\log\sin\frac{k\pi}{2m}-\tfrac{1}{2}\sqrt{2}\sum_{k=0}^{2m-1}(-1)^k\log\sin\frac{4k+1}{8m}\pi$$

$$+\tfrac{1}{2}\sqrt{2}\sum_{k=0}^{2m-1}(-1)^k\log\sin\frac{4k+3}{8m}\pi. \tag{49}$$

Denoting in (49) the summations in order by S_2, S_3 and S_4, we may write

$$S_2=-\sum_{k=1}^{2m-1}\log\sin\frac{k\pi}{2m}+2\sum_{k=1}^{m-1}\log\sin\frac{k\pi}{m}, \tag{50}$$

$$S_3=-\sum_{k=0}^{2m-1}\log\sin\frac{4k+1}{8m}\pi+2\sum_{k=0}^{m-1}\log\sin\frac{8k+1}{8m}\pi \tag{51}$$

$$=-S_{3,1}+S_{3,2}$$

$$S_4=-\sum_{k=0}^{2m-1}\log\sin\frac{4k+3}{8m}+2\sum_{k=0}^{m-1}\log\sin\frac{8k+3}{8m}\pi. \tag{52}$$

Now, by means of (44), (50) reduces to

$$S_2=-\log(2m)+(2m-1)\log 2-2(m-1)\log 2+2\log m$$

$$=\log m. \tag{53}$$

To reduce (51), we write

$$S_{3,1}=\log\prod_{k=0}^{2m-1}\left[\frac{i}{2}e^{\left(\frac{1}{4m}-\frac{4k+1}{8m}\right)\pi i}\left(e^{-\frac{\pi i}{4m}}-e^{\frac{2k\pi i}{2m}}\right)\right]. \tag{54}$$

Now $\quad e^{-\frac{\pi i}{4m}}-e^{\frac{2k\pi i}{2m}}$ is a factor of $x^{2m}-1$, when $x=e^{-\frac{\pi i}{4m}}$;

therefore

$$\prod_{k=0}^{2m-1}\left(e^{-\frac{\pi i}{4m}}-e^{\frac{2k\pi i}{2m}}\right)=\left(e^{-\frac{\pi i}{4m}}\right)^{2m}-1=e^{-\frac{\pi i}{2}}-1=\frac{\sqrt{2}}{i}e^{-\frac{\pi i}{4}} \tag{55}$$

and

$$S_{3,1}=\frac{1-4m}{2}\log 2. \tag{56}$$

In a similar way

$$S_{3,2} = \log \prod_{k=0}^{m-1} \left[\frac{i}{2} e^{\left(\frac{1}{4m} - \frac{8k+1}{8m}\right)\pi i} \left(e^{-\frac{\pi i}{4m}} - e^{\frac{2k\pi i}{m}} \right) \right], \tag{57}$$

from which $S_{3,2} = \frac{1-4m}{2} \log 2 + \log(\sqrt{2}-1)$ is obtained. (58)

Therefore

$$S_3 = \log(\sqrt{2}-1), \tag{59}$$

and similarly

$$S_4 = \log(\sqrt{2}+1). \tag{60}$$

Applying (53), (59) and (60) to (49) gives

$$S_1 = \log m + \sqrt{2} \log(\sqrt{2}+1). \tag{61}$$

Denoting the second summation in (48) by S_5, then if in S_1 in (48) n is written in place of m, we have

$$S_1 = -S_5 + 2 \sum_{k=1}^{4n-1} \cos \frac{k\pi}{2} \log \sin \frac{k\pi}{4n} \tag{62}$$

$$= -S_5 + 2 \sum_{k=1}^{2n-1} \cos k\pi \log \sin \frac{k\pi}{2n}$$

$$= -S_5 + 2 \sum_{k=1}^{2n-1} (-1)^k \log \sin \frac{k\pi}{2n} = -S_5 + 2S_6. \tag{63}$$

Now

$$S_6 = -\sum_{k=1}^{2n-1} \log \sin \frac{k\pi}{2n} + 2 \sum_{k=1}^{n-1} \log \sin \frac{k\pi}{n}, \tag{64}$$

which, by means of (44), reduces to

$$S_6 = \log n. \tag{65}$$

Applying (65) and (61) to (63), we obtain

$$S_5 = \log n - \sqrt{2} \log(\sqrt{2}+1), \tag{66}$$

and finally

$$S = \frac{\pi}{8}\sqrt{2} + \tfrac{1}{8} \log \frac{m}{n} + \tfrac{1}{4}\sqrt{2} \log(\sqrt{2}+1). \tag{67}$$

If $m = n$, then

$$\sum_{k=0}^{\infty} (-1)^k \frac{1}{1+4k} = \frac{\pi}{8}\sqrt{2} \log(\sqrt{2}+1). \tag{68}$$

In a similar way the sum of the series obtained by deranging

$$\sum_{k=0}^{\infty} (-1)^k \frac{1}{1+5k}$$

is

$$\frac{1}{10}\left(\log \frac{m}{n} + \frac{\pi}{5}\sqrt{5}\sqrt{10+2\sqrt{5}} + 2\sqrt{5} \log \frac{\sqrt{5}+1}{2} + 2 \log 2 \right). \tag{69}$$

4. While the series treated in this section do not come properly under the definition of deranged series, they are in a sense related to them.

(i) To find the value of

$$S = 1 - \frac{1}{10} + \frac{1}{11} - \frac{1}{20} + \frac{1}{21} - \frac{1}{30} + \frac{1}{31} - \dots, \tag{70}$$

which may be written symbolically thus:

$$S = \sum_{n=0}^{\infty} \frac{(-1)^n}{10\left[\frac{n+1}{2}\right] + \frac{1+(-1)^n}{2}}. \tag{71}$$

Let
$$S_x = \sum_{n=0}^{\infty} \frac{(-1)^n x^{10\left[\frac{n+1}{2}\right] + \frac{1+(-1)^n}{2}}}{10\left[\frac{n+1}{2}\right] + \frac{1+(-1)^n}{2}}; \tag{72}$$

then
$$S = S_x]_{x=1}.$$

But
$$\frac{dS_x}{dx} = \frac{1-x^9}{1-x^{10}};$$

hence
$$S = -\int_0^1 \frac{dx}{x^{10}-1} + \int_0^1 \frac{x^9\,dx}{x^{10}-1}. \tag{73}$$

Now
$$\int_0^1 \frac{dx}{x^{10}-1} = \tfrac{1}{2}\int_0^1 \frac{dx}{x^5-1} - \tfrac{1}{2}\int_0^1 \frac{dx}{x^5+1} = \tfrac{1}{2}I_2 - \tfrac{1}{2}I_1. \tag{74}$$

To find I_2, we denote in Ch. IX. (17) the terms in succession by T_1, T_2 and T_3; then, by means of Ch. IX. (48), we obtain

$$\int_0^1 T_1\,dx = \tfrac{1}{20}(\sqrt{5}-1)\log\frac{5-\sqrt{5}}{2} - \tfrac{3}{100}\pi\sqrt{10+2\sqrt{5}}, \tag{75}$$

$$\int_0^1 T_2\,dx = \tfrac{1}{20}(\sqrt{5}+1)\log\frac{5+\sqrt{5}}{2} + \tfrac{1}{100}\pi\sqrt{10-2\sqrt{5}}, \tag{76}$$

$$\int_0^1 T_3\,dx = \tfrac{1}{5}\log(1-x)]_{x=1}. \tag{77}$$

Therefore

$$\int_0^1 \frac{dx}{x^5-1} = \tfrac{1}{10}\sqrt{5}\log\frac{\sqrt{5}-1}{2} - \tfrac{1}{20}\log 5 - \frac{\pi}{100}(3\sqrt{10+2\sqrt{5}} + \sqrt{10-2\sqrt{5}}) + \tfrac{1}{5}\log(1-x)]_{x=1}; \tag{78}$$

and since
$$(3\sqrt{10+2\sqrt{5}} + \sqrt{10-2\sqrt{5}})^2 = 20(5+2\sqrt{5}),$$

$$\int_0^1 \frac{dx}{x^5-1} = \tfrac{1}{10}\sqrt{5}\log\frac{\sqrt{5}-1}{2} - \tfrac{1}{20}\log 5 - \frac{\pi}{50}\sqrt{5}\sqrt{5+2\sqrt{5}} + \tfrac{1}{5}\log(1-x)]_{x=1}. \tag{79}$$

This result can also be obtained directly from Ch. IX. (136). We then have

$$\int_0^1 \frac{dx}{x^5-1} = -\frac{\pi}{10}\cot\frac{\pi}{5} - \tfrac{1}{5}\log 2 + \tfrac{1}{5}\log(1-x)]_{x=1} + \tfrac{2}{5}\left(\cos\frac{2\pi}{5}\log\sin\frac{\pi}{5} - \cos\frac{\pi}{5}\log\sin\frac{2\pi}{5}\right),$$

which gives (79).

We also find

$$\int_0^1 \frac{dx}{x^5+1} = \frac{\pi}{50}\sqrt{5}\sqrt{10+2\sqrt{5}} + \tfrac{1}{5}\sqrt{5}\log\frac{\sqrt{5}+1}{2} + \tfrac{1}{5}\log 2. \tag{80}$$

Then, by means of (79) and (80), we obtain from (74)

$$\int_0^1 \frac{dx}{x^{10}-1} = -\frac{\pi}{100}\sqrt{5}\,(\sqrt{10+2\sqrt{5}}+\sqrt{5+2\sqrt{5}}) + \tfrac{1}{20}\sqrt{5}\log(\sqrt{5}-2)$$

$$-\tfrac{1}{40}\log 5 - \tfrac{1}{10}\log 2 + \tfrac{1}{10}\log(1-x)]_{x=1}. \tag{81}$$

But $\sqrt{10+2\sqrt{5}}+\sqrt{5+2\sqrt{5}} = \sqrt{5+2\sqrt{5}}+\sqrt{5-2\sqrt{5}}+\sqrt{5+2\sqrt{5}}$;

and since $(2\sqrt{5+2\sqrt{5}}+\sqrt{5-2\sqrt{5}})^2 = 5(5+2\sqrt{5})$,

therefore

$$\int_0^1 \frac{dx}{x^{10}-1} = -\frac{\pi}{20}\sqrt{5+2\sqrt{5}} + \tfrac{1}{20}\sqrt{5}\log(\sqrt{5}-2) - \tfrac{1}{40}\log 5$$

$$-\tfrac{1}{10}\log 2 + \tfrac{1}{10}\log(1-x)]_{x=1}. \tag{82}$$

This result could have been found directly from Ch. IX. (136).

Next $$\int_0^1 \frac{x^9\,dx}{x^{10}-1} = \tfrac{1}{10}\log 10 + \tfrac{1}{10}\log(x-1)]_{x=1} - \tfrac{1}{10}\log(-1)$$

$$= \tfrac{1}{10}\log 2 + \tfrac{1}{10}\log 5 + \tfrac{1}{10}\log(1-x)]_{x=1}. \tag{83}$$

Applying (82) and (83) to (73), we obtain

$$S = \frac{\pi}{20}\sqrt{5+2\sqrt{5}} - \tfrac{1}{20}\sqrt{5}\log(\sqrt{5}-2) + \tfrac{1}{8}\log 5 + \tfrac{1}{5}\log 2. \tag{84}$$

(ii) To find the value of

$$S = 1 - \frac{1}{10} - \frac{1}{11} + \frac{1}{20} + \frac{1}{21} - \frac{1}{30} - \frac{1}{31} + \dots \tag{85}$$

$$= \sum_{n=0}^{\infty} \frac{(-1)^{\left[\frac{n+1}{2}\right]}}{10\left[\frac{n+1}{2}\right] + \frac{1+(-1)^n}{2}}. \tag{86}$$

Following the method in (i), we find

$$S = \int_0^1 \frac{dx}{x^{10}+1} - \int_0^1 \frac{x^9\,dx}{x^{10}+1}. \tag{87}$$

Now $$\int_0^1 \frac{x^9 dx}{x^{10}+1} = \tfrac{1}{10}\log 2, \tag{88}$$

and by means of Ch. IX. (116), we obtain

$$\int_0^1 \frac{dx}{x^{10}+1} = \frac{\pi}{20}\operatorname{cosec}\frac{\pi}{10} + \frac{1}{5}\left(\cos\frac{\pi}{10}\log\cot\frac{\pi}{20} + \sin\frac{\pi}{5}\log\cot\frac{3\pi}{20}\right)$$

$$= \tfrac{1}{20}(\sqrt{5}+1)\pi + \tfrac{1}{20}\sqrt{10+2\sqrt{5}}\log(\sqrt{5}+1+\sqrt{5+2\sqrt{5}})$$

$$+ \tfrac{1}{20}\sqrt{10-2\sqrt{5}}\log(\sqrt{5}-1+\sqrt{5-2\sqrt{5}}). \tag{89}$$

Subtracting (88) from (89) gives (87).

The advantage of the use of the formula Ch. IX. (116) is evident in the evaluation of integrals like the first in (87).

Replacing in

$$\frac{10}{x^5+1}=\frac{2}{x+1}+\frac{(\sqrt{5}-1)x+4}{x^2+\frac{1}{2}(\sqrt{5}-1)x+1}+\frac{-(\sqrt{5}+1)x+4}{x^2-\frac{1}{2}(\sqrt{5}+1)x+1}, \tag{90}$$

x by x^2, we have

$$\frac{10}{x^{10}+1}=\frac{2}{x^2+1}-\frac{(1-\sqrt{5})x^2-4}{x^4+\frac{1}{2}(\sqrt{5}-1)x^2+1}+\frac{-(1+\sqrt{5})x^2+4}{x^4-\frac{1}{2}(\sqrt{5}+1)x^2+1}, \tag{91}$$

from which

$$\frac{20}{x^{10}+1}=\frac{4}{x^2+1}+\frac{\sqrt{10-2\sqrt{5}}\,x+4}{x^2+\frac{1}{2}\sqrt{10-2\sqrt{5}}\,x+1}+\frac{-\sqrt{10-2\sqrt{5}}x+4}{x^2-\frac{1}{2}\sqrt{10-2\sqrt{5}}\,x+1}$$
$$+\frac{\sqrt{10+2\sqrt{5}}\,x+4}{x^2+\frac{1}{2}\sqrt{10+2\sqrt{5}}\,x+1}+\frac{-\sqrt{10+2\sqrt{5}}\,x+4}{x^2-\frac{1}{2}\sqrt{10+2\sqrt{5}}+1}. \tag{92}$$

We then obtain

$$\int\frac{dx}{x^{10}+1}=\tfrac{1}{40}\sqrt{10-2\sqrt{5}}\log u+\tfrac{1}{40}\sqrt{10+2\sqrt{5}}\log v$$
$$+\tfrac{1}{20}(1+\sqrt{5})\,\theta-\tfrac{1}{20}(1-\sqrt{5})\,\phi+\tfrac{1}{5}\tan^{-1}x, \tag{93}$$

where $$u=\frac{x^2+\frac{1}{2}\sqrt{10-2\sqrt{5}}\,x+1}{x^2-\frac{1}{2}\sqrt{10-2\sqrt{5}}\,x+1},\qquad v=\frac{x^2+\frac{1}{2}\sqrt{10+2\sqrt{5}}\,x+1}{x^2-\frac{1}{2}\sqrt{10+2\sqrt{5}}\,x+1},$$

$$\theta=\tan^{-1}\frac{(1+\sqrt{5})x}{2(1-x^2)},\qquad \phi=\tan^{-1}\frac{(1-\sqrt{5})x}{2(1-x^2)};$$

and since $$\log u\Big]_{x=1}=2\log\frac{4+\sqrt{10-2\sqrt{5}}}{\sqrt{5}+1}=2\log(\sqrt{5}-1+\sqrt{5-2\sqrt{5}})$$

and $$\log v\Big]_{x=1}=2\log\frac{4+\sqrt{10+2\sqrt{5}}}{\sqrt{5}-1}=2\log(\sqrt{5}+1+\sqrt{5+2\sqrt{5}}),$$

therefore $$\int_0^1\frac{dx}{x^{10}+1}=\frac{\pi}{20}(\sqrt{5}+1)+\tfrac{1}{20}\sqrt{10+2\sqrt{5}}\log(\sqrt{5}+1+\sqrt{5+2\sqrt{5}})$$
$$+\tfrac{1}{20}\sqrt{10-2\sqrt{5}}\log(\sqrt{5}-1+\sqrt{5-2\sqrt{5}}),$$

which is the same as (89).

5. To find the value of the series obtained by retaining throughout

$$S=\sum_{n=1}^{\infty}\frac{(-1)^{n-1}}{n} \tag{94}$$

groups of p successive terms—beginning with the first term of the series—and omitting q successive terms after each of these groups.

Denoting the series thus obtained by $S_{p,q}$, then

$$S_{p,q}=\sum_{n=0}^{\infty}\sum_{m=1}^{p}\frac{(-1)^{n(p+q)+m-1}}{n(p+q)+m}. \tag{95}$$

We may write

$$S_{p,q}=\sum_{n=0}^{\infty}\sum_{m=1}^{p}\frac{(-1)^{n(p+q)+m-1}}{n(p+q)+m}r^{n(p+q)}\Big]_{r=1}$$

$$=\sum_{m=1}^{p}\frac{1}{r^m}S_m\Big]_{r=1}, \tag{96}$$

where
$$S_m=\sum_{n=0}^{\infty}\frac{(-1)^{n(p+q)+m-1}}{n(p+q)+m}r^{n(p+q)+m}. \tag{97}$$

Then
$$\frac{dS_m}{dr}=\sum_{n=0}^{\infty}(-r)^{n(p+q)+m-1}. \tag{98}$$

If we let $x=-r$, we have

$$\frac{dS_m}{dx}=-\sum_{n=0}^{\infty}x^{n(p+q)+m-1}=\frac{x^{m-1}}{x^{p+q}-1}$$

and
$$S_m=\int_0^x\frac{x^{m-1}dx}{x^{p+q}-1}, \tag{99}$$

where the upper limit $x=-1$.

Therefore
$$S_{p,q}=\sum_{m=1}^{p}\frac{(-1)^m}{x^m}\int_0^x\frac{x^{m-1}dx}{x^{p+q}-1}\Big]_{x=-1}. \tag{100}$$

Now, by Ch. IX. (48),

$$\int_0^x\frac{x^{m-1}dx}{x^n-1}=-\frac{2}{n}\sum_{k=1}^{\left[\frac{n-1}{2}\right]}\sin\frac{2k}{n}m\pi\tan^{-1}\frac{x\sin\frac{2k}{n}\pi}{1-x\cos\frac{2k}{n}\pi}$$

$$+\frac{1}{n}\sum_{k=1}^{\left[\frac{n-1}{2}\right]}\cos\frac{2k}{n}m\pi\log\left(1-2x\cos\frac{2k}{n}\pi+x^2\right)$$

$$+\frac{1}{n}\log(1-x)+\frac{(-1)^m}{2n}[1+(-1)^n]\log(1+x). \tag{101}$$

We shall next evaluate (101) for $x=-1$.

Denoting the first and second summations in (101) in order by S_1 and S_2, then

$$S_1\Big]_{x=-1}=-\sum_{k=1}^{\left[\frac{n-1}{2}\right]}\frac{k\pi}{n}\sin\frac{2k}{n}m\pi=-\frac{\pi}{n}S_1' \tag{102}$$

and
$$S_1'=(-1)^{m-1}\frac{n}{4}\cot\frac{m\pi}{n},\quad\text{when } n \text{ is even}, \tag{103}$$

$$=(-1)^{m-1}\frac{n}{4}\operatorname{cosec}\frac{m\pi}{n},\quad\text{when } n \text{ is odd}. \tag{104}$$

Therefore, whether n be even or odd and if m is not a multiple of n,

$$S_1\Big]_{x=-1} = (-1)^m \frac{\pi}{8}\left[\cot\frac{m\pi}{2n} - (-1)^n \tan\frac{m\pi}{2n}\right]. \tag{105}$$

We also find

$$S_2\Big]_{x=-1} = 2\log 2 \sum_{k=1}^{\left[\frac{n-1}{2}\right]} \cos\frac{2k}{n}m\pi + 2\sum_{k=1}^{\left[\frac{n-1}{2}\right]} \cos\frac{2k}{n}m\pi \log\cos\frac{k\pi}{n}; \tag{106}$$

and since

$$\sum_{k=1}^{\left[\frac{n-1}{2}\right]} \cos\frac{2k}{n}m\pi = -\tfrac{1}{2}[1+(-1)^m], \quad \text{when } n \text{ is even,} \tag{107}$$

$$= -\tfrac{1}{2}, \quad \text{when } n \text{ is odd,} \tag{108}$$

$$= -\tfrac{1}{4}[2+(-1)^m\{1+(-1)^n\}], \tag{109}$$

whether n be even or odd; hence

$$S_2\Big]_{x=-1} = 2\sum_{k=1}^{\left[\frac{n-1}{2}\right]} \cos\frac{2k}{n}m\pi \log\cos\frac{k\pi}{n} - \tfrac{1}{2}[2+(-1)^m\{1+(-1)^n\}]\log 2. \tag{110}$$

Applying (105) and (110) to (101) gives

$$\int_0^{-1}\frac{x^{m-1}dx}{x^n-1} = (-1)^{m-1}\frac{\pi}{4n}\left(\cot\frac{m\pi}{2n} - (-1)^n\tan\frac{m\pi}{2n}\right)$$

$$+\frac{2}{n}\sum_{k=1}^{\left[\frac{n-1}{2}\right]} \cos\frac{2k}{n}m\pi \log\cos\frac{k\pi}{n} + (-1)^{m-1}\frac{1+(-1)^n}{2}\log 2$$

$$+(-1)^m\frac{1+(-1)^n}{2n}\log(1-x)\Big]_{x=1}; \tag{111}$$

and by means of (111) we obtain from (100)

$$S_{p,q} = \frac{\pi}{4n}\sum_{m=1}^{p}(-1)^{m-1}\left(\cot\frac{m\pi}{2n} - (-1)^n\tan\frac{m\pi}{2n}\right)$$

$$+\frac{2}{n}\sum_{m=1}^{p}\sum_{k=1}^{\left[\frac{n-1}{2}\right]} \cos\frac{2k}{n}m\pi \log\cos\frac{k\pi}{n} + \frac{1+(-1)^n}{2n}\log 2\sum_{m=1}^{p}(-1)^{m-1}$$

$$+\frac{1+(-1)^n}{2n}\log(1+x)\sum_{m=1}^{p}\frac{1}{x^m}\Big]_{x=-1}. \tag{112}$$

In reducing (112) we distinguish between the cases when $n=p+q$ is even and when n is odd.

(i) Let n be even.

Now $$N = \log(1+x)\sum_{m=1}^{p}\frac{1}{x^m}\Big]_{x=-1} = \frac{1-x^p}{(1-x)x^p}\log(1+x)\Big]_{x=-1}.$$

Hence, when p is even,

$$N=\frac{1-x^p}{(1+x)x^p}\log(1-x)\Big]_{x=1}=0, \qquad (113)$$

and when p is odd
$$N=-\frac{1+x^p}{(1+x)x^p}\log(1-x)\Big]_{x=1}=\infty. \qquad (114)$$

Therefore, when n is even, (95) is convergent when p is even.

Next
$$\sum_{m=1}^{p}(-1)^{m-1}=\frac{1-(-1)^p}{2}$$

and
$$\frac{1+(-1)^n}{2n}\sum_{m=1}^{p}(-1)^{m-1}=\frac{1-(-1)^p}{2n}=0. \qquad (115)$$

Since
$$\sum_{m=1}^{p}\cos\frac{2k}{n}m\pi=\tfrac{1}{2}\sin(2p+1)\frac{k\pi}{n}\operatorname{cosec}\frac{k\pi}{n}-\tfrac{1}{2}, \qquad (116)$$

therefore

$$\sum_{m=1}^{p}\sum_{k=1}^{\frac{n-2}{2}}\cos\frac{2k}{n}m\pi\log\cos\frac{k\pi}{n}$$
$$=\frac{1}{2}\sum_{k=1}^{\frac{n-2}{2}}\sin(2p+1)\frac{k\pi}{n}\operatorname{cosec}\frac{k\pi}{n}\log\cos\frac{k\pi}{n}-\frac{1}{2}\sum_{k=1}^{\frac{n-2}{2}}\log\cos\frac{k\pi}{n}. \qquad (117)$$

Denoting by S_3 the second summation in the right-hand member of (117) and letting in it $\frac{n}{2}-k=k'$, then

$$S_3=\sum_{k=1}^{\frac{n-2}{2}}\log\sin\frac{k\pi}{n}=\sum_{k=1}^{\frac{n-2}{2}}N_k. \qquad (118)$$

Now
$$\sum_{k=1}^{n-1}N_k=\sum_{k=1}^{\frac{n-2}{2}}N_k+N_k\Big]_{k=\frac{n}{2}}+\sum_{k=\frac{n+2}{2}}^{n-1}N_k=2\sum_{k=1}^{\frac{n-2}{2}}N_k; \qquad (119)$$

hence
$$\sum_{k=1}^{\frac{n-2}{2}}\log\cos\frac{k\pi}{n}=\frac{1}{2}\sum_{k=1}^{n-1}\log\sin\frac{k\pi}{n} \qquad (120)$$

$$=\frac{1}{2}\log\frac{n}{2^{n-1}}, \text{ by Ch. IX. (146).} \qquad (121)$$

Applying (121) to (117) and the result, together with (113) and (115), to (112), writing $p+q$ for n, gives

$$S_{p,q}=\frac{\pi}{2(p+q)}\sum_{m=1}^{p}(-1)^{m-1}\cot\frac{m\pi}{p+q}+\frac{1}{p+q}\sum_{k=1}^{\frac{p+q-2}{2}}\sin(2p+1)\frac{k\pi}{n}$$
$$\operatorname{cosec}\frac{k\pi}{n}\log\cos\frac{k\pi}{n}-\frac{1}{2(p+q)}\log\frac{p+q}{2^{p+q-1}}. \qquad (122)$$

(ii) Let $n=p+q$ be odd.

To find the value of

$$S_4=[1+(-1)^n]\log(1+x)\sum_{m=1}^{p}\frac{1}{x^m}\Big]_{x=-1} \text{ in (112),} \tag{123}$$

we write
$$S_4=(1-x^n)\log(1-x)\sum_{m=1}^{p}\frac{1}{(-x)^m}\Big]_{x=1}; \tag{124}$$

and since
$$(1-x)\log(1-x)\Big]_{x=1}=0,$$

therefore
$$S_4=0. \tag{125}$$

Now, n being odd, the upper limits of the summations in (117) are $\frac{n-1}{2}$.

Letting $\frac{n-1}{2}-k=k'$ in

$$S_5=\sum_{k=1}^{\frac{n-1}{2}}\log\cos\frac{k\pi}{n}, \tag{126}$$

we have
$$S_5=\sum_{k=0}^{\frac{n-3}{2}}\log\sin\frac{2k+1}{2n}\pi \tag{127}$$

$$=-\tfrac{1}{2}(n-1)\log 2, \text{ by Ch. IX. (124).} \tag{128}$$

Applying (125) and (128) to (112), we obtain

$$S_{p,q}=\frac{\pi}{2(p+q)}\sum_{m=1}^{p}(-1)^{m-1}\operatorname{cosec}\frac{m\pi}{p+q}+\frac{p+q-1}{2(p+q)}\log 2$$
$$+\frac{1}{p+q}\sum_{k=1}^{\frac{p+q-1}{2}}\sin(2p+1)\frac{k\pi}{p+q}\operatorname{cosec}\frac{k\pi}{p+q}\log\cos\frac{k\pi}{p+q}. \tag{129}$$

6. If in (95) p is even and q is odd, or when p and q are both odd, the signs of the terms of the series do not alternate throughout. If the signs of the terms are changed so that they alternate, then (95) changes to

$$S_{p,q}=\sum_{n=0}^{\infty}(-1)^n\sum_{m=1}^{p}\frac{(-1)^{n(p+q)+m-1}}{n(p+q)+m}. \tag{130}$$

We may write
$$S_{p,q}=\sum_{m=1}^{p}\frac{1}{r^m}S_m\Big]_{r=1}, \tag{131}$$

where
$$S_m=(-1)^{m-1}r^m\sum_{n=0}^{\infty}\frac{(-1)^n(-r)^{n(p+q)}}{n(p+q)+m}. \tag{132}$$

Then
$$\frac{dS_m}{dr}=(-1)^{m-1}r^{m-1}\sum_{n=0}^{\infty}(-1)^n(-r)^{n(p+q)}; \tag{133}$$

and if we let $x=-r$, $$S_m=-\int_0^x \frac{x^{m-1}dx}{x^{p+q}-1}, \tag{134}$$
where the upper limit $x=-1$.

Therefore $$S_{p,q}=\sum_{m=1}^{p}\frac{(-1)^{m-1}}{x^m}\left[\int_0^x \frac{x^{m-1}dx}{x^{p+q}+1}\right]_{x=-1}. \tag{135}$$

Now, by Ch. IX. (47),

$$\begin{aligned}\int_0^{-1}\frac{x^{m-1}\,dx}{x^n+1}&=-\frac{2}{n}\sum_{k=0}^{\left[\frac{n-2}{2}\right]}\frac{2k+1}{2n}\pi\sin\frac{2k+1}{n}m\pi\\&-\frac{2}{n}\log 2\sum_{k=0}^{\left[\frac{n-2}{2}\right]}\cos\frac{2k+1}{n}m\pi-\frac{2}{n}\sum_{k=0}^{\left[\frac{n-2}{2}\right]}\cos\frac{2k+1}{n}m\pi\log\cos\frac{2k+1}{2n}\pi\\&+\frac{(-1)^{m-1}}{2n}[1-(-1)^n]\log(1+x)\Big]_{x=-1,\,0}.\end{aligned} \tag{136}$$

But $$\sum_{k=0}^{\left[\frac{n-2}{2}\right]}\frac{2k+1}{2n}\sin\frac{2k+1}{n}m\pi$$

$$=(-1)^{m-1}\frac{\pi}{4}\operatorname{cosec}\frac{m\pi}{n},\quad\text{when } n \text{ is even}, \tag{137}$$

$$=(-1)^{m-1}\frac{\pi}{4}\cot\frac{m\pi}{n},\quad\text{when } n \text{ is odd}, \tag{138}$$

$$=(-1)^{m-1}\frac{\pi}{8}\left(\cot\frac{m\pi}{2n}+(-1)^n\tan\frac{m\pi}{2n}\right), \tag{139}$$

whether n be even or odd, and if m is not a multiple of n.

Then, by the methods given above, we find:

(i) If $p+q$ is even, p and q must then both be odd,

$$\begin{aligned}S_{p,q}&=\frac{\pi}{2(p+q)}\sum_{m=1}^{p}(-1)^{m-1}\operatorname{cosec}\frac{m\pi}{p+q}+\frac{p+q-1}{2(p+q)}\log 2\\&+\frac{1}{p+q}\sum_{k=0}^{\frac{p+q-2}{2}}\sin\frac{2k+1}{2(p+q)}(2p+1)\pi\operatorname{cosec}\frac{2k+1}{2(p+q)}\pi\log\cos\frac{2k+1}{2(p+q)}\pi.\end{aligned} \tag{140}$$

(ii) If $p+q$ is odd, p must be even and q odd,

$$\begin{aligned}S_{p,q}&=\frac{\pi}{2(p+q)}\sum_{m=1}^{p}(-1)^{m-1}\cot\frac{m\pi}{p+q}-\frac{1}{2(p+q)}\log\frac{p+q}{2^{p+q-1}}\\&+\frac{1}{p+q}\sum_{k=0}^{\frac{p+q-3}{2}}\sin\frac{2k+1}{2(p+q)}(2p+1)\pi\operatorname{cosec}\frac{2k+1}{2(p+q)}\pi\log\cos\frac{2k+1}{2(p+q)}\pi.\end{aligned} \tag{141}$$

7. To find the value of

$$S_{5,7}=1-\frac{1}{2}+\frac{1}{3}-\frac{1}{4}+\frac{1}{5}-\frac{1}{13}+\frac{1}{14}-\frac{1}{15}+\frac{1}{16}-\frac{1}{17}+\frac{1}{25}-\frac{1}{26}+\dots. \tag{142}$$

Then, from (140),

$$S_{5,7}=\frac{\pi}{24}\sum_{m=1}^{5}(-1)^{m-1}\operatorname{cosec}\frac{m\pi}{12}+\frac{1}{12}\sum_{k=1}^{5}\sin(2k+1)\frac{11}{24}\pi\operatorname{cosec}\frac{2k+1}{24}\pi$$

$$\log\cos(2k+1)\frac{\pi}{24}-\frac{1}{12}\sum_{k=0}^{5}\log\cos(2k+1)\frac{\pi}{24}. \qquad (143)$$

Evaluating the summations in (143), we find

$$\sum_{m=1}^{5}(-1)^{m-1}\operatorname{cosec}\frac{m\pi}{12}=\frac{2}{3}\sqrt{3}+\sqrt{2}+2\sqrt{6}-2; \qquad (144)$$

and since $\sin(2k+1)\frac{11}{24}\pi=(-1)^k\cos(2k+1)\frac{\pi}{24}$,

the second summation in (143) becomes

$$\sum_{k=0}^{5}(-1)^k\cot(2k+1)\frac{\pi}{24}\log\cos(2k+1)\frac{\pi}{24}. \qquad (145)$$

Denoting by P_{2k+1} the expression under the summation sign in (145), then

$$\sum_{k=0}^{5}P_{2k+1}=\sum_{k=0}^{2}P_{2k+1}+\sum_{k=3}^{5}P_{2k+1}. \qquad (146)$$

Letting $5-k+k'$, the last summation in the second member of (146), we have

$$\sum_{k=3}^{5}P_{2k+1}=-\sum_{k=0}^{2}(-1)^k\cot\frac{12-(2k+1)}{24}\pi\log\cos\frac{12-(2k+1)}{24}\pi$$

$$=-\sum_{k=0}^{2}(-1)^k\tan(2k+1)\frac{\pi}{24}\log\sin(2k+1)\frac{\pi}{24}. \qquad (147)$$

Therefore

$$\sum_{k=0}^{5}P_{2k+1}=\sum_{k=0}^{2}(-1)^k\cot(2k+1)\frac{\pi}{24}\log\cos(2k+1)\frac{\pi}{24}$$

$$-\sum_{k=0}^{2}(-1)^k\tan(2k+1)\frac{\pi}{24}\log\sin(2k+1)\frac{\pi}{24} \qquad (148)$$

$$=(\sqrt{3}+\sqrt{2})(\sqrt{2}+1)\log\tfrac{1}{2}\sqrt{2+\sqrt{2+\sqrt{3}}}-(\sqrt{3}-\sqrt{2})(\sqrt{2}-1)\log\tfrac{1}{2}\sqrt{2-\sqrt{2+\sqrt{3}}}$$

$$+(\sqrt{3}+\sqrt{2})(\sqrt{2}-1)\log\tfrac{1}{2}\sqrt{2+\sqrt{2-\sqrt{3}}}-(\sqrt{3}-\sqrt{2})(\sqrt{2}+1)\log\tfrac{1}{2}\sqrt{2+\sqrt{2-\sqrt{3}}}$$

$$+(\sqrt{2}-1)\log\tfrac{1}{2}\sqrt{2-\sqrt{2}}-(\sqrt{2}+1)\log\tfrac{1}{2}\sqrt{2+\sqrt{2}} \qquad (149)$$

$$=(\sqrt{3}+\sqrt{2})[\sqrt{2}\log\tfrac{1}{4}(\sqrt{3}+\sqrt{2})+\log\tfrac{1}{2}(\sqrt{2}+1)(\sqrt{6}-\sqrt{2})]$$

$$-(\sqrt{3}-\sqrt{2})[\sqrt{2}\log\tfrac{1}{4}(\sqrt{3}-\sqrt{2})+\log\tfrac{1}{2}(\sqrt{2}+1)(\sqrt{6}+\sqrt{2})]$$

$$+\sqrt{2}\log(\sqrt{2}-1)-\log\tfrac{1}{4}\sqrt{2} \qquad (150)$$

$$=2\sqrt{6}\log(\sqrt{3}+\sqrt{2})+2\sqrt{3}\log(\sqrt{3}-1)+\sqrt{2}\log(\sqrt{2}+1)$$

$$-\tfrac{1}{2}(5+2\sqrt{3})\log 2. \qquad (151)$$

We also find $$\sum_{k=0}^{5} \log\cos(2k+1)\frac{\pi}{24} = -\frac{11}{2}\log 2. \tag{152}$$

Applying (144), (151) and (152) to (143), we obtain

$$S_{5,7} = \frac{\pi}{24}\left(2\sqrt{6}+\sqrt{2}+\frac{2}{3}\sqrt{3}-2\right)+\frac{1}{12}[2\sqrt{6}\log(\sqrt{3}+\sqrt{2})$$
$$+2\sqrt{3}\log(\sqrt{3}-1)+\sqrt{2}\log(\sqrt{2}+1)+(3-\sqrt{3})\log 2]. \tag{153}$$

8. Show that

(i) $$\sum_{k=1}^{n}(-1)^{\left[\frac{k}{2}\right]}\left[\frac{k}{2}\right] = \frac{1}{4}(-1)^{\left[\frac{n}{2}\right]}\left[\left\{1+(-1)^n\right\}\left\{1-(-1)^{\left[\frac{n}{2}\right]}\right\}\right.$$
$$\left.+\left\{1-(-1)^n\right\}\left\{n+(-1)^{\left[\frac{n+1}{2}\right]}\right\}\right]. \tag{154}$$

(ii) $$\sum_{k=1}^{\left[\frac{n}{2}\right]}\left[\frac{k}{2}\right] = \frac{1}{2}\left\{\left[\frac{n}{4}\right]-\left[\frac{n+2}{4}\right]\right\}+\frac{1}{2}\left\{\left(\left[\frac{n}{4}\right]\right)^2+\left(\left[\frac{n+2}{4}\right]\right)^2\right\} \tag{155}$$
$$= \frac{1}{4}\left(\left[\frac{n}{2}\right]\right)^2+\frac{1}{8}\left\{1-(-1)^{\left[\frac{n}{2}\right]}\right\}\left\{1+2(-1)^{\left[\frac{n}{2}\right]}\right\}. \tag{156}$$

(iii) $$\sum_{k=1}^{\left[\frac{n}{2}\right]}(-1)^k\left[\frac{k}{2}\right] = \frac{1}{2}\left\{\left[\frac{n}{4}\right]+\left[\frac{n+2}{4}\right]\right\}+\frac{1}{2}\left\{\left(\left[\frac{n}{4}\right]\right)^2+\left(\left[\frac{n+2}{4}\right]\right)^2\right\} \tag{157}$$
$$= \frac{1}{4}\left[\frac{n}{2}\right]\left\{1+(-1)^{\left[\frac{n}{2}\right]}\right\}. \tag{158}$$

(iv) $$\sum_{k=1}^{\left[\frac{n}{2}\right]}(-1)^{\left[\frac{k}{2}\right]}\left[\frac{k}{2}\right]$$
$$= \frac{1}{2}(-1)^{\left[\frac{n-2}{4}\right]}\left[\left\{1-(-1)^{\left[\frac{n}{2}\right]}\right\}\left[\frac{n+2}{4}\right]-1+(-1)^{\left[\frac{n+2}{4}\right]}\right]. \tag{159}$$

(v) $$\sum_{k=1}^{n}\left[\frac{k}{3}\right] = \frac{1}{2}\left\{\left[\frac{n}{3}\right]+\left[\frac{n+1}{3}\right]+\left[\frac{n+2}{3}\right]\right\}$$
$$+\frac{1}{2}\left\{\left(\left[\frac{n}{3}\right]\right)^2+\left(\left[\frac{n+1}{3}\right]\right)^2+\left(\left[\frac{n+2}{3}\right]\right)^2\right\}-\left\{\left[\frac{n+1}{3}\right]+\left[\frac{n+2}{3}\right]\right\} \tag{160}$$
$$= \frac{1}{6}(n-1)(n+4)-\left[\frac{2n-1}{3}\right]-\left\{(-1)^{\left[\frac{2n}{3}\right]}+(-1)^{n+\left[\frac{n}{3}\right]}\right\}. \tag{161}$$

(vi) $$\sum_{k=1}^{n}(-1)^k\left[\frac{k}{3}\right] = \frac{1}{4}\left\{(-1)^{\left[\frac{n}{3}\right]}+2(-1)^{\left[\frac{n}{3}\right]}\left[\frac{n}{3}\right]-1\right\}$$
$$-(-1)^{\left[\frac{n-1}{3}\right]}\frac{1-(-1)^{n+\left[\frac{n}{3}\right]}}{2}\cdot\left[\frac{n-1}{3}\right]. \tag{162}$$

CHAPTER XV.

THE NUMBERS OF BERNOULLI AND EULER. BERNOULLI'S FUNCTION.

IN this chapter expressions for the numbers of Bernoulli and Euler are derived. The results are believed to be simpler and the methods by which they have been obtained less laborious than those given heretofore.*

The numbers of Bernoulli and Euler enter as coefficients in many expansions, especially in those of the trigonometrical functions. The expression for the Bernoulli and Euler numbers will be obtained from their definitions. We shall denote the nth Bernoulli number by B_n and the nth Euler number by E_n.

1. (i) From the relation defining B_n,

$$B_n = \frac{2nT_{n-1}}{2^{2n}(2^{2n}-1)}, \tag{1}$$

where T_{n-1} is the coefficient of $\dfrac{x^{2n-1}}{(2n-1)!}$ in the expansion of $\tan x$, we have, from Ch. II. (16),

$$B_n = (-1)^n \frac{n}{2^{2n}-1} \sum_{k=1}^{2n-1} \frac{1}{2^k} \sum_{\alpha=1}^{k} (-1)^\alpha \binom{k}{\alpha} \alpha^{2n-1}, \tag{2}$$

and from Ch. II (37),

$$B_n = (-1)^{n-1} \frac{2n}{2^{2n}(2^{2n}-1)} \sum_{k=0}^{n-1} \frac{1}{2^{4k}} \binom{2k}{k} \sum_{\alpha=0}^{k} (-1)^\alpha \binom{2k+1}{k-\alpha} (2\alpha+1)^{2n-1}. \tag{3}$$

(ii) The definition

$$B_n = \frac{1}{2^{2n}} V_n, \tag{4}$$

where V_n is the coefficient of $\dfrac{x^{2n}}{(2n)!}$, in the expansion of $x \cot x$, gives

$$B_n = (-1)^n \sum_{k=1}^{n} \frac{k!\,(k-1)!}{(2k+1)!} \sum_{\alpha=1}^{k} (-1)^\alpha \binom{2k}{k-\alpha} \alpha^{2n} \text{ by Ch. X. (168)}, \tag{5}$$

and by Ch. II. (108) the form (2) is obtained.

* An expression attributed to Laplace is given by Lacroix, *Traité des différences et des Séries*, 1800, p. 106—and by the same author in *Traité du Calcul Différentiel et du Calcul Intégral*, second edition, vol. iii., 1819, p. 114.—Saalschütz, *Vorlesungen über die Bernoullischen Zahlen*, 1893.—Eytelwein, *Abhandlungen der Akademie der Wissenschaften zu Berlin*, 1816-1817, *Mathematische Klasse*.—Scherk, *Journal für Mathematik* (*J. f. M.*), vol. 4, 1829, pp. 299-304.—Stern, *J. f. M.* vol 26, 1843, pp. 88-90.—Schlömilch, *J. f. M.* vol. 32, 1846, pp. 360-364.—Bauer, *J. f. M.* vol. 58, 1861, pp. 292-300.—Worpitzky, *J. f. M.* vol. 94, 1883, pp. 203-232.—Kronecker, *J. f. M.* vol. 94, 1883, pp. 268-269.—Shovelton, *Quarterly Journal of Mathematics* (*Q.J.M.*), vol. 46, 1915, pp. 220-247.—Sheppard, *Q.J.M.* vol. 30, p. 31.

(iii) From the definition $B_n = \frac{1}{2(2^{2n-1}-1)} W_n,$ (6)

where W_n is the coefficient of $\frac{x^{2n}}{(2n)!}$ in the expansion of $x \operatorname{cosec} x$, and by means of Ch. II. (138)

$$B_n = (-1)^n \frac{2^{2n}}{2^{2n-1}-1} \sum_{k=1}^{n} \frac{1}{2^{4k}} \binom{2k}{k} \frac{1}{2k+1} \sum_{a=1}^{k} (-1)^a \binom{2k}{k-a} a^{2n} \tag{7}$$

is derived.

(iv) The definition

$$\phi(x, p) = p \sum_{n=1}^{x-1} n^{p-1} = x^p - \tfrac{1}{2} p x^{p-1} + \sum_{n=1}^{\left[\frac{p-1}{2}\right]} (-1)^{n-1} \binom{p}{2n} B_n x^{p-2n} \tag{8}$$

is given by Jacob Bernoulli, the originator of the Bernoulli numbers, in his *Ars Conjectandi*, p. 97, $\phi(x, p)$ is called the *Bernoulli function*. Writing in Ch. V. (95), $p-1$ for p, x for n and multiplying the result by p, we have

$$p \sum_{k=1}^{x-1} k^{p-1} = x^p - \tfrac{1}{2} p x^{p-1} + \sum_{k=1}^{\left[\frac{p-1}{2}\right]} \binom{p}{2k} \frac{k}{2^{2k}-1} \sum_{a=1}^{2k-1} \frac{1}{2^a}$$

$$\sum_{\beta=1}^{a} (-1)^{\beta-1} \binom{a}{\beta} \beta^{2k-1} x^{p-2k}. \tag{9}$$

Comparing (8) and (9), we obtain for B_n the expression (2).

2. Euler's numbers are defined as the coefficients of $\frac{x^{2n}}{(2n)!}$ in the expansion of $\sec x$, or

$$\sec x = \sum_{n=0}^{\infty} E_n \frac{x^{2n}}{(2n)!}. \tag{10}$$

We then have, from Ch. II. (55),

$$E_n = (-1)^n \sum_{k=1}^{2n} \frac{(-1)^k}{2^{k-1}} \binom{2n+1}{k+1} \sum_{a=0}^{\left[\frac{k-1}{2}\right]} \binom{k}{a} (k-2a)^{2n}; \tag{11}$$

from Ch. II. (69),

$$E_n = (-1)^n \sum_{k=0}^{2n} \frac{1}{2^k} \sum_{a=0}^{k} (-1)^a \binom{k}{a} (1+2a)^{2n}; \tag{12}$$

from Ch. II. (77),

$$E_n = (-1)^n \sqrt{2} \sum_{k=1}^{2n} \frac{1}{2^{k/2}} \cos (k+1) \frac{\pi}{4} \sum_{a=1}^{k} (-1)^a \binom{k}{a} a^{2n}; \tag{13}$$

and from Ch. II. (86),

$$E_n = (-1)^n 2^{2n+1} \sum_{k=1}^{n} \frac{1}{2^{4k}} \binom{2k}{k} \sum_{a=1}^{k} (-1)^a \binom{2k}{k-a} a^{2n}. \tag{14}$$

3. The coefficients of the expansion of

$$y=\tan x+\sec x=\tan\left(\frac{\pi}{4}+\frac{x}{2}\right) \tag{15}$$

are equal to E_n for even powers of x and to T_n—the coefficient of $\frac{x^{2n+1}}{(2n+1)!}$ in the expansion of $\tan x$—for odd powers of x.

Now $$y=-i+\frac{2i}{u+1},\quad \text{where } u=e^{i\left(\frac{\pi}{2}+x\right)};$$

then $$\frac{d^n y}{dx^n}=2i\sum_{k=1}^{n}\frac{(-1)^k}{k!}\sum_{a=1}^{k}(-1)^a\binom{k}{a}u^{k-a}\frac{d^n}{dx^n}u^a\frac{d^k}{du^k}\frac{1}{u+1} \tag{16}$$

and $$\left.\frac{d^n y}{dx^n}\right]_{x=0}=2i^{n+1}\sum_{k=1}^{n}\sum_{a=1}^{k}(-1)^a\binom{k}{a}a^n\left.\frac{i^k}{(u+1)^{k+1}}\right]_{x=0} \tag{17}$$

$$=i^n\sum_{k=1}^{n}\frac{1}{2^k}\sum_{a=1}^{k}(-1)^a\binom{k}{a}\left.(u+1)^{k+1}\right]_{x=0}$$

$$=\sqrt{2}i^n\sum_{k=1}^{n}\frac{1}{2^{k/2}}\sum_{a=1}^{k}(-1)^a\binom{k}{a}\left(\cos\frac{k+1}{4}\pi+i\sin\frac{k+1}{4}\pi\right). \tag{18}$$

Now, if n is even,

$$\left.\frac{d^{2n}}{dx^{2n}}y\right]_{x=0}=E_n=(-1)^n\sqrt{2}\sum_{k=1}^{2n}\frac{1}{2^{k/2}}\cos\frac{k+1}{4}\pi\sum_{a=1}^{k}(-1)^a\binom{k}{a}a^{2n}, \tag{19}$$

and if n is odd,

$$\left.\frac{dx^{2n+1}}{d^{2n+1}}y\right]_{x=0}=T_n=(-1)^{n-1}\sqrt{2}\sum_{k=1}^{2n+1}\frac{1}{2^{k/2}}\sin\frac{k+1}{4}\pi\sum_{a=1}^{k}(-1)^a\binom{k}{a}a^{2n+1}. \tag{20}$$

4. We shall now express the sum of the reciprocals of the powers of the series of natural numbers in terms of the Bernoulli and Euler numbers.

(i) By Ch. XI. (62) and (63),

$$\cot x=\frac{1}{x}-\sum_{n=1}^{\infty}\frac{1}{n\pi}\frac{1}{1-\frac{x}{n\pi}}+\sum_{n=1}^{\infty}\frac{1}{n\pi}\frac{1}{1+\frac{x}{n\pi}} \tag{21}$$

$$=\frac{1}{x}-\sum_{n=1}^{\infty}\frac{1}{n\pi}\frac{2x}{n\pi}\frac{1}{1-\frac{x^2}{n^2\pi^2}}$$

and $$x\cot x=1-\sum_{k=1}^{\infty}\frac{2}{\pi^{2k}}\sum_{n=1}^{\infty}\frac{1}{n^{2k}}x^{2k}. \tag{22}$$

Letting $$S_{2k}=\sum_{n=1}^{\infty}\frac{1}{n^{2k}}, \tag{23}$$

then
$$x \cot x = 1 - \sum_{k=1}^{\infty} \frac{2}{\pi^{2k}} S_{2k} x^{2k}; \tag{24}$$

and from the definition (4),
$$x \cot x = 1 - \sum_{k=1}^{\infty} 2^{2k} B_k \frac{x^{2k}}{(2k)!}. \tag{25}$$

Comparing (24) and (25) gives
$$S_{2k} = \frac{2^{2k-1}\pi^{2k}}{(2k)!} B_k, \tag{26}$$

and from (5) we have
$$S_{2k} = (-1)^k \frac{2^{2k-1}\pi^{2k}}{(2k)!} \sum_{\alpha=1}^{k} \frac{\alpha!\,(\alpha-1)!}{(2\alpha+1)!} \sum_{\beta=1}^{\alpha} (-1)^{\beta} \binom{2\alpha}{\alpha-\beta} \beta^{2k}. \tag{27}$$

Other expressions for S_{2k} are obtained from (2), (3) and (7).

5. To find
$$S'_{2k} = \sum_{n=1}^{\infty} (-1)^{n-1} \frac{1}{n^{2k}}. \tag{28}$$

Now
$$S'_{2k} = S_{2k} - \frac{2}{2^{2k}} S_{2k} = \frac{2^{2k-1}-1}{2^{2k-1}} S_{2k}, \tag{29}$$

and applying to (29) the expressions for S_{2k} we obtain corresponding expressions for S'_{2k}.

Values for S'_{2k} can also be derived as follows:

From Ch. XI. (84) and (85),
$$\operatorname{cosec} x = \frac{1}{x} + \sum_{n=1}^{\infty} \frac{(-1)^{n-1}}{n\pi} \frac{1}{1-\frac{x}{n\pi}} - \sum_{n=1}^{\infty} \frac{(-1)^{n-1}}{n\pi} \frac{1}{1+\frac{x}{n\pi}}$$
$$= \frac{1}{x} + \sum_{n=1}^{\infty} \frac{(-1)^{n-1}}{n\pi} \frac{2x}{n\pi} \sum_{k=0}^{\infty} \frac{x^{2k}}{(2k)!} \tag{30}$$

and
$$x \operatorname{cosec} x = 1 + 2\sum_{k=1}^{\infty} \frac{1}{\pi^{2k}} \sum_{n=1}^{\infty} \frac{(-1)^{n-1}}{n^{2k}} x^{2k}$$
$$= 1 + 2\sum_{k=1}^{\infty} \frac{1}{\pi^{2k}} S'_{2k} x^{2k}. \tag{31}$$

But, from the definition (6),
$$x \operatorname{cosec} x = 1 + 2\sum_{k=1}^{\infty} (2^{2k-1}-1) B_k \frac{x^{2k}}{(2k)!}. \tag{32}$$

Comparing (31) and (32), we have
$$S'_{2k} = \frac{(2^{2k-1}-1)\pi^{2k}}{(2k)!} B_k. \tag{33}$$

We then obtain

$$S'_{2k} = (-1)^k \frac{2^{2k}\pi^{2k}}{(2k)!} \sum_{\alpha=1}^{k} \frac{1}{4^{2\alpha}} \binom{2\alpha}{\alpha} \frac{1}{2\alpha+1} \sum_{\beta=1}^{\alpha} (-1)^\beta \binom{2\alpha}{\alpha-\beta} \beta^{2k}, \qquad (34)$$

from (7), and other expressions from (2), (3) and (5).

6. We shall next find the value of

$$U_{2k} = \sum_{n=1}^{\infty} \frac{1}{(2n-1)^{2k}}. \qquad (35)$$

Now, from Ch. XI. (51) and (52),

$$\tan x = \sum_{n=1}^{\infty} \frac{2}{(2n-1)\pi} \frac{1}{1 - \dfrac{2x}{(2n-1)\pi}} - \sum_{n=1}^{\infty} \frac{2}{(2n-1)\pi} \frac{1}{1 + \dfrac{2x}{(2n-1)\pi}} \qquad (36)$$

$$= \sum_{k=1}^{\infty} \frac{2^{2k+1}}{\pi^{2k}} \sum_{n=1}^{\infty} \frac{1}{(2n-1)^{2k}} x^{2k-1}$$

$$= \sum_{k=1}^{\infty} \frac{2^{2k+1}}{\pi^{2k}} U_{2k} x^{2k-1}. \qquad (37)$$

But, from the definition (1),

$$\tan x = \sum_{k=1}^{\infty} \frac{2^{2k}(2^{2k}-1)}{2k} B_k \frac{x^{2k-1}}{(2k-1)!}. \qquad (38)$$

Comparing (37) and (38), we have

$$U_{2k} = \frac{(2^{2k}-1)\pi^{2k}}{2(2k)!} B_k, \qquad (39)$$

and applying to (39) the values obtained for B_k gives corresponding values for U_{2k}.

Also, from (26),

$$U_{2k} = \frac{2^{2k}-1}{2^{2k}} S_{2k} \qquad (40)$$

$$= \frac{1}{2^{2k}} S_{2k} + S'_{2k}. \qquad (41)$$

7. To find the value of

$$U_{2k+1} = \sum_{n=1}^{\infty} \frac{(-1)^{n-1}}{(2n-1)^{2k+1}}. \qquad (42)$$

Now, from Ch. XI. (78) and (79), we have

$$\sec x = \sum_{n=1}^{\infty} (-1)^{n-1} \frac{2}{(2n-1)\pi} \frac{1}{1 - \dfrac{2x}{(2n-1)\pi}} - \sum_{n=1}^{\infty} (-1)^{n-1} \frac{2}{(2n-1)\pi} \frac{1}{1 + \dfrac{2x}{(2n-1)\pi}}$$

$$= \sum_{k=0}^{\infty} \frac{2^{2k+2}}{\pi^{2k+1}} \sum_{n=1}^{\infty} \frac{(-1)^{n-1}}{(2n-1)^{2k+1}} x^{2k}. \qquad (43)$$

Then
$$U'_{2k+1}=\frac{\pi^{2k+1}}{2^{2k+2}(2k)!}E_k, \tag{44}$$
and we obtain
$$U'_{2k+1}=(-1)^k\frac{\pi^{2k+1}}{2(2k)!}\sum_{\alpha=1}^{k}\frac{1}{4^{2\alpha}}\binom{2\alpha}{\alpha}\sum_{\beta=1}^{v}(-1)^{\beta}\binom{2\alpha}{\alpha-\beta}\beta^{2k}, \tag{45}$$
from (14), and other forms of U'_{2k+1} from (11), (12) and (13).

8. To find the value of $S=\sum_{n=1}^{\infty}\prod_{k=1}^{2n}\cot^p\frac{k\pi}{2n+1}.$ (46)

Now, by Ch. XII. (272), $S=\sum_{n=1}^{\infty}\frac{(-1)^{np}}{(2n+1)^p}$; (47)

then when p is even, $S=\sum_{n=1}^{\infty}\frac{1}{(2n+1)^{2p}}=\sum_{n=1}^{\infty}\frac{1}{(2n-1)^{2p}}-1$
$$=\frac{(2^{2p}-1)\pi^{2p}}{2(2p)!}B_p-1; \tag{48}$$
and when p is odd,
$$S=\sum_{n=1}^{\infty}\frac{(-1)^n}{(2n+1)^{2p-1}}=\sum_{n=1}^{\infty}\frac{(-1)^{n-1}}{(2n-1)^{2p-1}}-1 \tag{49}$$
$$=\frac{\pi^{2p-1}}{2^{2p-2}(2p-1)!}E_p-1. \tag{50}$$

If in (49) we let $p=1$, then from (50),
$$S=\sum_{n=1}^{\infty}\prod_{k=1}^{2n}\cot\frac{k\pi}{2n+1}=\frac{\pi}{4}-1,$$
which is the same as Ch. XII. (272).

9. Relations Involving the Numbers of Bernoulli and Euler.

Stern,* Glaisher,† Worpitzky,‡ Sheppard,§ and others have established recurring formulae for the Bernoulli and Euler numbers. But these results have, as a rule, been derived by the use of some artifice. The following methods enable us to obtain such relations in a more direct manner.

Let
$$\tan x=\sum_{k=0}^{\infty}T_k\frac{x^{2k+1}}{(2k+1)!} \tag{51}$$
and
$$\sec x=\sum_{k=0}^{\infty}E_k\frac{x^{2k}}{(2k)!}, \tag{52}$$
where
$$T_k=(2^{2k+2}-1)\frac{2^{2k+1}}{k+1}B_{k+1}. \tag{53}$$
$$T_0=1,\quad T_1=2,\quad T_2=16,\quad T_3=272,\ \text{etc.}$$
$$E_0=1,\quad E_1=1,\quad E_2=5,\quad E_3=61,\ \text{etc.}$$

* *J. f. M.*, vol. 26, p. 88.
† In numerous articles in the *Q.J.M.*
‡ *J. f. M.*, vol. 94, p. 203.
§ *Q.J.M*, vol. 30, p. 18.

(i) We shall first derive the relation

$$E_n = \sum_{k=0}^{n-1} \binom{2n-1}{2k} E_k T_{n-1-k}, \tag{54}$$

which was obtained by Stern and is reproduced by Saalschütz.*

Now, from (52), $$\frac{d}{dx} \sec x = \sum_{n=0}^{\infty} E_{n+1} \frac{x^{2n+1}}{(2n+1)!}. \tag{55}$$

Multiplying (51) and (52), we have

$$\sec x \tan x = \sum_{k=0}^{\infty} E_k \frac{x^{2k}}{(2k)!} \sum_{n=0}^{\infty} T_n \frac{x^{2n+1}}{(2n+1)!}. \tag{56}$$

Letting in (56) $n+k=n'$, then

$$\sec x \tan x = \sum_{k=0}^{\infty} E_k \frac{1}{(2k)!} \sum_{n=k}^{\infty} T_{n-k} \frac{x^{2n+1}}{(2n-k+1)!}$$

$$= \sum_{n=0}^{\infty} \frac{x^{2n+1}}{(2n+1)!} \sum_{k=0}^{n} \binom{2n+1}{2k} E_k T_{n-k}, \quad \text{by Ch. I. (68).} \tag{57}$$

Equating (55) and (57), we obtain

$$E_{n+1} = \sum_{k=0}^{n} \binom{2n+1}{2k} E_k T_{n-k}.$$

Writing $n-1$ for n gives the relation (54).

(ii) From $$\sec x = 1 + \tan x \tan \tfrac{1}{2} x \tag{58}$$

we will obtain a relation due to Scherk.

Applying (51) and (52) to (58), we have

$$\sum_{n=0}^{\infty} E_n \frac{x^{2n}}{(2n)!} = 1 + \sum_{k=0}^{\infty} T_k \frac{x^{2k+1}}{(2k+1)!} \sum_{n=0}^{\infty} \frac{1}{2^{2n+1}} T_n \frac{x^{2n+1}}{(2n+1)!} \tag{59}$$

or $$1 + \sum_{n=0}^{\infty} E_{n+1} \frac{x^{2n+2}}{(2n+2)!} = 1 + \sum_{n=0}^{\infty} \frac{1}{2^{2n+1}} \frac{x^{2n+2}}{(2n+2)!} \sum_{k=0}^{n} 2^{2k} \binom{2n+2}{2k+1} T_k T_{n-k}. \tag{60}$$

Equating in (60) the coefficients of equal powers of x, and writing $n-1$ for n, gives

$$E_n = \frac{1}{2^{2n-1}} S, \tag{61}$$

where $$S = \sum_{k=0}^{n-1} 2^{2k} \binom{2n}{2k+1} T_k T_{n-1-k}. \tag{62}$$

* *Vorlesungen über die Bernoullischen Zahlen*, 1893, p. 27. The relation is derived by means of the following expansions:

$$\log\left(E_0 + E_1 \frac{x^2}{2!} + E_2 \frac{x^4}{4!} + \dots\right) = T_0 \frac{x^2}{2!} + T_1 \frac{x^4}{4!} + T_2 \frac{x^6}{6!} + \dots,$$

$$\log \frac{\sin x}{x} = -\frac{2}{1} B_1 \frac{x^2}{2!} - \frac{2^3}{2} B_2 \frac{x^4}{4!} - \frac{2^5}{3} B_3 \frac{x^6}{6!} + \dots$$

and $$\log \cos x = -\frac{2(2^2-1)}{1} B_1 \frac{x^2}{2!} - \frac{2^3(2^4-1)}{2} B_2 \frac{x^4}{4!} - \frac{2^5(2^6-1)}{3} B_3 \frac{x^6}{6!} - \dots.$$

If n is odd,

$$S=\sum_{k=0}^{\frac{n-3}{2}} 2^{2k}\binom{2n}{2k+1} T_k T_{n-1-k}+2^{n-1}\binom{2n}{n} T_{\frac{n-1}{2}} T_{\frac{n-1}{2}}$$

$$+\sum_{k=\frac{n+1}{2}}^{n-1} 2^{2k}\binom{2n}{2k+1} T_k T_{n-1-k}. \qquad (63)$$

Letting in the second summation in (63) $n-1-k=k'$, it becomes

$$2^{2n-2}\sum_{k=0}^{\frac{n-3}{2}} \frac{1}{2^{2k}}\binom{2n}{2k+1} T_n T_{n-1-k}.$$

Therefore

$$E_n=\frac{1}{2^{2n}}\sum_{k=0}^{\frac{n-3}{2}} 2^{2k+1}(2^{2n-4k-2}+1)\binom{2n}{2k+1} T_k T_{n-1-k}+\frac{1}{2^n}\binom{2n}{n} T_{\frac{n-1}{2}} T_{\frac{n-1}{2}}. \qquad (64)$$

If n is even, the expression obtained differs from (64) in that the upper limit of k is $\frac{n-2}{2}$ and that the term outside the summation is wanting.

Therefore, whether n be even or odd,

$$E_n=\frac{1}{2^{2n}}\sum_{k=0}^{\left[\frac{n-2}{2}\right]} 2^{2k+1}(2^{2n-4k-2}+1)\binom{2n}{2k+1} T_k T_{n-1-k}+\frac{1-(-1)^n}{2^{n+1}} T_{\frac{n-1}{2}} T_{\frac{n-1}{2}}.^* \qquad (65)$$

(iii) Similar to the above many relations involving T_n, B_n and E_n may be obtained.

From
$$\sec x \cos x=1,$$

we have
$$\sum_{k=0}^{n}(-1)^k\binom{2n}{2k} E_k=0, \quad \text{if } n>0, \quad E_0=1. \qquad (66)$$

$$\cos x \tan x=\sin x$$

gives
$$\sum_{k=0}^{n}(-1)^k\binom{2n+1}{2k+1} T_k=1; \qquad (67)$$

from
$$\sec x \sin x=\tan x$$

we find
$$T_n=(-1)^n\sum_{k=0}^{n}(-1)^k\binom{2n+1}{k} E_k, \qquad (68)$$

and
$$B_n=(-1)^{n-1}\frac{n}{2^{2n-1}(2^{2n}-1)}\sum_{k=0}^{n-1}(-1)^k\binom{2n-1}{2n} E_k; \qquad (69)$$

and from
$$\sin x \tan x=\sec x-\cos x$$

* Saalschütz, *ibid.* p. 29.

we derive
$$E_n=(-1)^{n-1}\sum_{k=0}^{n-1}(-1)^k\binom{2n}{2k+1}T_k+(-1)^n, \tag{70}$$

and
$$E_n=(-1)^{n-1}\sum_{k=0}^{n-1}(-1)^k\binom{2n}{2k+1}2^{2k+1}(2^{2k+2}-1)\frac{B_{k+1}}{k+1}+(-1)^n. \tag{71}$$

10. We shall now find relations involving the coefficients of the expansions of $\cot x$ and $\operatorname{cosec} x$.

Let
$$\cot x=\frac{1}{x}+\sum_{k=0}^{\infty}V_k'\frac{x^{2k+1}}{(2k+1)!} \tag{72}$$

and
$$\operatorname{cosec} x=\frac{1}{x}+\sum_{k=0}^{\infty}W_k'\frac{x^{2k+1}}{(2k+1)!}, \tag{73}$$

where
$$V_k'=-\frac{2^{2k+1}}{k+1}B_{k+1} \quad\text{and}\quad W_k'=\frac{2^{2k+1}-1}{k+1}B_{k+1}. \tag{74}$$

(i) By means of (73), we have
$$\sin x\operatorname{cosec} x=\frac{\sin x}{x}+\sum_{k=0}^{\infty}W_k'\frac{x^{2k+1}}{(2k+1)!}\sum_{n=0}^{\infty}(-1)^n\frac{x^{2n+1}}{(2n+1)!}. \tag{75}$$

Letting $n+k=n'$, then (75) becomes
$$\sin x\operatorname{cosec} x=\sum_{n=0}^{\infty}(-1)^n\frac{x^{2n}}{(2n+1)}+\sum_{k=0}^{\infty}(-1)^kW_k'\frac{x^{2k+1}}{(2k+1)!}\sum_{n=k}^{\infty}(-1)^n\frac{x^{2n+2}}{(2\overline{n-k}+1)!}$$
$$=1-\sum_{n=0}^{\infty}(-1)^n\frac{x^{2n+2}}{(2n+3)!}+\sum_{n=0}^{\infty}(-1)^n\frac{x^{2n+2}}{(2n+2)!}\sum_{k=0}^{n}(-1)^k\binom{2n+2}{2k+1}W_k'; \tag{76}$$

and since $\sin x\operatorname{cosec} x=1$, therefore
$$\sum_{k=0}^{\infty}(-1)^k\binom{2n+2}{2k+1}W_k'=\frac{1}{2n+3}. \tag{77}$$

(ii) From $\sin x\cot x=\cos x$ we obtain
$$\sum_{k=0}^{n}(-1)^k\binom{2n+2}{2k+1}V_k'=\frac{1}{2n+3}-1. \tag{78}$$

Comparing (77) and (78) gives
$$\sum_{k=0}^{n}(-1)^k\binom{2n+2}{2k+1}(W_k'-V_k')=1 \tag{79}$$

and
$$\sum_{k=0}^{n}(-1)^k\binom{2n+2}{2k+1}\frac{2^{2k+2}-1}{k+1}B_{k+1}=1. \tag{80}$$

(iii) From $1+\cos 2x=\sin 2x\cot x$ we derive
$$\sum_{k=0}^{n}\frac{(-1)^k}{2^{2k}}\binom{2n+2}{2k+1}V_k=-\frac{2(2n+1)}{2n+3} \tag{81}$$

and
$$\sum_{k=0}^{n}\frac{(-1)^k}{k+1}\binom{2n+2}{2k+1}B_{k+1}=\frac{2n+1}{2n+3}. \tag{82}$$

11. NUMBERS RELATED TO EULER'S NUMBERS.

Glaisher* has by induction and comparison obtained the expansions

$$F(x)=\frac{\cos x}{\cos 2x}=\sum_{n=0}^{\infty} P_n \frac{x^{2n}}{(2n)!} \tag{83}$$

and

$$f(x)=\frac{\sin x}{\cos 2x}=\sum_{n=0}^{\infty} Q_n \frac{x^{2n+1}}{(2n+1)!}, \tag{84}$$

where

$$P_n=(-1)^n \sum_{k=0}^{n} (-1)^k \binom{2n}{2k} 2^{2k} E_k \tag{85}$$

and

$$Q_n=(-1)^n \sum_{k=0}^{n} (-1)^k \binom{2n+1}{2k} 2^{2k} E_k, \tag{86}$$

but no formula for E_k is given.

We shall consider here the more general expansions

$$F_p(x)=\frac{\cos^p a_1 x}{\cos^p a_2 x}=\sum_{n=0}^{\infty} P_{p,n} \frac{x^{2n}}{(2n)!} \tag{87}$$

and

$$f_p(x)=\frac{\sin^p a_1 x}{\cos^p a_2 x}=\sum_{n=0}^{\infty} Q_{p,n} \frac{x^{2n+1}}{(2n+1)!}, \tag{88}$$

and derive

$$P_{p,n}=(-1)^n \frac{a_1^{2n}}{2^{p-1}} \sum_{k=0}^{n} (-1)^k \binom{2n}{2k} \left(\frac{a_2}{a_1}\right)^{2k} \sum_{\gamma=0}^{\left[\frac{p-1}{2}\right]} \binom{p}{\gamma} (p-2\gamma)^{2n-2k} E_{p,k} - \frac{1+(-1)^p}{2^{p+1}} \binom{p}{\left[\frac{p}{2}\right]} a_2^{2n} E_{p,n} \tag{89}$$

and

$$Q_{p,n}=(-1)^n \frac{a_1^{2n+p}}{2^{p-1}} \sum_{k=0}^{n} (-1)^k \binom{2n+p}{2k} \left(\frac{a_2}{a_1}\right)^{2k} \sum_{\gamma=0}^{\left[\frac{p-1}{2}\right]} (-1)^\gamma \binom{p}{\gamma} (p-2\gamma)^{2n-2k+p} E_{p,k}, \tag{90}$$

where $E_{p,k}$ is the coefficient of $\frac{x^{2n}}{(2n)!}$ in the expansion of $\sec^p x$. The number $E_{p,k}$ is called the Euler number of order p.

By Ch. IV. (96),

$$E_{p,k}=(-1)^k \sum_{\alpha=0}^{2k} \binom{p+\alpha-1}{\alpha} \frac{1}{2^\alpha} \sum_{\beta=0}^{\alpha} (-1)^\beta \binom{\alpha}{\beta} (p+2\beta)^{2k}. \tag{91}$$

If $p=1$, $a=1$ and $b=2$, (89) and (90) reduce to Glaisher's expressions.

To derive (89) we multiply

$$\cos^p a_1 x=\frac{1}{2^p} \sum_{k=0}^{\infty} (-1)^k a_1^{2k} \frac{x^{2k}}{(2k)!} \sum_{\gamma=0}^{p} \binom{p}{\gamma} (p-2\gamma)^{2k} \tag{92}$$

by

$$\sec^p a_2 x=\sum_{n=0}^{\infty} a_2^{2n} \frac{x^{2n}}{(2n)!} E_{p,n}, \tag{93}$$

* *Q.J.M.*, vol. 29, pp. 59-69 and vol. 45, pp. 187-222.

giving

$$F_p(x)=\frac{1}{2^p}\sum_{k=0}^{\infty}(-1)^k a_1^{2k}\sum_{n=0}^{\infty}a_2^{2n}\frac{x^{2n+2k}}{(2n)!\,(2k)!}\sum_{\gamma=0}^{p}\binom{p}{\gamma}(p-2\gamma)^{2k}E_{p,n}. \qquad (94)$$

Letting $n+k=n'$,

$$F_p(x)=\frac{1}{2^p}\sum_{k=0}^{\infty}(-1)^k a_1^{2k}\sum_{n=k}^{\infty}a_2^{2(n-k)}\frac{x^{2n}}{(2\,\overline{n-k})!\,(2k)!}\sum_{\gamma=0}^{p}\binom{p}{\gamma}(p-2\gamma)^{2k}E_{p,\,n-k} \qquad (95)$$

$$=\frac{1}{2^p}\sum_{n=0}^{\infty}\sum_{k=0}^{n}(-1)^k a_1^{2k}\binom{2n}{2k}a_2^{2(n-k)}\sum_{\gamma=0}^{p}\binom{p}{\gamma}(p-2\gamma)^{2k}E_{p,\,n-k}, \text{ by Ch. I. (68)}, \qquad (96)$$

and letting $n-k=k'$, we obtain

$$F_p(x)=\frac{1}{2^p}\sum_{n=0}^{\infty}(-1)^n a_1^{2n}\sum_{k=0}^{n}(-1)^k\binom{2n}{2k}\left(\frac{a_2}{a_1}\right)^{2k}\frac{x^{2n}}{(2n)!}\sum_{\gamma=0}^{p}\binom{p}{\gamma}(p-2\gamma)^{2n-2k}E_{p,\,k}. \qquad (97)$$

Now, whether p be even or odd,

$$\sum_{\gamma=0}^{p}\binom{p}{\gamma}(p-2\gamma)^{2k}=2\sum_{\gamma=0}^{\left[\frac{p-1}{2}\right]}\binom{p}{\gamma}(p-2\gamma)^{2k},$$

and

$$=2\sum_{\gamma=0}^{\frac{p}{2}}\binom{p}{\gamma}-\binom{p}{\frac{p}{2}},$$

when p is even and $k=0$; therefore

$$P_{p,n}=(-1)^n\frac{a_1^{2n}}{2^{p-1}}\sum_{k=0}^{n}(-1)^k\binom{2n}{2k}\left(\frac{a_2}{a_1}\right)^{2k}\sum_{\gamma=0}^{\left[\frac{p-1}{2}\right]}\binom{p}{\gamma}(p-2\gamma)^{2n-2k}E_{p,k} - \frac{1+(-1)^\gamma}{2^{p+1}}\binom{p}{\left[\frac{p}{2}\right]}a_2^{2n}E_{p,n}. \qquad (98)$$

The coefficient of $\frac{x^{2n}}{(2n)!}$ in the expansion of

$$\frac{\cos^p a_1 x}{\cos^q a_2 x}$$

is of the same form as (98), except that in $E_{p,k}$ and $E_{p,n}$, q appears in place of n.

The expression for $Q_{p,n}$ is obtained by multiplying

$$\sin^p a_1 x=\frac{a_1^p}{2^{p-1}}\sum_{k=0}^{\infty}(-1)^k a_1^{2k}\frac{x^{2k+p}}{(2k+p)!}\sum_{\gamma=0}^{\left[\frac{p-1}{2}\right]}(-1)^\gamma\binom{p}{\gamma}(p-2\gamma)^{2k+p}$$

by the expansion of $\sec^p a_2 x$ and following the method by which $P_{p,n}$ was obtained.

12. (i) We shall next express the Bernoulli number—defined as the coefficient of $\frac{x^{2n}}{(2n)!}$ in the expansion of $\frac{x}{2}\cot\frac{x}{2}$—in form of a determinant.

For that purpose we first expand

$$f(x)=\frac{x}{2}\,\frac{e^x+1}{e^x-1}, \tag{99}$$

in powers of x.

Taking the $(2n+1)$st and then the $(2n+2)$nd derivative of

$$(e^x-1)\,f(x)=\frac{x}{2}\,(e^x+1),$$

we obtain
$$\sum_{k=0}^{2n+1}\binom{2n+1}{k}\frac{d^k}{dx^k}f(x)\,\frac{d^{2n+1-k}}{dx^{2n+1-k}}(e^x-1)=\frac{x}{2}\,e^x+\tfrac{1}{2}(2n+1)\,e^x \tag{100}$$

and
$$\sum_{k=0}^{2n+2}\binom{2n+2}{k}\frac{d^k}{dx^k}f(x)\,\frac{d^{2n+2-k}}{dx^{2n+2-k}}(e^x-1)=\frac{x}{2}\,e^x+\tfrac{1}{2}(2n+2)\,e^x. \tag{101}$$

Now, since $f(x)$ is an even function, we may write

$$f(x)=\sum_{n=0}^{\infty}v_{2n}\,\frac{x^{2n}}{(2n)!}, \tag{102}$$

where
$$v_{2n}=\frac{d^{2n}}{dx^{2n}}f(x)\Big]_{x=0}.$$

From (100) and (101) we obtain

$$\sum_{k=0}^{n}\binom{2n+1}{2k}v_{2k}=n+\tfrac{1}{2},\quad v_0=1, \tag{103}$$

and
$$\sum_{k=0}^{n}\binom{2n+2}{2k}v_{2k}=n+1. \tag{104}$$

Subtracting (103) from (104) gives

$$\sum_{k=0}^{n}\left[\binom{2n+2}{2k}-\binom{2n+1}{2k}\right]v_{2k}=\tfrac{1}{2}; \tag{105}$$

and since
$$\binom{2n+2}{2k}-\binom{2n+1}{2k}=\binom{2n+1}{2k-1},$$

therefore
$$\sum_{k=0}^{n}\binom{2n+1}{2k-1}v_{2k}=\tfrac{1}{2},\quad n=1,\,2,\,3,\,\ldots,\,n. \tag{106}$$

Solving the system of equations resulting from (106), we obtain

$$v_{2n}=\tfrac{1}{2}\begin{vmatrix}1 & \binom{2n+1}{4} & \binom{2n+1}{6} & \cdots & \binom{2n+1}{2n}\\ 1 & \binom{2n-1}{2} & \binom{2n-1}{4} & \cdots & \binom{2n-1}{2n-2}\\ 1 & 0 & \binom{2n-3}{2} & \cdots & \binom{2n-3}{2n-4}\\ \cdots & \cdots & \cdots & \cdots & \cdots\\ 1 & 0 & 0 & \cdots & \binom{3}{2}\end{vmatrix}\div\begin{vmatrix}\binom{2n+1}{2} & \binom{2n+1}{4} & \cdots & \binom{2n+1}{2n}\\ 0 & \binom{2n-1}{2} & \cdots & \binom{2n-1}{2n-2}\\ 0 & 0 & \cdots & \binom{2n-3}{2n-4}\\ \cdots & \cdots & \cdots & \cdots\\ 0 & 0 & \cdots & \binom{3}{2}\end{vmatrix}. \quad (1$$

The determinant of the denominator reduces to

$$\binom{2n+1}{2}\binom{2n-1}{2}\cdots\binom{5}{2}\binom{3}{2}=\frac{(2n+1)!}{2^n}. \tag{108}$$

If now in the determinant of the numerator $(2n+3-2\alpha)!$ be removed from the αth row, $\alpha=1, 2, 3, \ldots, n$, and $\frac{1}{(2n+1-2\beta)!}$ from the βth column, except the first, $\beta=2, 3, 4, \ldots, n$, the determinant becomes

$$\frac{(2n+1)!(2n-1)!\ldots 5!3!}{(2n-3)!(2n-5)!\ldots 3!1!}\begin{vmatrix} \frac{1}{(2n+1)!} & \frac{1}{4!} & \frac{1}{6!} & \cdots & \frac{1}{(2n)!} \\ \frac{1}{(2n-1)!} & \frac{1}{2!} & \frac{1}{4!} & \cdots & \frac{1}{(2n-2)!} \\ \frac{1}{(2n-3)!} & 0 & \frac{1}{2!} & \cdots & \frac{1}{(2n-4)!} \\ \cdots & \cdots & \cdots & \cdots & \cdots \\ \frac{1}{3!} & 0 & 0 & \cdots & \frac{1}{2!} \end{vmatrix}. \tag{109}$$

Therefore

$$v_{2n}=(-1)^{n-1}2^{n-1}(2n-1)!\begin{vmatrix} \frac{1}{4!} & \frac{1}{6!} & \frac{1}{8!} & \cdots & \frac{1}{(2n)!} & \frac{1}{(2n+1)!} \\ \frac{1}{2!} & \frac{1}{4!} & \frac{1}{6!} & \cdots & \frac{1}{(2n-2)!} & \frac{1}{(2n-1)!} \\ 0 & \frac{1}{2!} & \frac{1}{4!} & \cdots & \frac{1}{(2n-4)!} & \frac{1}{(2n-3)!} \\ \cdots & \cdots & \cdots & \cdots & \cdots & \cdots \\ 0 & 0 & 0 & \cdots & \frac{1}{2!} & \frac{1}{3!} \end{vmatrix}. \tag{110}$$

Denoting the determinant in (110) by Δ_n (Δ_0 not being defined), we have

$$f(x)=\frac{x}{2}\frac{e^x+1}{e^x-1}=1-\tfrac{1}{4}\sum_{n=1}^{\infty}(-1)^n 2^n \Delta_n \frac{x^n}{n!}. \tag{111}$$

Substituting in (111) $2i\theta$ for x gives

$$i\theta\frac{e^{i\theta}+e^{-i\theta}}{e^{i\theta}-e^{-i\theta}}=\theta\cot\theta=1-\sum_{n=1}^{\infty}2^{3n-2}\Delta_n\frac{\theta^{2n}}{n}; \tag{112}$$

therefore

$$\cot\theta=\frac{1}{\theta}-\sum_{n=1}^{\infty}2^{3n-2}\Delta_n\frac{\theta^{2n-1}}{n}, \tag{113}$$

and by the definition (4)

$$B_n=(2n-1)!\,2^{n-1}\Delta_n. \tag{114}$$

(ii) By means of $\tan\theta = \cot\theta - 2\cot 2\theta$,

we find
$$\tan\theta = \sum_{n=1}^{\infty} 2^{3n-2}(2^{2n}-1)\Delta_n \frac{\theta^{2n-1}}{n}, \tag{115}$$

which gives for B_n the same form as (114).

(iii) By the use of $\operatorname{cosec}\theta = \cot\frac{1}{2}\theta - \cot\theta$

we derive
$$\operatorname{cosec}\theta = \frac{1}{\theta} + \sum_{n=1}^{\infty} 2^{n-1}(2^{2n-1}-1)\Delta_n \frac{\theta^{2n}}{n}, \tag{116}$$

and obtain for B_n again the expression (114).

13. To represent Euler's number as a determinant.

Let
$$\sec x = \sum_{k=0}^{\infty} (-1)^k u_{2k} \frac{x^{2k}}{(2k)!}; \tag{117}$$

then from
$$\sec x \cos x = 1$$

we obtain
$$\sum_{k=0}^{n} \binom{2n}{2k} u_{2k} = 0, \quad n > 0, \quad u_0 = 1, \tag{118}$$

or
$$\sum_{k=1}^{n} \binom{2n}{2k} u_{2k} = -1, \quad n = 1, 2, 3, \ldots, n. \tag{119}$$

Solving the system of equations resulting from (119), we find

$$u_{2n} = \begin{vmatrix} -1 & \binom{2n}{2} & \binom{2n}{4} & \cdots & \binom{2n}{2n-2} \\ -1 & 1 & \binom{2n-2}{2} & \cdots & \binom{2n-2}{2n-4} \\ -1 & 0 & 1 & \cdots & \binom{2n-4}{2n-6} \\ \cdots & \cdots & \cdots & \cdots & \cdots \\ -1 & 0 & 0 & \cdots & 1 \end{vmatrix}. \tag{120}$$

Removing in (120) $(2n-2\alpha+2)!$ from the αth row and $\dfrac{1}{(2n-2\beta-2)!}$ from the βth column, we have

$$u_{2n} = -(2n)! \begin{vmatrix} \frac{1}{(2n)!} & \frac{1}{2!} & \frac{1}{4!} & \cdots & \frac{1}{(2n-2)!} \\ \frac{1}{(2n-2)!} & 1 & \frac{1}{2!} & \cdots & \frac{1}{(2n-4)!} \\ \frac{1}{(2n-4)!} & 0 & 1 & \cdots & \frac{1}{(2n-6)!} \\ \cdots & \cdots & \cdots & \cdots & \cdots \\ \frac{1}{2!} & 0 & 0 & \cdots & 1 \end{vmatrix} \tag{121}$$

or

$$u_{2n}=(-1)^n(2n)!\begin{vmatrix} \frac{1}{2!} & \frac{1}{4!} & \frac{1}{6!} & \cdots & \frac{1}{(2n-2)!} & \frac{1}{(2n)!} \\ 1 & \frac{1}{2!} & \frac{1}{4!} & \cdots & \frac{1}{(2n-4)!} & \frac{1}{(2n-2)!} \\ 0 & 1 & \frac{1}{2!} & \cdots & \frac{1}{(2n-6)!} & \frac{1}{(2n-4)!} \\ \cdots & \cdots & \cdots & \cdots & \cdots & \cdots \\ 0 & 0 & 0 & \cdots & 1 & \frac{1}{2!} \end{vmatrix}. \tag{122}$$

Denoting this determinant by Δ_n', then

$$u_{2n}=(-1)^n(2n)!\,\Delta_n'; \tag{123}$$

and since

$$E_n=(-1)^n u_{2n},$$

we have

$$E_n=(-1)^n(2n)!\,\Delta_n'. \tag{124}$$

We also find

$$\operatorname{cosec} x=\frac{1}{x}+\sum_{n=0}^{\infty}\Delta_n'' x^{2n-1}, \tag{125}$$

where

$$\Delta_n''=\begin{vmatrix} \frac{1}{3!} & \frac{1}{5!} & \frac{1}{7!} & \cdots & \frac{1}{(2n-1)!} & \frac{1}{(2n+1)!} \\ \frac{1}{1!} & \frac{1}{3!} & \frac{1}{5!} & \cdots & \frac{1}{(2n-3)!} & \frac{1}{(2n-1)!} \\ 0 & \frac{1}{1!} & \frac{1}{3!} & \cdots & \frac{1}{(2n-5)!} & \frac{1}{(2n-3)!} \\ \cdots & \cdots & \cdots & \cdots & \cdots & \cdots \\ 0 & 0 & 0 & \cdots & \frac{1}{1!} & \frac{1}{3!} \end{vmatrix}, \tag{126}$$

and by definition (6) we obtain

$$B_n=\frac{(2n)!}{2(2^{2n-1}-1)}\,\Delta_n''. \tag{127}$$

APPENDIX.

1. We shall give here expansions of a few expressions similar to Ch. I. (157) and (166), but of a more general type.

(i) To find the expansion in powers of x of

$$y=(3-4x^5+7x^{18})^p, \tag{1}$$

where p is any real number.

Expanding (1) by the Binomial Theorem, we have

$$y=3^p\sum_{k=0}^{\infty}(-1)^k\left(\frac{4}{3}\right)^k\binom{p}{k}x^{5k}\sum_{a=0}^{k}(-1)^a\binom{k}{a}\left(\frac{7}{3}\right)^a x^{13a}. \tag{2}$$

Letting
$$5k+13a=n, \tag{3}$$
we shall solve (3) for positive integral values of k and a. To this end we first find the smallest value a_0 of a and the corresponding value k_0 of k, satisfying

$$5k+13a=1. \tag{4}$$

Now a_0 is the solution of $13a\equiv 1\,(\text{mod } 5)$.

It is evident that the absolute value of a_0 is the denominator of the next to the last convergent of the continued fraction in which $\frac{13}{5}$ (the quotient between the coefficient of a and the coefficient of k) is converted, and the absolute value k_0 is the numerator of this convergent. We find $k_0=-5$ and $a_0=2$, and

$$\left.\begin{aligned} k&=-5n+13\left[\frac{2n}{5}\right]-13\gamma,\\ a&=\;\;\,2n-\;\,5\left[\frac{2n}{5}\right]+\;\,5\gamma. \end{aligned}\right\} \tag{5}$$

Now, since k and a are both positive and $k\geqq a$, it follows that

$$\gamma\geqq 0 \quad\text{and}\quad \gamma\leqq\left[\left[\frac{2n}{5}\right]-\frac{7n}{18}\right],$$

where if f is a proper fraction $[-f]$ is defined as zero.

Therefore

$$y=3^p\sum_{n=0}^{\infty}(-1)^n x^n\sum_{k=0}^{\left[\left[\frac{2n}{5}\right]-\frac{7n}{18}\right]}\left(\frac{4}{3}\right)^{-5n+13\left[\frac{2n}{3}\right]-13k}\left(\frac{7}{3}\right)^{2n-5\left[\frac{2n}{5}\right]+5k}$$
$$\binom{-5n+13\left[\frac{2n}{5}\right]-13k}{2n-5\left[\frac{2n}{5}\right]+5k}\binom{p}{-5n+13\left[\frac{2n}{5}\right]-13k}. \tag{6}$$

For example,

$$((x^{10}))(3-4x^5+7x^{18})^3 = 27\binom{4}{3}^2\binom{2}{0}\binom{3}{2} = 144\,;$$

$$((x^{9}))(3-4x^5+7x^{18})^3 = -27\binom{4}{3}^{-3}\binom{7}{3}^2\binom{-3}{2}\binom{3}{-6} = 0\,;$$

$$((x^{23}))(3-4x^5+7x^{18})^{\frac{1}{2}} = -3^{\frac{1}{2}}\binom{4}{3}^2\frac{7}{3}\binom{2}{1}\binom{\frac{1}{2}}{2} = \frac{28}{27}\sqrt{3}.$$

(ii) To expand in powers of x,

$$y = (1+x^8)^{p_1}(1+x^3)^{p_2}, \tag{7}$$

where p_1 and p_2 are any real numbers.

Then
$$\sum_{k=0}^{\infty}\binom{p_1}{k}x^{8k}\sum_{a=0}^{\infty}\binom{p_2}{a}x^{3a}. \tag{8}$$

Letting $8k+3a=n$, and following the method in (i), we find

$$\left.\begin{aligned} k &= -n+3\left[\frac{3n}{8}\right]-3\gamma, \\ a &= 3n-8\left[\frac{3n}{8}\right]+8\gamma, \end{aligned}\right\} \tag{9}$$

and
$$y = \sum_{n=0}^{\infty}x^n \sum_{k=0}^{\left[\left[\frac{3n}{8}\right]-\frac{n}{3}\right]}\binom{p_1}{-n+3\left[\frac{3n}{8}\right]-3k}\binom{p_2}{3n-8\left[\frac{3n}{8}\right]+8k}. \tag{10}$$

Denoting in (10) the product of the binomial coefficients by $P_{n,k}$, we have

$$(1-x^8)^{p_1}(1+x^3)^{p_2} = \sum_{n=0}^{\infty}(-1)^{n+\left[\frac{3n}{8}\right]}\sum_{k=0}^{\left[\left[\frac{3n}{8}\right]-\frac{n}{3}\right]}(-1)^k P_{n,k}. \tag{11}$$

Show that

$$(5-3x^4)^{1/3}(9-2x^7)^{1/5} = 5^{1/3}9^{1/5}\sum_{n=0}^{\infty}(-1)^{n+\left[\frac{n}{4}\right]}x^n\sum_{k=0}^{\left[\left[\frac{n}{4}\right]-\frac{2n}{9}\right]}(-1)^k\left(\frac{3}{5}\right)^{-2n+9\left[\frac{n}{4}\right]-9k}$$
$$\left(\frac{2}{9}\right)^{n-4\left[\frac{n}{4}\right]+4k}\binom{\frac{1}{3}}{-2n+9\left[\frac{n}{4}\right]-9k}\binom{\frac{1}{5}}{n-4\left[\frac{n}{4}\right]+4k}. \tag{12}$$

(iii) To expand in powers of x,

$$y = (1+x^m)^p\log(1+x^q). \tag{13}$$

Then
$$y = \sum_{k=0}^{\infty}\binom{p}{k}x^{mk}\sum_{a=0}^{\infty}(-1)^a\frac{x^{q(a+1}}{a+1}. \tag{14}$$

Letting $mk+qa=n$, we find

$$\left.\begin{aligned} k &= nk_0+q\left[\frac{na_0}{m}\right]-q\gamma, \\ a &= na_0-m\left[\frac{na_0}{m}\right]+m\gamma, \end{aligned}\right\} \tag{15}$$

where a_0 is the smallest value of a and k_0 the corresponding value of k satisfying

$$mk + qa = 1. \tag{16}$$

We then obtain

$$y = x^q \sum_{n=0}^{\infty} (-1)^{na_0 - m\left[\frac{na_0}{m}\right]} x^n \sum_{k=0}^{\left[\left[\frac{na_0}{m}\right]+\frac{nk_0}{q}\right]} \frac{(-1)^{mk}}{n_1} (P_{n_2}), \tag{17}$$

where

$$\left.\begin{aligned} n_1 &= na_0 - m\left[\frac{na_0}{m}\right] + mk + 1, \\ \text{and} \quad n_2 &= nk_0 + q\left[\frac{na_0}{m}\right] - qk. \end{aligned}\right\} \tag{18}$$

(iv) Show that

$$(a)\ \tan^{-1}x^9 \log(1+x^5) = x^{14} \sum_{n=0}^{\infty} (-1)^{n+\left[\frac{7n}{18}\right]} x^n \sum_{k=0}^{\left[\frac{2}{5}n - \left[\frac{7n}{18}\right]\right]} \frac{(-1)^k}{n_1 n_2}, \tag{19}$$

where

$$\left.\begin{aligned} n_1 &= \quad 4n - 10\left[\frac{7n}{18}\right] - 10k + 1, \\ \text{and} \quad n_2 &= -7n + 18\left[\frac{7n}{18}\right] + 18k + 1. \end{aligned}\right\} \tag{20}$$

If n_1 and n_2 either or both are negative, the corresponding term is zero.

$$(b)\ \tan^{-1}x^{\frac{1}{2}} \log(1+x^{\frac{1}{3}}) = x^{\frac{5}{6}} \sum_{n=0}^{\infty} (-1)^n x^{\frac{n}{3}} \sum_{k=0}^{\left[\frac{n}{3}\right]} \frac{1}{2k+1} \frac{1}{n-3k+1}, \tag{21}$$

$$(c)\ \tan^{-1}x^{\frac{1}{3}} \log(1+x^{\frac{1}{5}}) = x^{\frac{8}{15}} \sum_{n=0}^{\infty} (-1)^{\left[\frac{3n}{10}\right]} x^{\frac{n}{15}} \sum_{k=0}^{\left[\frac{n}{3} - \left[\frac{3n}{10}\right]\right]} \frac{(-1)^k}{n_1 n_2}, \tag{22}$$

where

$$\left.\begin{aligned} n_1 &= \quad 2n - 6\left[\frac{3n}{10}\right] - 6k + 1, \\ \text{and} \quad n_2 &= -3n + 10\left[\frac{3n}{10}\right] + 10k + 1. \end{aligned}\right\} \tag{23}$$

$$(d)\ \sin^{-1}x^{\frac{4}{5}} \tan^{-1}x^{\frac{3}{7}} = x^{\frac{43}{35}} \sum_{n=0}^{\infty} (-1)^n x^{\frac{2n}{35}} \sum_{k=0}^{\left[\frac{7n}{15} - \left[\frac{13n}{28}\right]\right]} \frac{1}{2^{2n_1}} \binom{2n_1}{n_1} \frac{1}{n_1 n_2}, \tag{24}$$

where

$$\left.\begin{aligned} n_1 &= \quad 14n - 30\left[\frac{13n}{28}\right] - 30k + 1, \\ \text{and} \quad n_2 &= -26n + 56\left[\frac{13n}{28}\right] + 56k + 1. \end{aligned}\right\} \tag{25}$$

2. Show that

$$\text{(i)}\ \sum_{k=0}^{\left[\frac{n}{2}\right]} \binom{n}{2k} \sin kx = 2^{n-1}\left[\cos^n \frac{x}{4} \sin \frac{nx}{4} + (-1)^n \sin^n \frac{x}{4} \sin\left(\frac{n\pi}{2} + \frac{nx}{4}\right)\right],$$

(ii) $$\sum_{k=0}^{\left[\frac{n}{2}\right]} \binom{n}{2k} \cos kx = 2^{n-1}\left[\cos^n \frac{x}{4} \cos \frac{nx}{4} + (-1)^n \sin^n \frac{x}{4} \cos\left(\frac{n\pi}{2} + \frac{nx}{4}\right)\right],$$

(iii) $$\sum_{k=0}^{\left[\frac{n-1}{2}\right]} \binom{n}{2k+1} \sin (2k+1)x$$
$$= 2^{n-1}\left[\cos^n \frac{x}{2} \sin \frac{nx}{2} - (-1)^n \sin^n \frac{x}{2} \sin (\pi + x) \frac{n}{2}\right],$$

(iv) $$\sum_{k=0}^{\left[\frac{n-1}{2}\right]} \binom{n}{2k+1} \cos (2k+1)x$$
$$= 2^{n-1}\left[\cos^n \frac{x}{2} \cos \frac{nx}{2} - (-1)^n \sin^n \frac{x}{2} \cos (\pi + x) \frac{n}{2}\right],$$

(v) $$\sum_{k=0}^{\left[\frac{n-1}{2}\right]} \binom{n}{2k+1} \sin kx$$
$$= 2^{n-1}\left[\cos^n \frac{x}{4} \sin (n-2) \frac{x}{4} - (-1)^n \sin^n \frac{x}{4} \sin \frac{1}{4}(2n\pi + \overline{n-2}\, x)\right],$$

(vi) $$\sum_{k=0}^{\left[\frac{n-1}{2}\right]} \binom{n}{2k+1} \cos kx$$
$$= 2^{n-1}\left[\cos^n \frac{x}{4} \cos (n-2) \frac{x}{4} - (-1)^n \sin^n \frac{x}{4} \cos \frac{1}{4}(2n\pi + \overline{n-2}\, x)\right],$$

(vii) $$\sum_{k=0}^{\left[\frac{n}{2}\right]} (-1)^k \binom{n}{2k} \sin kx$$
$$= 2^{n-1}\left[\cos^n \frac{\pi + x}{4} \sin \frac{\pi + x}{4} n + (-1)^n \sin^n \frac{\pi + x}{4} \sin \frac{1}{4}(2n\pi + \overline{\pi + x}\, n)\right],$$

(viii) $$\sum_{k=0}^{\left[\frac{n}{2}\right]} (-1)^k \binom{n}{2k} \cos kx$$
$$= 2^{n-1}\left[\cos^n \frac{\pi + x}{4} \cos \frac{\pi + x}{4} n + (-1)^n \sin^n \frac{\pi + x}{4} \cos \frac{1}{4}(2n\pi + \overline{\pi + x}\, n)\right],$$

(ix) $$\sum_{k=0}^{\left[\frac{n-1}{2}\right]} (-1)^k \binom{n}{2k+1} \sin kx$$
$$= 2^{n-1}\left[(-1)^n \sin^n \frac{\pi + x}{4} \cos \frac{1}{4}(3n\pi + \overline{n-2}\, x) - \cos^n \frac{\pi + x}{4} \cos \frac{1}{4}(n\pi + \overline{n-2}\, x)\right],$$

(x) $$\sum_{k=0}^{\left[\frac{n-1}{2}\right]} (-1)^k \binom{n}{2k+1} \cos kx$$
$$= 2^{n-1}\left[(-1)^{n-1} \sin^n \frac{\pi + x}{4} \sin \frac{1}{4}(3n\pi + \overline{n-2}\, x) + \cos^n \frac{\pi + x}{4} \sin \frac{1}{4}(n\pi + \overline{n-2}\, x)\right].$$

NOTES: **1.** Arrangement is alphabetical, by author. **2.** The item number (given in brackets) and author identifies title completely. Books may be ordered by item number and author. **3.** A Supplement to this Check List will be issued every three or four months.

MODERN PURE SOLID GEOMETRY

By N. ALTSHILLER-COURT

In this second edition of this well-known book on synthetic solid geometry, the author has supplemented several of the chapters with an account of recent results.

—Approx. 340 pp. 5⅜x8. [147] **In prep.**

STRING FIGURES, and other monographs

By BALL, CAJORI, CARSLAW, and PETERSEN

FOUR VOLUMES IN ONE:
String Figures, *by W. W. Rouse Ball;*

The Elements of Non-Euclidean Plane Geometry, *by H. S. Carslaw;*

A History of the Logarithmic Slide Rule, *by F. Cajori;*

Methods and Theories for the Solution of Problems of Geometrical Construction, *by J. Petersen*

—528 pp. 5¼x8. [130] Four vols. in one. **$3.95**

THÉORIE DES OPÉRATIONS LINÉAIRES

By S. BANACH

—1933. xii + 250 pp. 5¼x8¼. [110] **$3.95**

THEORIE DER FUNKTIONEN MEHRERER KOMPLEXER VERÄNDERLICHEN

By H. BEHNKE and P. THULLEN

—(Ergeb. der Math.) 1934. vii+115 pp. 5½x8½. [68] **$3.25**

CONFORMAL MAPPING

By L. BIEBERBACH

"The first book in English to give an elementary, readable account of the Riemann Mapping Theorem and the distortion theorems and uniformisation problem with which it is connected. . . . Presented in very attractive and readable form."
—*Math. Gazette.*

". . . thorough and painstaking . . . lucid and clear and well arranged . . . an excellent text."
—*Bulletin of the A. M. S.*

"Engineers will profitably use this book for its accurate exposition."—*Appl. Mechanics Reviews.*

—1952. vi + 234 pp. 4½x6½. [90] **$2.50**

BASIC GEOMETRY

By G. D. BIRKHOFF and R. BEATLEY

A highly recommended high-school text by two eminent scholars.

—Third edition. 1959. 294 pp. 5¼x8. [120] **$3.95**

KREIS UND KUGEL

By W. BLASCHKE

Isoperimetric properties of the circle and sphere, the (Brunn-Minkowski) theory of convex bodies, and differential-geometric properties (in the large) of convex bodies. A standard work.

—x + 169 pp. 5½x8½. [59] Cloth **$3.50**
[115] Paper **$1.50**

VORLESUNGEN ÜBER INTEGRAL-GEOMETRIE. Vols. I and II

By W. BLASCHKE

EINFÜHRUNG IN DIE THEORIE DER SYSTEME VON DIFFERENTIAL-GLEICHUNGEN

By E. KÄHLER

—222 pp. 5½x8½. [64] Three Vols. in One **$4.50**

VORLESUNGEN ÜBER FOURIERSCHE INTEGRALE

By S. BOCHNER

"A readable account of those parts of the subject useful for applications to problems of mathematical physics or pure analysis."

—*Bulletin of the A. M. S.*

—1932. 237 pp. 5½x8½. Orig. pub. at $6.40. [42] **$3.50**

ALMOST PERIODIC FUNCTIONS

By H. BOHR

Translated by H. COHN. From the famous series *Ergebnisse der Mathematik und ihrer Grenzgebiete*, a beautiful exposition of the theory of Almost Periodic Functions written by the creator of that theory.

—1951. 120 pp. 6x9. Lithotyped. German edition was $4.50.
[27] **$2.50**

LECTURES ON THE CALCULUS OF VARIATIONS

By O. BOLZA

A standard text by a major contributor to the theory.

—Ready June or July, 1961. Corr. repr. of first ed. xi + 267 pp. 5⅜x8. [145] Cloth **$3.25**
[152] Paper **$1.19**

THEORIE DER KONVEXEN KÖRPER

By T. BONNESEN and W. FENCHEL

"Remarkable monograph."

—*J. D. Tamarkin, Bulletin of the A. M. S.*

—1934. 171 pp. 5½x8½. Orig. publ. at $7.50 [54] **$3.95**

THE CALCULUS OF FINITE DIFFERENCES

By G. BOOLE

A standard work on the subject of finite differences and difference equations by one of the seminal minds in the field of finite mathematics.

Some of the topics covered are: *Interpolation, Finite Integration, Summation of Series, General Theory of Difference and Differential Equations of First Order, Linear DEqns with Variable Coefficients, Linear DEqns, Geometrical Applications.*

Numerous exercises with answers.

—Fourth edition. 1958. xii + 336 pp. 5x8. [121] Cloth **$3.95**
[148] Paper **$1.39**

A TREATISE ON DIFFERENTIAL EQUATIONS

By G. BOOLE

Including the Supplementary Volume.

—Fifth edition. 1959. xxiv + 735 pp. 5¼x8. [128] **$6.00**

THEORY OF FUNCTIONS

By C. CARATHÉODORY

Translated by F. STEINHARDT. The recent, and already famous textbook, *Funktionentheorie.*

Partial Contents: **Part One.** Chap. I. Algebra of Complex Numbers. II. Geometry of Complex Numbers. III. Euclidean, Spherical, and Non-Euclidean Geometry. **Part Two.** Theorems from Point Set Theory and Topology. Chap. I. Sequences and Continuous Complex Functions. II. Curves and Regions. III. Line Integrals. **Part Three.** Analytic Functions. Chap. I. Foundations. II. The Maximum-modulus principle. III. Poisson Integral and Harmonic Functions. IV. Meromorphic Functions. **Part Four.** Generation of Analytic Functions by Limiting Processes. Chap. I. Uniform Convergence. II. Normal Families of Meromorphic Functions. III. Power Series. IV. Partial Fraction Decomposition and the Calculus of Residues. **Part Five.** Special Functions. Chap. I. The Exponential Function and the Trigonometric Functions. II. Logarithmic Function. III. Bernoulli Numbers and the Gamma Function.

Vol. II.: **Part Six.** Foundations of Geometric Function Theory. Chap. I. Bounded Functions. II. Conformal Mapping. III. The Mapping of the Boundary. **Part Seven.** The Triangle Function and Picard's Theorem. Chap. I. Functions of Several Complex Variables. II. Conformal Mapping of Circular-Arc Triangles. III. The Schwarz Triangle Functions and the Modular Function. IV. Essential Singularities and Picard's Theorems.

"A book by a master . . . Carathéodory himself regarded [it] as his finest achievement . . . written from a catholic point of view."—*Bulletin of A.M.S.*

—Vol. I. Second edition. 1958. 310 pp. 6x9. [97] **$4.95**
—Vol. II. Second edition. 1960. 220 pp. 6x9. [106] **$4.95**

MEASURE AND INTEGRAL

By C. CARATHÉODORY

—About 360 pp. Translated from the German. **In prep.**

VORLESUNGEN ÜBER REELLE FUNKTIONEN

By C. CARATHÉODORY

This great classic is at once a book for the beginner, a reference work for the advanced scholar and a source of inspiration for the research worker.

—2nd, latest complete, ed. 728 pp. 5½x8½. Orig. publ. at $11.60. [38] **$8.00**

ELECTRIC CIRCUIT THEORY and the OPERATIONAL CALCULUS

By J. R. CARSON

"A rigorous and logical exposition and treatment of the Heaviside operational calculus and its applications to electrical problems . . . will be enjoyed and studied by mathematicians, engineers and scientists."—*Electrical World.*

—2nd ed. 206 pp. 5¼x8. [92] Cloth **$3.95**
[114] Paper **$1.88**

TEXTBOOK OF ALGEBRA

By G. CHRYSTAL

The usefulness, both as a textbook and as a work of reference, of this charming classic is attested to by the number of editions it has run through—the present being the sixth. Its richness of content can be only appreciated by an examination of the twelve-hundred-page book itself. **Thousands of valuable exercises (with solutions).**

6th ed. 2 Vols. 1235 pages. 5⅜x8. [84] Each volume **$2.95**

EIGENWERTPROBLEME UND IHRE NUMERISCHE BEHANDLUNG

By L. COLLATZ

"**Part I** presents an interesting and valuable collection of PRACTICAL APPLICATIONS.

"**Part II** deals with the MATHEMATICAL THEORY.

"**Part III** takes up various methods of NUMERICAL SOLUTION of boundary value problems. These include step-by-step approximations, graphical integration, the Rayleigh-Ritz method and methods depending on finite differences. **Here, as throughout the book, the theory is kept in close touch with practice by numerous specific examples.**"

—*Mathematical Reviews.*

—1945. 350 pp. 5½x8½. Orig. pub. at $8.80. [41] **$4.95**

ALGEBREN

By M. DEURING

—(Ergeb. der Math.) 1935. v + 143 pp. 5½x8½. Orig. pub. at $6.60. [50] **$3.95**

HISTORY OF THE THEORY OF NUMBERS

By L. E. DICKSON

"**A monumental work** . . . Dickson always has in mind the needs of the investigator . . . The author has [often] expressed in a nut-shell the main results of a long and involved paper *in a much clearer way than the writer of the article did himself*. The ability to reduce complicated mathematical arguments to simple and elementary terms is highly developed in Dickson."—*Bulletin of A. M. S.*

—Vol. I (Divisibility and Primality) xii + 486 pp. Vol. II (Diophantine Analysis) xxv + 803 pp. Vol. III (Quadratic and Higher Forms) v + 313 pp. [86] Three vol. set **$19.95**

STUDIES IN THE THEORY OF NUMBERS

By L. E. DICKSON

A systematic exposition, starting from first principles, of the arithmetic of quadratic forms, chiefly (but not entirely) ternary forms, including numerous original investigations and correct proofs of a number of classical results that have been stated or proved erroneously in the literature.

—1930. viii + 230 pp. 5⅜x8. [151] **In prep.**

THE INTEGRAL CALCULUS

By J. W. EDWARDS

A leisurely, immensely detailed, textbook of over 1,900 pages, rich in illustrative examples and manipulative techniques and containing much interesting material that must of necessity be omitted from less comprehensive works.

There are forty large chapters in all. The earlier cover a leisurely and a more-than-usually-detailed treatment of all the elementary standard topics. Later chapters include: Jacobian Elliptic Functions, Weierstrassian Elliptic Functions, Evaluation of Definite Integrals, Harmonic Analysis, Calculus of Variations, etc. Every chapter contains many exercises (with solutions).

—2 vols. 1,922 pp. 5x8. Originally published at $31.50 the set. [102], [105] Each volume **$7.50**

AUTOMORPHIC FUNCTIONS

By L. R. FORD

"Comprehensive . . . remarkably clear and explicit."—*Bulletin of the A. M. S.*

—2nd ed. (Cor. repr.) x + 333 pp. 5⅜x8. [85] **$4.95**

ASYMPTOTIC SERIES

By W. B. FORD

TWO VOLUMES IN ONE: *Studies on Divergent Series and Summability* and *The Asymptotic Developments of Functions Defined by MacLaurin Series.*

PARTIAL CONTENTS: I. MacLaurin Sum-Formula; Introduction to Study of Asymptotic Series. II. Determination of Asymptotic Development of a Given Function. III. Asymptotic Solutions of Linear Differential Equations. . . . V. Summability, etc. *I.* First General Theorem. . . . *III.* MacLaurin Series whose General Coefficient is Algebraic. . . . *VII.* Functions of Bessel Type. *VIII.* Asymptotic Behavior of Solution of Differential Equations of Fuchsian Type. Bibliography.

—1916; 1936-60. x + 341 pp. 6x9. [143] Two vols. in one. **$6.00**

THE CALCULUS OF EXTENSION

By H. G. FORDER

Partial Contents: I. Plane Geometry. II. Geometry in Space. III. Applications to Projective Geometry. . . . VIII. Applications to Systems of Linear Equations and Determinants. XII. Oriented Circle and Systems of Circles. XIII. The General Theory of Matrices . . . XV. Algebraic Products.

—1941-60. xvi + 490 pp. 5⅜x8. [135] **$4.95**

RUSSIAN MATHEMATICAL BIBLIOGRAPHY

By G. E. FORSYTHE

A bibliography of Russian Mathematics Books for the past quarter century. Supplements may be issued. Added subject index.

—1956. 106 pp. 5x8. [111] **$3.95**

CURVE TRACING

By P. FROST

This much-quoted and charming treatise gives a very readable treatment of a topic that can only be touched upon briefly in courses on Analytic Geometry. Teachers will find it invaluable as supplementary reading for their more interested students and for reference. The Calculus is not used.

Seventeen plates, containing over 200 figures, illustrate the discussion in the text.

—5th (unaltered) ed. 1960. 210 pp. + 17 fold-out plates. 5⅜x8. [140] **$3.50**

THE THEORY OF MATRICES

By F. R. GANTMACHER

Translated from the Russian, with further revisions by the Author.

This treatise by one of Russia's leading mathematicians gives, in easily accessible form, a coherent account of matrix theory with a view to applications in mathematics, theoretical physics, statistics, electrical engineering, etc. The individual chapters have been kept as far as possible independent of each other, so that the reader acquainted with the contents of Chapter I can proceed immediately to the chapters that especially interest him. Much of the material has been available until now only in the periodical literature.

Partial Contents. .VOL. ONE. I. Matrices and Matrix Operations. II. The Algorithm of Gauss and Applications. III. Linear Operators in an n-Dimensional Vector Space. IV. Characteristic Polynomial and Minimal Polynomial of a Matrix (Generalized Bézout Theorem, Method of Faddeev for Simultaneous Computation of Coefficients of Characteristic Polynomial and Adjoint Matrix, . . .). V. Functions of Matrices (Various Forms of the Definition, Components, Application to Integration of System of Linear Differential Eqns, Stability of Motion, . . .). VI. Equivalent Transformations of Polynomial Matrices; Analytic Theory of Elementary Divisors. VII. The Structure of a Linear Operator in an n-Dimensional Space (Minimal Polynomial, Congruence, Factor Space, Jordan Form, Krylov's Method of Transforming Secular Eqn, . . .). VIII. Matrix Equations (Matrix Polynomial Eqns, Roots and Logarithm of Matrices, . . .). IX. Linear Operators in a Unitary Space. X. Quadratic and Hermitian Forms.

VOLUME TWO. XI. Complex Symmetric, Skew-symmetric, and Orthogonal Matrices. XII. Singular Pencils of Matrices. XIII. Matrices with Non-Negative Elements (General Properties, Spectral Properties, Reducible Matrices, Primitive and Imprimitive Matrices, Stochastic Matrices, Limiting Probabilities for Homogeneous Markov Chain, Totally Non-Negative Matrices, Oscillatory Matrices . . .). XIV. Applications of the Theory of Matrices to the Investigation of Systems of Linear Differential Equations (Systems with Variable Coefficients, Lyapunov Transformations, Reducible Systems, Erugin's Theorem, Multiplicative Integral, Volterra's Calculus, Differential Systems in Complex Domain, Analytic Functions of Several Matrices, The Research of Lappo-Danilevskii, . . .). XV. The Problem of Routh-Hurwitz and Related Questions (Routh's Algorithm, Lyapunov's Theorem, Method of Quadratic Forms, Infinite Hankel Matrices of Finite Rank, Stability, Markov Parameters, Problem of Moments. Theorems of Markov and Chebyshev. Generalized Routh-Hurwitz Problem, . . .). Bibliography.

—Vol. I. 1960. x + 374 pp. 6x9. [131] **$6.00**
—Vol. II. 1960. x + 277 pp. 6x9. [133] **$6.00**

ARITHMETISCHE UNTERSUCHUNGEN

By C. F. GAUSS

The German translation of his *Disquisitiones Arithmeticae.*

—Repr. of 1st German ed. 860 pp. 5⅜x8. [150] **In prep.**

THEORY OF PROBABILITY

By B. V. GNEDENKO

Translated from the second Russian edition, with additions and revisions by Prof. Gnedenko.

Partial Contents: I. The Concept of Probability (Different approaches to the definition. Field of events. Geometrical Probability. Statistical definition. Axiomatic construction . . .). II. Sequences of Independent Trials. III. Markov Chains. IV. Random Variables and Distribution Functions (Continuous and discrete distributions. Multidimensional d. functions. Functions of random variables. Stieltjes integral). V. Numerical Characteristics of Random Variables (Mathematical expectation. Variance . . . Moments). VI. Law of Large Numbers (Mass phenomena. Tchebychev's form of law. Strong law of large numbers . . .). VII. Characteristic Functions (Properties. Inversion formula and uniqueness theorem. Helly's theorems. Limit theorems. Char. functs. for multidimensional random variables . . .). VIII. Classical Limit Theorem (Liapunov's theorem. Local limit theorem). IX. Theory of Infinitely Divisible Distribution Laws. X. Theory of Stochastic Processes (Generalized Markov equation. Continuous S. processes. Purely discontinuous S. processes. Kolmogorov-Feller equations. Homogeneous S. processes with independent increments. Stationary S. process. Stochastic integral. Spectral theorem of S. processes. Birkhoff-Khinchine ergodic theorem). XI. Elements of Statistics (Some problems. Variational series and empirical distribution functions. Glivenko's theorem and Kolmogorov's compatibility criterion. Two-sample problem. Critical region. Comparison of two statistical hypotheses . . . Confidence limits). TABLES. BIBLIOGRAPHY.

—Ready, 1961-1962. About 400 pp. 6x9. [132]

LES INTÉGRALES DE STIELTJES et leurs Applications aux Problèmes de la Physique Mathématique

By N. GUNTHER

—1932. 498 pp. 5½x8. [63] **$5.95**

LEÇONS SUR LA PROPAGATION DES ONDES ET LES ÉQUATIONS DE L'HYDRODYNAMIQUE

By J. HADAMARD

"[Hadamard's] unusual analytic proficiency enables him to connect in a wonderful manner the physical problem of propagation of waves and the mathematical problem of Cauchy concerning the characteristics of partial differential equations of the second order."—*Bulletin of the A. M. S.*

—viii + 375 pp. 5½x8½. [58] **$4.95**

REELLE FUNKTIONEN. Punktfunktionen

By H. HAHN

—426 pp. 5½x8½. Orig. pub. at $12.80. [52] **$4.95**

LECTURES ON ERGODIC THEORY

By P. R. HALMOS

CONTENTS: Introduction. Recurrence. Mean Convergence. Pointwise Convergence. Ergodicity. Mixing. Measure Algebras. Discrete Spectrum. Automorphisms of Compact Groups. Generalized Proper Values. Weak Topology. Weak Approximation. Uniform Topology. Uniform Approximation. Category. Invariant Measures. Generalized Ergodic Theorems. Unsolved Problems.

"Written in the pleasant, relaxed, and clear style usually associated with the author. The material is organized very well and painlessly presented. A number of remarks ranging from the serious to the whimsical add insight and enjoyment to the reading of the book."

—*Bulletin of the Amer. Math. Soc.*

—1960. (Repr. of 1956 ed.) viii + 101 pp. 5¼x8. [142] **$2.95**

INTRODUCTION TO HILBERT SPACE AND THE THEORY OF SPECTRAL MULTIPLICITY

By P. R. HALMOS

Prof. Halmos' recent book gives a clear, readable introductory treatment of Hilbert Space. The multiplicity theory of continuous spectra is treated, for the first time in English, in full generality.

—1957. 2nd ed. (c. repr. of 1st ed.). 120 pp. 6x9. [82] **$3.25**

RAMANUJAN: Twelve Lectures on His Life and Works

By G. H. HARDY

The book is somewhat more than an account of the mathematical work and personality of Ramanujan; it is one of the very few full-length books of "shop talk" by an important mathematician.

—viii + 236 pp. 6x9. [136] **$3.95**

GRUNDZÜGE DER MENGENLEHRE

By F. HAUSDORFF

Some of the topics in the Grundzüge omitted from later editions:

Symmetric Sets—Principle of Duality—most of the "Algebra" of Sets—most of the "Ordered Sets"—Partially Ordered Sets—Arbitrary Sets of Complexes—Normal Types—Initial and Final Ordering—Complexes of Real Numbers—General Topological Spaces—Euclidean Spaces—the Special Methods Applicable in the Euclidean plane—Jordan's separation Theorem—The Theory of Content and Measure—The Theory of the Lebesgue Integral.

—First edition. 484 pp. 5½x8¼. [61] **$4.95**

SET THEORY

By F. HAUSDORFF

Now for the first time available in English, Hausdorff's classic text-book has been an inspiration and a delight to those who have read it in the original German. The translation is from the Third (latest) German edition.

"We wish to state without qualification that this is an indispensable book for all those interested in the theory of sets and the allied branches of real variable theory."—*Bulletin of A. M. S.*

—1957. 352 pp. 6x9. [119] **$6.00**

VORLESUNGEN ÜBER DIE THEORIE DER ALGEBRAISCHEN ZAHLEN

By E. HECKE

"An elegant and comprehensive account of the modern theory of algebraic numbers."
—*Bulletin of the A. M. S.*

"A classic."—*Mathematical Gazette.*

—1923. 264 pp. 5½x8½. [46] **$3.95**

INTEGRALGLEICHUNGEN UND GLEICHUNGEN MIT UNENDLICHVIELEN UNBEKANNTEN

By E. HELLINGER and O. TOEPLITZ

"Indispensable to anybody who desires to penetrate deeply into this subject."—*Bulletin of A.M.S.*

—With a preface by E. Hilb. 1928. 286 pp. 5¼x8. [89] **$4.50**

Grundzüge Einer Allgemeinen Theorie der LINEAREN INTEGRALGLEICHUNGEN

By D. HILBERT

—306 pp. 5½x8¼. [91] **$4.50**

PRINCIPLES OF MATHEMATICAL LOGIC

By D. HILBERT and W. ACKERMANN

The famous *Grundüge der Theoretischen Logik* translated into English, with added notes and revisions by PROF. R. E. LUCE.

"The best textbook in a Western European language for a student wishing a fairly thorough treatment."—*Bulletin of the A. M. S.*

—1950-59. xii + 172 pp. 6x9. [69] **$3.75**

GEOMETRY AND THE IMAGINATION

By D. HILBERT and S. COHN-VOSSEN

The theme of this book is *insight.* Not merely proofs, but proofs that offer *insight*—intuitive understanding—into *why they are true.* Not merely properties of the hyperboloid or of Pascal's hexagon, but insight into *why they have these properties.* In this wide-ranging survey, one of the world's greatest and most original mathematicians uses insight as both his technique and his aim. Both the beginner and the mature mathematician will learn much from this fascinating treatise.

Translated from the German by P. NEMENYI.

CHAPTER HEADINGS: I. The Simplest Curves and surfaces. II. Regular Systems of Points. III. Projective Configurations. IV. Differential Geometry. V. Kinematics. VI. Topology.

"A mathematical classic . . . The purpose is to make the reader *see* and *feel* the proofs."—*Science.*

"A fascinating tour of the 20th-century mathematical zoo."—*Scientific American.*

"Students . . . will experience the sensation of being taken into the friendly confidence of a great mathematician and being shown the *real significance* of things."—*Science Progress.*

"A glance down the index (*twenty-five columns of it*) reveal the breadth of range:—

"Annulus; Atomic structure; Automorphic functions; Bubble, soap; Caustic Curve; Color problem; Density of packing, of circles; Four-dimensional space; Gears, hyperboloidal; Graphite; Lattices; Mapping; "Monkey Saddle"; Table salt; Zinc.

"*These are but a few of the topics* . . . The title evokes the imagination and the text must surely capture it."—*Math. Gazette.*

—1952. 358 pp. 6x9. [87] **$6.00**

SQUARING THE CIRCLE, and other Monographs

By HOBSON, HUDSON, SINGH, and KEMPE

FOUR VOLUMES IN ONE.

SQUARING THE CIRCLE, by *Hobson*. A fascinating account of one of the three famous problems of antiquity, its significance, its history, the mathematical work it inspired in modern times, and its eventual solution in the closing years of the last century.

RULER AND COMPASSES, by *Hudson*. "An analytical and geometrical investigation of how far Euclidean constructions can take us. It is as thoroughgoing as it is constructive."—*Sci. Monthly*.

THE THEORY AND CONSTRUCTION OF NON-DIFFERENTIABLE FUNCTIONS, by *Singh*. I. Functions Defined by Series. II. Functions Defined Geometrically. III. Functions Defined Arithmetically. IV. Properties of Non-Differentiable Functions.

HOW TO DRAW A STRAIGHT LINE, by *Kempe*. An intriguing monograph on linkages. Describes, among other things, a linkage that will trisect any angle.

"Intriguing, meaty."—*Scientific American*.

—388 pp. 4½x7½. [95] Four vols. in one **$3.25**

SPHERICAL AND ELLIPSOIDAL HARMONICS

By E. W. HOBSON

"A comprehensive treatise . . . and the standard reference in its field."—*Bulletin of the A. M. S.*

—1930. 512 pp. 5⅜x8. Orig. pub. at $13.50. [104] **$6.00**

DIE METHODEN ZUR ANGENÄHERTEN LÖSUNG VON EIGENWERTPROBLEMEN IN DER ELASTOKINETIK

By K. HOHENEMSER

—(Ergeb. der Math.) 1932. 89 pp. 5½x8½. Orig. pub. at $4.25. [55] **$2.75**

ERGODENTHEORIE

By E. HOPF

—(Ergeb. der Math.) 1937. 89 pp. 5½x8½. [43] **$2.75**

HUDSON, "Ruler and Compasses," see Hobson

THE CALCULUS OF FINITE DIFFERENCES

By CHARLES JORDAN

"... destined to remain the classic treatment of the subject . . . for many years to come."—*Harry C. Carver, Founder and formerly Editor of the* ANNALS OF MATHEMATICAL STATISTICS.

—1947. Second edition. xxi + 652 pp. 5½x8¼. [33] **$6.00**

THEORIE DER ORTHOGONALREIHEN

By S. KACZMARZ and H. STEINHAUS

The theory of general orthogonal functions. *Monografje Matematyczne*, Vol. VI.

—304 pp. 6x9. [83] **$4.95**

KÄHLER, see Blaschke

DIFFERENTIALGLEICHUNGEN: LOESUNGSMETHODEN UND LOESUNGEN

By E. KAMKE

Everything possible that can be of use when one has a given differential equation to solve, or when one wishes to investigate that solution thoroughly.

PART A: General Methods of Solution and the Properties of the Solutions.

PART B: Boundary and Characteristic Value Problems.

PART C: Dictionary of some 1600 Equations in Lexicographical Order, with solution, techniques for solving, and references.

"A reference work of outstanding importance which should be in every mathematical library."

—*Mathematical Gazette.*

—Third ed. 692 pp. 6x9. Orig. Publ. at $15.00. [44] **$9.50**

KEMPE, "How to Draw a Straight Line," see Hobson

ASYMPTOTISCHE GESETZE DER WAHRSCHEINLICHKEITSRECHNUNG

By A. A. KHINTCHINE

—1933. 82 pp. (Ergeb. der Math.) 5½x8½. Orig. pub. at $3.85. [36] Paper **$2.00**

ENTWICKLUNG DER MATHEMATIK IM 19. JAHRHUNDERT

By F. KLEIN

Vol. I deals with general Advanced Mathematics of the prolific 19th century. Vol. II deals with the mathematics of Relativity Theory.

—616 pp. 5¼x8¼. Orig. $14.40. [74] 2 Vols. in one **$7.50**

VORLESUNGEN ÜBER HÖHERE GEOMETRIE

By FELIX KLEIN

In this third edition there has been added to the first two sections of *Klein's* classical work a third section written by Professors *Blaschke, Radon, Artin* and *Schreier* on recent developments.

—Third ed. 413 pp. 5½x8. Orig. publ. at $10.80. [65] **$4.95**

THEORIE DER ENDLICHEN UND UNENDLICHEN GRAPHEN

By D. KÖNIG

"Elegant applications to Matrix Theory . . . Abstract Set Theory . . . Linear Forms . . . Electricity . . . Basis Problems . . . Logic, Theory of Games, Group Theory."—*L. Kalmar, Acta Szeged.*

—1936. 269 pp. 5¼x8¼. Orig. publ. at $7.20. [72] **$4.50**

DIOPHANTISCHE APPROXIMATIONEN

By J. F. KOKSMA

—(Ergeb. der Math.) 1936. 165 pp. 5½x8½. Orig. publ. at $7.25. [66] **$3.50**

FOUNDATIONS OF THE THEORY OF PROBABILITY

By A. KOLMOGOROV

Translation edited by N. MORRISON. With a bibliography and notes by A. T. BHARUCHA-REID.

Almost indispensable for anyone who wishes a thorough understanding of modern statistics, this basic tract develops probability theory on a postulational basis.

—2nd ed. 1956. viii + 84 pp. 6x9. [23] **$2.50**

EINFÜHRUNG IN DIE THEORIE DER KONTINUIERLICHEN GRUPPEN

By G. KOWALEWSKI

—406 pp. 5¼x8¼. Orig. publ. at $10.20. [70] $4.95

DETERMINANTENTHEORIE EINSCHLIESSLICH DER FREDHOLMSCHEN DETERMINANTEN

By G. KOWALEWSKI

PARTIAL CONTENTS: Definition and Simple Properties . . . Systems of Linear Equations . . . Symmetric, Skew-symmetric, Orthogonal Determinants . . . Resultants and Discriminants . . . Linear and Quadratic Forms... Functional, Wronskian, Gramian determinants . . . Geometrical applications ... Linear Integral Equations ... Theory of Elementary Divisors.

"A classic in its field."—*Bulletin of the A. M. S.*

—Third edition. 1942. 328 pp. 5½x8. [39] **$4.95**

IDEALTHEORIE

By W. KRULL

—(Ergeb. der Math.) 1935. 159 pp. 5½x8½. Orig. publ. (paper bound) at $7.00. [48] Cloth, **$3.95**

GROUP THEORY

By A. KUROSH

Translated from the second Russian edition and with added notes by PROF. K. A. HIRSCH.

A complete rewriting of the first, and already famous, Russian edition.

Partial Contents: PART ONE: The Elements of Group Theory. Chap. I. Definition. II. Subgroups (Systems, Cyclic Groups, Ascending Sequences of Groups). III. Normal Subgroups. IV. Endomorphisms and Automorphisms. Groups with Operators. V. Series of Subgroups. Direct Products. Defining Relations, etc. PART TWO: Abelian Groups. VI. Foundations of the Theory of Abelian Groups (Finite Abelian Groups, Rings of Endomorphisms, Abelian Groups with Operators). VII. Primary and Mixed Abelian Groups. VIII. Torsion-Free Abelian Groups. Editor's Notes. Bibliography.

Vol. II. PART THREE: Group-Theoretical Constructions. IX. Free Products and Free Groups (Free Products with Amalgamated Subgroup, Fully Invariant Subgroups). X. Finitely Generated Groups. XI. Direct Products. Lattices (Modular, Complete Modular, etc.). XII. Extensions of Groups (of Abelian Groups, of Non-commutative Groups, Cohomology Groups). PART FOUR: Solvable and Nilpotent Groups. XIII. Finiteness Conditions, Sylow Subgroups, etc. XIV. Solvable Groups (Solvable and Generalized Solvable Groups, Local Theorems). XV. Nilpotent Groups (Generalized, Complete, Locally Nilpotent Torsion-Free, etc.). Editor's Notes. Bibliography.

—Vol. I. 2nd ed. 1959. 271 pp. 6x9. [107] **$4.95**
—Vol. II. 2nd ed. 1960. 308 pp. 6x9. [109] **$4.95**

DIFFERENTIAL AND INTEGRAL CALCULUS

By E. LANDAU

Landau's sparkling *Einführung* in English translation. Completely rigorous, completely self-contained, borrowing not even the fundamental theorem of algebra (of which it gives a rigorous elementary proof), it develops the entire calculus including Fourier series, starting only with the properties of the number system. A masterpiece of rigor and clarity.

—2nd ed. 1960. 372 pp. 6x9. [78] **$6.00**

ELEMENTARE ZAHLENTHEORIE

By E. LANDAU

"Interest is enlisted at once and sustained by the accuracy, skill, and enthusiasm with which Landau marshals . . . facts and simplifies . . . details."

—*G. D. Birkhoff, Bulletin of the A. M. S.*

—1927. vii + 180 + iv pp. 5½x8¼. [26] **$3.50**

ELEMENTS OF ALGEBRA

By HOWARD LEVI

"This book is addressed to beginning students of mathematics. . . . The level of the book, however, is so unusually high, mathematically as well as pedagogically, that it merits the attention of professional mathematicians (as well as of professional pedagogues) interested in the wider dissemination of their subject among cultured people . . . a **closer approximation to the right way to teach mathematics to beginners than anything else now in existence.**"—*Bulletin of the A. M. S.*

—Third ed. 1960. xi + 161 pp. 5⅜x8. [103] **$3.25**

LE CALCUL DES RÉSIDUS

By E. LINDELÖF

Important applications in a striking diversity of mathematical fields: statistics, number theory, the theory of Fourier series, the calculus of finite differences, mathematical physics and advanced calculus, as well as function theory itself.

—151 pp. 5½x8½. [34] **$3.25**

THE THEORY OF MATRICES

By C. C. MacDUFFEE

"No mathematical library can afford to be without this book."—*Bulletin of the A. M. S.*

—(Ergeb. der Math.) 2nd edition. 116 pp. 6x9. Orig. publ. at $5.20. [28] **$2.95**

MACMAHON, "Introduction . . ." see Klein

COMBINATORY ANALYSIS, Vols. I and II

By P. A. MACMAHON

TWO VOLUMES IN ONE.

A broad and extensive treatise on an important branch of mathematics.

—xx + 300 + xx + 340 pp. 5⅜x8. [137] Two vols. in one. **$7.50**

FORMULAS AND THEOREMS FOR THE FUNCTIONS OF MATHEMATICAL PHYSICS

By W. MAGNUS and F. OBERHETTINGER

Gathered into a compact, handy and well-arranged reference work are thousands of results on the many important functions needed by the physicist, engineer and applied mathematician.

Translated by J. WERMER.

—1954. 182 pp. 6x9. German edition was $7.00. [51] **$3.90**

THE PROBLEM OF PLATEAU

By T. RADO

—(Ergeb. der Math.) 1933. 113 pp. 5½x8. Orig. publ. (in paper binding) at $5.10. [81] Cloth, **$2.95**

EINFÜHRUNG IN DIE KOMBINATORISCHE TOPOLOGIE

By K. REIDEMEISTER

Group Theory occupies the first half of the book; applications to Topology, the second. This well-known book is of interest both to algebraists and topologists.

—221 pp. 5½x8¼. [76] **$3.50**

KNOTENTHEORIE

By K. REIDEMEISTER

—(Ergeb. der Math.) 1932. 78 pp. 5½x8½. [40] **$2.25**

FOURIER SERIES

By W. ROGOSINSKI

Translated by H. COHN. Designed for beginners with no more background than a year of calculus, this text covers, nevertheless, an amazing amount of ground. It is suitable for self-study courses as well as classroom use.

"The field covered is extensive and the treatment is thoroughly modern in outlook . . . An admirable guide to the theory."—*Mathematical Gazette.*

—Second ed. 1959. vi + 176 pp. 4½x6½. [67] **$2.25**

CONIC SECTIONS

By G. SALMON

"The classic book on the subject, covering the whole ground and full of touches of genius."

—*Mathematical Association.*

—6th ed. xv + 400 pp. 5¼x8¼. [99] Cloth **$3.25**
[98] Paper **$1.94**

HIGHER PLANE CURVES

By G. SALMON

CHAPTER HEADINGS: I. Coordinates. II. General Properties of Algebraic Curves. III. Envelopes. IV. Metrical Properties. V. Cubics. VI. Quartics. VII. Transcendental Curves. VIII. Transformation of Curves. IX. General Theory of Curves.

—3rd ed. xix + 395 pp. 5⅜x8. [138] **$4.95**

ANALYTIC GEOMETRY OF THREE DIMENSIONS

By G. SALMON

A rich and detailed treatment by the author of *Conic Sections, Higher Plane Curves*, etc.

—Seventh edition. (V. 1). 496 pp. 5x8. [122] **$4.95**

INTRODUCTION TO MODERN ALGEBRA AND MATRIX THEORY

By O. SCHREIER and E. SPERNER

An English translation of the revolutionary work, *Einführung in die Analytische Geometrie und Algebra*. Chapter Headings: I. Affine Space. Linear Equations. (Vector Spaces). II. Euclidean Space. Theory of Determinants. III. The Theory of Fields. Fundamental Theorem of Algebra. IV. Elements of Group Theory. V. Matrices and Linear Transformations. **The treatment of matrices is especially extensive.**

"Outstanding . . . good introduction . . . well suited for use as a text . . . Self-contained and each topic is painstakingly developed."

—*Mathematics Teacher.*

—Second ed. 1959. viii + 378 pp. [80] **$6.00**

PROJECTIVE GEOMETRY OF *n* DIMENSIONS

By O. SCHREIER and E. SPERNER

Translated from the German by CALVIN A. ROGERS.

A textbook on the analytic projective geometry of n dimensions whose clarity and explicitness of presentation can hardly be surpassed.

Suitable for a one-semester course on the senior undergraduate or first-year graduate level. The background required is minimal: The definition and simplest properties of vector spaces and the elements of matrix theory. For the reader lacking this background, suitable reference is made to the Authors' companion volume *Introduction to Modern Algebra and Matrix Theory.*

There are exercises at the end of each chapter to enable the student to test his mastery of the material.

CHAPTER HEADINGS: I. n-Dimensional Projective Space. II. General Projective Coordinates. III. Hyperplane Coordinates. The Duality Principle. IV. The Cross Ratio. V. Projectivities. VI. Linear Projectivities of P_n onto Itself. VII. Correlations. VIII. Hypersurfaces of the Second Order. IX. Projective Classification of Hypersurfaces of the Second Order. X. Projective Properties of Hypersurfaces of the Second Order. XI. The Affine Classification of Hypersurfaces of the Second Order. XII. The Metric Classification of Hypersurfaces of the Second Order.

—1961. 208 pp. 6x9. [126] **$4.95**

PROJECTIVE METHODS IN PLANE ANALYTICAL GEOMETRY

By C. A. SCOTT

The original title of the present work, as it appeared in the first and second editions, was "An Introductory Account of Certain Modern Ideas and Methods in Plane Analytic Geometry." The title has been changed to the present more concise and more descriptive form, and the corrections indicated in the second edition have been incorporated into the text.

CHAPTER HEADINGS: I. Point and Line Coordinates. II. Infinity. Transformation of Coordinates. III. Figures Determined by Four Elements. IV. The Principle of Duality. V. Descriptive Properties of Curves. VI. Metric Properties of Curves; Line at Infinity. VII. Metric Properties of Curves; Circular Points. VIII. Unicursal (Rational) Curves. Tracing of Curves. IX. Cross-Ratio, Homography, and Involution. X. Projection and Linear Transformation. XI. Theory of Correspondence. XII. The Absolute. XIII. Invariants and Covariants.

—Ready, Summer, 1961. 3rd ed. xiv + 288 pp. 5x8. [146] Probably **$3.50**

LEHRBUCH DER TOPOLOGIE

By H. SEIFERT and W. THRELFALL

This famous book is the only modern work on *combinatorial topology* addressed to the student as well as to the specialist. It is almost indispensable to the mathematician who wishes to gain a knowledge of this important field.

"The exposition proceeds by easy stages **with examples and illustrations at every turn.**"

—*Bulletin of the A. M. S.*

—1934. 360 pp. 5½x8½. Orig. publ. at $8.00. [31] **$4.95**

SHEPPARD, "From Determinant to Tensor," see Klein

HYPOTHÈSE DU CONTINU

By W. SIERPIŃSKI

An appendix consisting of sixteen research papers now brings this important work up to date. This represents an increase of more than forty percent in the number of pages.

"One sees how deeply this postulate cuts through all phases of the foundations of mathematics, how intimately many fundamental questions of analysis and geometry are connected with it . . . a most excellent addition to our mathematical literature."

—*Bulletin of A. M. S.*

——Second edition. 1957. xvii + 274 pp. 5x8. [117] **$4.95**

SINGH, "Non-Differentiable Functions," see Hobson

DIOPHANTISCHE GLEICHUNGEN

By T. SKOLEM

"This comprehensive presentation . . . should be warmly welcomed. We recommend the book most heartily."—*Acta Szeged.*

—(Ergeb. der Math.) 1938. ix + 130 pp. 5½x8½. Cloth. Orig. publ. at $6.50. [75] **$3.50**

ALGEBRAISCHE THEORIE DER KOERPER

By E. STEINITZ

"Epoch-making."—*A. Haar, Aca Szeged.*

—177 pp. including two appendices. 5¼x8¼. [77] **$3.25**

INTERPOLATION

By J. F. STEFFENSEN

"A landmark in the history of the subject.

"Starting from scratch, the author deals with formulae of interpolation, construction of tables, inverse interpolation, summation of formulae, the symbolic calculus, interpolation with several variables, in a clear, elegant and rigorous manner . . . The student . . . will be rewarded by a comprehensive view of the whole field. . . . A classic account which no serious student can afford to neglect."—*Mathematical Gazette.*

—1950. 2nd ed. 256 pp. 5¼x8¼. Orig. $8.00. [71] **$4.95**

A HISTORY OF THE MATHEMATICAL THEORY OF PROBABILITY

By I. TODHUNTER

Introduces the reader to *almost every process and every species of problem which the literature of the subject can furnish.* Hundreds of problems are solved in detail.

—640 pp. 5¼x8. Previously publ. at $8.00. [57] **$6.00**

SET TOPOLOGY

By R. VAIDYANATHASWAMY

In this text on Topology, the first edition of which was published in India, the concept of partial order has been made the unifying theme.

Over 500 exercises for the reader enrich the text.

CHAPTER HEADINGS: I. Algebra of Subsets of a Set. II. Rings and Fields of Sets. III. Algebra of Partial Order. IV. The Closure Function. V. Neighborhood Topology. VI. Open and Closed Sets. VII. Topological Maps. VIII. The Derived Set in T_1 Space. IX. The Topological Product. X. Convergence in Metrical Space. XI. Convergence Topology.

—2nd ed. 1960. vi + 305 pp. 6x9. [139] **$6.00**

LECTURES ON THE GENERAL THEORY OF INTEGRAL FUNCTIONS

By G. VALIRON

—1923. xii + 208 pp. 5¼x8. [56] **$3.50**

GRUPPEN VON LINEAREN TRANSFORMATIONEN

By B. L. VAN DER WAERDEN

—(Ergeb. der Math.) 1935. 94 pp. 5½x8½. [45] **$2.50**

LEHRBUCH DER ALGEBRA

By H. WEBER

The bible of classical algebra, still unsurpassed for its clarity and completeness. Much of the material on elliptic functions is not available elsewhere in connected form.

PARTIAL CONTENTS: *VOL. I.* CHAP. I. Rational Functions. II. Determinants. III. Roots of Algebraic Equations. V. Symmetric Functions. V. Linear Transformations. Invariants. VI. Tchirnhaus Transformation. VII. Reality of Roots. VIII. Sturm's Theorem. X. Limits on Roots. X. Approximate Computation of Roots. XI. Continued Fractions. XII. Roots of Unity. XIII. Galois Theory. XIV. Applications of Permutation Group to Equations. XV. Cyclic Equations. XVI. Kreisteilung. XVII. Algebraic Solution of Equations. XVIII. Roots of Metacyclic Equations.

VOL. II. CHAPS. I.-V. Group Theory. VI.-X. Theory of Linear Groups. XI.-XVI. Applications of Group Theory (General Equation of Fifth Degree. The Group G_{168} and Equations of Seventh Degree . . .). XVII.-XXIV. Algebraic Numbers. XXV. Transcendental Numbers.

VOL. III. CHAP. I. Elliptic Integral. II. Theta Functions. III. Transformation of Theta Functions. IV. Elliptic Functions. V. Modular Function. V. Multiplication of Elliptic Functions. Division. VII. Equations of Transformation. VIII. Groups of the Transformation Equations and the Equation of Fifth Degree... XI.-XVI. Quadratic Fields. XVII. Elliptic Functions and Quadratic Forms. XVIII. Galois Group of Class Equation. XIX. Computation of Class Invariant . . . XII. Cayley's Development of Modular Function. XXIII. Class Fields. XXIV.-XXVI. Algebraic Functions. XXVII. Algebraic and Abelian Differentials.

—Ready, Fall, '61. 3rd ed. (C. repr. of 2nd ed.). 2,345 pp. 5x8.
[144] Three vol. set. Probably **$19.50**

DAS KONTINUUM,
und andere Monographien

By H. WEYL, E. LANDAU, and B. RIEMANN

FOUR VOLUMES IN ONE.

DAS KONTINUUM (Kritische Untersuchungen ueber die Grundlagen der Analysis), by *H. Weyl.* Reprint of 2nd edition.

MATHEMATISCHE ANALYSE DES RAUMPROBLEMS, by *H. Weyl.*

DARSTELLUNG UND BEGRUENDUNG EINIGER NEURER ERGEBNISSE DER FUNKTIONENTHEORIE, by *E. Landau.* Reprint of 2nd edition.

UEBER DIE HYPOTHESEN, WELCHE DER GEOMETRIE ZU GRUNDE LIEGEN, by *B. Riemann.* Reprint of 3rd edition, edited and with comments by H. Weyl.

—83 + 117 + 120 + 48 pp. 5¼x8. [134] Four vols. in one.
$6.00

THE THEORY OF GROUPS

By H. J. ZASSENHAUS

In this considerably augmented second edition of his famous work, Prof. Zassenhaus puts the original text in a lattice-theoretical framework. This has been done by the addition of new material as appendixes, so that the book can also continue to be read, as before, on a strictly group-theoretical level. The new edition has sixty percent more pages than the old.

The number of exercises, also has been greatly increased.

"A wealth of material in compact form."

—*Bulletin of A. M. S.*

—Second edition. 1958. viii + 265 pp. 6x9. [53] **$6.00**

Prices subject to change without notice